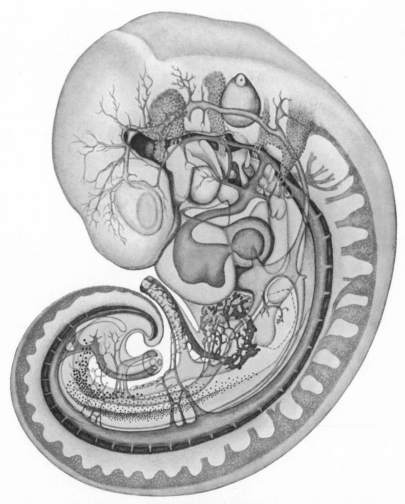

Human embryo of 32 somites, 4½ weeks old. (For explanations see Fig. 318.)

EMIL WITSCHI

Professor of Embryology and Endocrinology

The State University of Iowa

Development

of

Vertebrates

W. B. SAUNDERS COMPANY

Philadelphia   1956   London

Preface

Among the many problems that command a general human interest, questions about reproduction and the origin of life have long occupied a prominent place. In our day they are gaining new meaning and importance, for research has carried mankind to the very threshold of willfully directed reproduction. Discoveries in the fields of controlled reproduction and prenatal care have already attained considerable practical and economic importance in medicine and in livestock breeding. The example of the honey bee that controls sex determination as well as queen-worker differentiation, encourages even much bolder expectations for the future of our young developmental technology. In fact, basic research of the last century and particularly of recent decades already has revealed enough about conditions, agents, and mechanisms of developmental processes, that practical applications of far-reaching consequences can distinctly be foreseen.

The change of embryology from a contemplative science, supplying the substance for philosophical constructions and discussions, to one of mechanical analysis and active control is closely connected with the introduction of experimental research methods. While exact descriptive study of the developmental process may lead to preliminary speculations about its inherent mechanisms, only experimental testing can confirm or decisively rule out assumed causal relationships.

The present text is primarily written for premedical students and zoology majors who have completed a course in general biology. Therefore, it aims at the presentation of developmental concepts on an advanced basis, while introducing the subject matter of vertebrate embryology. Research methods are considered to the extent required for the understanding of the results of important investigative work. Modern dynamic embryology occupies itself primarily with the mechanisms of change of one form into another. Yet descriptive morphology remains inseparably connected with this physiology of development, and at least

v

17175

the beginning and the end of every experiment have to be related to definite morphologic stages. To avoid intolerable cramming of a one-semester course, the descriptive material contained in the representative life histories is rigidly systematized. Taxonomy and classification are not in themselves stimulating subjects, but they are the means by which large accumulations of objects or of knowledge may be surveyed and mastered. The system of analytical staging employed in this book is furthermore intended to relieve the memory of the student by making the book an easily usable guide to factual information. The goal of an introductory course in embryology, toward which also this book aims to contribute, is a realization, by the student, that development is a natural process which is open to scientific analysis by research methods not essentially different from those of the inorganic sciences. At the same time, teaching should avoid oversimplification through unjustified reliance on diagrams and on summary concepts which fail to present the actual complication in composition and structure of living organization that is the product of an evolutionary history of a thousand million years or more.

Since the most direct and least time-consuming method of teaching morphology necessitates a liberal use of well labeled pictures, great care was given to the illustration of this book. It was decided not to employ a standard pattern of reproduction, but to make use of different suitable techniques, from photography to line drawing. This combines the advantage of adaptability to the nature of the object with a demonstration of principal methods of scientific illustration. The new figures were prepared by the author, often assisted by students and associates. Those reproduced from other publications are usually rendered in the original techniques. Several authors, and particularly the Department of Embryology of the Carnegie Institution, have aided by furnishing original prints. To all these collaborators the author expresses his appreciation and sincere thanks.

EMIL WITSCHI

May, 1956

Contents

I. Introduction

II. Multiplication and Maturation of Germ Cells

III. The Start of Ontogenesis

IV. Amphibians

V. Fishes

VI. Birds

VII. Mammals

Section One

Introduction

Chapter 1

Basic Concepts and

Technical Terms

The word *embryo* originally referred broadly to *the unborn,* also the unhatched bird, and even the germ of a plant within the seed shells. Though in scientific application one now tends to restrict the name to relatively early stages, the branch of biology which is called *embryology* deals with the entire reproductive processes. *Vertebrate embryology* therefore is concerned with the life cycles of fishes, amphibians, reptiles, birds, and mammals.

Life Cycles and Evolution. Development is one of the outstanding characteristics of life. It has no real beginning within a life cycle. The fertilized egg itself is the product of antecedent processes of egg and sperm formation and thus issues from a parental cycle. Individual development, or *ontogeny,* is only one segment of a much longer train of events, namely the evolution of the species, or *phylogeny.*

Evolution may be graphically visualized as a tight coil in which every turn represents the equivalent of one life cycle or one *generation.* The sequences of turns in the longitudinal dimension of the coil add up to evolution. According to best estimates, primitive life seems to have started about two billion years ago. Of the first billion almost no documentary evidence has been discovered so far. We think of this epoch mainly as one of chemical evolution. Processes of photosynthesis

2

and enzymatic oxidation must have arisen early. For only after solar radiation had become utilizable for the synthesizing of high energy compounds, was the scene set for the evolution of complex, large organisms.

It may well have taken one billion years for the evolution of organized cells with a nucleus and other essential cell structures. About the same epoch, primitive forms of sexuality may have arisen which served as a basis for the establishment of simple life cycles. The only information that we may gain about evolution in those distant eons is by analogy from studies on today's protozoans, bacteria, and viruses.

Figure 1 presents the primitive but solidly established life cycle of *Trichosphaerium*. This species resembles both amebas and foraminifers. Its cycle begins with the *copulation of two gametes*. This event is the equivalent of *fertilization* of an egg by a sperm, as observed in higher animals. But in *Trichosphaerium* the fusing germ cells are morphologically alike; they are *isogametes*. Each has an oval cell body with a

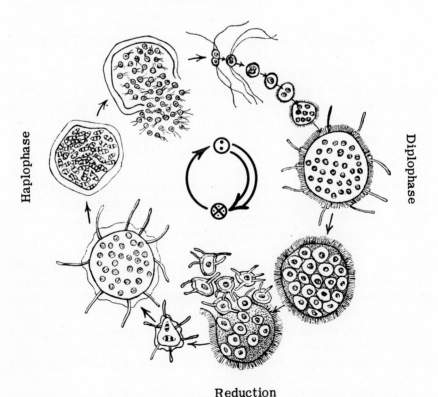

Fertilization

Haplophase

Diplophase

Reduction

Figure 1.   Life cycle of the protozoan *Trichosphaerium* (adapted from Schaudinn 1899).

nucleus, and two long cilia. Copulation is followed by complete union of the cell bodies and of the nuclei, and by resorption of the cilia. The fusion cell or *zygote* is diploid (double-weight), since the chromatin elements of two haploid (single-weight) gametes were added together. After a while the nucleus of the zygote begins to multiply. The plasmatic body grows; its surface membrane becomes fortified and transforms into a shell. Finally the cytoplasm divides into individual ameboid cells which leave the bursting shell. Apparently, during the last two divisions the nuclei return to the haploid state, a process which is called *meiosis*. Similar reduction divisions will be described more fully in the chapters on spermatogenesis and ovogenesis.

Each small haploid ameba soon grows into another multinucleated body. No solid shell is formed this time; but later, rapidly progressing cell divisions result in the liberation of a large number of small isogametes, each provided with a pair of cilia. This completes the life cycle. As is easily seen, it is composed of two parts which differ in nuclear constitution: a *diplophase* and a *haplophase*. They change alternatingly one into the other through *fertilization* (copulation) and *meiosis* (reduction) (Fig. 1).

Germ Plasm and Soma. In the life history of *Trichosphaerium* every cell remains always within the reproductive cycle. Artificial destruction may occur, but inherently every cell has a capacity for life that is not limited by time. This situation becomes radically changed in the many-celled animals, the *metazoa*. Here, sooner or later in the course of development, some cells specialize for particular services, such as nutrition, protection, contractility, irritability. Subsequently they lose the capacity of transforming into gametes; they have become body cells. Together they represent the *soma* and differ from the reproductive cells, the *germ plasm*, by having a limited life duration.

The separation of soma and germ plasm is more definite in the higher metazoa than in some lower forms. An example of clear differentiation is offered by the small crustacean *Tisbe* (Fig. 2). At the end of the sixth cleavage division of its egg, a large globular cell at the vegetal pole of the germ is distinguished by the inclusion of many mitochondria (Fig. 2d). Subsequently it divides in two and then in four cells (Fig. 2e-h). Of the latter, the inner two, which contain most of the mitochondria, are the *primordial germ cells*. All other cells, now about 250, represent the soma. While they develop rapidly into a little nauplius larva, the germ cells remain passive; during this early period they do not even multiply; as a pair they take their places left and right, near the body cavities, where later the sex glands will be located (Fig. 2i-k).

In the vertebrates the primordial germ cells probably separate from the soma also following about the eighth cleavage division. At this early stage, they are not as easily identified as in *Tisbe*, but their specific nature and their separation from somatic cells become clearly apparent in slightly older embryos (Fig. 312).

Recapitulation Theory. It is rather surprising that during metazoan evolution the soma became much more profoundly changed than the germ plasm. The only general difference between the germ-cell cycle of man and the life history of *Trichosphaerium* consists in the differentiation of separate female and male gametes. *Eggs* and *sperms* are formed, instead of morphologically uniform isogametes.

On the other hand, the soma, in the course of over 500 million years, has evolved step by step into progressively more complex organisms. Illustrative examples chosen from man's ancestry would be sponges, celenterates, echinoderms, protochordates, fishes, amphibians, reptiles, and mammals. The fact that today representatives of this entire evolutionary sequence are living side by side with man, can be explained on the basis of two well founded assumptions. First, it is

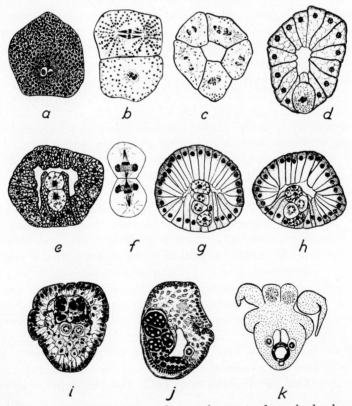

Figure 2. Separation of germ plasm and soma in the early development of the crustacean *Tisbe* (Witschi 1934). *a–c,* Cleavage; *d,* blastula with large stem cell; *e–h,* gastrulation; the second division of the stem cell is unequal (*f*), results in two primordial germ cells (center), and two endoderm cells; *i–k,* differentiation of the nauplius larva, which still has only two germ cells.

probable that life originated not only once, but repeatedly through long spaces of time. Secondly, it is certain that direction and speed of evolution are not the same for all individuals. Thus it comes about that the direct but fragmentary evidence of evolution presented by the fossils can be so widely supplemented through studies in the comparative morphology of the living species.

However, it was a matter of great surprise when in the early years of the Darwinian epoch Haeckel and other leading embryologists put forward the idea that the course of the evolutionary history of a species is also reflected in its individual ontogeny. Some of the hottest battles about scientific theory were fought against the implication that the developing human embryo itself should testify for man's descent from primitive animal ancestors. Today there remains no reasonable doubt about the fundamental fact that developing vertebrates pass through series of stages which in general recapitulate the evolutionary progression. But it is also recognized that the ancestral history is not faithfully repeated in full detail. Many short-cuts are taken, and most stages exhibit modifications in the nature of *adaptations to changed environmental conditions*. Often ancestral organs are no longer used and consequently show various conditions of reduction. The gill slits and branchial arches in human embryos are without physiologic importance for the individual. But the fact of their embryonic appearance places emphasis on the close relationship of man with all other vertebrates and particularly with the amphibians and fishes, in which these structures are important parts of functional respiratory organs.

The ontogenetic study of life histories has yielded relatively little information concerning the over-all process of evolution that was not obtainable also from the paleontologic records and by deduction from the facts of comparative morphology. However, it is only by observation of live, developing organisms that one may get a coherent aspect of the flow of transformation, rather than a pieced together and incomplete mosaic picture. Watching a tadpole metamorphose into a frog, one attends a performance of one of the most portentous events in vertebrate evolution: the conversion of an aquatic fish into a terrestrial tetrapod. Of course, in many preceding generations the act has been amply rehearsed—perhaps as often as 100 million times. It now runs off with mechanized precision within a few days or weeks. No record tells of the first hesitant steps, trials, errors, and casualties under which the labyrinthodonts, primitive amphibians of the carboniferous period, finally succeeded in climbing onto land. But faithfully repeated are the successful morphologic and physiologic changes that must have attended also the original evolutionary progress.

Stages of Vertebrate Development. Recapitulation of common ancestral history in the course of ontogenesis explains the essential similarity of development in all vertebrate classes. This statement must be amended with reference to the higher classes, in which development proceeds beyond the fish stage. At the amphibian level the metamorphic stages become added, and the life histories of birds and mammals are further extended by fetal stages.

Extension of life histories by addition of terminal stages is exactly the mode of evolution that must be expected on the basis of the recapitulation theory. However, it would be wrong to assume that the early ontogenetic stages were immutable. Quite to the contrary they are open to adaptive variation, in response to environmental changes. For instance fish and amphibian eggs, embryos, and larvae usually have protective colorations; but if normally they are deposited in hidden, dark places, they are colorless. Similarly embryos and fetuses of mammals lack pigment until the time of birth. Pigmentation obviously often does not follow the rule of recapitulation.

Changes in egg size, in nutritional, and in respiratory conditions are causes of even more pronounced secondary variations. Usually adaptive and basic characters may easily be distinguished. The former are also subject to recapitulation. This becomes most evident in cases where function again was lost. Thus the yolk sac of the mammals was obviously acquired by reptilian ancestors in response to increasing egg size. With the development of placental nutrition it lost its functional value; but generation after generation it still forms and expands as if it were to enclose a large yolk mass. A similar situation exists in regard to a respiratory organ, the allantois. However, it is a remarkable fact that in many instances, and particularly in human development, both vesicles attain only a rudimentary stage of development. Obviously nonfunctional characters tend to become reduced. Thus the evolutionary history, as reflected in ontogeny, becomes blurred through three modifying processes: (1) secondary adaptations at the embryonic level, (2) recapitulation of obsolete adaptive characters, and (3) reduction of non-functional characters.

The fundamental similarities in the life histories of all vertebrates furnish the basis for a system of developmental stages of all classes. As indicated in Table 1, the course of ontogenesis can be divided into a succession of easily recognizable *periods* (column 2). Even though differentiation processes may overlap across the indicated boundary lines, each period is characterized by some distinctly new features (column 3). For the practical purpose of designating the developmental condition of all kinds of embryos some of these periods are too inclusive, and it is necessary to subdivide them in a number of smaller units or stages (column 1). The number and length of such stages is partly a matter of convenience. Embryologists more often work with early than with late stages of development. Thus the chronologic time value of the developmental stages increases in a nearly logarithmic progression. Since it would be difficult to find characteristic short names for all stages, the continuous numbering method was adopted and has been found of practical value by many embryologists.

The right side of Table 1 presents some major events of the phylogeny of the vertebrates and of man in parallel with the ontogenetic periods. At some levels the similarity may at first not seem very obvious, as for instance between the primitive streak stage of a vertebrate and the echinoderm and ascidian types. Later in this text it will be shown that the primitive streak stage is one of early mesoderm differentiation and, of course, echinoderms and ascidians are prototypes of the two major modes of mesoderm evolution.

Table 1

Corresponding Ontogenetic and Phylogenetic Periods of the Vertebrates

ONTOGENY			PHYLOGENY	
1 STAGES	2 PERIOD	3 CHARACTERISTICS	4 CORRESPONDING ANCESTORS	5 APPROXIMATE APPEARANCE OF ANCESTORS (YEARS B.C.)
1–6	Cleavage	Cell clusters	Protozoans	1,000,000,000
7	Blastula	One layer	Sponges	600,000,000
8–11	Gastrula	Two layers	Celenterates	500,000,000
12	Primitive streak	Three layers	Echinoderms Ascidians	400,000,000
13–17	Neurula	Notochord	Protochordates	360,000,000
18–24	Tailbud	Somite proliferation		
25	Fish Larva Embryo	Visceral arches Single circuit Paired paddles	Fishes	300,000,000
26–33	Metamorphosis	Closed gill slits Partly doubled circulation Pentadactyle ap- pendages	Amphibians	250,000,000
34	Fetus I	Fetal membranes Near double cir- cuit	Reptiles	200,000,000
35	Fetus II	Sealed eyelids Double circuit with atrial foramen	Primitive mammals	100,000,000
36	Fetus III	Reopened eyelids Extended fetal pe- riod Complete double circuits at birth, homothermy	Higher mammals Man	35,000,000 1,000,000

Columns 1 and 2: for illustrations see Figures 42 and 292 to 336.

For *fishes,* Stage 25 leads up to the end of the developmental history. However, *amphibians* and all higher classes pass now through changes that are so extensive, and of a nature so different from the course of preceding stages, that one speaks of a *transformation* or *metamorphosis.* The reason for such radical reorientation is easily recognizable. In evolution, going on land implied leaving an environment in which up to this time all life had taken its course. This was possible only by drastic reconstruction of many organs, particularly the locomotor and the respiratory systems. The aquatic organism had to be readapted for life in a terrestrian environment.

Of all tetrapod vertebrates, only amphibians recapitulate metamorphosis faithfully in both the morphologic and the functional sense. With the advent of the *reptiles* a *new type* of *eggs* developed, carrying very large stores of yolk enclosed in solid shells. Many of these eggs were deposited on land, others were retained in the oviducts for a long time. In either case, a large part of the development took its course within protective shells. Thus, an entirely new situation had arisen. In amphibians and all their antecedents the entire development from the egg on up to the adult proceeded in an open environment, the young starting early to procure its own food. Beginning with the reptiles the parents by one method or another provided for the adequate supply of all materials necessary for sustenance and growth, with the exception only of oxygen. The young, removed from contacts with the outside, suffered a consequent reduction of many structures that fell in disuse. Particularly, adaptive characters of the amphibian larval period tended to disappear. On the other hand, development in confinement necessitated also the acquisition of new organs such as the *fetal membranes.* They are formed by the embryo, but are mere appendages of the main body. They might be considered as a set of larval organs, since they disappear at the time of hatching or of birth.

Reduced to unpigmented, insensitive cave animals, the developing young of today's amniotes (reptiles, birds, mammals) have become the objects of more and more prolonged parental care. Of the three fetal stages which gradually become added after the metamorphic period, the reptiles acquire only the first. Birds and mammals have all three. They are also the only vertebrates in which the blood-vascular circuits become fully doubled. Homothermal control of the body temperature becomes established during the last two fetal stages, confirming the rule that the characteristics of higher organization are late additions to the developmental history.

Experimental Embryology. Speculative mechanistic or materialistic concepts of life appear time and again throughout the history of philosophy, but only during the last one hundred years have cause-analytic methods been employed systematically and successfully in biologic research. Experimental techniques being highly characteristic for this approach, the branch dealing with development is now usually designated as *experimental embryology*. A more fundamental trait is the search for causal relationships between successive steps of developmental processes and particularly of differentiation. This was expressed in the originally proposed name *Entwicklungsmechanik* (mechanics of development) which, however, is no longer in common usage.

Though the ultimate goal of describing and explaining development and evolution entirely in terms of physics and chemistry is still far afield, the results obtained in recent years have already profoundly changed the whole aspect of embryology. Formerly purely descriptive, it has become, at least in principle, a dynamic science, with teaching and research interests centered on the exposition of causal relationships.

Comparative Embryology.   Most students of embryology are primarily interested in the life history of man, i.e., in "ourselves unborn." As human materials for systematic and experimental studies often are not easily obtainable, it is fortunate that for many purposes embryos from other species can be used as substitutes. This emphasizes again the close relationship that connects all vertebrates and encourages the comparative study of various classes and species. As one of the many interesting results of such efforts appears the much discussed distinction between *homologous* and *analogous organs*. The term *homology* expresses a kinship of common derivation in the evolutionary sense, such as exists between pectoral fins of teleosts, wings of birds, and the arms of man. On the other hand, the resemblances which may develop in non-homologous organs that have become adapted to identical functions are classed as *analogies*. The structural and functional analogies of gills, lungs, and chorioallantoic membranes are easily recognized; yet these three organs of respiration originate from quite different parts of the embryos. They are not homologous.

Some biologists have objected to the evolutionary interpretation of similarities in life cycles, mostly as being too speculative. Instead similarities are contemplated as variants of a number of basic types which thus become considered as the nucleus of a formal *idealistic morphology*. Such abstract constructions are bound to lose adherence as paleontologic research adds more and more detail to the outline of the actual course of evolution.

Technical Terms.   The biologic sciences are burdened with an unnecessarily vast and complicated terminology. The traditional use of Greek and Latin names is slowly changing and modern language designations and practices are gaining favor. *Egg* very commonly is given preference over either *oön* or *ovum,* even in strictly scientific publications. The English language is particularly suited to absorb and anglicize foreign elements. This is a great esthetic as well as practical asset. In an English sentence, designations like arterial duct and arterial ligament blend easily, while ductus arteriosus and ligamentum arteriosum sound pompous, awkward, and obviously foreign. There exists really no good reason why in compounding one should not mix Latin and Greek roots. All living languages, and particularly the American, freely combine heterogeneous elements, even Indian and Greek, in compounding characteristic new names. In the interest of simplification, a rule for uniformity should be generally accepted. Since *ovary* is distinctly preferred over *oöphoron,* and usually *ovum* over *oön,* it seems legitimate to use the Latin root consistently, i.e., also in combinations like *ovoplasm, ovocyte, ovogonium* and so forth.

In the following chapters synonyms will only be mentioned if they

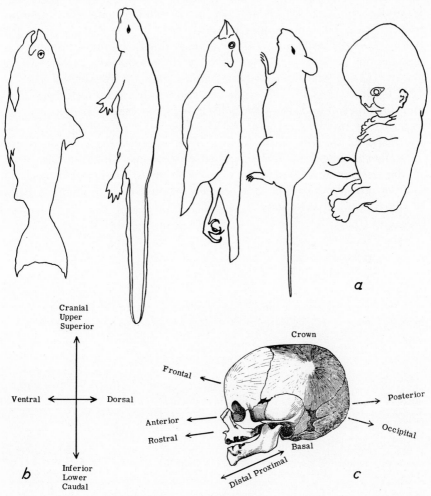

Figure 3.   Standard positions and directions. *a,* Left lateral views of fish, salamander, bird, rodent, and human fetus; *b,* directional designations applying to the specimens shown in *a; c,* terms particularly used for locations and directions pertaining to the head (skull of newborn after Corning, 1925).

are very frequently used or have some distinct advantage. Proper names should enter terminology as little as possible and be carried only as long as the nature of a structure or process remains unsettled. The name *mesonephric duct,* to mention one example, replaces the much used *Wolffian duct.* Convenience and preciseness should be leading principles in all matters of terminology.

Positions and Directions.   Considerable disagreement exists in the usage of certain directional terms. What in human anatomy is called the *superior caval vein* often goes under the name of *anterior caval vein* in animal morphology. It seems that originally the word *up* also was used for *head.* It is not intended to solicit here support from Icelandic philology. Yet, at any rate, it seems more natural to agree on *upward (superior)* rather than forward (anterior) as a designation for the head-ward direction in both man and animals. Figure 3 explains the designations used in the present text. Representatives of the major classes and a human fetus are lined up in standard left side view (Fig. 3*a*). The diagram (Fig. 3*b*) indicates corresponding terms for positions and directions. The head with its high degree of differentiation presents a particular problem in man. As a consequence of erect posture, the rostral end of the longitudinal axis is bent ventrally. Figure 3*c* indicates a number of more commonly applied expressions, which are also used in the description of head structures in animals. Designations such as *anterior* and *posterior semicircular canals* should refer to identical parts in the ears of all vertebrates.

Multiplication and Maturation

of Germ Cells

Chapter 2

Spermatogenesis

1. THE GERM CELLS IN SEXUAL REPRODUCTION

In sexual reproduction the material link between parents and offspring is formed by the *germ cells* which during the maturation process differentiate into *eggs* and *sperms*. The eggs of fishes, amphibians, reptiles, and birds attain considerable size through accumulation of large stores of yolk and other nutritious materials. Those of the mammals are smaller, barely large enough to be visible without the help of lenses; but even they conform to the rule that the egg is the largest cell of the species. On the other hand, sperms are of microscopic size, and smaller than most body cells.

Although the fertilized human egg is diminutive and weighs only about a microgram, it contains a microstructure which determines the general type of a human being, as well as a multitude of racial, familial, and personal traits. In the course of development, an individual increases more than 100 billion times in weight, becomes very complex chemically and physically, and repeatedly changes its general appearance (the so-called phenotype); but it retains a stable constitution (its genotype), the elements of which in due course may be passed on again to following generations.

During the second half of the nineteenth century, intensive studies of the cell and of the fertilization process led to the realization that the *chromatic substance of the nucleus* is particularly important as a substrate of basic constitution. More recently, when cytologists combined

14

their research methods with those of students of inheritance, the old theories gained a much broader and more exact foundation. This work now culminates in the *gene concept* of hereditary constitution. The genes are localized in the chromosomes. Their total number in the genotype of any one organism can only be estimated, but certainly amounts to several thousand in the case of man. It is possible that each darkly staining band in the chromosomes of salivary gland cells of flies (Fig. 4) is the locus of a single gene. The chromosomes of most other cells are less favorable for microscopic study, and their composition of *chromomeres* and *interchromomeres* becomes visible only during certain phases of their development (Fig. 11). Chemical analysis shows that the chromomeres consist largely of desoxyribonucleic acid (DNA) compounds; the interchromomeres are mostly globulins. The former contain phosphorus and are believed to be essential constituents of the substance of the genes.

In the course of development, *all cells of an embryo receive identical sets of chromosomes.* Nevertheless they differentiate into tissues and organs of very diverse character. Hence, constitution cannot be vested in chromosomal genes only. A *supplementary category of differentiating factors* must be contained in the egg, most likely not in the nucleus, but *in its cell body.* Since differentiation is the most outstanding general feature of development, these cytoplasmic agents are of particular interest to the embryologist. Experiments with eggs and early embryos indicate that they are chemicals, and localized in definite parts of the cell body. Summarily they are called *morphogenic substances,* the name referring to their role as inductors of morphologic differentiation. The spatial arrangement of these agents in the egg is of greatest importance and consequence, since it determines the pattern of their unequal distribution during cleavage and gastrulation. Obviously the morphogenic

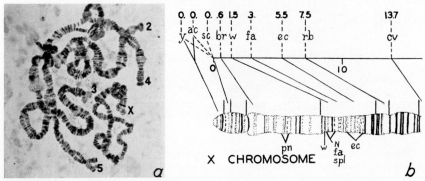

Figure 4.   Salivary chromosomes of flies (Painter 1935, 1937). *a,* Somatic chromosome conjugation in *Simulium;* the darkly staining bands are *chromomeres,* loci of genes. *b, below,* Part of salivary chromosome of *Drosophila melanogaster; above,* correlated gene map.

substances create conditions which favor the realization of one group of genic potentialities in some cells, and of another group in other cells. However, the exact nature of the interactions between cytoplasmic and nuclear determinants is not yet known.

The question of the *origin of the morphogenic substances* has often been raised. Its solution seems linked to that of the origin of the chromosomes and the genes. Of the two possibilities, namely, that they are newly formed in each generation under control of the nucleus, or that they are inherited by direct cytoplasmic transmission, the latter gains some support from the observation that the cell body is never a homogeneous mass. Structural differentiation and polarity are recognizable even in primordial germ cells.

In ovogenesis and spermatogenesis the histories of the nuclei and chromosomes are closely related, while those of the cytoplasm and its inclusions differ greatly according to sex. Ovogenesis results in the accumulation of nutritious reserves, and spermatogenesis in the development of an intricate apparatus of locomotion. Other characteristic traits are linked with these major differences.

In the tailless amphibians, and in all the higher vertebrates, *sperma-*

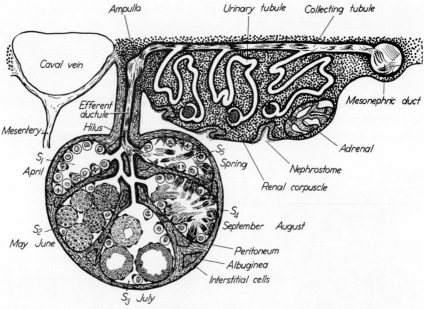

Figure 5.   Seasonal spermatogenic cycle in the frog. Diagrammatic cross section through testis and mesonephros. S_1–S_5, Seminal tubules containing progressive stages of spermatogenesis. S_1, Primary spermatogonia; S_2, four large follicles with secondary spermatogonia; S_3, two follicles with 1st and 2nd meiotic divisions, one with spermatids; S_4, spermiogenesis and transformation of follicular cells into sustentacular cells; S_5, release of sperms into rete and efferent ductules during breeding season. *Residual spermatogonia* in all seminal tubules.

togenesis takes its course within the seminal tubules of the testes (Fig. 5). The *primary spermatogonia* are fastened to the tubular walls. Each gonium is invested in a *follicle cell* (Fig. 6). Active spermatogenesis, which often is restricted to a short season in summer, begins with a rapid succession of mitotic divisions. Daughter cells resulting from spermatogonial divisions are supplied with an individual follicle cell. A number of so-called *residual spermatogonia* maintain this condition permanently and become the source for germ cell proliferations in subsequent years. The majority soon form clusters within common follicles (Fig. 6), and pass rapidly through a series of changes by which they transform into *sperms* (Fig. 7). Every summer the testes of the frog produce millions of sperms which derive from a comparatively small number of primary spermatogonia by repeated mitotic divisions, maturation, and spermiogenesis. The following presentations are based on the frog, but spermatogenesis proceeds similarly in all vertebrates.

2. MULTIPLICATION PHASE OF SPERMATOGENESIS

Resting (not dividing) *primary spermatogonia* (Fig. 6) are single and relatively large globular cells with clear *cytoplasm* and a large

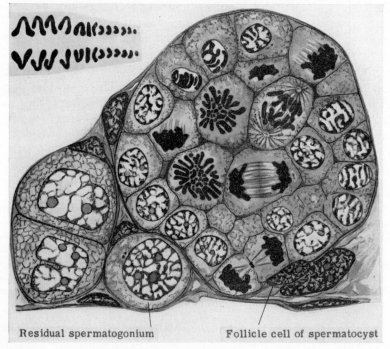

Residual spermatogonium   Follicle cell of spermatocyst

Figure 6.   Spermatogenesis in the frog: Multiplication phase. Residual spermatogonium and two follicles attached to the wall of a seminal tubule of the frog. Early follicle contains only two secondary spermatogonia, the advanced one over one hundred; resting, or in mitotic division. At upper left the 26 metaphasic chromosomes of a spermatogonium, arranged in pairs; × 1600.

nucleus. Their fine *chromatin network* spreads mainly along the inner surface of the *nuclear membrane,* with strands also attached to the centrally located *nucleoli.* In the cytoplasm, special techniques reveal the usual inclusions of granular type: *liposomes* (often called Golgi bodies) and *mitochondria.* The *central body* with two *centrioles* lies close to the nuclear membrane. *Secondary spermatogonia* (Fig. 6), lying in clusters within a common follicular cyst, decrease in size as they multiply; their resting nuclei become gradually more darkly stainable with hematoxylin and other basic dyes; one says they are now *basophil.*

Because of the high rate of multiplication, the secondary spermatogonia serve favorably for a study of the *mitotic process* (Fig. 6). It starts (*prophase*) with dissolution of the nucleoli and condensation of the chromatin network into 26 *chromosomes* of characteristic shapes. The central body divides and the daughter centers move apart. Next (*metaphase*) the nuclear membrane dissolves and the chromosomes assemble in the equatorial plane of the quickly forming *achromatic spindle.* A double set of 26 strong spindle fibers (traction fibers) connect the chromosomes with the central bodies. They fasten to the angle of the large V-shaped chromosomes, and slightly subterminally to rod-shaped chromosomes. At the place of attachment, a small corpuscle, the *kinetochore,* appears imbedded in the chromosome. Directed studies show that metaphasic chromosomes are double structures with halves separated by a very fine cleft. Each half has its own kinetochore, the two being attached to opposite spindle poles. Thus, in metaphase, everything is set for a division which will result in two daughter cells with 26 chromosomes each. While the spindle fibers contract, the twin chromosomes separate and move to the opposite poles (*anaphase*), where the reconstruction of daughter nuclei immediately begins (*telophase*). Nuclear division is followed by constriction of the cytoplasm and completion of cell division.

It is not known exactly when and how *duplication of chromomeres* occurs, though it can be safely assumed that new chromosomes are synthesized during the interkinetic phase. Recent spectrometric determinations of DNA content support this view and indicate that synthesis follows immediately after each cell division. According to all available evidence, chromosomes are never formed by free synthesis; even the smallest fragments, if lost, are not regenerated. In consideration of the necessary intricacy of chromosomal structure, the apparent ease, precision, and speed with which multiplication proceeds is truly remarkable.

A careful accounting of spermatogonial chromosomes in metaphasic plates shows that each morphologic type is twice represented. Hence, one can line up the 26 chromosomes of the frog in a series of 13 pairs (upper left of Fig. 6), each of which consists of a member of maternal and one of paternal origin. Members of such pairs are homologous and equivalent, except that in hybrids not all corresponding genes (or alleles) may be identical. In frogs every normal male is heterozygous, for one of the sex-determining genes. This means that a particular chromosome pair is made up of unequal partners. One, usually called the *X-chromosome,* contains a higher quantitative variant of a sex determining factor (F) than the other, the so-called *Y-chromosome* (with factor f). In Figure 6 this pair of *sex chromosomes* is probably the fourth from the left. In many other species X and Y show distinct size differences (Fig. 366).

3. MATURATION PHASE

a. Chromosome Conjugation (Synapsis). After a variable number of spermatogonial divisions, the mitotic process within the *follicular cysts* comes to a standstill, and a new series of changes is initiated which leads to the reduction of the chromosome number to one-half. During this phase, it is customary to designate the germ cells as *spermatocytes.* As they issue from the last spermatogonial division, their chromatin is a dense and regular network throughout the nucleus (Fig. 7a). A brief growth period follows, during which the chromatin network transforms into a number of long and very fine threads. One observes a tendency of these chromosomes to run parallel in pairs (Fig. 7b). During the characteristic *synaptene stage* (Fig. 7c) they are U-shaped loops, distinctly paired (conjugated), and with ends pointed toward the central body, while the curved middle parts pile up in the opposite half of the nuclear cavity.

The synaptic spermatocytes are relatively small and hard to preserve in a condition that would permit a detailed study of the *chromosome conjugation.* The corresponding stages in ovogenesis will be found more favorable for this purpose.

The polarization of the chromosome pairs disappears again while they contract (Fig. 7d, e) in preparation for the meiotic divisions. The composite nature of the pairs remains easily visible; but in fact each member chromosome is itself already a double thread or rod, as a result of the internal duplication which followed the last spermatogonial division. Therefore each "pair" of synaptic chromosomes actually consists of four threads. They are *tetrads,* 13 of them, and this term will be employed from here on, even if routine analysis of microscopic preparations permits clear recognition of only two elements.

From the above description of the course of events, it follows that of the four elements of a tetrad, two are of maternal and two of paternal descent. But certain genetic facts, known under the terms of *crossing over* and *recombination,* prove that equivalent pieces may become exchanged between conjugated maternal and paternal threads. As a result, each of the four threads of a postsynaptic tetrad may be composed differently of maternal and paternal segments. From here on one can no longer speak of maternal and paternal chromosomes. A true integration of the parental chromosomes has finally taken effect.

b. Reduction Divisions (Meiosis).   Conjugation is followed by two reducing or *meiotic divisions* (Fig. 7*f–n*). As a result, every spermatocyte yields four *spermatids,* each of which contains a single centriole and a single set of chromosomes (13 in the frog). Conventionally, one calls this the haploid number (n) as distinct from the diploid chromosome number $(2n)$, which was present in the spermatogonia (Fig. 6).

c. Spermiogenesis.   The spermatids are only one-fourth the size

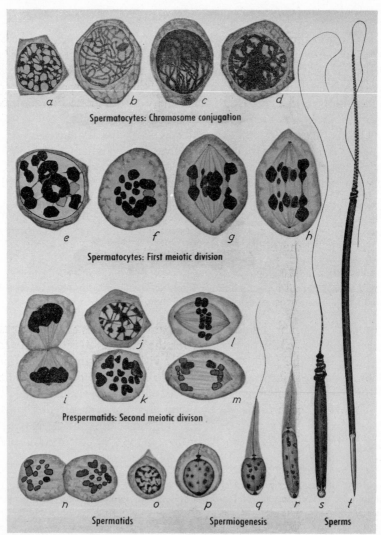

Figure 7.   *Spermatogenesis in the frog: Maturation phase.* Drawings of single cells arranged in a progressive series, from secondary spermatogonium just transforming into a spermatocyte (*a*), to mature sperms; the short and blunt *sylvatica* type (*s*) is more common than the pointed *temporaria* type (*t*); × 1900.

of a spermatocyte. While they transform into sperms (Fig. 7*o–t*) they diminish again by casting off some of their cytoplasm. Each nucleus retains the haploid complement of chromosomes and becomes the major part of the *head* of a sperm. The tip or *acrosome* starts as a derivative of the central body. The latter assumes an essential role also in the formation of the *middle piece* and the *tail filament*. With the bulk of cytoplasm shed as a *remnant body*, large numbers of mitochondrial granules also become discarded, though some remain included in the middle piece. Thus, only essential parts of the cell are retained, particularly the *chromosomes* which are the major hereditary substance of the sperm cell, the *central body* which furnishes the propelling apparatus in middle piece and tail, and the *liposomes* which enter into the formation of the acrosome. The possible importance of the retained *mitochondria* as carriers of enzymes or as morphogenic substances has often been alluded to, but remains undecided. The extreme reduction of the cytoplasm suggests that protoplasmic inheritance may be reserved mostly for the egg.

Having rid itself of nearly all encumbering elements, the sperm becomes dependent on the environment for sustenance. This is received temporarily from the *sustentacular cells* (of Sertoli) which first were associated with the primary spermatogonia and the spermatocytes as *follicle cells* (Fig. 6). At the time when the tails of the immature sperms grow out and the follicular cysts burst open into the lumen of

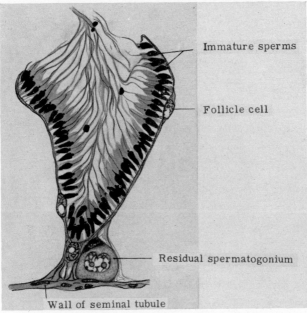

Immature sperms

Follicle cell

Residual spermatogonium

Wall of seminal tubule

Figure 8.   Frog, spermatogenesis. A follicle with immature spermatozoa breaks open; origin of sustentacular cells; × 600.

the seminal tubule (Figs. 5, 8), each follicle cell attracts a bundle of sperms and transforms simultaneously into a goblet-shaped nurse or sustentacular cell (Fig. 9). In frogs, sperms remain attached throughout the winter, often as long as six months. Once detached, they still may be stored for a short time in the mesonephric tubules and in the deferent ducts (Fig. 5). However, their vitality and capacity to fertilize eggs diminish rather quickly in this free condition.

The preceding description of spermatogenesis, though based on a study of amphibian material, also applies in all major points to the conditions in the other vertebrates. There are, of course, variations in less important features. The testicular structure shows a characteristic line of evolution from the lowest to the highest vertebrates. In the *lamprey*, the testis is not connected with the mesonephros. Sperms are released into the body cavity when the follicular cysts burst. In *selachians*, a urogenital connection through a system of tubules becomes first established. For *birds* and *mammals* it is characteristic that the follicle cells separate early from the spermatogonia, directly assuming their roles as sustentacular cells.

Considerable attention has been given to the taxonomic variation in *chromosome numbers*. Among mammals, some marsupials have as few as 6 but some rodents and carnivores as many as 40 chromosomes in the haploid sets. To mention a few specific cases, the haploid number is 11 in the opossum, 20 in the mouse, 21 in the rat, 39 in the dog, and

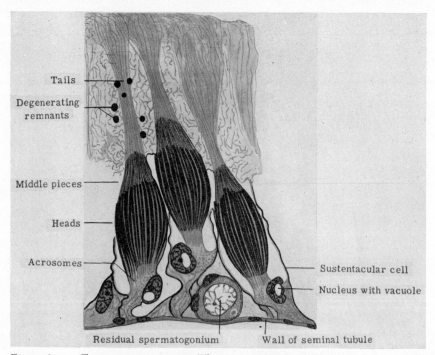

Figure 9.   Frog, spermatogenesis. Three sustentacular cells, each with a bundle of mature sperms; × 900.

24 in man. In the other vertebrate classes, one finds an even wider range. It is obvious that a haploid set represents the complete nuclear hereditary material of the species. The number of particles called chromosomes, into which this material is subdivided, seems rather irrelevant.

Sperms of various species differ remarkably in shape and size (compare Figs. 7s and t). The nuclear part of the head may be round and wedge-shaped or elongated to the extent that it resembles a fine needle. In some species, the acrosome assumes a bizarre form; the tail piece may carry undulating membranes. The significance of these wide variations is not clear. Gross differences are not necessary in order to prevent crossbreeding. Many fairly closely related species have similarly shaped sperms and yet do not interbreed. Nevertheless, the shape is probably not entirely without importance for the capacity of penetration. Among frogs the species temporaria, which has the longest and most sharply pointed sperm head (Fig. 7t), is also the most successful in cross-fertilizations.

Chapter 3

Ovogenesis

The development of the egg differs in important ways from that of the sperm. Its outstanding characteristics derive from the excessive growth of the cell body during the maturation phase. This trait is linked with other distinctive features such as immobility of the egg, low number of ovogonial mitoses, and early start of the maturation processes.

Spermatogonia and ovogonia both start development from similar numbers of primary gonia which are of identical size. But during later development, mitotic multiplication in the testis by far exceeds that in the ovary. One cubic centimeter of normal human seminal fluid contains from 60 million to 100 million sperms and the total number of spermatocytes produced in a lifetime is estimated as of the order of one million millions (10^{12}). On the other hand, the total ovocyte production of a normal woman is probably not exceeding 5 million and of that number only rarely as many as 500 will completely mature and be released from the ovarian follicles.

The diameters of early synaptic spermatocytes and ovocytes show only a 2:3 ratio (10 μ and 15 μ in the frog); but the mature human egg has about *1000* times the volume of a spermatid and more than *10,000* times that of a sperm. In the frog the latter ratio is about 1:300 million. In sharks, birds, and many other vertebrates, the relative size of the egg is even more impressive.

24

The remarkable growth of the egg takes place during the *auxocyte stage* which follows synapsis and lasts, often with interruptions, until the start of the meiotic divisions. It is during this time that the ovocyte becomes the largest of all cells, in almost every vertebrate species. Even the nucleus may become perceptible by the naked eye. It contains large quantities of fluid and sometimes is called a *germinal vesicle*.

The eggs of amphibians may be considered as representative of the primitive vertebrate type while those of birds and mammals are extreme modifications in opposite directions. The development of the three types will be described separately.

1. AMPHIBIAN OVOGENESIS

The following outline is based on observations on salamanders and frogs. As in spermatogenesis, one distinguishes a *multiplication phase* and a *maturation phase*. Ovogonial multiplication takes place in the surface layer of the ovary, called the *cortex*. In adult females it becomes a seasonal occurrence, high mitotic activity usually following ovulation by one or two months. Cytologically, the ovogonia do not differ from spermatogonia (Fig. 10a, 10b). They contain double sets of chromo-

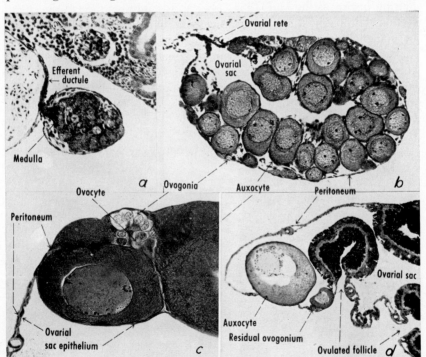

Figure 10.   Sex glands of the wood frog (*R. sylvatica*). Cross sections through immature testis (*a*) and ovary (*b*), at the metamorphosis stage; × 135. *c*, Germ patch in the wall of the adult ovary with residual ovogonia and ovocytes; × 200. *d*, Adult ovary after ovulation, with empty follicle and two immature ovocytes; × 66.

somes (26 in most frog species, 28 in salamanders, and 22 or 24 in newts). *Residual ovogonia* are found throughout life. In the adult ovary they lie concentrated in small *germ patches* which are distributed over the otherwise much reduced, thin, and sterile cortex (Fig. 10). After a series of free ovogonial mitoses, a brief follicular cyst stage follows. The number of secondary ovogonial divisions being low, the cysts contain only small numbers of ovocytes (2–32) when maturation starts.

After the synaptene stage, the follicle cells furnish each ovocyte with an individual envelope, the *granulosa*. Time relations differ widely from those in spermatogenesis. As a rule the ovocyte stage lasts from one to two years, i.e., until ovulation (Fig. 10*d*), contrasting with the duration of only about one month for the entire spermatocyte development.

a. Chromosome Conjugation (Synapsis).   In females, the maturation process starts much earlier than in the males (compare Figs. 10*a*, *b*). At metamorphosis, the ovaries contain not only synaptic ovocytes, but also fairly large auxocytes, i.e., growing immature eggs (Fig. 10*b*). In the ovocytes of salamanders, the conjugation of the chromosomes is more clearly displayed than in almost any other material (Fig. 11). Pairing begins at the ends (Fig. 11*a*) and progresses toward the middle sections. Probably the gross arrangement in polarized pairs is effected by some chromosome-centriole relationship. In the finer adjustments for homologous conjugation and in the final approach of corresponding chromomeres, attraction forces of small electrical charges may conceivably play a role. Photomicrographs show that the chromatic nodules unite more closely than the achromatic parts of the chromosomes (Fig. 11*b*).

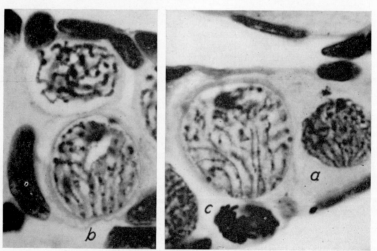

Figure 11.   Synaptic ovocytes of the salamander (*Ambystoma maculatum*). *a, b, c,* Three successive stages; × 1000.

Synaptic ovocytes differ from spermatocytes by the persistence of a large nucleolar body in the animal half of the nuclear cavity (cf. Figs. 11 and 7*b, c, d*). The movements and arrangements of the conjugating chromosomes are obviously the same as in spermatogenesis. It is only toward the end of the synaptene stage that the ways of male and female germ cell development definitely part. Instead of contracting, the ovocyte chromosomes are spreading (Fig. 11*c*). A multitude of very delicate branches or loops become visible which create the peculiar fuzzy appearance that suggested for them the name of *lampbrush chromosomes* (Figs. 12*c*, 12*d*). Nucleus and cell body now enter the period of extensive growth.

b. Auxocyte Stage. In ovocytes of the early growth stage, new, small *nucleoli* appear like droplets of dew, scattered over the delicate chromatin threads. As they grow, they disengage, float in the nuclear sap, and then collect under the inner surface of the nuclear membrane (Fig. 12). This pattern of nucleolar development remains unchanged for about one year, during which period the lampbrush chromosomes attain their maximal elaboration (Figs. 12*c*, 12*d*).

About the middle of the second summer, when the egg has grown to the size of 0.5 mm., the chromosomes concentrate in the center of the nucleus (Fig. 13*a*). This results in a striking arrangement. The inner nuclear space is filled with chromosomes and a fine dust of chromidia, while the peripheral zone contains the nucleoli. In the latter half of the second summer, the eggs attain full size. While the germinal vesicle further increases, the chromosomes and nucleoli remain confined to its central region (Figs. 13*a*, 14). The major part of the vesicle contains only clear nuclear fluid. At the approach of the breeding season in spring, it moves toward the animal pole where it becomes flattened against the inner surface of the egg. The chromosomes ascend to the top of the nucleolar cloud (Fig. 14).

The described nuclear changes are accompanied by a remarkable *development of the cell body*. Polarity and a visible diversity of cytoplasmic differentiation along the main axis are in evidence at all stages, from ovogonia to mature eggs. The *central body* lies on the vegetal side of the ovocyte nucleus. Together with the center of the nucleus, it positions the *main axis of the cell*. The clear *ground substance* or *matrix* of the cytoplasm contains a loose network of *protein fibrils*. They assume shorter or globular shapes while changing from the half-solid to a fluid consistency (gel ⇌ sol conditions).

Rapidly growing ovocytes are always darkly staining with basic dyes. This reaction indicates the presence of large quantities of *ribonucleic acid*. The acid is not evenly distributed but associated with the fibrils. The latter are dotted with minute *chromidia* and simulate the chromosome structure, on a smaller scale. The *basophil reaction* disappears in the full-grown egg, which lies inactive in its ovarian follicle.

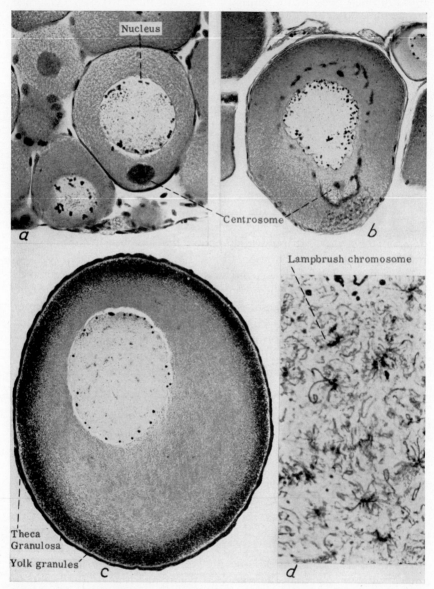

Figure 12.   Growth stages of ovocytes in amphibians: *a,* at the end of the first season, prominent central bodies with two centrioles; frog, × 270; *b,* early in the second season, dispersion of the central mitochondria (dark) and liposomes (numerous light vacuoles); frog, × 135; *c,* slightly older ovocyte, start of yolk formation (black granules), vesicular nucleus with nucleoli (dark dots), and lampbrush chromosomes; *Ambystoma maculatum,* × 135; *d,* lampbrush chromosomes from specimen in previous figure; × 500.

Some of the fibrils are *lipoproteins,* that is, conjugated proteins with fatty acids. If oriented in parallel bundles, they show birefringence. This is the case in the clear layer of centrifuged cells, but also in mitotic spindles.

The growing ovocytes become food stores, accumulating non-living, so-called *deutoplasmic granules* of various chemical compositions and different size ranges. In frog eggs one distinguishes at least three types of very fine *mitochondria, liposomes, yolk platelets,* and *fat* or *oil droplets.*

The *central mitochondria,* at the beginning aggregated with the centrosome (Fig. 12*a*), later spread around the nucleus and toward the periphery (Figs. 12*b,* 14). Possibly these granules are identical with the above described chromidia of protein fibrils. The second type appears in the growing ovocytes soon after the synaptic stage. One may characterize them as *diffuse mitochondria* since they are distributed through the entire cell body. Lastly, the *peripheral* (or *cortical*) mitochondria are present during the time of most rapid growth of the ovocyte in the clear zone immediately beneath the egg membrane (Fig. 12*c*). It is evident that, in its growth, the ovocyte depends entirely on supplies which it receives through the encasing follicle cells. These materials pass through the follicular and ovocyte membranes as solutes. It is probable that the *peripheral mitochondria* are temporary precipitates of recently absorbed proteins. They do not accumulate in very large amounts but seem to become converted readily into other types of cell constituents.

In post-synaptic auxocytes the *central body* is still closely attached to the wall of the nucleus. It then moves deeper into the cytoplasm and swells through accumulation of *liposomes* (Golgi bodies) and *mitochondria* around the *centrioles* (Fig. 12*a,* diameter 125 μ). In tangential sections (upper left of Fig. 12*a*), one recognizes easily the two chromophobe centrioles. The main body appears vacuolated because the liposomes dissolve in sections prepared by standard techniques. During the first summer, the development of most ovocytes does not progress much beyond this stage. But in the following spring, in eggs nearly half a millimeter in diameter, the central body begins to dissociate (Fig. 12*b,* diameter 350 μ). The centrioles fragment into a dozen or more small pieces which disperse in the cytoplasm. It is probable that some later partake in the formation of the polar spindles. The *mitochondria* and the *liposomes* spread in a characteristic pattern around the nucleus and toward the vegetal pole (Fig. 12*b*). The distribution of the liposomes is linked with the production of *yolk platelets,* which starts in the vegetal polar cap. Yolk first appears in the peripheral zone of eggs about the middle of the second summer (Fig. 12*c*).

In the *full-grown egg* of about 2 mm. diameter (Fig. 14) yolk platelets are scattered throughout the cell body. The largest ones are contained in a cup-shaped zone, rising from the vegetal pole toward and beyond the equator. Finer platelets fill the hollow of this cup, up to the animal surface of the egg. *Pigment granules* are mixed with the finer type of yolk (Fig. 13c). They accumulate in a dense layer under the surface of the animal half of the egg, thinning out toward the vegetal pole. Pigmentation is found in most species that deposit eggs in places where they are exposed to bright light. It protects nuclei and cytoplasm against injurious irradiation.

During the last phase of ovocyte growth, the *cell membrane* becomes conspicuously thickened, partly by apposition from the outside. Consisting of very clear and transparent material, it corresponds to the pellucid membrane of mammalian eggs but more usually it is given the name of *vitelline membrane*.

c. Reduction Divisions (Meiosis).   In the further development, several events become closely coupled. In frogs, ovulation normally occurs after a female has been clasped by a male. In a very short time, often within minutes, a hundred to several thousand eggs become released from their follicular membranes and drop into the body cavity. The nuclear membrane dissolves, nucleoli and nuclear fluid mix with the surrounding yolk, and the chromosomes move to a place slightly beneath the egg membrane at the animal pole. The compact tetrads arrange themselves in the equatorial plane of the quickly forming first polar spindle of the egg (Fig. 13b). The first meiotic division follows while the eggs are still in the body cavity, or during their descent through the oviducts. Occasionally it is delayed until the eggs have reached the lower oviducts, called uteri. While the eggs assemble here, the first polar body, containing half the chromosomal material, is cut off. Accordingly, into the second polar spindle enter the remaining n chromosome *dyads* (half-tetrads; Fig. 13c). At this stage, the autonomous development comes to a standstill. Unless the eggs become fertilized or artificially stimulated, they will not give off the second polar body or start embryonic development. Normally, the developmental arrest at the stage of the second polar spindle lasts only a few hours, and ends when the eggs are extruded from the uteri and become inseminated. The activation of the egg by the entering sperm induces completion of the second meiotic division.

The meiotic chromosomes of frogs are less contracted in ovogenesis than in spermatogenesis; the longer ones are V-shaped, not ovoid. As in spermatogenesis the morphologic pictures might seem to suggest that the first meiotic division segregates the original conjugants which lined up during the synaptic stage. But as a result of crossing over, the post-synaptic chromosomes actually are composites of maternal and paternal segments. At completion of the second meiotic division the egg retains a pro-nucleus with only the haploid number of single chromosomes (Fig. 14).

d. Follicular Apparatus. From the start of their development, the female germ cells are located between two epithelia, the peritoneum and the ovarial sac (Fig. 10*b*). Moreover, the individual ovogonia as well as the auxocytes are tightly encased in *follicle cells*. At the end of the synaptic stage the follicle cells start to multiply (Fig. 11*c*) and thus give rise to the many-celled *granulosa*, which is applied to the egg membrane. Its outside originally borders on the loose stroma which fills the open spaces between the peritoneum and ovarial sac. The blood vessels also run through this stroma, and some become closely associated with the surface of the granulosa. They are the supply lines through which oxygen and food are carried toward the growing egg cells. As the auxocytes continue growing they project more and more deeply into

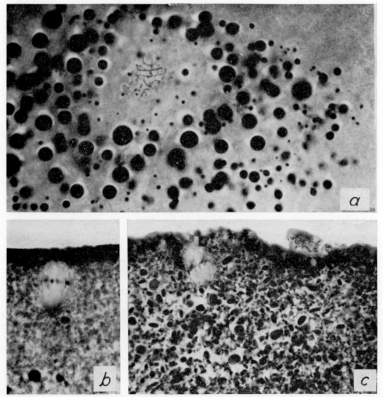

Figure 13. Meiosis in the frog egg; × 600. *a*, Part of nucleus of full grown ovocyte at start of breeding season; nucleolar aggregation and contracting tetrad chromosomes. *b*, First meiotic spindle (metaphase) at animal pole of ovulated egg; with tetrad chromosomes. *c*, First polar body and second meiotic spindle of egg from the uterus; dyad chromosomes.

the ovarial sacs (Fig. 10*b*) and thus receive a second epithelial envelope—the *theca* (Figs. 10*c*, 10*d*, 12*b*). Little stroma remains between granulosa and theca, though in this narrow space a system of fine capillaries persist which continue supplying the egg. The granulosa serves as a system of nurse cells, placed between the blood vessels and the egg. The theca fastens the egg to the surface of the ovary (Figs. 10*d*, 12*b*), leaving the part of the granulosa uncovered which borders

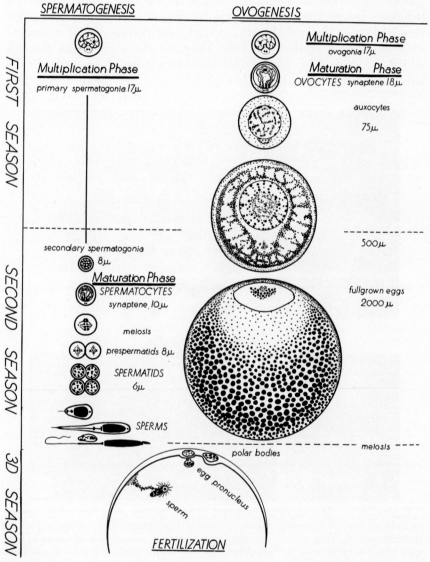

Figure 14.   Succession of major events in amphibian spermatogenesis and ovogenesis; diagram.

on the peritoneum. At the time of ovulation, only granulosa and peritoneum rupture; the theca remains intact. With the expulsion of the egg, the entire follicular apparatus contracts into a compact body (Fig. 10d) which resembles empty follicles of mammalian ovaries but fails to transform into a luteal body.

e. **Comparison of Spermatogenesis and Ovogenesis in Amphibia.** Figure 14 illustrates diagrammatically the essential similarities and differences in spermatogenesis and ovogenesis, namely: (1) reduction of diploid gonial chromosome sets to haploid sets in the mature gametes of both sexes; (2) time differences in start and duration of the maturation process; (3) increase of cell size in ovogenesis and decrease in spermatogenesis; (4) polar body formation in the egg—each ovocyte produces only one mature egg, while each spermatocyte furnishes four mature sperms; (5) disappearance of the centrioles in the egg and their persistence in the sperm.

2. AVIAN OVOGENESIS

The development of birds' eggs is similar to that of amphibians, and a description of the multiplication and early maturation phases would be repetitious except for minor and unessential detail. But there are four distinguishing features, all representing adaptations to special conditions of avian reproduction, which call for a short discussion.

a. **Reduction of the Reproductive Rate.** It is a widely observed rule that the reproductive rate declines as the chances of survival improve. While a single frog may release up to 10,000 eggs in every breeding season, the common starling lays only from five to seven. Yet, within 60 years following its importation into America, this bird has increased from 120, the number released in Central Park, New York, to a population of many millions—possibly close to one billion.

Though the cause of the restriction of reproduction remains obscure, its working mechanism is quite obvious. As a rule, female starlings do not ovulate more than a total of 50 eggs in a lifetime. Yet in the ovary of a hatching (13-day-old) nestling one counts about 100,000 ovocytes. Similar conditions prevail in all birds (Fig. 15). By selective breeding of best-laying flocks of domestic chickens and ducks, egg production has been increased, and may total over 1000—sometimes over 300 in a year. But even under such artificial conditions, the number of mature and ovulated eggs is small if compared with that of the ovocytes present in the ovaries of hatching chicks.

Egg production in birds becomes reduced by two means. First, the *multiplication phase becomes restricted* to the prehatching period. About four days to one week before hatching, most ovogonia transform into ovocytes. No germ patches remain from which, as in amphibians, new sets of ovocytes might arise in subsequent years. At hatching time, the number of ovocytes is so high that further production would be mere waste.

The second control measure is linked with the *seasonal breeding habits* of wild birds. The ovary of starlings weighs about 8 mg. during early winter and contains ovocytes measuring between 15 and 500 μ. In spring, as many as 100 or more ovocytes grow beyond that size. In February, the ovarian weight already averages 50 mg. and by mid-April, immediately before egg-laying begins, it attains 220 mg., nearly 30 times the original weight of the inactive season (Fig. 16). The largest ovocytes have diameters up to 4 mm. During the following days, from five to eight eggs are ovulated. The remaining enlarged ovocytes disappear by resorption within the ovary. Degenerating follicles are numerous throughout the incubation period, and nodules of remnant follicle cells may still be found late in November. Thus the second means of reducing the reproductive rate is the *follicular resorption of ovocytes*. From the presented facts, it appears that atresia (non-opening) is by far the more common fate of a follicle than ovulation.

A simple experiment proves that all enlarging follicles would be capable of maturing. If one removes daily one egg from a sparrow nest, beginning on the second day of laying, the female continues production for a considerable time.

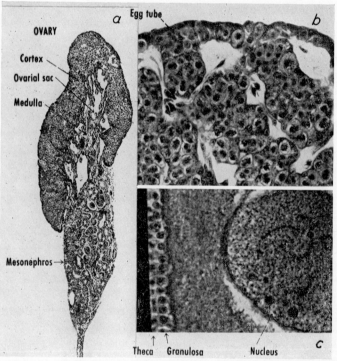

Figure 15. *a,* Cross section through ovary and mesonephros of a redwing blackbird (*Agelaius phoeniceus*) at the time of hatching. The cortex of this section contains close to one thousand synaptic ovocytes; the entire ovary over 100,000; $\times$ 50; *b,* part of cortex enlarged; $\times$ 333. *c,* Starling, part of ovarial auxocyte with large follicle cells; nucleus with lampbrush chromosomes; $\times$ 333.

More than 50 normal eggs may be delivered. This shows that broodiness, which in the sparrow will not develop unless three to five eggs are in the nest, is linked with the cessation of egg production.

b. Prominence of the Follicular Apparatus. As in amphibians, the auxocyte is enclosed in a *granulosa* and a *theca*. The origin of these envelopes is the same in both classes. The theca is composed of some stroma cells which grow out from the ovarial sacs (Fig. 15) and penetrate between the post-synaptic follicles. The development of the granulosa offers a striking picture. It starts from the follicle cells of the ovogonia, which multiply rapidly at the early auxocyte stage and form a single-layered squamous epithelium, much as in amphibians. But as the egg continues to grow, the granulosa cells become cuboid and then cylindric. When the diameter of the egg measures 1 mm. they are very large, each with a round nucleus and a prominent central body in the peripheral cytoblast (Fig. 15c). Later, the granulosa becomes two or three layers deep, and its cells decrease in size as they become more numerous. At all stages one observes clear signs of the nursing functions which the granulosa cells assume, supplying the egg with all materials necessary for its tremendous growth.

c. Final Growth Period. The most distinctive character of the avian egg, its extreme size, is acquired during about seven or eight days preceding ovulation. At the start of this period the structure of the auxocytes is essentially that of ripe amphibian eggs (Fig. 14). A lens-shaped or almost globular body of cytoplasm in the animal hemisphere contains the nucleus and some finely granulated yolk. It is partly enclosed in the mass of heavier yolk of the vegetal hemisphere. Every day of the week preceding laying the diameter of the hen's egg in-

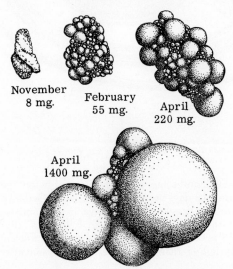

November
8 mg.

February
55 mg.

April
220 mg.

April
1400 mg.

Figure 16.   Four starling ovaries illustrating seasonal growth of egg follicles; × 2.

creases about 4 mm. Starling and sparrow eggs add about 2.5 and 2.0 mm. (Figs. 16, 17). The spurt of growth is graphically illustrated in Figure 17. It continues day and night, but from midnight until morning the added material contains relatively little fat and more protein and water. The high fat content of the yolk deposited in day-time is responsible for its deeper yellow color, because in the fats concentrate the yellow carotenoids that are ingested with the food. Thus, a thin layer of white and a heavy layer of yellow yolk are added every day. The concentric arrangement is interrupted beneath the animal pole. Since the nucleus follows the surface layer of the growing egg, and is always surrounded by ovoplasm containing little fat, a column of white yolk material extends from the center of the egg (the latebra) to the surface (Fig. 17).

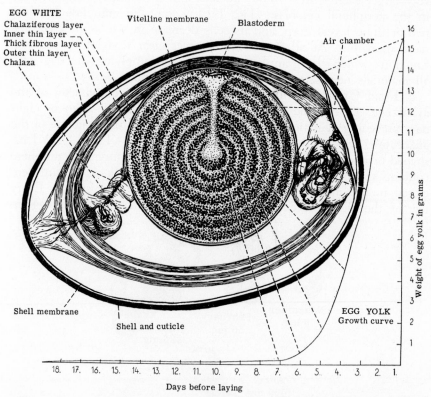

Figure 17.   Growth and composition of hen's egg before incubation. (Weight curve of ovocyte during 18 days preceding laying, after Gerhartz 1914.) The cells of the *blastoderm* are drawn relatively too large in size and too few in number. *White yolk* is lightly stippled, *yellow yolk* is heavily stippled (the central white yolk was called *latebra of Purkinje,* that below the blastoderm *nucleus of Pander*). Egg yolk, being relatively lighter than egg white, tends to ascend toward the highest part of the shell.

Song birds lay their clutch in daily succession, usually without interruptions. Consequently in ovaries collected at the beginning of the laying season, the four or five largest eggs illustrate the daily amount of growth during this period (Figs. 16, 18).

d. Assemblage and Laying of the Cleidoic Egg.   At the time of ovulation the avian egg contains large stores of proteins, fats, vitamins, and mineral salts. But to cover the needs of growth and subsistence up to hatching time, it is still short of the larger parts of water and proteins. Both become added in the form of a thin solution of albumen, the *egg white*, during the passage through the oviduct and the sojourn in the uterus. When it is ready to be laid, the bird's egg within its shell is a self-sufficient unit, depending on the environment only for oxygen supply. It is a closed-type or *cleidoic egg*.

The ovulating avian egg falls into the body cavity, and is fertilized immediately or after its entrance into the *infundibulum* or *funnel* part of the oviduct, within about 15 minutes. In all birds, the left duct alone grows to functional size, and with a few exceptions, such as accipitrine hawks, only the left ovary matures eggs. The egg is conveyed through the short infundibulum and after another 15 minutes (in the hen) it enters the longest section of the oviduct, the *magnum* (Fig. 18). The walls of this part contain large and numerous albumen-secreting glands. They produce a coat of albumen which becomes applied to the surface of the egg. It consists of several chemically separate proteins, but mainly of ovalbumin (about 80%) and ovomucoid (glycoproteins, 10 to 20%).

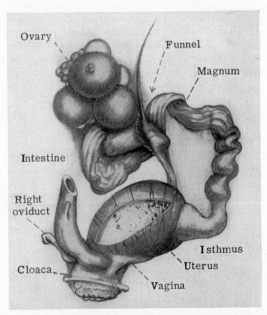

Figure 18.   Ovary and oviduct of a sparrow after artificial stimulation of egg growth and ovulation with gonadotrophic hormone of pregnant mare serum. Uterus partly opened to show ovulated egg with colored shell (Witschi 1935); × 1.4.

From the magnum, the egg passes into the thinner-walled *isthmus* where the shell membrane, consisting of keratin fibers, is added. Finally, it enters the *uterus* (Fig 18). Here its volume becomes doubled through absorption of *water*. This involves a considerable stretching of the shell membrane. The albumen now becomes distinctly stratified; an inner-most fine layer, containing many mucin fibers, forms a capsule around the yolk and projects from opposite sides in the shape of twisted cords (chalazae), toward the pointed and the blunt ends of the egg (Fig. 17). The egg white is stratified in three layers, which, according to differences in fluidity, are designated as the inner thin, the thick, and the outer thin albumen. They differ more in colloidal structure than in protein content.

While the shell membrane is still expanding, crystals of calcium carbonate (calcite) become deposited on its surface. This leads to the formation of a *shell* which has a rather spongy structure in its deeper part, but is more dense, though still porous, at its surface. Keratin fibers fill the pores and also form a fine cuticular film over the entire surface. The shell serves a variety of purposes. It gives mechanical protection and, together with the shell membrane, guards against loss of too much water. At the same time it permits the free exchange of respiratory gases. The *air chamber,* at the broad end of the egg, makes its appearance only after the egg has been laid. It slowly enlarges as some water is lost by evaporation.

Shells of hens' eggs are only faintly pigmented, while those of many other species show a double *coloration.* A general diffuse color, often green-blue (ovo-cyan), is produced in the wall of the uterus and deposited together with the calcite. Spots and streaks of brown (ovoporphyrin) are most often added, together with the cuticle, to the surface of the shell. This pigment forms in the upper parts of the oviduct and floats in droplets in the albumen which is to form the

Table 2

Composition of the Egg of the Domestic Hen

Average weight 58 gm.

CONSTITUENTS	EGG YOLK 32%	EGG WHITE 57%	SHELL 11%	TOTAL 100%
	%	%	%	%
Water	50	86	—	65
Protein	16 (3 gm.)	13 (4 gm.)	—	12.5
Fat	32 (6 gm.)	traces	—	10
Calcite	—	—	94	
Shell keratin	—	—	4	11
Other*	2	1	2	1.5
Total	100	100	100	100

* Carbohydrates total some 300 mg. of which 200 mg. is free glucose (80 mg. in the yolk, 120 mg. in the egg white).

keratinous fibers of the cuticle of the shell. Since the egg lies in the uterus with the broad end toward the oviduct (Fig. 18), it is understandable that generally the heaviest sprinkling with brown dots is found in a zone around this pole. Large droplets sometimes get caught between the uterine wall and the shell, or move straight downward, and inscribe on the shells "kymograph recordings" of the intra-uterine rotations of the eggs. Occasionally, even the turning of the egg, which leaves the uterus with the broad end first, becomes recorded (Fig. 19). All shell colors are derivatives of hemoglobin.

The *material composition of the hen's egg* has been studied in great detail. It is summarized in Table 2. The abundance of fats is an adaptation of the energy metabolism to the cleidoic condition. In amphibians, in which the nitrogenous waste products immediately pass into the ambient water, up to 30 per cent of the original protein stores are burned and serve as a source of energy before feeding begins. The corresponding figure in the chick is below 4 per cent. Instead of proteins, a large quantity of fat is utilized, which gives carbon dioxide and water as end products.

In the domestic chicken the normal interval between *ovulation and laying* is from 25 to 26 hours. Of these the egg spends about three in the magnum, one in the isthmus, and 20 in the uterus. In pigeons and doves, which produce clutches of only two, the interval is from 38 to 39 hours. Most song birds, with clutches of from four to seven, are daily layers. Ovulation of a new egg often follows laying of the preceding one within half an hour. Possibly the two processes are stimulated by a common hormonal factor. In this habit of serial egg production, the birds differ from reptiles which grow, ovulate, and lay their large clutches at one time. It is quite probable that the condition in birds developed as an adaptation to their aviatic life habits.

Birds' eggs are relatively large, exceeding in some small species 10 per cent of the adult body weight. Enclosed in unelastic, breakable shells they can only be laid, because the avian pelvis has not the shape of a girdle but is wide open, ventrally.

Figure 19.   Egg shells of the redwing with natural color marks; the downward movement of the cuticle-forming albumen (perpendicular lines) as well as the right turning rotation of the egg shells in the uterus (horizontal lines) becomes registered when the shells make contact with large drops of dye; × 1.

3. MAMMALIAN OVOGENESIS

Ovogonial multiplication is also in mammals restricted to the embry-onic and fetal stages (including nestling stages with sealed eyelids, in small species). In the human, one observes first synaptic ovocytes in fetuses of over 10 weeks and 50 mm. crown-rump length. At 15 weeks (100 mm.) the ovocytes have become predominant and ovogonial mul-tiplication is nearing its end. An estimate on the basis of partial counts places the number of germ cells in the neighborhood of 5 million. During the second part of pregnancy, follicular degeneration sets in which partly offsets further increases. The ovaries of a newborn female child contain somewhere between 5 and 10 million ovocytes; but no ovogonia are left. Through the years of childhood and maturity this number decreases until about age 45, when the last ovocytes disappear. The exhaustion of the germ cell component of the ovaries is followed by physiologic disturbances and readjustments which mark the so-called climacteric period in the life of women.

During a woman's reproductive years not over 400 eggs are actually ovulated. Thus, a majority of several millions end by degeneration within the ovaries. Resorbing eggs and follicles are widely observed in the ovaries of all mammalian females of reproductive age. *Atretic degeneration* must be regarded as a normal and well regulated process. It results in a reduction of reproductive rates to levels which differ from species to species, but always are quite low.

While the *growth or auxocyte period* in avian ovogenesis extends beyond the amphibian prototype, it is relatively shortened in all mam-mals above the monotremes. In the latter, the eggs ("yolks") still attain diameters of 3 to 5 mm. In marsupials and eutherians growth stops much earlier (Table 3, page 65). The human egg with an average of 130 μ is one of the largest, having nearly twice the diameter of rat and mouse eggs.

The *mature egg* of the mouse has a homogeneous, finely granular cytoplasm. That of the rat contains clouds of a coarser type of inclu-sions (Fig. 23). In the hamster even some true yolk is formed. Of course, all mammalian eggs must contain nutritious stores sufficient to sustain life and development during cleavage and up to implantation. They are acquired mainly during the development of the secondary ovarian follicles, preceding final maturation and ovulation, when the ovocytes grow from 15 μ or less to the characteristic ovulation size of the species (70 μ in the rat; Figs. 20a, b, c, 21).

As in amphibians and birds, the *follicular apparatus* consists of *granulosa* and *theca*. Its development during the stage of the early auxocyte is essentially identical with that of the avian type. Later, when the growth of the egg lags, the follicle still continues enlarging. The granulosa becomes many layers thick and clefts appear within its cell mass (Fig. 20). At this characteristic stage, the follicle of the rat measures about 150 μ and the egg 60 μ; in man the corresponding figures are 300 μ and 100 μ. With continued follicular growth the clefts coalesce and form large *follicular cavities* or *antrums* (Figs. 20, 21, 22). At the approach of ovulation the follicles expand more rapidly, measuring ultimately about 1.5 mm. in the rat and 15 mm. in man. The follicular fluid has a high content of sex hormones, which indicates that the follicular apparatus grows beyond the size of the egg because it has to fulfill its functions as a gland of internal secretion. During all these transformations, the ovocyte is surrounded by a distinct *pellucid membrane* and deeply embedded in a mass of granulosa cells, the *cumulus,* which projects into the follicular cavity (Fig. 21).

The *final stages of the maturation process,* with the meiotic divisions, occur during ovulation and fertilization. Soon after dissolution of the nuclear membrane, the cumulus, by liquefaction at its base, begins to separate from the investment layer of the granulosa. Simultaneously the

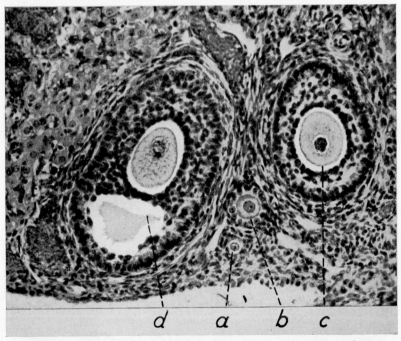

Figure 20.   Part of section of adult rat ovary, showing four early stages of auxocyte and follicle development. *a,* Beginning growth stage, ovocyte with two squamous follicle cells; *b,* enlarged ovocyte within follicular capsule (granulosa) of cuboidal cells (16 in this section); *c,* nearly full grown ovocyte with pellucid membrane; granulosa several layers thick; distinct theca; *d,* ovocyte full grown; granulosa and theca enlarge rapidly; small follicular cavity (antrum) within the granulosa; × 250.

follicle begins to thin out where it borders on the ovarian capsule. The latter process is independent of the original location of the cumulus (Fig. 22).

Because of their relatively small size, the mammalian eggs are well suited for a study of the *meiotic process*. In mice and rats the first cleavage spindle arises near the center of the egg, within a zone of clear ovoplasm. It then moves nearer to the animal pole, where the egg is capped by a thickened vitelline membrane (Fig. 23). It contains 20 tetrads in the mouse, 21 in the rat. During the later metaphase and throughout the anaphase it seems as if the entire egg were going to divide equally (Fig. 23*d, e*). A cleavage plate rises from the center of the spindle toward the surface, where it divides the thickened part of the membrane. But some changes, occurring during early telophase, initiate the unequal division of the cell body. The broad mitochondrial plate in the center of the spindle becomes attached between the halves of the polar membrane (Fig. 23*e*). Next, one pole of the spindle, together with the compact mass of n chromosome dyads, swings up toward the surface of the egg (Fig. 23*f*). Then the chromosomes slip under the adjacent polar membrane, and a protoplasmic bud is constricted off, the small *first polar body* (Fig. 23*f–i*). As a rule, the first

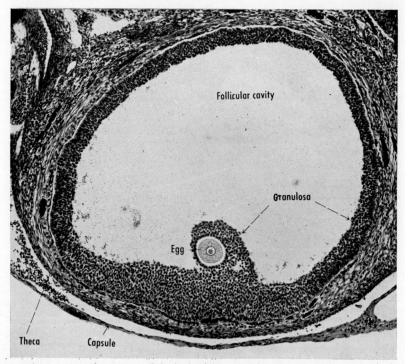

Figure 21.   Full grown ovarian follicle with large cavity; from female rat, immediately before ovulation. Around the ovocyte the granulosa rises in the cumulus; × 100.

polar body divides completely or partially, soon after its formation (Fig 23*i*).

By this time the cumulus has become detached and the egg floats toward the thin end of the follicle, where an *ovulation pore* forms, piercing granulosa and peritoneal epithelium. Some follicular fluid seeps out and carries the egg into the ovarian capsule (Fig. 24). The cumulus cells, now the *corona* of the egg, become partly mucified and produce long fibroid streamers.

During ovulation (Fig. 24*b*) and while the eggs pass from the ovarian capsule through the funnel or infundibulum into the oviduct (Fig. 24*c, d*), the *second meiotic spindle* with *n* chromosome dyads becomes organized. As one might expect, the spindle lies under the remaining thickened membrane, parallel to the surface and perpendicular to the position of the first spindle (Fig. 25*a*).

If no spermatozoa are present in the oviducts, the second meiotic division is not carried to normal completion. About 24 hours after ovulation, unfertilized eggs of the rat have lost their corona and fragment irregularly. The pieces may first resemble normal blastomeres but the chromosomal distribution is irregular and within another day the entire batch disappears.

In the normal course of reproduction, the eggs meet with sperms in the upper, distended oviduct (Fig. 25*a*). They are still surrounded

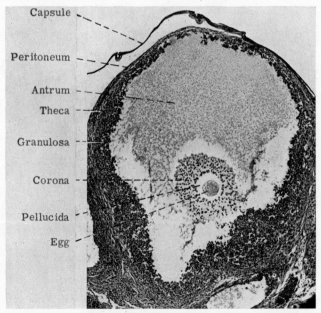

Figure 22. Mature follicle, early phase of ovulation. Under the ovarial surface, granulosa and theca have become very thin. Cumulus, detaching from parietal granulosa, transforms into corona. Female rat, 8 hours after copulation; × 66.

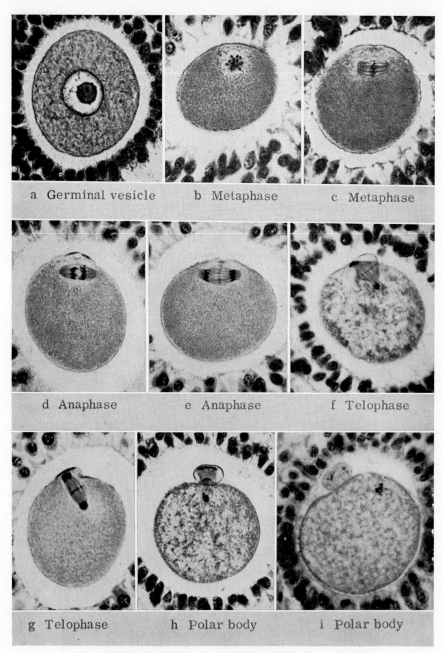

Figure 23.   Stages of maturation of the ovocyte within the ovarian follicle. *a,* Same egg as in Fig. 21; *b–h,* first meiotic division; *,* division of the first polar body, formation of the second polar spindle; the pellucid membrane swells. *a, f, h,* and *i* from the rat, others from the mouse; all × 450.

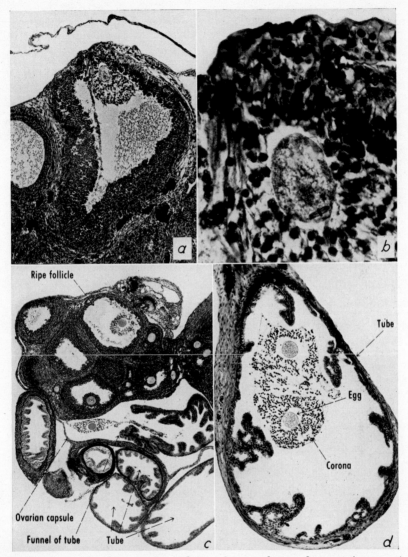

Figure 24.   *Ovulation. a,* Rat, 8 hours after copulation; the egg is just entering the follicular ovulation pore; nearly half of the corona has passed into the ovarian capsule, turning to the right; follicle contracting; × 66. *b,* Same follicle, more enlarged detail, showing second meiotic spindle, structure of corona, theca, and granulosa cells; × 265. *c,* Section through ovary and oviduct of mouse during ovulation. In the ovary a large follicle with detaching ovocyte. In the ovarian capsule an ovocyte with corona, being drawn into the funnel of the tube; several loops of the tube are sectioned, some highly distended; × 40. *d,* Two fertilized eggs in the tube of a rat, 10 hours after copulation; the corona cells begin to dissociate; × 66.

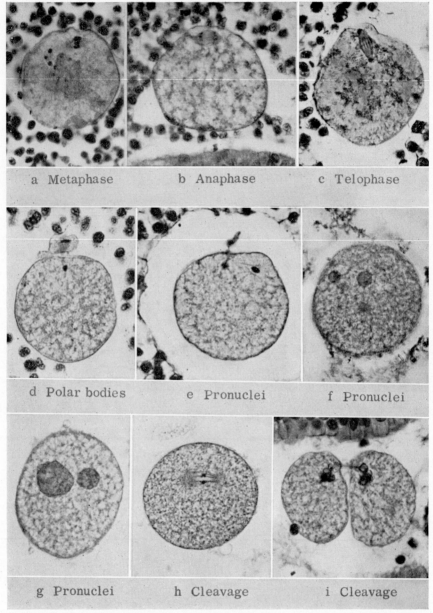

a Metaphase   b Anaphase   c Telophase

d Polar bodies   e Pronuclei   f Pronuclei

g Pronuclei   h Cleavage   i Cleavage

Figure 25.   *Rat eggs in the tube;* fertilization, second meiotic division and first cleavage division. *a,* Newly fertilized egg; second polar spindle; two sperms between vitelline membrane and surface of the egg (at 6 and 7 o'clock); 8 hours after copulation. *b, c,* Second meiotic division, 10 h. *d,* Second polar body close to remnant of the first one; sperm head near surface (at 10 o'clock) in small area of dense cytoplasm; 11 h. *e,* Both pronuclei small and dense; sperm pronucleus in center of large protoplasmic sphere; 12 h. *f, g,* Pronuclei become vesicular, corona disintegrates; 12–24 h. *h,* First cleavage spindle with polar asters, in excentric position; 30 h. *i,* Early two-cell stage, remnants of cleavage spindle; vesicular chromosomes begin to fuse; 35 h. × 450.

46

by mucified corona cells which seem to present no obstacle to approaching sperms. As the first sperm head pierces the vitelline membrane the meiotic process becomes reactivated. The anaphasic and telophasic events closely resemble those of the first division. The spindle remains parallel with the surface during anaphase (Fig. 25b), then rises to a radial position initiating the deflection of the plane of cell division. As a sequel to these changes the second polar body is formed, by unequal cell division. The furrow that is indicated first in the anaphase stage, instead of progressing radially, veers tangentially (Fig. 25c) and a second polar body is cut off which is of nearly the same size as the first (Fig. 25d). By this time, the first polar body usually has degenerated or completely disappeared.

A single set of chromosomes now remains in the egg, first as a compact body; but within the next few hours it transforms into a vesicular egg-pronucleus (Fig. 25e–g), preparatory to fusion with the sperm nucleus and initiation of cleavage (Fig. 25h, i).

Section Three

The Start of Ontogenesis

Chapter 4

Fertilization

1. AMPHIMIXIS AND ACTIVATION

Fertilization is complicated by a number of intricate arrangements which promote the successful union of egg and sperm. However, the elements of chance and hazard are never fully eliminated. The sperms are suspended by millions in the spermatic fluid or semen. Though motile, their propelling force is small, and usually inadequate to account for the entire journey to the eggs and penetration of their envelopes and membranes.

Most fishes, frogs, and toads eject eggs and sperms into the water, the males usually squirting the semen over the eggs. In such *external fertilization,* a close synchronization is essential, since the eggs can be fertilized only immediately after discharge. Sperms may retain their motility and capacity of fertilization for several hours, even if the semen ("milk" of the male fish) is diluted with water. Eggs, however, become non-fertilizable after contact with water, probably because their swollen membranes are impenetrable for sperms. *Artificial insemination* of frog and trout eggs, to be successful, must be done by the "dry method," that is, by spreading sperm suspensions over mature eggs before submersion in water.

Newts and salamanders have a peculiar method of *internal fertilization.* The males enclose drops of spermatic fluid in coagulating albuminous secretions of the cloacal glands, and deposit them on twigs and stones at the breeding places. These *spermatophores* are picked

50

up by the females, and the sperms become stored in recesses of the cloaca. The eggs are inseminated as they leave the oviducts and pass through the cloaca. They are deposited singly, or in small clusters. If the sperms ascend into the oviducts, intra-uterine development of embryos and larvae can follow.

Internal fertilization through copulation is practiced by a few groups of teleosts (e.g., the viviparous *Poeciliidae*), by the sharks, and by all reptiles, birds, and mammals. During ejaculation, the semen is moved with considerable speed from the storage places (testis, epididymis, deferent duct, seminal vesicles) through the peripheral sex ducts of the male, by pressure created in the muscular walls of these organs. The ascent through the female ducts is slower. In some mammals (rabbit, cat, dog, rat) peristaltic movements in the uterus churn the contents of this part of the genital tract, so that after a short time a nearly homogeneous sperm suspension fills the lumen from the vagina to the tubal ends of uterine horns. In the rat and the dog, sperms reach the uterine opening of the oviducal tubes about 30 seconds after ejaculation, in the rabbit only after about 10 minutes. In the lining of the tubes, one can see bands of ciliated cells, most or all of which beat downward. By their action, they move the liquid contents so that they stream down along the wall and reascend in counter currents through the center. This circulation may help the progress of sperms in the tubes. It has also been suggested that movements of inner folds of the tubes (Fig. 24d) sustain the migration. But the possibility of sperms making this stretch of their journey by self-propulsion is not ruled out. Mammalian sperms in favorable media and under normal temperature conditions can travel from 3 to 6 mm. per minute. This rate would seem adequate for the task, since the ascent actually takes several hours (about four in the rabbit). In mammals, the large majority of the sperms remain in the uteri and disintegrate. The upper parts of the tubes, where fertilization actually takes place, never contain them in very large numbers.

Male gametes retain full viability and fertilizing power over long periods, when stored in the testes or male sex ducts (half a year in the testis of frogs, one month in the epididymis of the guinea pig). After ejaculation, their life duration usually becomes limited to less than one day. Notable exceptions to this rule are furnished by some teleosts, birds, and bats, in whose oviducts sperms remain alive for weeks or months.

Human sperms may ascend to the upper parts of the oviducts in about six hours. They lose their fertilizing capacity within 12 to 48 hours. However, opinions quite at variance with these have also been given. The viability of unfertilized ovulated eggs diminishes rapidly. Frog eggs may be retained in the uteri four to ten days, depending on temperature. Mammalian eggs remain fertilizable from four to possibly 20 hours.

In the final union of eggs and sperms, *chemical substances* play important roles. Three groups of substances can be distinguished:

(a) Substances released by the eggs into the ambient water, which serve to orient the sperm movement toward the surface of the egg. They also increase the activity and the metabolic rate of the sperms. Chemically they seem to differ widely according to species and therefore may selectively attract sperms of their own or of closely related species only. The term *gamone* has been introduced for this class of hormone-like substances released by gametes into the surrounding media.

(b) Complementary substances (possibly glycoproteins), which have been extracted from eggs and sperms and given the names *fertilizin* and *antifertilizin*. If added to a suspension of sperms, fertilizin will cause agglutination (sticking together) and formation of clumps of sperms. Similarly, antifertilizin agglutinates eggs. In solution both are an impediment to fertilization. But normally, they are located on the surface of the eggs (fertilizin) and sperms (antifertilizin). Their reaction may be essential for the early stages of the fertilization process, probably by fixation of the sperm to the egg membrane.

(c) *Proteolytic enzymes* of the sperm, which cause disintegration of follicle cells and membranes around the eggs and of the cortical substance of the egg itself. They are stored in the acrosomal part of the sperm. They prepare a path for the entrance of the sperm and activate the egg, inducing resumption of its development. Their chemical nature is unknown, though they show a suggestive resemblance to tryptic enzymes.

The proteolytic enzymes produce extensive visible reactions in the cortical cytoplasm of the eggs. Vacuolation of the surface layer, starting from the entrance point of the sperm (Fig. 26a), quickly spreads and leads to the shedding of the cell membrane now called *fertilization membrane*.

In most eggs, and particularly those of large size, sperms gain entrance close to the animal pole (Fig. 25). Exceptions to this rule are, however, frequently observed in small eggs (Fig. 33). According to some reports, the tail of the sperm, instead of following head and middle piece into the egg, may break off. If the whole gamete enters, the substances of the tail do not play any obvious role in the further progress of fertilization, but soon disappear in the cell body of the egg (Fig. 26). The middle piece exhibits striking signs of activity. Its centriole becomes the center of a sphere of clear protoplasm from which astral rays radiate into the body of the egg (Figs. 25e, 26b, 27b, 33). This aster moves toward the main axis of the egg, followed by the sperm-head that transforms into the vesicular *sperm pronucleus*. It regresses before the final approach of the pronuclei (Fig. 27c), but reappears in preparation for the first cleavage division. In amphibians the entrance point of the sperm on the surface and its track through the ovoplasm remain recognizable for some time because of the accumulation of numerous brown pigment granules (Figs. 26b, 29a).

The haploid *egg pronucleus* which forms after completion of the second meiotic division (Fig. 27a) steadily grows and at the same time moves in the direction of the center of the egg, until it meets with the sperm pronucleus (Figs. 25d–g, 26b). It is significant that the egg pronucleus, though growing to even larger size than the sperm pronucleus, accomplishes its movements in the absence of astral formations, and that no pigments are deposited to mark its path. In birds and mammals, sperm asters are indistinct spheres of cytoplasm (Fig. 25e). The nuclei themselves seem to be passive, and moved by protoplasmic forces to the physiologic center of the cell.

Counting from the time of sperm entrance, the second polar body is given off within half an hour in birds and frogs, one hour in newts, and two hours in rats. The pronuclei meet after about half an hour in birds, one hour in frogs, two or three hours in newts, and 10 to 15 hours in rats.

In some species the pronuclei unite into a single *fusion nucleus*. More often they remain separate through the prophase of the first cleavage division (Fig. 27c–e). In amphibians and birds the first cleavage mitosis follows almost immediately upon the meeting of the pronuclei. In mammals a considerable delay occurs (Fig. 25f–i), so that the two-cell stage is reached only from 12 (rabbit) to 24 hours (hamster, guinea pig, rat) after entrance of the sperm.

Effects of Fertilization.   The direct effect of the entrance of the sperm is the *activation of the egg*. The developmental arrest into which the egg lapsed after completion of the first meiotic division is overcome, and the maturation process is completed. Since the sperm lies at a

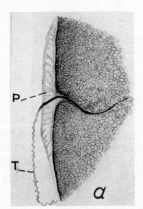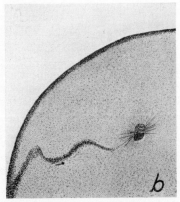

Figure 26.   Fertilization in the newt *Taricha torosa* (Daniel and Yarwood 1939). *a,* Entrance of sperm (*T,* tail; *P,* foam-like ovoplasm surrounding sperm head); *b,* sperm track, pronuclei, aster of first cleavage spindle.

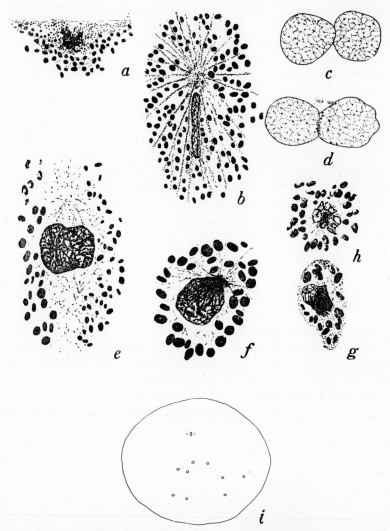

Figure 27.   Nuclear development following fertilization in the newt (Fankhauser 1932, 1941). *a,* Telophase chromosomes of second meiotic division of the egg. *b,* Same egg, sperm head in transformation to pronucleus; with aster; 2 hours after insemination; *c,* the pronuclei meet, at 4 hours; *d,* reappearance of centrosomes close to the pronuclei, at 5 hours; *e,* formation of cleavage spindle; *f,* aster of degenerating accessory sperm, 7 hours after insemination; *g* and *h,* degenerating accessory sperms at the four-cell stage, about 12 hours after insemination; × 425. *i,* Position of cleavage spindle and accessory sperms in newt egg, 7 hours after insemination; × 15.

considerable distance from the polar spindle, activation must be effected by transmission through chemical agents. It seems most likely that the proteolytic enzymes of the sperm, reacting with the cortical cytoplasm of the egg, are responsible for this activation, as well as the blocking of entrance of more sperms, and the shedding of the fertilization membrane.

A far-reaching consequence of fertilization is *amphimixis*, i.e., the bringing together of two chromosome sets with their hereditary potentialities. Numerically, fertilization restores the diploid chromosome condition, as it existed in the germ cells (ovogonia and spermatogonia) before the onset of the maturation process. But with respect to genetic quality, the fusion nucleus (or zygotic nucleus) receives maternal and paternal elements in a wide array of combinations.

2. ARTIFICIAL INSEMINATION

For many experimental purposes, but also in livestock breeding and occasionally in clinical practice, artificial insemination has become a valuable technique. It consists in the collection of sperm suspensions from testes or ejaculates, their proper storage, and their transmission into the female genital ducts or bringing them into direct contact with the eggs. Sperms collected in test tubes can be stored for hours and days (up to one week in some instances), if carefully sealed with exclusion of air and kept at low temperature (3 to 10° C.). Of late, methods of deep freezing have been developed which seem to open possibilities of storage over almost unlimited times. Recently some normal human offspring have been delivered as the result of artificial inseminations with semen that had been stored at −70° C. Artificial insemination of fish and amphibian eggs by the dry method is easily performed. Newly ovulated eggs of laboratory rodents may be transferred to glass dishes, inseminated and then returned into the oviducts or uteri of the same or some other female. In poultry and livestock breeding, artificial insemination by injection of sperm suspensions into the uterine sections of the genital ducts has now become a standard technique of wide application. One of the economically important aspects is the possibility of dividing one ejaculate of a valuable sire into a number of fully potent portions.

3. POLYPLOIDY

In rare cases, animals may develop with more than the usual two sets of chromosomes. This condition may arise in several ways, but most often through participation of more than one single set of ovocyte chromosomes in the formation of the cleavage nucleus. Extreme temperature and anesthetics have a tendency to suppress cell division, often without interfering with chromosome duplication. Recently it has been discovered that exposure of freshly fertilized eggs of newts and salamanders to extreme temperatures—from 0° to 3° C. for a duration of about 20 hours or from 35° to 37° C. for five minutes—results in high percentages of triploid larvae. It seems quite probable that the treatment suppresses the completion of the second meiotic division, and that the dyads of the spindle $(2n)$ together with the chromosomes of the sperm (n) give origin to the triploid cleavage nucleus. Tetraploid and pentaploid larvae are even more rare than triploids. Incomplete nuclear division without subsequent cell division is the probable source of such high chromosome numbers.

4. POLYSPERMY

Eggs of small size, such as those of ascidians and mammals and even those of frogs, effectively control insemination, preventing entrance of more than one sperm. Contact with the first sperm elicits a reaction in the surface layer of the egg which normally spreads fast enough to make the egg impervious to any which arrive later. This mechanism can be upset experimentally by damaging agents or by artificial insemination with highly concentrated spermatic fluids. However, the entrance of more than one sperm does not lead to triploidy or any other form of regular polyploidy. Each sperm introduces a centriole, which later gives origin to two astral centers. Hence, the cleavage spindles are doubled, or multipolar, and the cleavage process is irregular, often leading to early degeneration and death of the germs.

The larger eggs of selachians, reptiles, and birds, and also those of salamanders and newts, are slower in the prevention of superfertilization. In many species polyspermy becomes the rule. In order to prevent fusion of more than one sperm with the egg pronucleus, or interference of additional centrosomes with the formation of a normal cleavage spindle, new control mechanisms have developed, acting inside the ovoplasm. In newts, from one to twenty sperms enter the egg, mostly its animal hemisphere (Fig. 29A). When their asters begin to grow and enlarge, they repulse each other. They therefore become rather evenly spaced if present in large numbers. Toward the end of the third hour, the egg pronucleus comes in contact with the aster of the sperm nearest its path toward the egg center. During the next four hours, while the egg pronucleus unites with the principal sperm pronucleus and the first cleavage spindle is formed, the accessory sperm pronuclei are pushed into the yolk-filled vegetal hemisphere (Fig. 27i), where after some abortive attempts at mitotic division, they degenerate (Fig. 27f–h). Later they are resorbed or extruded into the cleavage cavity.

In sharks and birds the number of accessory sperms has been seen to vary from one to 60. Many accessory sperm nuclei divide several times but, as cleavage progresses, they are pushed into the outer plasmatic zone, where they degenerate and disappear. All attempts to ascribe a physiologic meaning to these cases of polyspermy remain unsatisfactory. Obviously, the egg develops just as well without, or with only few accessory sperms, as with large numbers. Very high numbers may prevent normal development. In the mammalian egg, as a rule, several sperms penetrate through the pellucid membrane, but only one actually enters the cell body (Fig. 25a, b). Polyspermy occurs also in the large egg of the duckbill (*Ornithorhynchus*).

5. PARTHENOGENESIS

Occasionally eggs can undergo development without the participation of sperms. In a number of invertebrates, such as plant lice, *spontaneous parthenogenesis* occurs as a regular form of reproduction. In mammals, degenerating unfertilized eggs in the ovaries or the oviducts often pass through a series of abnormal cell divisions, but development stops early, before initiation of embryo formation. Nevertheless, it is probable that *ovarian tumors,* which often contain histologically well differentiated embryomas, arise from parthenogenetically developing eggs. An interesting photograph published by Neumann shows an ovary with two independent teratomas, one with black, the other with blond hair (Fig. 28). Apparently Mendelian segregation had occurred; at least one polar body must have been given off by each egg.

Pincus performed experiments on *parthenogenesis* with unfertilized rabbit eggs, using exposure to low temperature (6° C. for 10 to 30 minutes) or hypotonic and hypertonic media as stimulating agents. More than half the number of tubal eggs thus treated gave some evidence of development, i.e., formation of the second polar body, and a few cleavage divisions. By reimplanting activated eggs into foster does, four normally born and viable rabbits were obtained from a total of some 800 eggs. The eggs of brook lampreys respond to chemical double

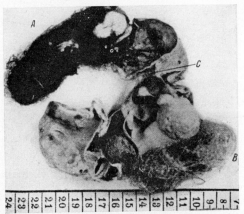

Figure 28.   Human ovary (C) with two embryomas; one with black (A) the other with blonde hair (B) (Neumann 1925).

treatments much like those of the sea urchin. But the resulting development is abnormal and never goes much beyond the gastrula stage.
Work with frog eggs proved most successful. Bataillon, by pricking
with fine needles near the animal pole, induced normal cleavage in a
large percentage of unfertilized eggs, and complete larval and adult
development in more exceptional cases. The chromosome number often
remains haploid; it can, however, become diploid or triploid by mechanisms that are not yet fully understood. Haploid embryos have a low
viability; they have never been seen to develop beyond larval stages.

At first sight the various methods of parthenogenetic stimulation
seem unrelated. Yet a further analysis suggests that all serve to substitute, directly or indirectly, for the effects of the proteolytic enzymes
of entering sperms.

If the technique of induced parthenogenesis could be improved,
it might become of value in the production of homozygous strains in
livestock breeding. Most promising are some methods of *partial parthenogenesis,* in which the stimulating factor of the entering sperm is
preserved while amphimixis is prevented. Two lines of experimentation
lead toward this goal: merogony and chromosome elimination by irradiation.

Merogony, or development of an egg fragment, usually is started by
fertilization of a normal egg. Soon afterward, the egg pronucleus is
removed by pipetting (Fig. 29C) or the egg is slowly constricted in
two by ligation (Fig. 29B). In the latter case, though the nuclear

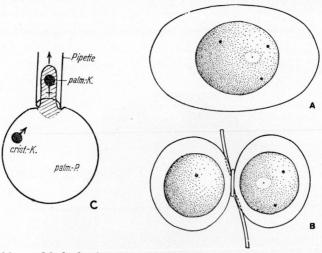

Figure 29.   Methods of merogony. *Right figures:* A, fertilized egg of a newt
with polar area (egg nucleus) and entrance points of three sperms; B, same egg
after ligation, divided in two parts; one contains only a sperm nucleus, the other
the egg nucleus and two sperm nuclei (Fankhauser 1932). C, Removal of the
polar spindle (ovocyte nucleus) from a *Triton palmatus* egg shortly after entrance
of a cristatus sperm (Hadorn 1936).

components become differently distributed, both parts may develop. The resulting possibilities are indicated diagrammatically in Figure 30. Constriction will not activate the egg; without fertilization, fragments with the second meiotic spindle remain quiescent (Fig. 31a). On the other hand, if ligated five to 30 minutes after fertilization, egg fragments without sperms but with the meiotic spindle give off the second polar body like normal eggs (Fig. 31b). Such activation of the egg may also lead to abortive attempts at cleavage. However, the nuclear divisions proceed abnormally, without polar asters and spindles (Fig. 31c–f). Apparently the missing centrioles cannot be restored.

Fragments containing one or several sperms may develop nearly normally. In favorable experimental series, over 10 per cent may resemble normal cleaving eggs insofar as one spindle with double asters (Fig. 31g) occupies a central position while additional sperms become displaced and degenerate. The resulting embryos and larvae are haploid. They rarely reach the stage of metamorphosis (Fig. 32). Since such *merogones* derive from egg fragments with maternal cytoplasm and paternal chromosomes, they may be expected to give conclusive information about the role of the cytoplasm in inheritance. Similar arrangements are also obtained through removal of the ovocyte chromosomes with a fine pipette, shortly after insemination of an egg (Fig. 29C). The results of some such experiments suggest that the development of certain epidermal characters is controlled by plasmatic factors.

Irradiation of the sperms with fairly high dosages of *x-rays* can damage the chromosomes to the extent that sooner or later following

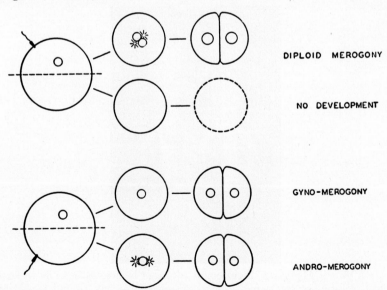

DIPLOID MEROGONY

NO DEVELOPMENT

GYNO-MEROGONY

ANDRO-MEROGONY

Figure 30.   Four types of egg fragments obtained by ligation of fertilized newt eggs (Fankhauser 1937).

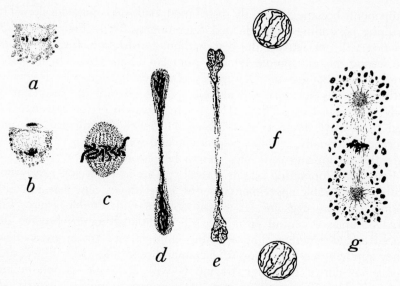

Figure 31.   Nuclear conditions in fragments of ligated newt eggs. *a,* Second meiotic spindle (metaphase) in fragment of ligated unfertilized egg, 24 hours after laying (no development); *b–f,* stages of nuclear development in fragments from fertilized eggs which contain the egg nucleus but no sperm; *b,* formation of polar body 1 hour 15 minutes after insemination, *c–f,* abnormal, anastral mitotic division of nuclei in unfertilized egg fragments. *g,* Normal cleavage spindle with haploid number of chromosomes from a fragment with sperm only; × 300 (Fankhauser 1937, 1932).

Figure 32.   *Merogony.* Right: most advanced haploid salamander so far obtained from any egg fragment without egg nucleus. At left, control animal from normal, fertilized egg. Both near end of metamorphosis; × 2.5 (Fankhauser 1937).

fertilization they degenerate and disappear. The possibilities of this method of production of offspring with chromosomes arising from only the female parent have not yet been fully explored.

This survey of experiments may suffice to show that the process of fertilization permits of many variations. Eggs can develop with chromosome numbers which greatly deviate from those of normal diploid sets. On the other hand large parts of the cell body can be removed and the remainder still may develop into an embryo. Since chromosomes and cytoplasm are the essential elements of the egg, and must contain all the factors that determine specific development, these results are very puzzling, at least at first sight. However, further careful study soon reveals that the possibilities of variation are definitely restricted. Embryos cannot develop very far if the egg had not at least one complete haploid set of chromosomes. Similarly, certain plasmatic elements cannot be dispensed with. Obviously the more penetrating analysis of the conditions involved in the activation and fertilization of the egg furnishes a means for the identification of these very factors of determination which, as a group, represent the *constitution of the developing egg.*

Chapter 5

Cleavage and

Gastrulation

1. CLEAVAGE AND BLASTULA FORMATION (ST. 1–7)

The patterns of cleavage and gastrulation are determined primarily by amount and distribution of the yolk. The eggs of chordates are of the telolecithal type, showing concentration of deutoplasmic substances toward the vegetal pole, and of finely structured protoplasm toward the animal pole. But the degree of axial differentiation varies widely between the very small and nearly yolk-free eggs of *Amphioxus* or mammals, and the extremely large eggs of selachians or birds. Yolk, an inert material, slows the progress of cell division in the vegetal parts. As a consequence, cleavage, which is nearly equal in *Amphioxus* and many ascidians (Fig. 33), becomes unequal (Fig. 34a) or partial (Fig. 34b). One distinguishes completely dividing or *holoblastic* and partially dividing or *meroblastic* eggs. The latter type leads to a disc-shaped accumulation of cleavage cells on top of an undivided yolk mass (Fig. 34b, c).

Egg size is not the only factor controlling the cleavage type. The degree of separation of deutoplasm and protoplasm is also of importance. In fertilized teleost eggs, it becomes almost complete. Their protoplasm collects at the surface, especially near the animal pole, while the yolk granules flow together into a single globular mass, which also includes the fat droplets (Fig. 34). This clean separa-

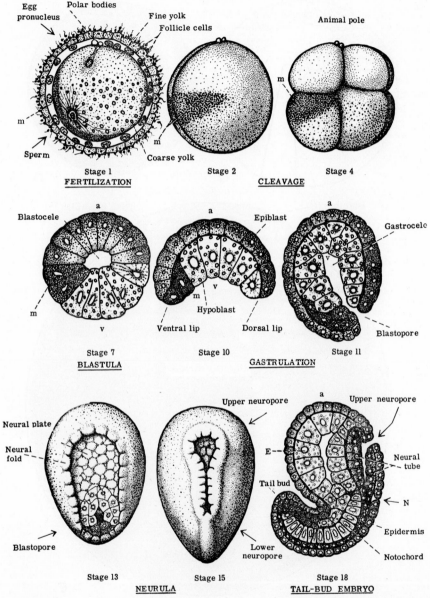

Figure 33.   Ascidian egg (*Ascidia mentula*); fertilization and early stages of development. The newly fertilized egg (St. 1) is shown within its follicular envelopes, which are omitted in the later stages. Large numbers of supernumerary sperms are attached to the surface of the follicle; *a,* animal pole, *m,* mitochondrial aggregations in prospective ventral mesoderm cells, *v,* vegetal pole. Stages 2 and 4 are left lateral views, 13 and 15 dorsal views, all others show sagittal sections.

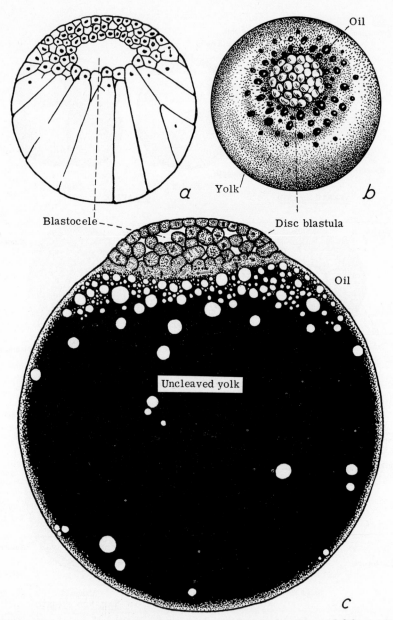

Figure 34.   *a,* Sagittal section through early blastula of ganoid fish; unequal but total cleavage (St. 7); × 16. *b,* Blastodisc and yolk sphere of the trout, 1 day after fertilization (St. 7); × 12. *c,* Trout, axial section through similar stage (St. 7); irregular cleavage cavity (blastocele) separates epiblast and hypoblast; basal layer forms a syncytium; protoplasmic surface layer (stippled) encloses yolk mass (black) and oil droplets (white); × 30.

tion is the cause for the meroblastic cleavage type of all teleost eggs, most of which are only of moderate size. As may be seen from Table 3, the cleavage type remains fairly constant within large taxonomic groups—notwithstanding considerable variation in the egg size. The cells along the periphery and at the base of the *blastodiscs* may remain in open communication with the yolk mass (blastocones, Fig. 35), or form a continuous syncytium (Fig. 34).

The small eggs of mammals resemble those of ascidians and of *Amphioxus*. However, their dearth in yolk is not primitive, but acquired following the evolution of placental feeding methods. In the duck-bill (*Ornithorhynchus*) cleavage is of the discoid type (Fig. 36), the same as in reptiles and birds. In the smaller eggs of marsupials, an extrusion of yolk occurs which is reminiscent of the meroblastic type (Figs. 37, 38). Even the eggs of the eutherian mammals which are of a similar size range to those of ascidians and *Amphioxus*, follow a pattern more closely related to that of the meroblastic monotremes than primitive holoblastic types.

Cleavage furrows show a tendency to become oriented after a generalized pattern. Usually, the first two cut each other at right angles in the polar axis and the third one stands nearly at right angles to the first two. While the former are meridional in position, the third one is latitudinal (Figs. 33, 42, St. 1–4). Later, with increase in number and decrease in size of the cells, the regularity of pattern becomes less pronounced.

Evidence is accumulating that vertebrate eggs have a bilaterally symmetric as well as a polar structure, even before fertilization. This structure, together with such modifying factors as gravity and accidental position of the sperm entrance point, determines the position of the

Table 3

Egg Size and Cleavage Type in Various Groups of Chordates

TAXONOMIC GROUP	SIZE IN MM.	CLEAVAGE TYPE
Ascidians	0.1–0.7	Holoblastic
Amphioxus	0.12	Holoblastic
Lampreys (Hyperoartia)	1.0	Holoblastic
Hagfish (Hyperotretia)	22 × 8	Meroblastic
Selachians	15–100	Meroblastic
Teleosts	0.8–6	Meroblastic
Ganoids	2–3.5	Holoblastic
Dipnoans	3–7	Holoblastic
Amphibians	1–7	Holoblastic
Reptilians, oviparous	8–40	Meroblastic
Reptilians, smallest viviparous	3	Meroblastic
Birds	6–85	Meroblastic
Monotremes	3–4.5	Meroblastic
Marsupials	0.15–0.25	Holoblastic, with yolk extrusion
Eutheria	0.06–0.14	Secondarily
Man	0.12–0.14	holoblastic

cleavage planes. The first furrow most often coincides with the future sagittal plane of the embryo (separating left and right halves) and the second furrow with the frontal plane (separating dorsal and ventral parts). However, exceptions occur frequently. The first furrow may have the frontal position or form various angles with the sagittal plane. Such variations are without consequence for the orientation of the developing embryo. Cleavage planes merely tend to follow the pre-

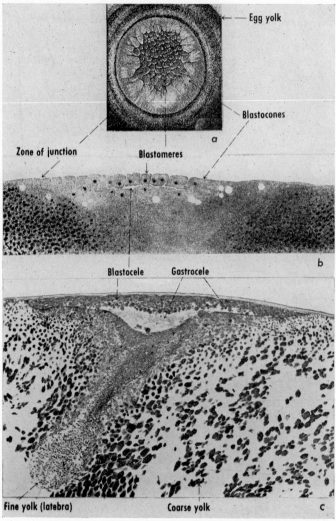

Figure 35.   Chick; *a,* surface view and *b,* axial section of disc blastula of uterine egg (St. 7); both show closed and open cells (blastomeres and blastocones); irregular cleavage cavity (blastocele) between epiblast and hypoblast; × 7.2 and × 34 Duval 1889). *c,* Sagittal section through disc gastrula of the sparrow (St. 9); at the dorsal circumference (left) the edge is thick; ventrally it is thin; epiblast and hypoblast are closely apposed; × 40.

existing structural patterns, but neither determine nor modify the main axes of the germ.

At the free surface of cleaving germs, the blastomeres are highly coherent and assume an epithelial character, while in their depth they have rounded surfaces and remain more independent. As a consequence, there appear open spaces that coalesce and form a continuous *cleavage cavity*. This is called the *blastocele*, when the germ reaches the blastula stage (Figs. 33, 34c, 39, St. 7).

Amphioxus and ascidians furnish chordate embryology with the ideal prototype of a *blastula*. It consists of an epithelial blastoderm, only one cell deep, which encloses a spherical blastocele (Fig. 33). In the holoblastic eggs of frogs and salamanders, the blastocele locates in the animal hemisphere (Fig. 39). At the beginning of gastrulation, the wall of the blastula is thin and epithelial in the animal half, but consists of a solid mass of cuboidal cells in the vegetal half of the germ. In ganoids, dipnoans, and amphibians with very large eggs (Table 3), the cavity is small, lens-shaped, and lies in the polar region of the germ (Fig. 34a). Finally, in meroblastic *disc blastulae* of teleosts and birds it is reduced to a narrow and irregular cleft (Figs. 34c, 35b).

2. GASTRULATION (ST. 8-11)

So far, the embryonic development has consisted mainly of mitotic activity, but *differentiation* becomes of predominant importance with the beginning of gastrulation. Literally, and when applied to celenterate development, the term *gastrulation* means stomach formation. But its technical use is extended, and refers to a period in development during which the primitive germ assumes a *two-layered condition*. The processes by which this is attained differ in various taxonomic groups and cleavage types; but at the end, always a separation into an outer layer, the *epiblast,* and an inner layer, the *hypoblast,* is accomplished. The

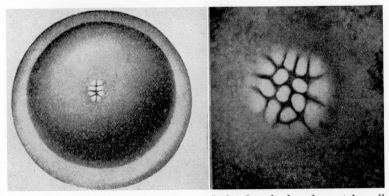

Figure 36. Cleavage in monotremes. Left: *Ornithorhynchus,* eight cells on top of the large yolk mass (St. 4); right: *Echidna,* blastodisc of 16 cells (St. 5); (J. P. Hill, from Brachet-Dalcq 1935.)

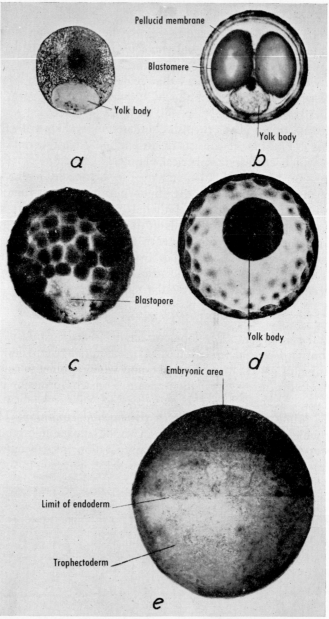

Figure 37.   Early stages of the marsupial *Dasyurus* (J. P. Hill 1910). *a,* Egg, at the time of the first cleavage division (St. 1); note yolk body near vegetal pole; *b,* two-cell stage (within membrane); yolk body extruded (St. 2); *c, d,* early blasto-cysts, showing delayed closure of ectotrophoblast at vegetal pole; yolk body within the central cavity (St. 7); *e,* late blastocyst, (St. 13). *a–d* × 75; *e* × 10.

hypoblast borders on a cavity, the *gastrocele* or *archenteron,* which usually communicates to the outside through an opening of variable size and shape, the *blastopore.*

a. AMPHIOXUS AND ASCIDIANS

In *Amphioxus* and ascidians, the single-layer blastula becomes a double-layer gastrula by *invagination* of the vegetal hemisphere (Fig. 33, St. 7–10) and succeeding *epiboly* or overgrowth of the hypoblast by the epiblast (Fig. 33, St. 11). During these developments the blastocele becomes gradually compressed. The cells of the vegetal hemisphere of the blastula become the hypoblast, and those of the animal hemisphere become the epiblast. The hypoblast consists of fewer but larger cells than the epiblast and contains stores of nutritious materials. While the blastocele disappears, a new cavity forms in the hollow of the invaginating hypoblast. This is the *gastrocele.* At the beginning, it has a wide opening, the *blastopore,* which, in the course of the epibolic process, narrows to a small passage (Fig. 33, St. 10, 11).

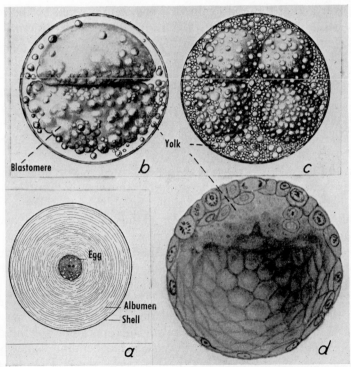

Figure 38.   Early stages of the development of the opossum (marsupials). *a,* Tubal egg with pellucid zone, albumen, and shell membrane (total diameter 0.6 mm., St. 1); *b,* two cells (St. 2), yolk elimination starting; *c,* four cells (St. 3), yolk elimination far progressed; *d,* blastocyst (St. 7), with primitive endoderm layer; yolk in the upper blastocyst cavity (gastrocele). (E. McCrady 1938.)

b. AMPHIBIANS

In amphibians, differences in the coloration of the animal and vegetal hemispheres, but also of the ventral and dorsal sides of the blastulae, have been given a great deal of attention. Although the general appearance seems to indicate a radial symmetry of all parts around the main axis, a close study of the distribution of the surface pigments of most species reveals the presence of a gray crescent below the equator, with pointed ends reaching about halfway around the circumference of the eggs (Fig. 42, St. 7, 8). The center of this gray crescent is in the dorsal midline. Together with the two poles of the egg, it determines the *sagittal plane*. The existence of a bilateral symmetry of plasmatic structure can be traced back even to the unfertilized egg.

The course of gastrulation (Fig. 42, St. 8–11) is rendered more complicated than in *Amphioxus,* by the presence of considerable amounts of yolk in the vegetal blastomeres (Fig. 39). In principle, it still consists of *invagination* and *epiboly,* the two processes running concurrently. Downgrowth of the animal hemisphere is conspicuous from the very beginning. The vegetal half becomes tucked in and turned over and at the end is almost completely covered by the former animal hemisphere, now the epiblast. In their participation in this process, ventral and dorsal parts differ markedly. Around the dorsal lip, relatively small cells of prospective oral endoderm, head mesenchyme, and notochord move swiftly to the inside. On the ventral side, where the yolk mass remains attached to the blastopore lip, invagination is almost at a standstill. Consequently, the completed gastrula has the shape of a pouch with a lining that is very thick on one side. Otherwise, it resembles that of *Amphioxus* rather closely (compare Fig. 39, St. 11 with Fig. 33, St. 11).

From the outside, gastrulation is first indicated by the appearance of a slightly bent furrow below the center of the gray crescent (Fig. 42, St. 8). The fold above this furrow is the dorsal lip of the blastopore. As gastrulation proceeds, lateral and ventral lips become added and the blastopore becomes successively sickle-shaped and finally circular (Fig. 42, St. 9, 10). The yolk mass slowly sinks to the inside. During late gastrula stages it still protrudes through the pore as a so-called *yolk plug,* reducing the opening to a circular cleft (Fig. 42, St. 11). This cleft is shallow ventrally, but gradually deepens toward the dorsal side.

From the depth of the dorsal gastrulation furrow arises the *invagination canal*. It forms immediately following the appearance of the dorsal blastopore lip, and plunges into the yolk mass, bending somewhat to the dorsal side. As it approaches the blastocele, the end of the canal begins to widen (Fig. 39, St. 8). Distending like an inflated rubber balloon, it becomes the *gastrocele* which gradually displaces the blastocele (Fig. 39, St. 10, 11). By the end of gastrulation, the blastocele has become reduced to a narrow cleft between the epiblastic and hypo-

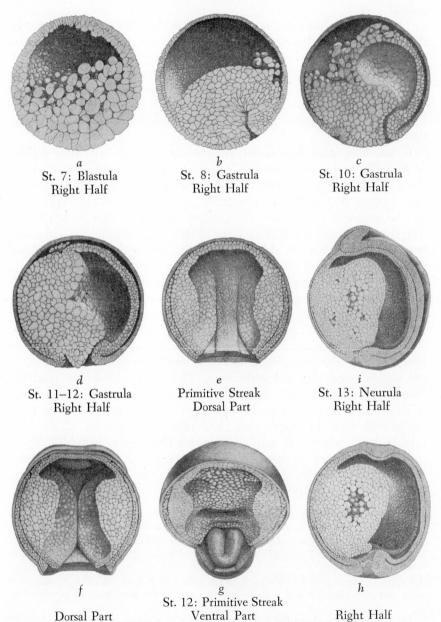

a
St. 7: Blastula
Right Half

b
St. 8: Gastrula
Right Half

c
St. 10: Gastrula
Right Half

d
St. 11–12: Gastrula
Right Half

e
Primitive Streak
Dorsal Part

i
St. 13: Neurula
Right Half

f
Dorsal Part

g
St. 12: Primitive Streak
Ventral Part

h
Right Half

Figure 39.   Early differentiation in the salamander (*Taricha torosa*); internal
aspects of hardened and split germs. Stages 7–13; × 20.

blastic cell layers and a somewhat wider space ventrally below the animal pole.

The gastrocele does not at any time break through into the blastocele. At stage 10 the wall which separates the two cavities is fairly thin and composed of loose, round cells; however, they fit tightly together on the side toward the gastrocele. The material that builds the expanding walls of the gastrocele comes from the surface of the blastula. From all sides, cells converge toward the blastopore, disappear in the cleft, slide inside along the narrow invagination canal, and fan out again to line the gastrocele.

By *marking with vital stains*, such as neutral red, Nile blue sulfate, or Bismark brown, it is possible to follow the gastrulation process more closely. Best results are obtained by pressing dye-saturated platelets of agar against the surface of the germ. The gelatinous envelopes must first be removed, but usually the vitelline membrane may be left intact. The dye penetrates the surface layer of the germ, combining with some granular cell inclusions. Living cells may retain the dyes for several days, and after the use of special fixation techniques the marks remain visible even in microtome sections. Figure 40 shows the displacements of 24 color marks applied along the dorsal and ventral midlines of a blastula. Invagination begins under the center of the gray crescent, about 30° below the equator. In the course of gastrulation, the material of this region (marks 8–9) is carried inside and up until it comes to lie directly under the animal pole where it forms the endodermal lining of the foregut, and the oral membrane. This region, and that near the animal pole (marks 1-2), stretch less than those between marks 3 and 6. Evidently areas forming the lower parts of the gastrula grow more extensively than the upper ones. The vegetal hemisphere of the blastula, with its heavy yolk content, becomes the ventral hypoblast of the gastrula. It changes its shape to some degree but does not stretch much in the axial direction. The original vegetal pole (mark 12) does not ascend to the top of the gastrocele, but comes to lie in its ventral floor.

Experimental evidence proves that gastrulation rests on the activity of the participating individual cells and cell groups rather than on pressure or traction from outside. Its normal progress depends on the rate of cell division in certain regions, but even more on the change in shape of individual cells. Forces of cohesion between the surfaces of neighboring cells also play an important role. The free cell surfaces unite into a continuous tough *coat* which also lines the invagination canal and the gastrocele and probably plays a role in the mechanics of gastrulation.

Invagination and *epiboly* are not the only means of material transfer during gastrulation. Many cells do not follow the surface along blastopore and invagination canal, but take a course through the depth of the cell layers. This is particularly so in the vegetal hemisphere, where the bulk of large cells glide inward by *ingression* rather than by invagination. Ingression movements directed from the vegetal pole toward

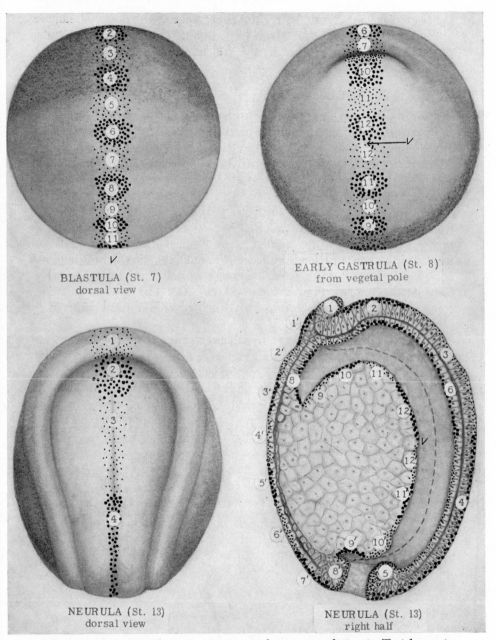

BLASTULA (St. 7)
dorsal view

EARLY GASTRULA (St. 8)
from vegetal pole

NEURULA (St. 13)
dorsal view

NEURULA (St. 13)
right half

Figure 40.   Morphogenic movements during gastrulation in *Taricha*, as indicated by deformation and displacement of 24 artificial color marks (based on Vogt, Schechtman and others). Fine dots: neutral red; heavy dots: Nile blue sulfate. Numbering system: at the blastula stage the marks along the dorsal midline are numbered 1 to 12 from the animal to the vegetal pole; the corresponding ventral marks are numbered 1' to 12'. *v*, vegetal pole; × 33.

the blastocele start shortly before the appearance of the dorsal blastopore lip. Similar cell migrations, which bring about internal rearrangements, continue until disappearance of the yolk plug, at the stage of closure of the blastopore (St. 12).

c. VERTEBRATES WITH MEROBLASTIC EGGS

In fishes, reptiles, and birds gastrulation is not as obvious a process as in ascidians and amphibians. The two-layer condition is prearranged already in the disc blastula with its cleft-like segmentation cavity (Figs. 34c, 35b). Gastrulation consists in (1) a more definite differentiation of epiblastic and hypoblastic layers, (2) the compression and virtual disappearance of the blastocele, and (3) the formation of a gastrocele.

In *birds* the latter arises through separation of the hypoblast cells from the uncleaved yolk mass (Fig. 35c). The hypoblast applies itself to the epiblast. Only the circular edge of the blastoderm remains attached to the yolk in what is called the *zone of junction*. The similarity of this disc gastrula to the invagination gastrula of an *Ascidia* is easily recognized (compare Figs. 35c and 33, St. 10). The zone of junction corresponds to the blastopore lips and the opening of the blastopore is plugged with the yolk mass.

In *fishes* a large part of the hypoblast assumes a syncytial character and remains attached to the yolk (Fig. 34). This is the *extra-embryonic hypoblast,* which later becomes the endodermal layer of the yolk sac. The *embryonic hypoblast* is the under layer of the projecting dorsal circumference of the double layered blastodisc (Fig. 143). Its cells later contribute to the development of the embryo proper, as described in the chapter on fish development.

Figure 41.   Postgastrulation development in the salmon (St. 14, 15, 17, 18), illustrating the simultaneous progress of epiboly and embryo formation in teleosts (Wilh. His 1874). Black: embryo; white: covered part of the yolk; shaded: uncovered yolk area.

In all meroblastic eggs the closure of the blastopore is delayed far beyond the gastrula stage, usually to tailbud and even later stages. The reason for this is the necessity of investing the large uncleaved yolk. The formation of a *yolk sac* is accomplished by continued epibolic growth of the blastopore lips, which so to speak swallow up the yolk mass (Fig. 41). The lips of the *yolk sac blastopore* differ essentially from those of the gastrula blastopore by being three-layered. Hence, they produce a three-layered yolk-sac epithelium.

Gastrulation in *mammals* is definitely of the avian and reptilian type, but further modified by the reduction or absence of uncleaved yolk. The monotremes and marsupials with their relatively large eggs link the mammalian and avian types (Figs. 36–38).

* * *

Beginning with the gastrula stages, adaptive modifications create distinctly divergent types of life histories for the various vertebrate classes. In the following chapters the more important ones are presented in a succession which deviates somewhat from the taxonomic system. The amphibians are given first place, because their eggs and early developmental stages seem less changed by secondary adaptations than those of almost any of the fishes. Besides, they are so widely in use for embryologic laboratory work that it seems expedient as well as scientifically justified to use them as the basic type in the study of vertebrate embryology.

Amphibians

Chapter 6

Normal Stages and

Fate Maps

A. SURVEY OF PERIODS AND STAGES (TABLE 4)

The *external changes* occurring in the development of the frog are shown in Figure 42. They do not progress in an even flow, but from time to time assume a distinctly new character. This makes it possible to recognize a sequence of periods, most of them extending over a considerable length of time. Thus during early development mitotic cell division is the characteristic developmental process. Later follow the distinctive cell displacements which usually are described as invagination and epiboly. This permits us to distinguish the periods of *cleavage* and *gastrulation* (St. 1–6 and 8–11). Between the two is placed the *blastula stage* (St. 7), which serves as a landmark in embryologic development.

The *primitive streak stage* (St. 12), issuing at the end of gastrulation, is most clearly defined as one of beginning third layer formation. In amphibians it becomes established when the yolk plug is withdrawn and the lateral lips of the blastopore move together (St. 11–12, Figs. 39, 42). The dorsal lip becomes the *primitive node*. Between the lateral lips, now called *primitive folds,* persists for a while a deep furrow, the *primitive groove;* its lower end marks the position of the *cloacal pore* of the embryo.

78

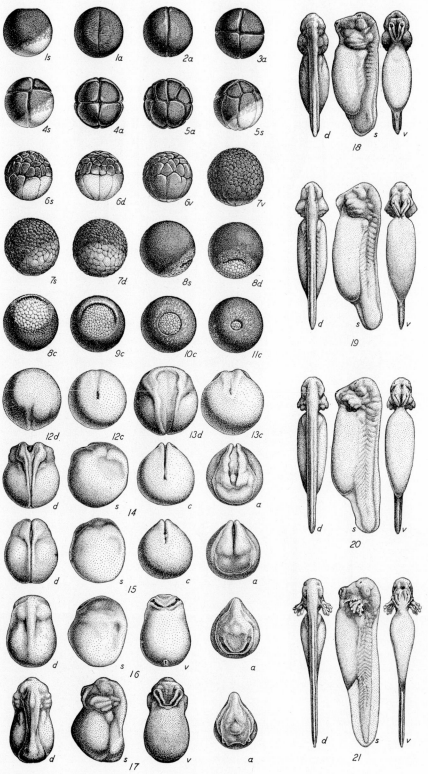

Fig. 42A

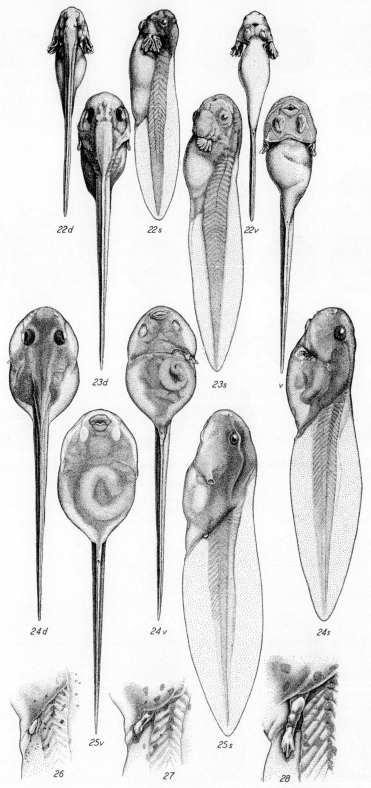

22d 22s 22v

23d 23s v

24d 24v 24s

25v 25s

26 27 28

Fig. 42B

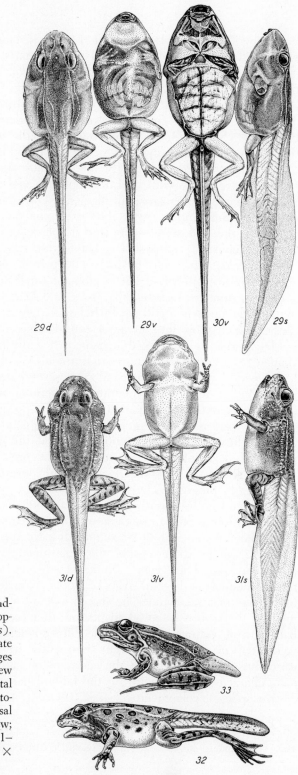

Figure 42A–C. Standard stages of frog development (*Rana pipiens*). Numbers 1–33 designate the developmental stages (cf. Table 4). *a,* View from animal pole (frontal view); *c,* caudal (blastoporal) view; *d,* dorsal view; *s,* left lateral view; *v,* ventral view. Stages 1–25 × 6.5; stages 26–28 × 3; stages 29–33 × 1.2.

Fig. 42C

The period of *neurula stages* (St. 13–17) is named for the externally visible differentiation of the neural tube. It starts with the appearance of *neural folds* which border a broad *neural plate*. This phase ends after the lateral folds have completely fused, dorsally. One may distinguish between *open neurulae* (St. 13–15) and *closed neurulae* (St. 16, 17). The entire embryo is finally covered with epidermis. During the *tail-bud stages* (St. 18–24), the embryo gains rapidly in length by prolifera-tion of the terminal blastema, which is the tailbud.

The *fully formed embryo* (St. 25) of most amphibian species is a *free swimming larva* with well developed visceral arches in the foregut region, some of which carry gill filaments. Distinctive is the *termination of tailbud proliferation*. After the last of the tail segments have been produced, the bud seems spent and its blastema used up or scattered. Usually, hatching occurs shortly before this stage; frog larvae acquire closed gill sacs, and start feeding. The paired appendages make their appearance in the form of flat or globular small buds. The entire stage is of short duration in toads, tree frogs, and some frogs which metamor-phose early and when still small. It lasts longer in bull frogs and other species which grow into larvae of considerable size.

Metamorphosis is a long-drawn-out period during which amphibians change from aquatic into terrestrial animals. It includes the secondary larval period which may expand over several years. In fact perenni-branchiate species like the mudpuppy, *Necturus*, never progress beyond the larval condition. The period, therefore, appears clearly subdivided. The first part is one of preparatory or *incipient metamorphosis* (St. 26–29), during which adaptations to larval life dominate the general picture of development while metamorphic processes easily escape at-tention. The casual observer usually is not aware that metamorphosis is already in progress. The second part is more dramatic, especially in anurans, and is distinguished as *climactic metamorphosis* (St. 30–33).

Only anurans pass through a complete metamorphosis. The tailed amphibians metamorphose incompletely. *Necturus*, one of the most primitive, grows short legs of the quadruped type but stops at the termination of about stage 30; newts advance to stage 31; none of the salamanders go beyond stage 32. Some characteristic stages from the life history of a salamander are shown in Figure 43. The early develop-ment of the arms is a special adaptation; they seem to substitute for the balancers of younger stages. Time-shifts (heterochronies) in the de-velopment of appendages occur frequently in many species of all vertebrate classes. Evidently the cessation of tailbud proliferation is a more characteristic end-point for the tailbud period than any condition of arm or leg development.

Table 4 presents in the first and second columns the adaptation of the stages of general vertebrate development to the class of amphibians (compare with Fig. 42). The standard stages 1–25 in the second column are similar to the stages of

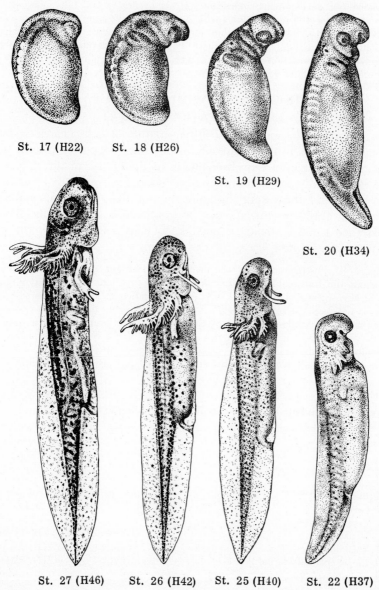

St. 17 (H22)   St. 18 (H26)

St. 19 (H29)

St. 20 (H34)

St. 27 (H46)   St. 26 (H42)   St. 25 (H40)   St. 22 (H37)

Figure 43.   Development of the salamander (*Ambystoma maculatum*) from closed neurula through tailbud and early larval stages (St. 17–27, Harrison's Stages 22–46); hatching occurs before stage 25 (H40). (After Detwiler's 1937 edition of parts of the unpublished Harrison series.) Upper row approx. × 10; lower row × 8.

frog development proposed by Pollister and Moore, and by Shumway. In regard to salamander development, Harrison (for *Ambystoma*) and Glaesner (for *Triturus*) have proposed normal series with nearly twice the number of stages (Table 4, third column). This means that most stages represent quite short steps in development. The equivalents of these stages in the standard system may be recognized by comparison of the third with the second column in Table 4 and Figure 43 with Figure 42.

B. MORPHOGENIC MOVEMENTS AND FATE MAPS

1. GASTRULATION (ST. 8–11)

Organs often do not arise by differentiation of cells nearest at hand, but take their origin from elements moved into place from distant parts. This discovery had already been made in the course of direct observations on normally and abnormally developing germs. But its formulation was vague and the extent and direction of the movements remained uncertain, until the introduction of the technique of artificial color marks (see p. 72 f.) made it possible to map out accurately the prospective *organ-forming areas* on early germs.

Figure 40 illustrates the practical method and the general principle of finding out about the foreseeable or *prospective fate* of any definitely located group of cells at the surface of a blastula. Of great assistance in the placement of color marks is the fact that from the beginning the polar bodies indicate the position of the animal pole, while the center of the gray crescent locates dorsal midline and sagittal plane. The comparison of the distribution of the color marks at stage 13 in Figure 40 with their original placement at stage 7 discloses immediately that at the blastula stage it was the *prospective fate* of regions 1–3 (including a part

Table 4

Periods and Standard Stages of Amphibian Development[1]

PERIOD	STANDARD STAGES[2]	SALAMANDER STAGES[3]
I Cleavage	1–6	1–7
II Blastula	7	8
III Gastrula	8–11	9–12
IV Primitive Streak	12	13
V Neurula	13–17	14–24(H), 14–21(G)
VI Tailbud	18–24	25–39(H), 22–34(G)
VII Larva (primary larval period)	25	40(H), 35(G)
VIII Metamorphosis		
a incipient m. or secondary larval period	26–29	36–52(G)
b climactic m.	30–33	53–56(G)

[1] The third column contains salamander stages in accordance with the *Ambystoma* series of Harrison (H) and the *Triturus* series of Glaesner (G). By comparison with the second column it will be possible to convert salamander stages into standard stages, with fair approximation.

[2] Compare Fig. 42.

[3] Compare Fig. 43.

of 4) to become neural tissue; and that the region marked with dot 8 was to become the endodermal layer of the oral membrane. By systematic extension of such work it is therefore possible to locate even in the blastula or in the gastrula the yet undifferentiated cell groups which, much later, will serve as the materials in the formation of the various tissues and organs. This leads to the construction of *fate maps*, like those shown in Figure 44. The entire surface becomes divided up into *areas of prospective organ differentiation*. The comparison of fate maps of a series of stages from the early gastrula (St. 8) to the neurula (St. 14) provides a graphic picture of the extent of the *morphogenic movements* which precede actual histologic differentiation. At the last stage all materials are at, or near, the places where they will take part in organogenesis.

Fate maps of the various amphibian species differ only in unessential detail. Figure 44, which is based on location work on several anuran and urodele species, represents the generalized *amphibian type*. Variations are brought about by differences in egg size, yolk content, and other hereditary factors, but also by environmental conditions such as changes in temperature, chemical composition of the water, degree of maturity of the egg and many more. The results are easily recognized as modifications of the general type.

At the time when gastrulation starts (St. 8, Fig. 44*a, b*), the animal hemisphere of the germ consists mainly of *prospective ectoderm* or ectoblast, subdivided into prospective epiderm and neuroderm, separated by a narrow band of neural crest (stippled). The lower vegetal hemisphere with its large yolk-filled cells is the *prospective endoderm* region (endoblast). The *prospective mesoderm* or mesoblast forms a nearly complete belt around the equator. It is broadest on the dorsal side, and has a narrow gap at the ventral surface. Here endoblast and ectoblast meet, superficially, in the area of the prospective proctodeum. The mesoblast ring is made up of crosswise areas of prospective *notochord, somites, nephric blastema*, and *lateral mesoderm*. These parts are so arranged that their tail ends extend along the animal border of the belt, while the frontal regions are oriented toward the blastoporal furrow, below the vegetal border. This arrangement involves an extreme lateral spreading of the prospective mesoderm of the lower body region.

The prospective tail somites 20 to 40 (or 50) are located in a narrow zone extending from the center to near the dorsal edge of the map (Fig. 44, fine stipple). The prospective somites 10 to 20 of the lower trunk and the root of the tail form a narrow, laterally stretched band (solid lines). The 10 first somites (broken lines), all of the prospective trunk region, are located in a field that narrows in the blastoporal direction and then passes continuously into the area of head mesenchyme. The latter arches frontally around the notochordal area and establishes a connection with the mesenchyme and somite field of the right side of the germ. The head mesenchyme is stippled in such a fashion that the sites of prospective otic and preotic somites (in front of somite 1) as well as the prospective prechordal plate become recognizable. The areas of prospective neuroderm and notochord are in direct contact in a narrow border zone. This is the *prospective axial rudiment*. From it issue the floor plate of the neural tube and the notochord of the lower trunk and the tail regions.

Invagination begins in the prospective foregut area of the vegetal hemisphere (St. 9, Fig. 44c, d). The first mesoblastic material to pass inside is the prechordal area, followed by the frontal part of the notochordal field. The first few somites become involved only when the yolk plug assumes a closed circular outline. At the end of gastrulation less than half of the prospective mesoderm has become invaginated

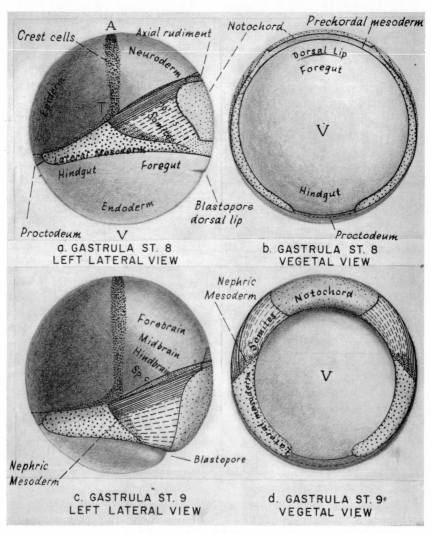

Fig. 44a–d

(Fig. 44e, f). The remainder is still a part of the epiblast. The incompleteness of invagination of the prospective mesoderm during gastrulation is a characteristic departure from the condition in ascidians and in Amphioxus where the entire mesoblast is contained in the hypoblast of the gastrula (Fig. 45).

2. PRIMITIVE STREAK STAGE (ST. 12)

Immediately following the yolk plug or gastrula stage begins *mesoderm formation*. By sheering and folding, the roof of the hypoblast

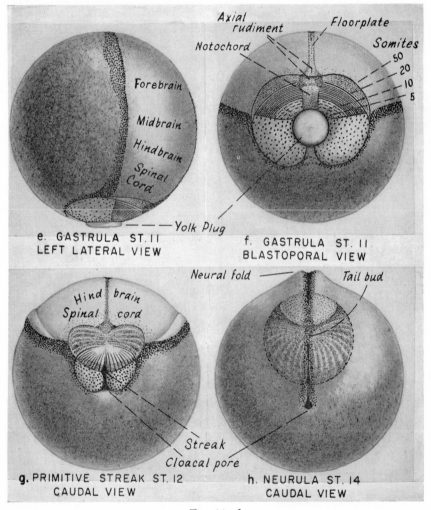

Fig. 44e–h

Figure 44.   Generalized amphibian type; *maps of areas of prospective fate* (fate maps) outlined on the external surface of a series of embryos. A, Animal pole; V, vegetal pole; about × 25.

separates into mesodermal and endodermal plates which slide along
each other, one in the ventral, the other in the dorsal direction. As
these movements progress, left and right endodermal wings rise and
finally fuse in the dorsal midline (Figs. 39e, f, h, 46, 54). At the same
time the mesoderm continues spreading ventrally (Fig. 54) and orally.
Thus, the entire endodermal tube and part of the mesodermal layer
arise from the hypoblast of the gastrula.

These developments in the hypoblast are accompanied by the transformation of the round blastopore into a *primitive streak* (Figs. 42, 44,
St. 11, 12). While the yolk plug withdraws to the inside, the lateral
lips of the pore move together and form a deep slit. Round dimples
appear at the upper and lower ends which are the *primitive pit* and the
primitive cloacal pore. The upper one is often compressed and may
disappear early. The lower persists and becomes the cloacal opening.
If viewed from the inside of an opened germ, the primitive streak
protrudes into the central cavity in the shape of two thick *lateral folds*,
which, above, unite into a median *node*. Below, these folds end at the
level of the cloacal pore (Fig. 39f, g).

By this time areas of at least 10 somites have disappeared from the
surface (Fig. 44g). They have become invaginated together with large
parts of the lateral plate areas. Their blastemic cell masses now form the
substance of the thick primitive folds, but are also spreading laterally
and orally, contributing to the rapid expansion of the middle layer. This
characteristic penetration into the old blastocelic cleft is recognizable
in the parts of embryos shown in Figure 39e–h.

Also the notochord has completely disappeared from the surface. Its
upper part, which first was included in the roof of the archenteron,
becomes "middle layer" and disappears from direct view, through the
upward growth of the endodermal wings (Fig. 39e, f). The lower,
last invaginated part is now entirely contained in the primitive node.
At the outer surface the left and right prospective somite-blastemas

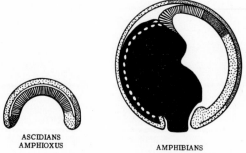

ASCIDIANS
AMPHIOXUS

AMPHIBIANS

Figure 45.   Location of equivalent areas in the gastrulae of ascidians and of
amphibians. Epithelial endoderm (hatched); yolk endoderm (black); epidermis
(light stipple); neuroderm (denser stipple); notochord (light stipple); prechordal
plate and ventral mesoderm (darkest stipple).

move together and partly fuse, covering the end of the neural plate as well as the entire axial rudiment (Fig. 44g).

It is now possible to construct a *fate map for the archenteric roof and the primitive streak.* Figure 46 shows the pattern of prospective areas in the roof of a germ at the early primitive streak stage. The endodermal wings have barely started to rise and still leave a wide open gap, in which large parts of prospective mesoderm remain visible. The node part of the primitive streak contains the remnant of notochord blastema and particularly the axial rudiment. The primitive folds consist of somitic, nephric, and lateral plate segments. All these accumulations of undifferentiated embryonic cells are ready to spread in the space between the ectodermal and endodermal layers. Thus *the primitive streak is an organ of direct mesoderm formation.* The cells which issue from it never enter the hypoblast, but directly join the mesodermal cell plates which separate from the hypoblast.

3. NEURULA STAGES 13–17

The most obvious morphogenic movements during early neurulation occur in the *ectoderm.* The open neural plate transforms into a tubular central nervous system, and the epiderm, which always remains in

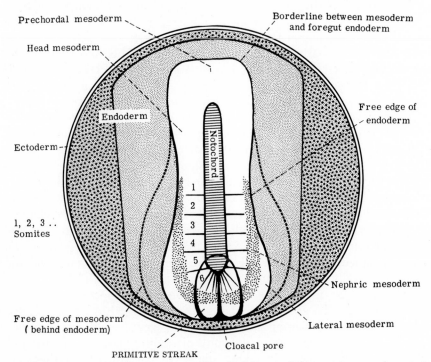

Figure 46.   Inside view of cut-off roof of the amphibian embryo at the primitive streak stage, with map of prospective mesodermal differentiations; the cut endodermal surfaces are coarsely stippled.

contact with the medullary folds, becomes a thin epithelium, now called *epidermis,* that covers the entire surface of the germ.

In the formation of the neural tube, two structures play a prominent role, namely the *neural folds,* which rise along the border of the neuroderm with the epiderm (Fig. 44g), and the *floor plate.* The latter is a product of the *axial rudiment.* As indicated in the successive stages of Figure 44, the axial rudiment moves during gastrulation from its original place above the equator into the lip of the blastopore of the late gastrula (compare Fig. 40, mark 4). While doing so, it leaves a trail of proliferated cells, which usually form a shallow groove in the center of the lengthening medullary plate. This is the beginning of the *floor plate.* As is indicated in the fate maps, the tip of this strip of tissue lies in the lower prosencephalic region. As the plate grows, it is laterally joined by the series of prospective mesencephalic, rhombencephalic, and spinal areas. The floor plate continues this independent growth by proliferation from the axial rudiment. Spliced between the converging left and right areas of prospective brain and spinal cord, it becomes, so to say, the midrib of the central nervous system from the lower prosencephalic region to the tail end of the spinal tube.

Beginning at the primitive streak stage the *lateral neural folds* advance dorsally. They move faster at the spinal and rhombencephalic level than in the forebrain region (Fig. 42, St. 12–15). While in the brain region the lateral folds roll in sufficiently to fuse above a central canal, in the spinal region they simply push together and form a solid cord. The floor plate thus gets buried under a mass of neural cells. It becomes recognizable again later, when after absorption of the yolk the histology of the spinal tube becomes more differentiated.

The movements in the *epidermal field* are from the start completely adapted to those of the neighboring areas; but after completion of gastrulation the epidermis spreads also over the uninvaginated mesoderm and covers the entire neural system. The extent of displacement changes greatly within the area of prospective epidermis. The corner designated by T in Figure 44a contains the *prospective tail epidermis.* The small *proctodeal area* between the ventral prongs of the mesoblastic belt moves down to the cloacal pore and partly enters it, to line the terminal part of the intestinal tract. While these two regions travel great distances, the ventral epiderm between the animal pole and the equator remains almost stationary.

Morphogenic movements continue also in the mesoblastic areas. Between stages 12 and 14 (Fig. 44g, *h*) another 10 to 15 prospective somites and the remaining lateral mesoderm pass through the primitive streak. In the earlier invaginated cords of somitic blastema the first five or six somites are actually taking shape. In consequence of these developments, the lower part of the primitive streak and the cloacal pore become lined or covered with epidermis (Fig. 44h), while the upper part is still bordered on each side by an area of uninvaginated prospective mesoderm, the equivalent of the last 20 to 30 tail somites.

4. TAILBUD FORMATION

During the later neurula stages (St. 14 to 17) the folds of the primitive streak flatten and disappear. The function of mesoderm formation is taken over by a new organ, the *tailbud*. It becomes organized as a composite of the axial rudiment, the blastemic end of the neural cord, and the remnants of uninvaginated prospective mesoderm, consisting now almost exclusively of prospective caudal somites. These elements seemingly fuse into a disc of blastemic tissue (Fig. 44*h*) which gradually swells and grows to a protruding tailbud (Fig. 42, St. 17, 18). However, it is still possible to recognize the constituent elements (Figs. 58, 59, 61). The axial rudiment is deeply buried, and from it issue notochord and floor plate. The neural blastema reaches toward the dorsal surface but is always covered by epidermis and partly by somitic blastema. With the help of color marks it can be shown that the latter still executes simplified invagination movements, turning over as it gradually joins the lower ends of the somitic cords (Fig. 59). This process continues until completion of the entire tail at about stage 24.

5. THREE WAYS OF MESODERM FORMATION BY INVAGINATION

The formation, in the amphibians, of mesoderm from cells that never were incorporated in the hypoblast represents a new though not a fundamentally different process. Compared with the ancestral ascidian type of separation from the hypoblast (Figs. 33, 45), proliferation from the primitive streak and from the tailbud is more direct and represents a simplification of the procedure. However, invagination movements are a characteristic element of all three modes of mesoderm production.

The course of third layer formation is summarized in Table 5. The three modes are characterized by the place from which the cells immediately move into third

Table 5

Progress of Invagination of the Prospective Mesoderm in Amphibians

STAGE	IMMEDIATE SOURCE	SOMITES	LARVAL LEVEL
Early gastrula St. 9	hypoblast	(presomitic mesoderm)	head
Late gastrula St. 10–11	hypoblast	1–3	trunk
Primitive streak and neurula St. 12–17	primitive streak	4–20	trunk and root of tail
Tailbud St. 18–24	tailbud	20–50	tail

layer position (second column). It is easily seen that the limit between body and tail is not directly determined by the change from primitive streak to tailbud proliferation. In the frog the cloacal pore is located at about the level of the thirteenth somite. Accordingly, the last of the lateral mesoderm disappears through the primitive groove at the inception of the neurula stage. The trunk of the salamander is considerably longer. The cloacal pore lies at the height of the nineteenth somite. As therefore one might expect, some visceral mesoderm remains at the surface until the end of the neurula stages. In frogs, prospective tail somites move in at both neurula and tailbud stages, while in salamanders, this process is almost exclusively limited to the tailbud stage. The occurrence of such differences proves that the various modes of mesoderm formation are functionally equivalent, and not necessarily linked with the differentiation of the major body regions. One might also conclude that the trunk of the anurans became secondarily shortened by contraction of the visceral parts.

Chapter 7

Differentiation of

Preprimordia

A. DETERMINATION OF EMBRYONIC DIFFERENTIATION

Before proceeding to the description of the next following steps of development, it is necessary to give brief consideration to the *factors which control differentiation*. We are entering here a field that presents the investigator with perplexing difficulties. Unencumbered by much factual knowledge, philosophers of even the very remote ages harbored general notions about a material and machine-like nature of organisms. However, the steady progress of science more and more led to the realization that living things are structurally and functionally of a high complexity which may seem more amenable to non-mechanical, vitalistic interpretation. Thus it was an undertaking of daring as well as vision, when in the latter part of the nineteenth century Wilhelm Roux proposed the creation of a new branch of embryologic research, which should be devoted to the discovery and study of the *causes* of developmental processes, and for which he proposed the programmatic name *Entwicklungsmechanik* or *mechanics of development*.

It was important for the success of the new discipline that work on the most complex problems, such as the nature of life or the complete synthesis of cellular organisms, was postponed in favor of exact and quantitative studies of single steps or phases in the developmental chain of events. Such scrutiny still bears on matters of very diverse degrees of complexity; but while in themselves often of trifling significance, they all reflect some light on the basic problems of constitution and differentiation of the living organism. In recent years research in this field has yielded many significant results. They are briefly reviewed in the present chapter.

1. THE ORGANIZATION CENTER

A causal analysis of the factors that are responsible for the differentiation of organs and tissues is only possible by experimental methods. In 1891 Driesch reported that blastomeres of the sea urchin, separated at the two-cell stage, each develop into a complete larva. More recent experiments with amphibians, by Spemann, prove that in the developing egg, a *center of organization* is so located that it becomes evenly divided by the sagittal plane. If by constriction in this direction an egg, morula, or blastula is divided into equal halves, two small but complete embryos are obtained—true identical twins (Fig. 47c). However, if the separation is made in the frontal plane, so that the gray crescent comes to lie almost entirely in one half, this dorsal part alone yields an embryo. The ventral half goes on with cell divisions, yet is unable to gastrulate (Fig. 47a, b). This is manifest proof that *growth and differentiation can be dissociated*. The dorsal half includes a factor that brings about embryonic organization. Spemann called it the *organizer*.

2. INDUCTION OF DIFFERENTIATION

By the time of gastrulation the organizer lies above the dorsal lip of the blastopore. If a piece of it is transplanted to the lower ventral side of another gastrula, it invaginates and induces a secondary embryo (Fig. 48a–c). This twin is mostly of host material. Its neural tube and otic vesicles are formed from what had been prospective ventral epidermis; the notochord and the somites from prospective ventral epidermis and tail mesoderm; and the pharynx, stomach, liver, and small intestine from prospective yolk endoderm of the host. The implant itself becomes fully integrated, but usually contributes only a small part of the entire cellular material (Fig. 48d).

At stage 8 the *inductive potency* is spread over nearly the entire area of the prospective mesoderm (Fig. 49a). However, there occur considerable *quantitative differences*, the capacity being greatest in the dorsal lip and all but disappearing toward the ventral side. Moreover, *qualitative differences* of a type that is indicated by the distinction of *head inductor* and *rump inductor* are discernible. With a subtle testing technique Holtfreter has revealed the existence of an intrinsic pattern of considerable complexity in the organizer, before its invagination; it corresponds to the manifoldness of inductions after invagination.

The above mentioned *integration of the implanted tissue* illustrates the fact that the original organizer later comes under the inductive influence of its own creations; as may be seen from Figure 48, it partakes in the differentiation of neural tube, notochord, and somites in a harmonious way, i.e., in response to environmental factors. Obviously the organizer concept suffers from oversimplification. In fact, organization is the result of a multitude of induction processes. The *head inductor,* invaginated during gastrulation, becomes the archenteron roof. It induces the differentiation of the primitive brain with the eyes, and probably also that of the visceral apparatus. In their turn the *prosencephalon* induces the nasal placodes and hatching glands, the *eye* induces the formation of lens and cornea, and the *rhombencephalon* induces otic and epibranchial placodes. Yet the sequences of inductions

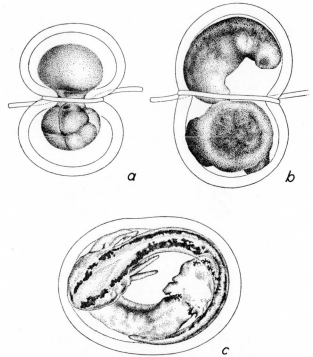

Figure 47.   Constriction of the egg of the newt, *Triturus,* and eventual separation in equal sized parts (Spemann 1928). *a,* The fertilization nucleus was included in the ventral half. After the second division one of the four cleavage nuclei passed through the narrow into the upper dorsal half. Soon afterward the halves were completely separated. *b,* The ventral half (with three of the four cleavage nuclei) produced an unorganized abdominal blastema, while the dorsal (starting with only one nucleus), developed into a small but complete embryo; the dorsal half included the organization center. *c,* In a second experiment the ligature passed through the sagittal instead of the frontal plane. It halved the organization center; each half egg developed into an embryo (identical twins).

are not in the form of a branching tree but often appear like a lacework, with double and multiple connections. The latter provide a basis for so-called *double assurances* of differentiation. This relationship is illustrated by lens formation in the species *Rana palustris*. It may be induced by the brain as well as by the optic bulb. Consequently, if the bulb is early transplanted to another body region, two lenses can form, one near the brain and the other near the transplanted eye.

3. SELF-DIFFERENTIATION

If blastomeres or parts of blastulae and early gastrulae are isolated, they manifest various capacities of independent differentiation. As

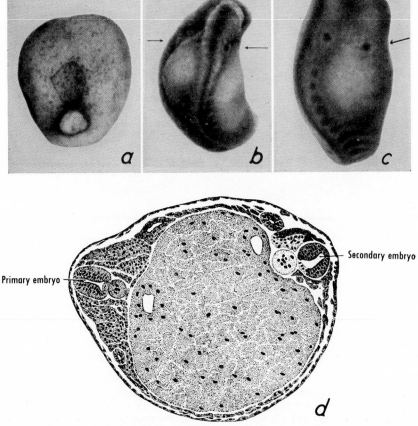

Figure 48.   Induction of secondary embryo formation (*a–c*, Spemann 1931, *d*, Spemann and Hilde Mangold 1924). *a*, Late gastrula of *Triturus*, ventral aspect, implanted and invaginated dorsal lip of donor visible through the prospective ventral epidermis of the host. *b*, *c*, Views of resulting primary and secondary embryos; arrows point to otic vesicles of the latter. *d*, Cross section through a similar specimen; tissues of the secondary embryo that derived from donor-implant appear in light stipple.

above mentioned, ventral halves of blastulae are nearly *nullipotent,* dorsal halves *totipotent.* A thorough investigation of early gastrulae (St. 8) was made by Holtfreter. Small pieces of known prospective fate were cultivated in vitro, in dishes containing a weak solution of mineral salts. Sufficient food in the form of yolk, fat, and carbohydrates is contained in these cells for the few days which they need, to display their capacities for autonomous differentiation. Pieces of prospective endoderm, and of marginal mesoderm (heart, kidney), develop essentially in the same way as they would within the normal embryo. They exhibit the condition of complete *determination.*

On the other hand, pieces of prospective neural and epidermal ectoderm have no capacity at all for self-differentiation. They merely develop into sheets of epithelial cells (epidermis) without specified character and thus prove to be in a state of *indetermination.*

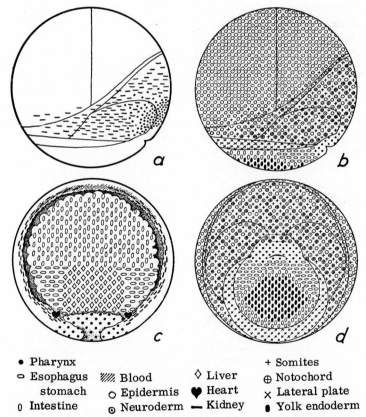

• Pharynx			+ Somites
○ Esophagus	▨ Blood	◇ Liver	⊕ Notochord
stomach	○ Epidermis	♥ Heart	× Lateral plate
0 Intestine	◉ Neuroderm	— Kidney	▮ Yolk endoderm

Figure 49.   *a,* Distribution of inductive capacity in the early gastrula (St. 8); left side view; stippled: head inductor; hatched: rump and tail inductor. *b–d,* Distribution of capacities of self-differentiation in the early gastrula (St. 8) with key printed below; *b,* left side view, *c,* inside view of vegetal hemisphere after removal of the animal hemisphere, *d,* view from vegetal pole side (Holtfreter 1938).

Most remarkable is the behavior of pieces of prospective mesoderm, especially from the region of the prospective notochord. They develop some notochord, but also somites, lateral plate mesoderm, and neural tissue (Fig. 49*b, c, d*). In other words, the organizer region can differentiate not only in accordance with its prospective fate, but may produce in addition the tissues which normally it induces to differentiate from other sources. It manifests various degrees of *labile determination*.

4. REACTIVE COMPETENCE

As a rule, the *competence* of embryonic cells to respond to inductors, by a plurality of types of differentiation, is in inverse proportion to their state of determination. In the early gastrula, the prospective endoderm is least responsive to inductive stimuli. Its ventral yolk cells may be induced to form a second intestinal tube with an extra liver and other secondary differentiations (Figs. 48*d*, 50*b*); but only under very special conditions has it been possible to obtain mesodermal or ectodermal structures from prospective endoderm. On the other hand, the great importance which inductive factors can assume is best demonstrated by small pieces of indetermined prospective ectoderm. Dependent upon induction from outside, it is competent to respond to a wide range of inductors. Any piece may produce epidermis, neural tissue, sensory organs, or even mesodermal tissues, according to the character of the inductive influence to which it becomes subjected.

The ventral half of a blastula which, isolated, is not capable of self-differentiation, proves fully competent to react by formation of an entire embryo, if supplied with adequate induction.

Competence of a given embryonic area changes with the *age*. At the blastula or early gastrula stage the prospective forebrain and eye region may still be induced to differentiate into almost any other kind of ectodermal or some mesodermal tissues. But at the late gastrula stage the same area is rigidly determined and will only produce forebrain and eyes, even if it is heterotopically transplanted, i.e., placed into a different region of another embryo. The range of competence becomes restricted as the degree of determination increases.

5. NATURE OF THE INDUCTOR

As already pointed out, the original organizer concept had to undergo radical changes. First it was found that organizers are taxonomically unspecific. Implants of frog dorsal lip induce embryonic differentiation on salamanders and vice versa; however, the resulting embryos are of host specificity. Conversely the small contributions of graft tissue are donor-specific even though integrated into the induced embryo. This *lack of specificity of induction* became reaffirmed when dead inductor tissue, killed by drying, boiling, or dehydration with alcohol, was found capable of evoking the same differentiations as the living. Even living and dead tissues from almost any kind of adult animals, e.g., liver and kidney of rodents, can induce secondary embryo formation in amphibians.

Such experiences favor the assumption that induction is effected by chemical means. The search for specific substances in the dorsal blastopore region yielded suggestive facts about concentration differentials of glycogen, adenosine triphosphate, sulfhydryls, and nucleoproteins. Implantation experiments gave positive reactions with a multitude of organic and inorganic materials. Some estrogenic steroids and cancerogenic compounds proved most effective (Needham, Waddington). Far from answering, these investigations rather complicate the question regarding the nature of induction. However, they all point to the foremost importance of the reacting substratum, the living cells, in the determination of the character of induction.

Significant in this connection is Holtfreter's discovery that *dead or injured pieces* of prospective epidermis are of good inductive quality. Since similar pieces in healthy living condition lack this capacity (Fig. 49a), it may be surmised that they carry the inductor in an inactive form. This suggests the possibility that most or all substitutes are not inductors themselves, but merely agents that liberate inductors, through injury to cells of a competent substratum.

6. ACCESSORY INDUCTORS AND TWINNING

The reported experiments on induction furnish also a basis for the understanding of twinning. Splitting of the center of organization, as in the constriction experiments, is not indicated as the usual mechanism of duplication. Direct observations on early stages of twinning, as well as the study of the morphology of twin relationships in more advanced cases, reveal a closer resemblance with experimental twin formation through implantation of a second organizer. Regarding the origin of accessory induction, the above mentioned observation by Holtfreter on tissue damage is most suggestive. In experiments on the effect of delay of fertilization in ovulated amphibian eggs it was found that from overripe eggs twins and other duplications (polymelia, polydactyly) develop at a relatively high frequency. As the accompanying illustrations (Figs. 50, 51) show, the accessory embryos may be of varied size and perfection; if they are not of full length, the head end is defective, with rostral parts completely missing. As a rule the lower body regions are fused.

Overripeness of frog eggs is a condition of deterioration which develops if females with ovulated eggs in their uteri are prevented from laying. At low room temperature (18° C.) signs of damage appear about the fourth day. At the end of one week the eggs usually are no longer capable of development. At the present time it is not possible to characterize the changes in any but general terms. After fertilization

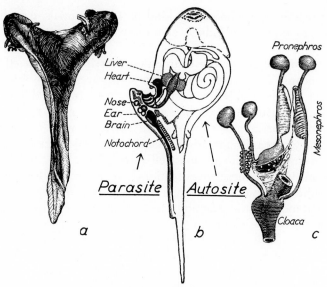

Figure 50.   Twinning in frogs, caused by overripeness of the egg. *a*, Nearly equal twins (× 10). *b*, Unequal twins, dissection; organs of autosite in outline, those of parasite darkly shaded and labelled; × 4. *c*, Urogenital organs and cloaca of twins *b*; scattered germ cells (white dots) in the common lower mesentery; × 8. (Witschi 1952.)

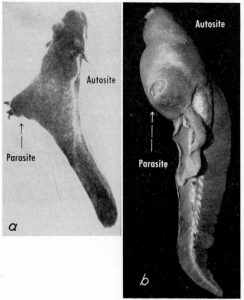

Figure 51.   Unequal sized twins from overripe eggs of the frog. The parasite becomes reduced to an embryoma that is progressively assimilated, and overgrown by the tissues of the autosite (Witschi 1952).

overripe eggs do not cleave as regularly as normal eggs. The pigmentation is more diffuse and usually no gray crescent becomes recognizable. At the time of gastrulation blastopore formation is irregular, often multiple, and delayed. Evidently in some cases the chemical changes result in liberation of inductor substances, with such quantitative variations that sometimes secondary centers of organization become established. From the composition of the twin embryos it can be deduced that such centers always are located in the prospective endoderm near the mesodermal border. The proximity of the twins is a direct function of the distance between primary and accessory inductors, while their size and completeness probably depends on quantitative properties of the inductor. The establishment of secondary inductors changes the prospective fates of the parts of the gastrulae which fall under their influence. The resulting relationships are diagrammatically expressed in Figure 52. In the parlance of Dalcq, such twin development represents a case of *paragenesis*, i.e., one of many possible alternates of the *normogenesis* as mapped out in Figure 44a.

B. GERM LAYERS AND PREPRIMORDIA (ST. 12–17)

Although the fates of the prospective areas of mesoderm and ectoderm may be deflected by inductive influences, the once differentiated germ layers are not likely ever to change their denomination. This stability justifies the general practice of classifying tissues as belonging

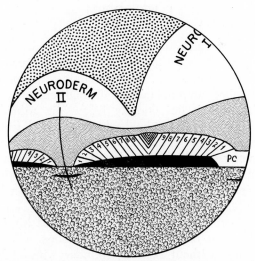

Figure 52.   Fate map of twin development; the accessory twin II is presumed to have a defective forehead; at the neighboring sides fusion would start at the level of the ninth somites. *Coarse stipple,* prospective epidermis; *fine stipple,* p. notochord; *1–9,* beginning of the series of p. somites; *PC,* prechordal mesoderm; *bubble,* p. endoderm. Two places of initial invagination are located in the endodermal area.

to the *ectoderm, endoderm,* or *mesoderm.* In some invertebrates reserves of residual *blastema cells* are set aside and carried over into the adult stage. In cases of regeneration, or budding, such blastemas often are capable of producing gonia as well as tissues of all three germ layers. In the vertebrate body blastema-like cells play an important part in the regeneration of epithelia, epidermis, lining of the intestines, in wound healing, and in the restitution of limbs and lenses in salamanders. Weiss has shown that the regeneration blastema of salamander tail, if transplanted to the base of a forelimb, is able to produce an arm. This does not, however, involve a change of germ layer values, since tails and limbs are made up of similar tissue elements. The high regenerative capacity of salamander blastema cells is an isolated phenomenon among vertebrates, which otherwise are characterized by a fairly strict tissue specificity.

In recent years doubts have arisen about the validity of the concept of *germ-layer specificity*. The above mentioned fact that prospective ectoderm may be induced to produce mesodermal tissues obviously calls for some limitation of its application. However, one must also remember that *prospective* ectoderm is not yet ectoderm at all. Its declared fate still rests on the tacit assumption that the future course of development will take a normal course. Specificity, as a rule, seems firmly established after morphologic separation into germ layers has once occurred. In a more theoretical sense one may also date it from the time of *determination*. It was found that the endoderm is almost irreversibly determined even before the beginning of gastrulation.

1. ECTODERM

Following the primitive streak stage the ectoderm separates into *epiderm* and *neuroderm,* the boundary being in general indicated by rising *neural folds* (Fig. 44, St. 12). When they first become noticeable, these folds divide the ectoderm approximately into dorsal and ventral halves. In the tailed amphibians the frontal curvature includes the animal pole; in frogs it lies dorsally below the animal pole. While the lateral folds move toward the back, the frontal wall remains stationary. The neural plate thus becomes laterally compressed, and assumes the character of a high, pseudostratified, and later many-layered epithelium (Figs. 53, 54). While in process of folding, the neural plate starts to show signs of partial segmentation (Fig. 53), which gradually leads to the differentiation of the *primary brain vesicles:* forebrain (prosencephalon), midbrain (mesencephalon), and hindbrain (rhombencephalon). The last one also shows indications of still further segmentation. It leads, without definite boundary, into the *spinal cord.*

Since the cranial folds move relatively slowly, the front of the tube remains open for a while in the so-called *neuropore* (Fig. 42, St. 15). After its closure, the brain grows beyond and around the frontal surface of the germ. As a consequence, two characteristic bends arise in the head region, the *cranial and the cervical flexures* (Figs. 58, 59). Simultaneously, the segmentation or neuromery of the brain becomes more noticeable.

Within the lateral neural folds, along the borderlines of neural and epidermal ectoderm, lie strands of cells which do not become permanently included either in the epidermis or the neural tube (darkly stippled zones in Fig. 44). These are the *neural crest cells,* so called

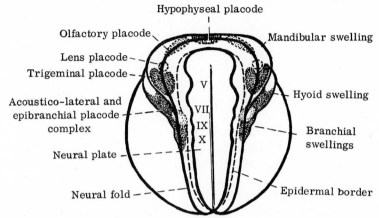

Figure 53.   Amphibian neurula (St. 13); frontal parts slightly raised. Epidermis grows over the neural folds. Distribution of placodes in relation to cranial neural folds and marginal swellings indicated by stippled areas; ear placodes lightly stippled. V, VII, IX, X, nuclei of the corresponding trigeminal, facial, glossopharyngeal, and vagal nerves. (Diagram, partly after Knouff.)

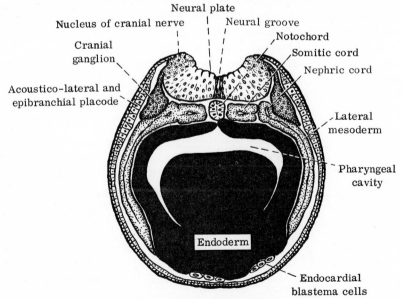

Figure 54.   Tree-frog (*Hyla crucifer*). Cross section through open neurula (St. 13), level of the nucleus of the cranial nerve IX; × 80.

because in the spinal region they become temporarily massed together in or above the dorsal crest of the neural tube (Fig. 55). In the head region they separate from the neural plate while it is still open (Fig. 54). This cranial crest material is bulky; it gives origin to the major part of the *cartilaginous skeleton of the larval head* (Figs. 64, 65), and contributes also some neurons to the formation of the *cranial ganglia*. On the other hand, the spinal division consists of relatively few cells, does not produce any cartilage, but gives origin to the entire *spinal ganglia* which come to lie between the somites and the spinal cord. The crest contributes also the *mesenchyme of the dorsal and ventral tail* fins (Fig. 42, St. 18–25, Fig. 68a). Obviously, the area of prospective neural crest is not restricted to the border zone between the neural and epidermal territories, but continues further along the edge of the latter toward the prospective cloacal pore region (Fig. 44).

In the head region, essential parts of the sensory nervous system originate from *placodes* which are located outside the neural folds. At the open neurula stage, the epiderm is composed of a thin covering or *periderm* layer, and a subjacent layer. This latter often consists only of loosely arranged squamous or cuboidal cells. However the placodes arise as local thickenings (Fig. 54) in the same deeper layer. In the open neurula they are not yet well defined, but form an almost continuous horseshoe-shaped plate, which is noticeable as a *marginal swelling* around the cranial neural folds. As diagrammatically indicated in Figure 53, its frontal center becomes the primordium of the *buccal hypophysis*. Along the mandibular swellings lie the paired *olfactory, lenticular,* and *trigeminal placodes*. Over much of the hyoid and branchial swellings of each side, spreads a large complex which later separates into a dorsolateral and a ventral series of placodes. After closure of the neural tube, the former subdivides into *otic, preotic,* and *postotic placodes,* the latter into a number of *epibranchial placodes,* one at the dorsal edge of each gill cleft. Though the fully differentiated

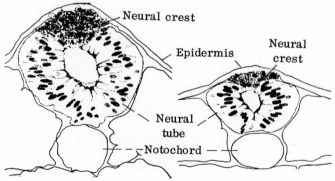

Figure 55.   *Ambystoma* of stage 17; cross sections of spinal cord at the level of the third and the seventh segments; neural crest (Detwiler 1937); × 96.

buccal hypophysis and the eye lenses show no striking histologic relationship to neural tissues, their developmental history marks them as specialized derivatives of the placode series.

2. ENDODERM

At the end of gastrulation the endoderm has the shape of a bowl with the opening turned toward the notochordal and blastoporal regions (Fig. 39d, e). Its hollow is the gastrocele. The ventral and lateral walls consist of large yolk-laden cells (Figs. 39, 40). In front it remains in direct contact with the epidermis, contributing to the formation of the *oral membrane*. In dissected embryos of the primitive streak stage, the rims of the lateral walls of the endoderm are plainly visible (Figs. 39, 46). In the middle region they run along the notochord. At the level of the primitive streak they circle at some distance around the primitive folds, but finally close in from both sides and meet below the cloacal end of the primitive groove. Here, the endoderm remains attached to the proctodeal ectoderm (Fig. 44).

During the neurula stage the endodermal folds fuse beneath the notochord (Fig. 54). This leads to the formation of an endodermal channel, the *gut*. At the same time, the prechordal mesoderm plate separates from the endoderm (Fig. 58). At the lower end of the embryo the endodermal ridges close in around the hindgut and become attached to the proctodeum (Fig. 58). The roof of the hindgut for a short while maintains a contact with the notochord and projects into the base of the tailbud; this is the ephemeral *tailgut*.

The *primitive gut* is divided in three main sections: foregut, midgut, and hindgut. In neurulae, the *foregut* originally encloses a large hepatopharyngeal cavity (Fig. 39h, i). But at the tailbud stage, concurrent with the development of the heart, it separates into *pharynx* and *liver diverticulum* (Fig. 58). The *oral cavity* makes its first appearance as a pocket of the pharynx which pushes toward a corresponding epidermal depression, the *oral pit*. The *midgut* has a very narrow lumen which temporarily becomes occluded at several places. Its thick ventral wall serves as the main storage place for the yolk material. The *hindgut* is set off from the midgut by a sharp ventral flexure, and gradually differentiates into a *cloaca*.

3. MESODERM

In regard to both origin and differentiation, the mesoderm is more complex than the other germ layers. We can distinguish at least three types which will be described as invagination mesoderm, angioblastema, and neural crest mesoderm.

a. **Invagination Mesoderm.** The early history of this by far the largest component of the mesoderm was traced before and summarized in Table 5 (p. 91). During the late neurula and the tailbud stages it separates into seven longitudinal bands (Figs. 54, 58, 59). In the dorsal midline lies the *notochord* (axial mesoderm). To its left and right appear a pair of *somitic cords* (the paraxial mesoderm or epimere), which early begin to divide into cube-shaped somites. Along their ventral borders run the *nephrogenic cords* (intermediate mesoderm or mesomere) and, more ventrolaterally, the plates of *visceral mesoderm* (lateral mesoderm or hypomere).

When at the beginning of the tailbud stages the upper part of the *notochord* assumes a characteristic histologic structure, its flattened cells cease to multiply. Mitotic figures are now only found at the blastemic upper and lower ends. At stage 18 (Fig. 58) the differentiated cord reaches only to a rhombencephalic level; later it extends further, until it comes to its final stop below the infundibulum of the diencephalon (Figs. 81, 83).

The *somitic cords* are direct continuations of the prechordal plate and the head mesenchyme. Segmentation begins with three *cranial somites* which contribute to the formation of the occipital and basilar parts of the skull. But the three segments are not equivalent in frogs and salamanders. A comparison of Figures 81 and 83 will show that the first muscle segment or *myomere* of *Taricha* lies behind the ear, at the level of the ninth cranial ganglia. In frogs, it lies at the base of the ear while the second segment is matched with the ninth ganglia. Consequently the assumption that the head of the salamanders has absorbed one more somite than that of the frogs seems well founded. Externally only the *spinal somites* are easily recognizable. They are numbered in accordance with the spinal nerves and are helpful in the definite localization of the sites of many organs. In frogs the first and the second myotomes disappear during the chondrification of the skull. In the *septums* between the second and the third form the *occipital arches,* which border the *foramen magnum,* the main outlet of the brain case. The first vertebral ring, called *atlas,* appears about the same stage (late St. 25) in the septums between the third and the fourth myotomes.

With the notochord also the somitic cords enter into the formation of the tailbud and eventually extend to the very tip of the tail.

The notochord plays an important role in the development of the axial morphology. Or rather, the role is played by the *axial rudiment* from which the floor plate of the neural tube and the notochord arise. It lies in the dorsal blastopore lip of the late gastrula (Fig. 44, St. 11), and persists as a blastema complex in the tailbud, at the border of the prospective neural and notochordal areas (Fig. 58). In the course of the further development it continues the production of floor plate and notochord. At the same time, while moving in the caudal direction, it serves as a cleaver that splits the invaginating median somitic mass into left and right blastema cords. The common dependence of these three developments on the axial rudiment is revealed by their simultaneous reduction and disappearance in *microcephalic and acephalic embryos*. This malformation is not caused by terminal blastemic degeneration, but develops following incomplete gastrulation. In cases of twinning it is particularly easy to determine the segmental value of the missing parts in the parasite (Figs. 50–52). If only forebrain and midbrain are absent (Fig. 56a), the embryo is a *microcephalus*, and the arrangement of its notochord-floorplate-somite complex is essentially unchanged. However, if also the larger part of the rhombencephalon and at least the first five somites are missing (Fig. 56c), the embryo is an *acephalus* (Fig. 56b). In the latter case the spinal tube develops as an almost solid round cord, without floor plate; the notochord is absent and the somitic mesoderm is a continuous unpaired mass. Solid muscle bundles develop directly under the neural tube; the spinal ganglia fuse and form an unpaired median chain (Fig. 56d). Thus, the failure of formation of an axial rudiment leads to the characteristic complex of three or four deficiencies which is comprised under the summary designation of *axial syndrome*.

Incomplete gastrulation with subsequent acephalic development and axial syndrome have been produced by overripeness of the egg (Witschi), treatment with lithium chloride (Lehmann, Pasteels), and hybridization (Witschi and Chang). The failure of differentiation of an axial rudiment, if gastrulation invagination is not deep enough, indicates the existence of gradients and regional differences in the blastula. The invaginating organizer induces forehead and notochord differentiation only if it is carried into territories close to the animal pole.

Nephric blastema cords (intermediate mesoderm; mesomeres) and *lateral plates* (lateral mesoderm; hypomeres) remain restricted to the trunk region or barely enter the root of the tail. Primary segmentation

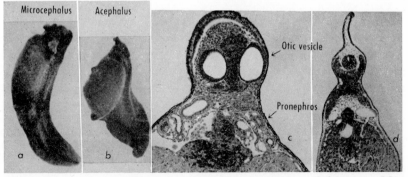

Figure 56.   Frog, malformations caused by overripeness of the egg. *a*, Microcephalus; × 7.5. *b*, Acephalus; × 7.5. *c*, Cross section through upper part of an acephalus with two otic vesicles and fused acoustic ganglia but without rhombencephalon; × 50. *d*, Cross section through lower body region of acephalus exhibiting the *axial syndrome*: absence of notochord and neural floor plate, non-separation of the median somitic mass, and single ventromedial spinal ganglion; × 25. (Witschi 1952.)

occurs mainly in the head and upper body regions (Fig. 59). The lateral mesoderm splits early into a *somatic* and a *splanchnic* sheet. The former applies itself to the body wall, the latter to the endodermal organs (viscera). Between them develop rapidly expanding *celomic cavities.*

b. **Angioblastema.**   The origin of the blood cells and endothelia of the blood vessels has long been a controversial subject. Blood islands and vessels first become recognizable in tailbud embryos. They are located between the splanchnic mesoderm and the endoderm. While most often they give the impression of being mesodermal differentiations, in some instances an origin from the superficial endoderm may seem suggested. This ambiguity becomes understandable if the *history of the angioblastema* is traced from the amphibian blastula. At this early stage (St. 7, 8), the blastema is located along the lower and inner edge of the mesodermal belt, bordering on that part of the prospective endoderm which faces the blastocele and which in the course of gastrulation becomes the surface layer of the gut and yolk endoderm (Fig. 57a). During gastrulation it is carried along by the endoderm and becomes rearranged, as indicated in Figure 57b. The dorsal limbs of

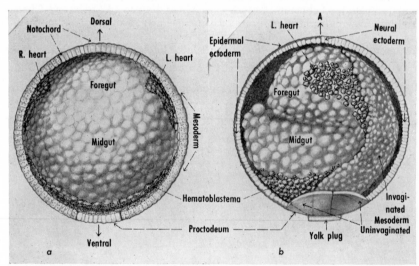

Figure 57.   Location of the angioblastema in the amphibian blastula and its displacements during gastrulation. *a,* Blastula (St. 7) after removal of the animal hemisphere. The floor of the blastocelic cavity is formed by large endodermal cells (prospective fore- and midgut), the cut edge by prospective mesoderm and ectoderm (proctodeal plate). Wedged between the two is the angioblastema (partly based on Holtfreter, cf. Fig. 49c). *b,* Late gastrula (St. 11). Left lateral view after removal of the ectodermal epiblast, but sparing the uninvaginated mesoderm. The involuted endoderm is divided into foregut and midgut (solid yolk sac) portions. Dorsally the mesoderm prepares to fold off from the hypoblast. The *hematoblastema* advances ventrally along the surface of the midgut, the *endothelioblastema* dorsally along midgut and foregut.

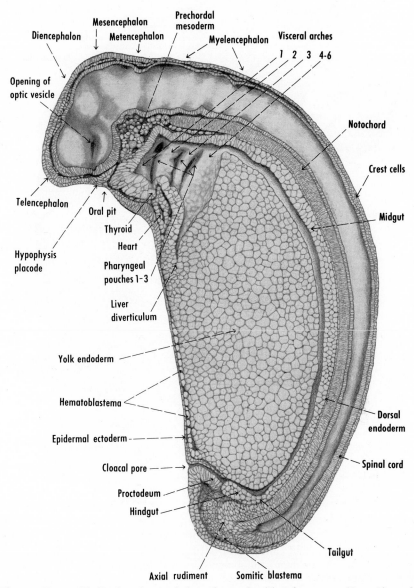

Figure 58.   Tailbud embryo of the salamander *Taricha torosa* (St. 18), right
half, medial aspect; × 30.

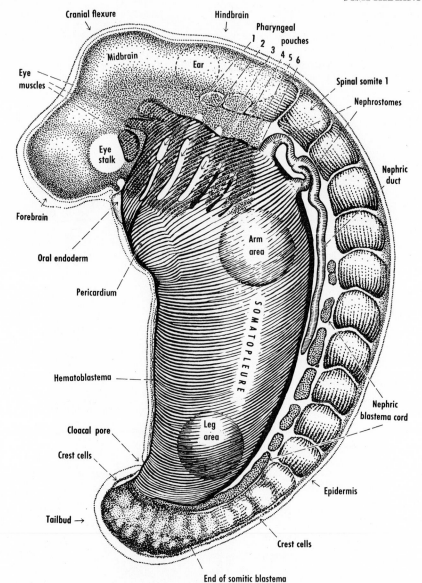

Figure 59. Tailbud embryo of a salamander (St. 19); left lateral view. By dissecting away the epidermis most mesodermal differentiations become exposed (slightly diagrammatic). *Crest derivatives* (stippled): envelopes around central nervous system (primordial meninges), dorsal and ventral fin mesenchyme, primordial chondrocranium, primordia of visceral cartilages. *Paraxial mesoderm:* 3 cranial somites; 10 free spinal somites; invaginated part of somitic blastema cord with 11 or 12 somites marked off by constrictions; non-invaginated median part of the somitic mesoderm. *Nephric mesoderm:* two pronephric segments, growing nephric duct, and mesonephric blastema cord. *Lateral mesoderm* (hatched): three primordia of eye muscles; six visceral arches (still incompletely differentiated); primordial celomic sac; primordial *pericardial sac;* discs in the lateral wall (somato-

the crescent spread out over the thin-walled foregut and the dorsal midgut, and later give origin to the endothelia of the *heart* and the *blood vessels*. The medioventral part remains attached to the ventral side of the yolk mass, between cloaca and hepatic rudiment. Experiments indicate that this is the exclusive source of all *blood cells*. The two divisions of the angioblastema are accordingly designated as *endothelioblastema* and *hematoblastema* (Fig. 60).

c. **Ectomesenchyme.**   While the first two types of mesoderm

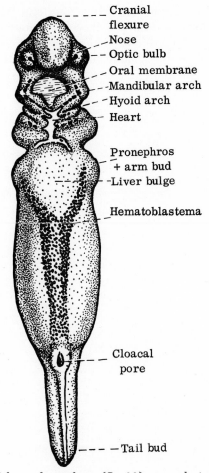

Cranial
flexure
Nose
Optic bulb
Oral membrane
Mandibular arch
Hyoid arch
Heart

Pronephros
+ arm bud
Liver bulge

Hematoblastema

Cloacal
pore

Tail bud

Figure 60.   Salamander embryo (St. 20), ventral view. Endothelioblastema (white and hatched) and hematoblastema (heavy stipple) shown as if shining through the covering mesoderm and epidermis; × 16.

pleure) indicate location of the preprimordia of *fore and hind limbs*. At this stage only three pharyngeal pouches are actually present; the fourth to the sixth, in solid black, mark prospective differentiations. The *angioblastema* is covered by the lateral mesoderm except in ventral midline; × 30.

arise from the equatorial belt of the blastula, the third one has an entirely different origin. It is called the *neural crest mesoderm* or *ecto-mesenchyme,* both terms referring to its peculiar early history. In the blastula the prospective crest cells are situated along the border of the prospective epiderm (Fig. 44). Included in the neural folds, they shift dorsally during neurulation. The differences in the later history of the cranial and the spinal divisions of the crest cells were described above (p. 104). From the crest material arise diverse ectodermal structures, but also the mesenchyme which furnishes large parts of the cartilaginous skeleton of the head (Fig. 65), and the mesenchyme of the dorsal and ventral fins. Many of its cells migrate extensively before they reach the site of final differentiation (Fig. 59). But the nature of their movements shows no relationship with the later ectodermal or mesodermal differentiation. It is not yet clear when and how the various types segregate.

Chapter 8

Integration of Larval

Organs and Organ Systems

The early phases of differentiation, as described so far, resulted in the assemblage and preliminary organization of groups of uniform, little differentiated cells into *preprimordia* and *primordia*. Both differ from mere prospective areas of gastrulae by a higher degree of determination. Transplanted to other parts of the embryonic body they still will develop as if they had been left in place. Primordia have advanced beyond the condition of preprimordia by assuming directly recognizable, characteristic shapes. For instance the tailbud (St. 18) is the primordium of the tail, while at stage 14 the general region above the cloacal pore may be said to contain its preprimordium (Fig. 44*h*). Location and limits of preprimordia must be determined by indirect methods, transplantation, color marks, or careful backward tracing of the normal process of development.

During the tailbud stages elements that are heterogeneous by origin or through divergent differentiation, form composite *organs*. *Organogenesis* progresses speedily, while the embryo develops into a larva (St. 18–25). Though the free-swimming tadpole represents the very prototype of the embryos of higher vertebrates, it has been named a *larva* because it differs so greatly from the adult form as to mask its specific identity. The reason for this can be seen in the necessity for special

113

adaptations to life in an open aquatic environment. Whereas practically all organs begin differentiating during the tailbud and larval
stages, there are two major systems which in frogs so exclusively serve
the needs of the aquatic phase that they are properly classified as larval
organs. They sustain the functions of locomotion and respiration, and
are structurally represented by fins and gills.

1. THE LARVAL LOCOMOTOR ORGAN

The larva swims by undulating movements of its body and the long
muscular *tail*. The latter grows throughout the entire tailbud period
(Figs. 42, 43, St. 18–24). Through proliferative activity of the tailbud
up to 50 segments are added to those of the body. The last ones are
formed at stage 24, when the larvae of most amphibians already move
about freely. The core of the tail consists of notochord and spinal cord.
Both taper off into filamentous ends that remain attached to each other

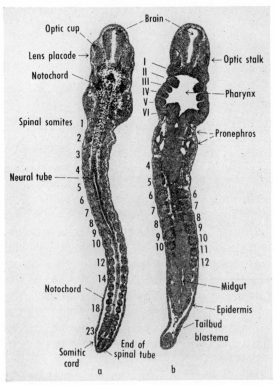

Figure 61.   *Taricha torosa* (St. 20); swimming posture. Two frontal sections:
a, Cut at level of notochord and neural tube; on the left two vanishing postotic
myomeres and 23 permanent myomeres or somites can be counted; in the head
region eye cups and lens placodes. Below the eye: cords of crest cells and epibranchial placodes. *b,* Cut at level of pharynx and midgut; five pharyngeal pouches;
pronephric bodies; on the left a nephrostome at the level of the fourth (first spinal)
somite. I–VI, visceral arches; 1–23, permanent myomeres and somites; × 15.

near the tip. This axis lies embedded between the two fillets of longitudinal tail muscle. In frog larvae up to 40 pairs of segments may be
counted. Gradually they become smaller, less distinctly separated, and
finally merge in an unsegmented strand of tissue which still has the
length of from five to ten somites. Only the proximal segments are
provided with spinal ganglia (Figs. 66, 70a). Mesenchyme, derived
from the neural crest, forms the supporting substance of the dorsal and
ventral fins. Hindgut and cloaca end in the proximal part of the ventral
fin. Also small vestiges of tailgut may be included in the root of the
tail. The dorsal aorta supplies the organ through the caudal artery.
Some blood is also contributed by the lower vertebral artery. These
vessels spread out into a rich network of capillaries, which collect again
in an efferent vessel, the caudal vein (Fig. 63). The surface is formed
by an epidermis with numerous large mucus cells.

In frogs the tail is the major organ of locomotion of the larvae up to the last
stages of metamorphosis. Muscular contractions in rump muscles may be observed
as early as stage 18. At stage 19 waves of such contractions running from the head
toward the tail may be elicited in embryos taken from their jelly envelopes. In
sections (Fig. 61) one finds the somitic segments of the concave sides shorter than
those of the relaxed convex sides. By stage 21 or 22 freed larvae are able to swim
short distances, but spontaneous sustained swimming usually begins only some
time after normal hatching stages have been attained.

2. THE RESPIRATORY AND VASCULAR SYSTEMS OF THE LARVAE

Most characteristic for the larval period is the *branchial apparatus*
which develops in the foregut region. During the tailbud stage the
upper lateral body walls become segmented through the development
of *pharyngeal pouches* (Figs. 58, 61, 62) and corresponding *visceral
grooves* of the external surface (Figs. 42, 43, St. 17–20). They set apart
six pairs of visceral arches. One distinguishes a pair of mandibular, a
pair of hyoid, and four pairs of branchial arches (Figs. 65, 66). The
last branchial pair shows degrees of reduction in various species, and
is absent in *Necturus, Proteus* and other perennibranchiates. Cus-
tomarily, the *pharyngeal pouches* are given the order number of the
preceding visceral arches. Thus the first pair of pouches are located
between the mandibular and hyoid arches. They never break through
to the outside. In salamanders they disappear early, whereas in most
frog larvae they persist in a rudimentary condition (Fig. 65) until
metamorphosis, when they become a part of the accessory hearing apparatus. At this stage the second to the fifth pouches rupture and
become *gill clefts*. The sixth pouches remain rudimentary and parts of
their epithelial linings assume a glandular structure.

During the later tailbud stage, protuberances appear at the surface
of some of the branchial arches near their dorsal roots. These are the
gillbuds (Figs. 42, 43, St. 20, 21). While they grow into long, branch-

ing tufts of filamentous *external gills,* they become covered by endodermal epithelium which grows out from the pharyngeal pouches and replaces the epidermis of the external gills. About the time of hatching, through simultaneous rupture of the third gill cleft and the oral membrane, a passage becomes cleared for the circulation of respiratory water.

Newt and salamander larvae have three pairs of *gills,* which are attached to the third, fourth, and fifth visceral arches (Fig. 43). In newts, the sixth arch exceptionally carries an additional small and lightly branched filament. The external gills persist throughout the larval period and grow into large, plume-like structures. Along the ventral part of the branchial arches rises a lamella which is the *gill plate.* It seems to have some protective value. The first visceral arches (mandibular arches) carry neither gills nor gill plates. In newts and salamanders (except *Ambystoma tigrinum* and viviparous European salamanders) they acquire an ephemeral pair of *balancers* (Fig. 43). Also the second or hyoid arches carry no gills; but from their outer edges arise the lamellar *opercula* (covers) which are enlarged homologues of the gill plates of the branchial arches (Fig. 43). They merge ventrally into a continuous crosswise fold.

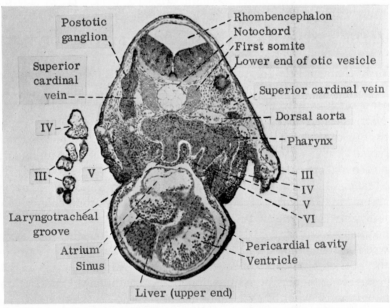

Figure 62.   Hatching frog larva (*Rana sylvatica,* St. 21). Oblique cross section, on the left (right side of figure) passing through dorsal root of third visceral arch (open gill cleft), on the right side through the fifth arch. The laryngotracheal groove is the common primordium of left and right seventh pharyngeal pouches. The mesoderm lamella between it and the sixth pouch is a rudimentary seventh visceral arch; it contains a small pulmonary artery (seventh aortic arch); III to VI, visceral arches; × 50.

Hatching frog larvae have two pairs of *external gills,* each consisting of a single small tree (Fig. 42, St. 21, 22). They originate near the center of the third and the fourth visceral arches. The esophagus remains occluded until about a week after hatching, when yolk and other reserves have become used up and the larvae begin to feed. On the

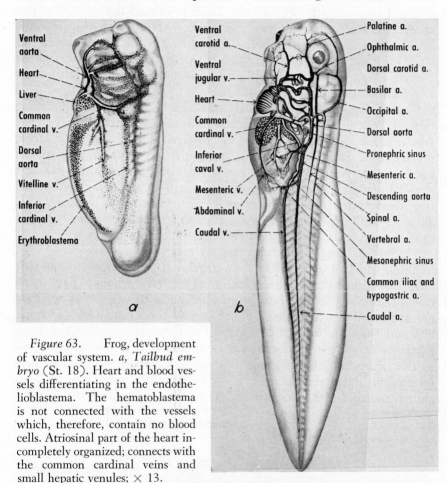

Ventral aorta

Heart

Liver

Common cardinal v.

Dorsal aorta

Vitelline v.

Inferior cardinal v.

Erythroblastema

Ventral carotid a.

Ventral jugular v.

Heart

Common cardinal v.

Inferior caval v.

Mesenteric v.

Abdominal v.

Caudal v.

Palatine a.

Ophthalmic a.

Dorsal carotid a.

Basilar a.

Occipital a.

Dorsal aorta

Pronephric sinus

Mesenteric a.

Descending aorta

Spinal a.

Vertebral a.

Mesonephric sinus

Common iliac and hypogastric a.

Caudal a.

a   *b*

Figure 63.   Frog, development of vascular system. *a, Tailbud embryo* (St. 18). Heart and blood vessels differentiating in the endothelioblastema. The hematoblastema is not connected with the vessels which, therefore, contain no blood cells. Atriosinal part of the heart incompletely organized; connects with the common cardinal veins and small hepatic venules; × 13.

b, Larva (St. 25). Functional circulatory system. *Hatched:* ventricle and aortic bulb; *stippled:* atrium and venous sinus; *reticulated:* liver. In this drawing the plexuses of the aortic arches are simplified. Actually, the first and second are capillary networks supplying the first and second visceral arches. The third to the sixth show, in reverse order, steps in the formation of branchial plexuses. The seventh or pulmonary arch has a common dorsal root with the sixth arch and forms a capillary plexus around the surface of the small lung sacs; then it returns the blood to the heart, entering through the dorsal wall of the atrium. The peripheral part of the superior cardinal vein is not represented. The inferior cardinal veins (renal portal veins) form plexuses of lacunae in the nephric bodies which drain partly through the cardinal veins by way of the pronephric bodies, and partly through the newly developing, unpaired, inferior caval vein; × 8.

ventral surface of the mandibular arches develop the *glandular suckers*
(Fig. 42, St. 16–22). In the young larva they serve as *adhesive organs*
but disappear about the time when the larvae begin feeding (Fig. 63*b*,
St. 24, 25). During the days following hatching, the *opercula*, growing
down from the second visceral arches, form a pair of lids over the gill
slits and external gills (Fig. 42, St. 23–25). Toward the end of the first
week their free edges fuse with the *cervical folds* which rise from the
body wall below the heart bulge. Thus the gills of anuran larvae become enclosed in *gill sacs*. On the left side remains an open drain, the
spiracle (Fig. 42); the right gill sac communicates with the left one by
a narrow ventral passage (Fig. 65).

By this time, the second, fourth, and fifth gill slits are also breaking
through, opening into the common gill sacs (branchial or cervical
sinuses). Enclosed in these sacs the external gills of the early larvae
remain small, and the respiratory function is largely taken over by the
so-called *internal gills*. These are highly branched, short tufts that
sprout from the gill plates (Fig. 67). In half-grown larvae of the bull
frog, the fourth and fifth arches each carry four rows of about 15 little
gill trees—60 in all; they give the arches an appearance of brushes. The
third and sixth arches carry similar gills, in smaller numbers.

The visceral arches are supported by a *cartilaginous skeleton* (Figs.
65, 66), which is attached to the ventral and lateral neurocranium by
means of ligaments and muscles. The *visceral cartilages* have been
called the "ribs" of the cranial and pharyngeal region. However, they
derive from the neural crest (Fig. 59), and their histogenesis is quite
different from that of vertebral ribs. The first arch contains two large
cartilages of which the dorsal one, or *quadrate,* becomes solidly fused
to the neurocranium. In urodele larvae it maintains the dorsoventral
orientation and is fastened only by its proximal end (Fig. 64). In
anuran tadpoles (Figs. 65, 66, 73), it assumes a longitudinal direction

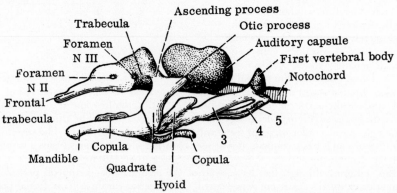

Figure 64.   Chondrocranium of salamander larva; stippled parts are derived
from prechordal and paraxial mesenchyme, others from crest mesenchyme; 3–5,
branchial cartilages (after Hoerstadius 1945).

alongside the ventrolateral edge of the cranium. In addition to the anchoring at the ear capsule, it is also fastened in the region between nose and eye (i.e., to the orbitonasal lamina). As a consequence, the joint with the lower jaw is carried far rostrally; the mouth becomes a relatively small opening and the ventral cartilage or *mandible* is short and has an almost crosswise position.

The *horny teeth* of the frog are fastened to pairs of upper and lower *rostral cartilages* (Figs. 65, 66) which alone carry on the functions of biting and mastication. The question has been raised whether these cartilages might be remnants of a premandibular arch. However, they

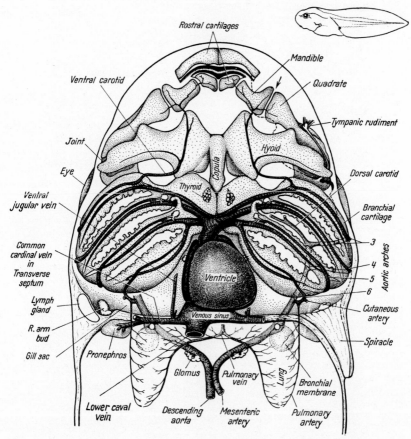

Figure 65. Frog larva (*Rana catesbeiana*, St. 26); cartilaginous skeleton and vascular system of the pharyngeal region; ventral aspect. Atrium (dark) mostly hidden by ventricle of the heart. Aortic trunk branching into four pairs of aortic arches (3 to 6). Interaortic septums occur near the ventral roots of the third to the fifth arches; afferent and efferent limbs of the sixth arch communicate through direct anastomoses. Paired thyroid glands (on the basal plates of the branchial cartilages); two pairs of parathyroids (at the ventral roots of the fourth and fifth aortic arches); paired ultimobranchial bodies, near the heart (Witschi 1949); × 10.

are not of general occurrence in vertebrates, and even in primitive fishes there is little evidence found in support of the theory of another visceral segment in front of the mandibular. It seems preferable to consider all cartilages of the lower jaw as parts of the first visceral arch. The upper rostralia arise as parts of the chondrocranium.

Much of the floor of the oral cavity is supported by a pair of broad

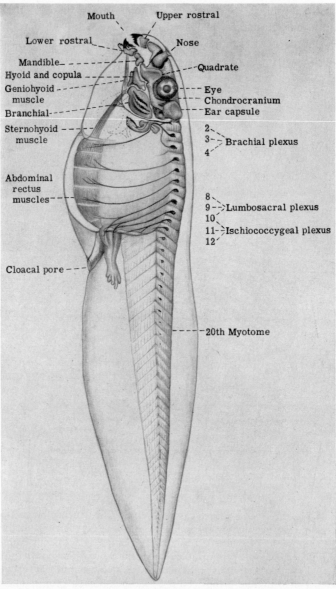

Figure 66.   Frog larva (*R. catesbeiana*, St. 28); partially dissected to show segmental arrangement of muscles, nerves and some parts of the visceral skeleton; × 2.

hyoid cartilages. In frogs they become attached, secondarily, to the quadrate cartilage by a joint below the eyes and in front of the auditory tubes. Ventrally they fuse with the median, unpaired *copula* (Figs. 65, 66, 73).

The cartilages of the third to the sixth arches, or *branchial cartilages,* are connected with each other ventrally as well as dorsally, forming shallow cups with three slits (Figs. 65, 66). The entire branchial skeleton gives somewhat the impression of a basket (the "gill basket"). On its inside, each cartilage carries spiny *gill rakers.* Over their outside surfaces run the *aortic arches,* deeply hidden beneath the thick velvet of thousands of *gill filaments.*

The gills contain an elaborate network of finely branching *blood vessels* which arise from the *branchial aortic arches.* The development of this branchial system starts in embryos of the early tailbud stage, when irregular open spaces lined with endothelial cells appear in the third visceral arch (Fig. 63*a*). Gradually, four pairs of vessels become organized which ascend from the aortic trunk through the branchial visceral arches to the dorsal aortae (Fig. 63*b*). As gills bud and sprout, the adjacent parts of the aortic arches transform into a network of arterioles, the loops of which enter every filament (only grossly indicated in Fig. 63*b*). As a consequence of this development, each arch is divided into an *afferent* and an *efferent* vessel (Figs. 65, 67), the former bringing blood to the gills, and the latter carrying it away. In species without gills or the sixth arches, the corresponding aortae may still persist (they do in *Ambystoma,* but not in *Necturus*). They may

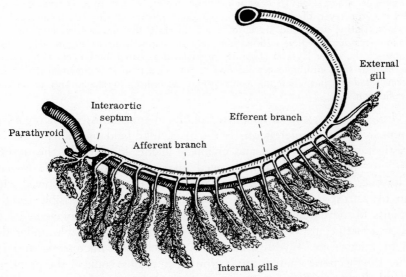

Figure 67.   Frog larva (St. 29); left fourth aortic arch with gills; efferent branch opens into left dorsal aorta; frontal view; × 14.

also acquire a vestigial plexus of arterioles, reminiscent of gill circulation.

The primordia of the first and second aortic arches transform directly into *ventral carotids* and a *lingual plexus* of blood vessels (Fig. 63). The failure of these arches to develop regular aortic passages is correlated with the absence of gills, but mainly with the relative tardiness of all vascular developments in amphibians. The development of the seventh aortic arches will be described jointly with that of the lungs.

In *Xenopus,* the African clawed toad, the larvae do not acquire gills. Their respiratory function is taken over by the highly developed gill rakers, which form large, branching filters in bulging chambers. The branchial capillary plexuses are only indicated in very early embryos and soon regress. The gill rakers are supplied by inner branches from the fourth aortic arch and probably also from the root of the fifth and the sixth. These branches are known also in the ranid frogs as *filter arteries.* They are drained by various veins that are contributory to the common cardinal veins.

3. EPIGENESIS OF THE LARVA

The progress of differentiation of embryonic primordia and histologic systems during amphibian development is summarily presented in Table 6. It provides an impressive picture of the increase in morphologic manifoldness that occurs within the first week. The list of some 60 items in the last column even falls short of the number of actual differentiations embodied in a newly hatched larva.

Diagrams and classifications like this one are short summaries of greatly diverse facts. As abstractions they are afflicted with some inadequacies, which eventually may lead to misinterpretations. Thus, the indicated lineage of the *ectomesenchyme* at about stage 18 does not intend to imply that in a general way the outer germ layer of stage 12 may produce either ectodermal or mesodermal tissues. Rather it should serve to recall the fact that ectomesenchyme derives from a restricted region within this area, as mapped out in Figure 44g. More correctly the outer layer at stage 12 might be designated as the *ecto-18crestmesoderm.* But such cumbrous terminology is unnecessary if it is understood that the term *ectoderm* has changing connotations according to stages and regions of application.

Epigenesis, or the development of the manifoldness of an organism from a visbly simpler germ, is the particular field of embryologic investigation. The physical and chemical agents involved in the normal and in the experimentally changed process are its *epigenetic factors.* However, the egg, far from being unorganized matter, is endowed with an ultrastructure that is even more fundamentally responsible for the results of development than the epigenetic factors. The elements of such structure are below the size ranges that become visible under the light microscope. Investigations with the electron microscope and indirect cytogenetic analysis are beginning to resolve some of the problems of this *basic constitution,* which is inherited, by way of the germ plasm, from long sequences of ancestral generations. The development of the larva from the egg represents, not a case of creation of organization, but an *epigenetic elaboration of visible manifoldness, on the basis of inherited ultrastructure.*

Table 6

Progress of Embryonic Differentiation during Premetamorphic Periods

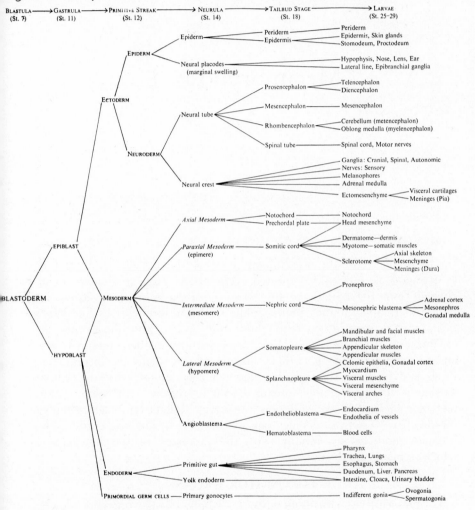

Chapter 9

Metamorphosis. I

In the ontogeny of the amphibians the evolutionary change from fish to tetrapod is faithfully repeated, generation after generation. The change from the aquatic to the terrestrial form is more extensive in some orders and families than in others. Perennibranchiates like *Necturus* and *Proteus* retain throughout their life a prevailingly piscine organization. Various larval characters persist also in the common newts and salamanders, so that their metamorphosis really is incomplete. Frogs and toads go through the most extensive transformations. Their locomotor and respiratory organs become entirely remodeled. After metamorphosis they develop new nutritional habits, and, accordingly, the digestive system undergoes radical changes. In fact the entire body becomes more or less rebuilt, with the exception of the sex glands, which remain unaffected.

1. LOCOMOTOR ORGANS

a. **Descriptive Morphogenesis.** Many changes prepare slowly during the period of incipient metamorphosis. In *frog larvae,* the *limb buds* make their appearance at the time when the gill sacs close. At stage 24, before formation of the spiracle, the *primordia of the hindlegs* are seen on sections through the body at the level of the lowest part of the celomic cavity. At stage 25 they become externally visible as slight, unpigmented protuberances (Fig. 42). In most newt and salamander larvae the forelimbs develop precociously. They are externally recog-

124

nizable at stage 21 (Fig. 43), while the hind limbs are still rudimentary at stage 27. A notable exception, *Ambystoma tigrinum* has no balancers and the forelegs are not precocious.

At the beginning of leg formation a *mesenchymal blastema* fills the entire thickness of the somatopleure between the peritoneum and the slightly bulging and thickened epidermis (Fig. 68). The cells are most densely packed beneath the basement membrane of the epidermis; some are in mitotic division. In frogs, the limb bud remains blastemic throughout stage 25 and its epidermis is unpigmented; it elongates slowly into a plainly visible oval body. At stage 26 (Fig. 42) it shows a segmentation into two parts. Both contain *precartilaginous condensations*, the upper a femur, the lower fibula and tibia. The dorsal (fibular) surface usually is pigmented. Stage 27 (Fig. 42) is externally characterized by the addition of a notched *foot plate*, mainly representing the tarsal part of the leg. New cartilaginous elements belong to the *pelvic girdle* and the tarsal and metatarsal part of the limb. Stage 28 (Figs. 42, 66) is conspicuous for the outgrowth of the *five toes* and the development of *muscles*, especially in the upper leg. The *functional condition* is attained at stage 29 (Fig. 42), the larva making use of the legs as balancers and pushers. All parts are now assembled but the skeleton is still entirely cartilaginous. Ossification begins during climactic metamorphosis, at stage 30.

In frog larvae the arms protrude into the gill sacs (Fig. 65) where

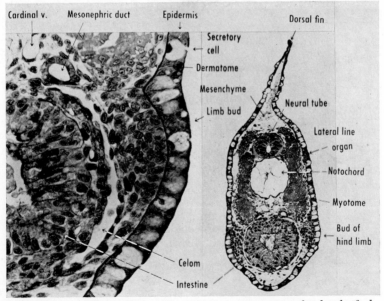

Figure 68.   *Taricha torosa* (St. 25); cross section at the level of the primordium of the hindlimb; × 48. *At the left,* section through bud at higher magnification; × 200.

they remain enclosed until metamorphosis. While the dorsum of the developing foot faces toward the outside (supination, Fig. 66), the distal part of the forelimb rotates at an early stage so that the palm of the hand comes to rest on the opercular wall of the gill sac (Fig. 42). The cartilages of the forearm (ulna and radius) are partially crossed when they begin to differentiate, and they fuse in this position of half-pronation. When breaking to the outside (Fig. 42, St. 31–33) the forearm contains a single cartilage, with distally forking ends of ulna and radius. This arrangement becomes stiffened later by ossification, so that the hand remains fixed in pronation. The first digit is rudimentary; externally visible are only the second to the fifth fingers. The fourth (next to the last) finger and the fourth toe are the longest in their series.

Branches of *spinal nerves* grow early into the limb buds (Fig. 69). At stage 26 the basic pattern of the final distribution is recognizable. During the later larval stages the nerves follow the growth of the limbs. In frogs, the arm is supplied by a *brachial plexus* made up of branches from spinal nerves 2 to 4 (Fig. 66). The hindlegs are similarly supplied by the *lumbosacral plexus,* from spinal nerves 8 to 10. In salamanders the corresponding plexuses are formed by spinal nerves 3 to 5 and 15 to 18.

A rapid growth of the legs during the final two weeks of larval life

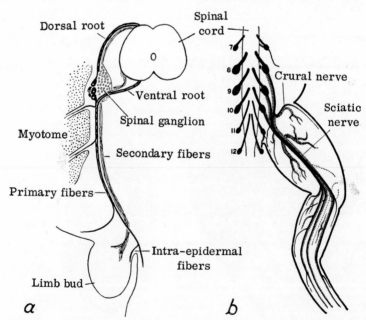

Figure 69.   Innervation of the leg of the frog from the lumbosacral plexus (spinal nerves 8 to 10). *a,* Early larva (St. 25); the nerves entering the bud form a crural and a sciatic bundle. *b,* Late larva (St. 29) (Taylor 1943, 1944).

leads up to the climax of metamorphosis, the beginning of which is marked by the sudden emergence of the fully developed forelegs. The left one pushes out through the spiracle while the right one breaks through a perforation in the opercular wall of the gill sac (Fig. 42, St. 31). While mechanical pressure may speed the formation of this opening, it is not its main cause. A foramen develops by local histolysis even in the absence of a foreleg, as after surgical ablation of the pre-primordial limb bud.

When the arms emerge from the gill sacs, the *larval tail* is still intact; one or two days later its fins start to wither (St. 32), and within a week or ten days the entire tail becomes resorbed. The involution starts suddenly with tissue degeneration and is rapidly carried toward completion, through the phagocytic (i.e., ingestive) action of invading white blood cells. Early in this process the degenerating tissues become sharply delimited, and near its completion the short cone of discolored degenerating tissue contrasts strangely with the healthy skin of the body (Fig. 42, St. 31–33).

The small number of vertebrae which is characteristic for living anurans is a recent adaptation to their peculiar, hopping type of locomotion. Fossil ancestral frogs had up to 26 presacral vertebrae instead of the 8 of present-day species. Frog larvae first develop a regular series of 11 to 12 vertebrae (Fig. 70a). During metamorphosis, the ninth becomes a *sacral vertebra* by developing strong lateral processes that articulate with the iliac wings (alae) of the pelvis (Fig. 70b). At the same time the tenth, eleventh, and twelfth vertebrae fuse into a single bone, the urostyle (or coccyx), which projects dorsally over the opening of the now long and slender pelvis. Strong muscles between pelvis and urostyle make this lower part of the "broken" back an integral part of the catapulting mechanism of the lower extremities (Fig. 70b).

Metamorphosis in salamanders is not marked by any sudden changes in the locomotor organs. The fins may become reduced to varying degrees depending on the life habits of the species, but the muscular and skeletal parts of the tail are retained by all species. The legs are short and the body always drags on the ground.

b. The Experimental Analysis of Limb Development.   Such analysis is largely the work of Braus, Harrison and their collaborators. In *Taricha torosa* and *Ambystoma maculatum* armbuds organize at stage 21 and legbuds at stage 27. Since transplants of the earliest limb buds to neutral sites on the embryonic body, on the head, the tail, or in the lateral body wall, always grow into exactly the same kind of limb that they would have furnished at their normal site, it is obvious that visible buds are already completely *determined*. Consequently experiments had to be made with younger stages. Usually the pre-primordium of a donor, excised and freed of its epidermis, is pushed into a small pocket prepared under the epidermis of the host. It is easily seen that the transplant may be made to the same or to the opposite side, and any or several of its three axes may be rotated. Fore- and hindlimb blastemas may be exchanged. Since buds at the time of their appearance had proved to be fully determined, it was necessary to transplant the *prospective areas of limb formation*. Their position in early tailbud embryos is indicated by circles in Figure 59 (St. 19). The results of transplantations are as follows:

(1) The blastema of the prospective armbud is determined for arm-bud quality and longitudinal axis, as early as the open neurula stage. After transplantation to the site of the prospective leg, it produces an arm and not a leg.

(2) The same type of determination still holds at the early tailbud stages 18 and 19. Transplants with reversal of the dorsoventral axis still develop into normally oriented arms (Fig. 71a). However, reversal of the longitudinal axis results in reversed arms (left arm on right side, Fig. 71b).

(3) Finally, the dorsoventral axis becomes fixed at stage 20 and the mediolateral at stage 21.

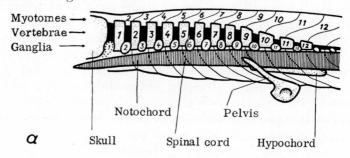

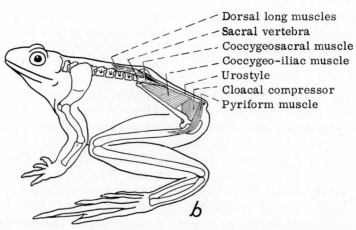

Figure 70.   Development of muscles and bones of frogs during metamorphosis (Hodler 1949); *a,* before metamorphosis; *b,* adult conditions.

Surprisingly, the determination of the corresponding characteristics in the much later growing legs occurs at about the same embryonic stages as in the arms.

The reported evidence suggests that the arm is induced at the end of the gastrula stage, possibly the archenteron being its inductor. From the beginning the area acquires the arm quality and not that of a limb in general. Also the longitudinal axis seems determined from the start. Quite differently, the dorsoventral and the mediolateral axes become fixed much later by inductive influences from the environment, i.e., from the neighboring tissues of the embryo. Similar considerations apply to the determination of the legbuds, except that the initial induction occurs at a somewhat later stage. In either case *determination* usually precedes by several days its manifestation in the form of visible *differentiation*.

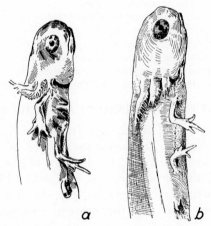

Figure 71.   Result of transplantation of prospective armbud mesoderm of *Ambystoma maculatum* to mid-body region, at stage 18. *a,* Longitudinal axis unchanged, dorsoventral and mediolateral axes reversed. Result: normal right limb (Harrison 1925). *b,* Longitudinal and mediolateral axes reversed, dorsoventral axis unchanged. Result: mirror image of normal right arm (Harrison 1925, 1921).

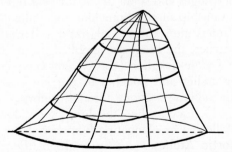

Figure 72.   Graphic pictures of a field of determination; vertical lines: gradients; horizontal lines: isopotentials (Ten Cate 1953).

Donor embryos, though deprived of a prospective limb area, sometimes are able not only to close their wound, but also to grow at its place one or several limbs. This led Harrison to investigate the possible range of limb production. It was found that this potency is highest in the center of the established area and gradually falls off at the periphery. This condition can be graphically represented as a *field of determination* (Fig. 72) with gradient and isopotential curves. Such a presentation conforms with a trend of thought common to most workers in this field, but particularly formulated by Weiss. It is applicable likewise to organizers and inductors.

The limb area may also be considered as a *field of induction,* since under its influence other tissues can become engaged in arm or leg formation. Moreover, it is evident that in the later progress of limb differentiation an entire series of inductions are involved. In any of these applications the "fields" are not themselves agents of differentiation, but represent summary quantitative appraisals of morphogenic factors. About the nature of the latter we have only such indirect information as derives from the study of the induced reactions. Structure at the macromolecular level, specific chemical composition, enzyme factors, and the like, are believed to hold the cues in the riddle of determination.

Balinsky has shown that supernumerary limbs may grow from the lateral body wall of newts after implantation, at stage 19–20, of an otic vesicle or, at least in one case, of a piece of celloidin. This gives evidence of a high competence of this region for limb formation; but the experiment seems also to indicate that certain types of cell damage tend to release inherent, inactive inductor potentialities. The similarity to the above reviewed work on primary organization is obvious.

2. ORGANS OF RESPIRATION AND CIRCULATION

a. **Larval Lungs.** The change from branchial to pulmonary respiration is prepared by developments starting at very early stages. In embryos ready to hatch (St. 21) the floor of the pharynx forms a narrow depression, the *laryngotracheal rudiment* (Fig. 62). From its lowest part arise two lateral diverticula, representing a *seventh pair of pharyngeal pouches.* They are the primordia of paired *bronchi* and *lungs.*

During the larval period the lungs serve as hydrostatic as well as respiratory organs. Like the swim bladders of fishes, they tend to adjust the specific gravity of the entire body to that of the water and may be used to shift the gravitational center. The respiratory surface becomes increased by inner ridges and septa in the *alveolar lung sacs* (Fig. 113).

The close relationship of the branchial and pulmonary organs is reflected in their innervation and vascularization. Together with the last three branchial arches, the lungs are supplied by the *vagus nerve.* The proximity of the *nodose ganglion* (the visceral component of the vagus ganglion) to the arches and pouches of the lower pharynx is plainly visible in slightly oblique sections through embryos of the early gill-bud stage (Fig. 62). Later, when the lungs grow down into the body cavity, they are followed by elongating branches of the nerve.

b. **Larval Aortic Arches.** The origin of the *aortic arches* was outlined in preceding sections (Figs. 63, 65). The fifth to the seventh do not develop as independently as do the third and the fourth. When, in frog embryos of about 7 mm., the sixth appears, it branches off from the fifth and again returns to it. Moreover, its efferent part soon establishes a connection with the seventh or pulmonary arch. The short common vessel through which the sixth and seventh open into the dorsal aorta is the *arterial duct*. During the late larval period the dorsal root of the fifth arch also connects with the arterial duct (Figs. 73, 74). The *cutaneous artery,* which supplies much of the skin, originates from the dorsal segment of the sixth arch (Figs. 65, 74).

Pulmonary arteries and *pulmonary veins* are the afferent and efferent vessels of the seventh aortic arch. The pulmonary plexus takes the place of a branchial capillary network. The blood flows dorsoventrally, that is, opposite to the direction of that taken in the four branchial arches. This is a consequence of the fusion of the ventral seventh arch with the atrium of the heart, where the blood pressure is lower than in the arterial duct (Fig. 63). In the perennibranchiate *Necturus,* a sixth aortic arch does not develop. Nevertheless the pulmonary vessels form as in other amphibians, proving the independence of the seventh from the sixth arch. The origin of the pulmonary circuit near the dorsal aorta and the dorsoventral direction of its blood flow resemble

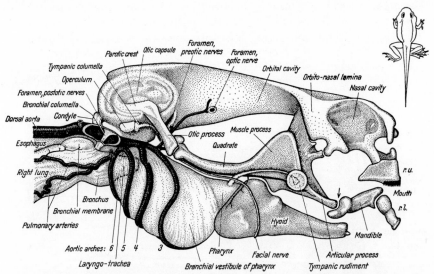

Figure 73.   Frog (*R. catesbeiana*) during early metamorphosis (St. 31). Cartilaginous skeleton of the head, tympanic organ, gill sac, and aortic system. The horny teeth of the lower jaws have been lost completely, those of the upper jaws partially. Arrow points to quadrato-mandibular joint. The primordial tympanic columella of the ear ends in a mesenchymatic cord which is accompanied by the facial nerve. The dorsal carotid divides into external (palatine) and internal branches; the latter, passing along the base of the chondrocranium, divides into a cerebral branch (entering the cranial cavity) and the ophthalmic artery. (Witschi 1949); × 8.

conditions in fishes, where the swim bladders are supplied by vessels from the dorsal aorta.

Before they reach the *heart,* the left and right pulmonary veins unite into a single vessel (Fig. 65). In small larvae of the bullfrog (18 mm.) this *common pulmonary vein* passes over the dorsal circumference of the venous sinus, then widens and applies itself broadly to the primary atrium. In several places, perforations permit the venous blood to enter the atrium. Later, this attachment becomes fully incorporated, so that the seventh aortic arch contributes materially to the formation of the left atrial chamber. The wall of the pulmonary vein is superficially attached to the arterial bulb by a solid ligament which lies in a groove of the expanding atrium. It may be called the *septal ligament,* since it lies over the root of the *atrial septum.* In metamorphosing anuran larvae the separation of the atrium into two chambers is complete. The importance of the pulmonary vein for the development of the second chamber is also indicated by the fact that lungless salamanders retain an undivided atrium.

c. Supplementary Respiratory Organs.   During the larval period, *cutaneous respiration* is far more important than pulmonary. Even in adult frogs, the skin releases more carbon dioxide than the lungs. *Buccopharyngeal* respiration is harder to evaluate quantitatively, but often seems to be as efficient as the pulmonary, even in adult frogs. The oxygenated blood from skin and pharynx is returned through a

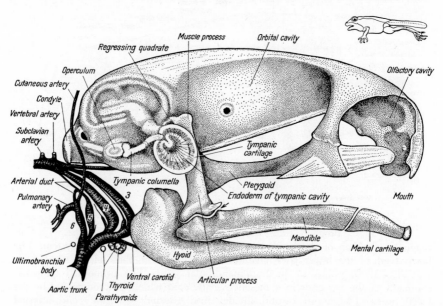

Figure 74.   Frog (*R. catesbeiana*) during metamorphosis (St. 32–33). Chondrocranium and early ossifications. Arrow points to quadrato-mandibular joint. 3–6, Aortic arches. (Witschi 1949); × 8.

pair of cutaneous veins, and a pair of ventral jugular veins, into the common cardinal veins and the venous sinus. Only the pulmonary veins, which carry little oxygen, return directly to the atrium. Such facts make it seem unlikely that the evolution of a separate pulmonary circuit might have originated on grounds of physiologic conditions. Accidental topographic relationships, but particularly the embryologic derivation of heart and aortic arches from a common blastemic area, apparently prepared the way for the evolutionary development of the *pulmonary respiratory system.*

d. **Changes at Metamorphosis.**   The *involution of the gills* begins shortly before the arms break through the branchial sacs and proceeds at about the same pace as the resorption of the tail. When the latter has become reduced to a short stump (St. 33), the gills appear like wilted leaves that fill the shrinking branchial sacs (compare Figs. 77 and 78). They plug up the gill slits, which are much reduced in size. The fine filaments have disappeared and circulation through the gills is almost abolished. Histolysis, that is dissolution of their tissue, is near the final stage, as indicated also by the presence of numerous, large round *phagocytes,* which ingest the remnants of the soft parts. When the resorption of the tail is complete, the gills, gill slits, and gill sacs also have vanished, except for insignificant fibrous remnants and pigment masses.

The *topography of the aortic arches and the visceral skeletal aparatus* changes more extensively in frogs than in salamanders. Only the former are considered in the following description. During early metamorphosis (St. 30–31) the larval organization of the *vascular system* is still essentially intact (cf. Figs. 65 and 73). Rapid changes follow the regression of the gills. While the afferent branches and gill capillaries shrink, the blood from the ventral aortae is forced through preexisting and now widening pores of the *interaortic septums* into the efferent limbs of the aortic arches (Figs. 65, 67, 74).

Special conditions develop at the root of the third arch. At the time of the development of the larval branchial plexus, the direct communication between ventral aorta and ventral carotid (Fig. 63) had become throttled through the development of a thick *interaortic septum* (Figs. 65, 77). From then on the ventral carotid was supplied from the gills, by way of the efferent branch of the aortic arch. However, the septum always retained some potential anastomoses. At metamorphosis they are forced open, when the gill capillaries close and regress. Thus, the ventral carotid becomes again a direct branch of the aortic trunk. During these changes a prominent swelling develops at the root of the dorsal carotid, which is the *carotid body* (Figs. 75, 76). Sections show that it consists of a porous diagonal membrane, and a sponge-like body in the median wall of the vessel (Fig. 78). The main current of blood flows through the pores, while a smaller amount seeps through a

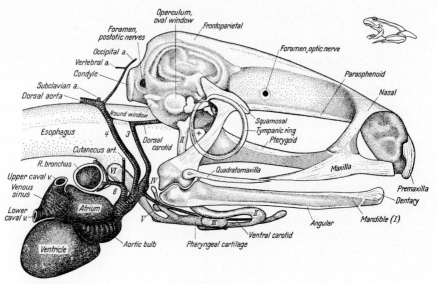

Fig. 75

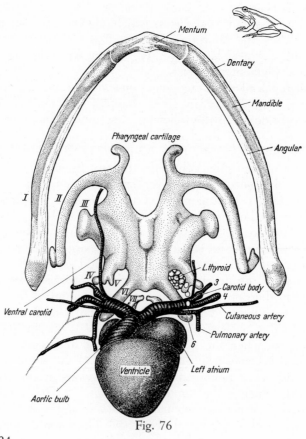

Fig. 76

spongy pad. The functional importance of these bodies is unknown. The interaortic septums of the fourth and the fifth arches disappear without leaving similar remnant structure.

Up to stage 31, the efferent limbs of all arches open into an uninterrupted dorsal aorta, where free passage exists, in both the rostral and the caudal directions. At the climax of metamorphosis (Fig. 74, St. 32) the fifth arch undergoes a rapid reduction, starting with the constriction of its ventral root and occlusion of its dorsal segment. A similar reduction of the dorsal part of the sixth arch initiates the transformation of the *arterial duct* system into an *arterial ligament*. The proximal part of the sixth arch persists and serves as the common root of the cutaneous and the pulmonary arteries.

With the shrinkage of the gill baskets (branchial vestibula) in the transition from stage 31 to 33 the aortic arches shorten to less than half their length. In Figure 73 only the dorsal efferent roots are visible, the gill-carrying parts of the arches lying ventrally under the branchial vestibule. On the other hand, in Figure 74 the aortic system is fully visible in lateral view.

The adult condition becomes established during the late stages of metamorphosis (Figs. 75, 76, St. 33). The fifth arch and the arterial ligament disappear completely. The dorsal aorta between the third and the fourth arches becomes reduced to a fibrous *aorticocarotid ligament*, completing the separation of *carotid* (third) and *systemic* (fourth) *arches*.

3. VISCERAL ARCHES

The pharyngeal apparatus of segmental arches becomes radically reconstructed. The larval arrangement of cartilages and muscles (Figs. 65, 66), besides serving branchial respiration, also satisfies the particular requirements of mud-eating frog tadpoles. The mouth has a small opening, and large lateral sacs with gill rakers. Since metamorphosis in frogs involves not only the loss of the gills, but also a change in food habits, the jaws and the oral opening become as extensively transformed as the branchial arches.

In the *mandibular arch* region, changes start with the shedding of the horny teeth (St. 31). Then the quadrate cartilage rotates ventrally around the point of its attachment at the ear capsule (Figs. 65, 66 and 73–76). At stage 33 it projects at right angles from the body of the

---

Figures 75, 76.   Frog (*R. catesbeiana*) at end of metamorphosis. Lateral and ventral views; cartilaginous and osseous parts of head skeleton, heart, and aortic system. II, Hyoid process, III–VI, branchial processes of the pharyngeal cartilage. 3, Carotid arch; 4, systemic arch; 6, common root of cutaneous and pulmonary arteries. On the right side of Figure 76 two parathyroids and an ultimobranchial body are shown, below the thyroid. Figure 75 shows the middle ear after removal of the tympanic membrane and of the endoderm of tympanic cavity; + marks the entrance of the auditory tube into the oral cavity ×8 (Witschi 1949).

skull and later it slants decidedly in the caudal direction. Throughout this process, the attachment to the orbitonasal lamina is preserved. This involves a considerable stretching of the connecting *pterygoid process* of the quadrate. The lower jaw grows in length at the same rate as its joint with the quadrate moves caudally. At the end of metamorphosis, it is about six times as long as it was at the start.

These changes are accompanied by progressive *ossification* (cf. p. 138). In the upper jaw the place of the rostral cartilages is taken by the *premaxillary bones*. In the lower jaw the rostral cartilages fuse with the mandibles (pars mentalis) and both parts become covered by the *dentary*. In the upper jaw a clasp develops laterally around the masticating muscles, through the outgrowth of a *caudal process* from the *maxilla*, and of a rostral extension of the lateral surface of the quadrate; this *quadrato-maxilla* becomes a major part of the upper jaw, while

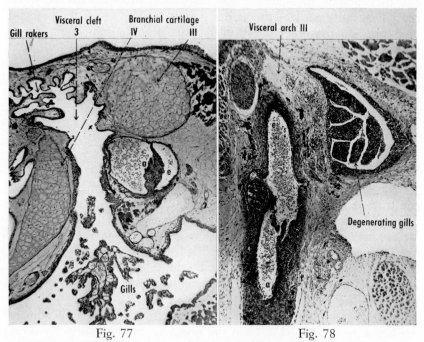

Fig. 77   Fig. 78

Figure 77.   Interaortic septum of the third aortic arch of a tadpole (*R. catesbeiana*, St. 28); part of a sagittal section which passes through the cartilages of the third and the fourth visceral arches. Highly vascularized terminal branches of gills in the third visceral cleft. *a,* Afferent (ventral) limb, *e,* efferent (dorsal) limb of third aortic arch; × 40.

Figure 78.   Interaortic septum of the third aortic arch of a frog in metamorphosis (*R. catesbeiana*, St. 33); part of a cross section showing the porous septum through which the blood passes from the afferent (*a*) into the efferent (*e*) aortic limb. The regressing dorsal limb of the afferent vessel combines with the interaortic septum in the formation of the *carotid body*. The gills (upper right) are poorly vascularized and degenerating; the gill slit is closing; × 40.

the *pterygoid,* curving medially around the masticating muscles, is included in the roof of the oral cavity.

The *cartilages of the second to the sixth visceral arches* fuse into one broad plate, the *pharyngeal cartilage,* which is embedded in the floor of the oral cavity and the root of the tongue. From its body project paired lateral processes which are derived from the second to the sixth visceral arches (Figs. 75, 76). The hyoid process attains a considerable length and takes the shape of a slender rod. It curves caudally around the tympanic cavity and attaches itself to the auditory capsule near the oval foramen. The distal parts of the branchial cartilages melt away until only short processes and ridges remain. They still serve for the attachment of muscles which formerly controlled the movements of the branchial apparatus and now assume analogous functions in the buccopharyngeal respiratory system. The last process is turned slightly dorsally; left and right members form the prongs of a fork which partly encloses the larynx and the *laryngotracheal cartilages,* derivatives of the seventh visceral arches (Figs. 75, 76VII).

The *muscles* which attach to the pharyngeal cartilage are either visceral or somitic in origin. Of the former, the four petrohyoid (petropharyngeal) muscles are derived directly from the levators of the branchial arches. Dorsally, they start from the parotic crest of the ear capsule and their contractions lift the floor of the pharyngeal (oral) cavity. The first one is supplied by the glossopharyngeal nerve; the other three receive branches of the vagus. Below the last of the branchial levator muscles, and belonging to the same series, follows the laryngeal levator, a muscle of the seventh visceral arch. At metamorphosis the center of this muscle becomes attached to the lowest process (VI) of the pharyngeal cartilage; the dorsolateral part disappears, and the ventromedial portion transforms into the laryngeal musculature of the adult frog. The laryngeal nerves are branches of the vagus nerve.

The strong levator of the hyoid arch, the orbitohyoid, is a purely larval muscle and disappears during metamorphosis.

The sternohyoid and the geniohyoid may be considered as upper terminal segments of the abdominal rectus muscle (Fig. 66). Contractions of the former lower the floor of the oral cavity. Both are supplied by the second spinal nerve (which also contains the remnants of the first and some fibers from the third). Like the branchial levators, these longitudinal muscles are little changed in the metamorphic process.

4. ALIMENTARY TRACT

The *small intestine* of anuran tadpoles is a long and slender tube, coiled into a double spiral of several complete revolutions (Fig. 42, St. 25, 29, 30). During metamorphosis it becomes shortened to about one-eighth of its larval length (Table 7). But the digestive surface is not proportionately reduced, since the formerly smooth walls now become covered with many septal folds. While involution and reconstruction proceed, food intake is completely suspended.

5. OSSIFICATION

Ossification of the skeleton is not entirely a characteristic of metamorphosis. The fact that ganoids and teleosts have bones structurally similar to those of terrestrial salamanders and frogs proves that, in certain groups, the evolution of bone preceded the advent of the tetrapods. However, as a rule, salamanders which become terrestrial have more heavily ossified skeletons than their perennibranchiate relatives (Fig. 79a–d). In the ontogenesis of present-day amphibians, ossification starts much earlier in salamanders than in frogs. In *Triturus* and *Ambystoma,* ossified tips of teeth appear even before hatching; shortly afterward the basal plates of such teeth fuse into larger pieces which constitute the first system of bones. When feeding begins, the larvae have several pairs of tooth-bearing bones in their upper jaws, and along the base of the cranium (Fig. 80). Other ossifications follow in the course of larval development, so that at the onset of metamorphosis, the adult bony skeleton is nearly complete. In frogs, ossification occurs mainly during metamorphosis. The jaw bones form particularly late and true teeth appear only at the end of metamorphosis (Figs. 75, 76, 80).

The progressive series of ossification from perennibranchiates to terrestrial salamanders (Fig. 79) is paralleled by the developmental stages observed in frogs. In long bones, perichondral bone becomes deposited in the form of a cylinder around the middle part (diaphysis) while the ends (epiphyses) remain uncovered. Then, as in *Necturus,* the perichondral (membranous) tissue begins to invade the partly calcified cartilage, forming a well vascularized primary marrow tissue. Eventually it also enters the epiphyses (Fig. 79d). Along its surface, a spongy system of secondary or endochondral bone develops. The absence of independent epiphyseal nuclei of ossification is characteristic for amphibians. Ossification is very incomplete in all modern amphib-

Table 7

Changes in Length of the Small Intestine in Rana sylvatica

After R. G. Janes (1934)

STAGE	TOTAL LENGTH (BODY + TAIL)	LENGTH OF SMALL INTESTINE
26 (Beginning of feeding)	22 mm.	50 mm.
29 (End of feeding)	44 mm.	128 mm.
33 (End of metamorphosis)	15 mm.	15 mm.

ians. The chondrocranium essentially persists in the adult, but the cartilage becomes fortified, and locally even replaced by bone (Figs. 73–76).

6. EXCRETORY ORGANS

The origin and the early history of the excretory organs are outlined by Figures 44, 46, 54, and 59. The designation *intermediate mesoderm*

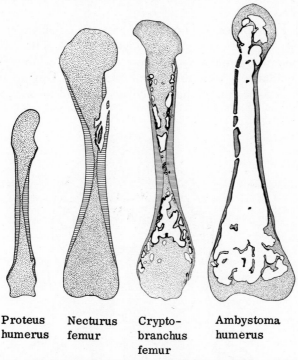

| Proteus humerus | Necturus femur | Crypto- branchus femur | Ambystoma humerus |

Figure 79.   Conditions of ossification in long bones of four amphibian species; *stippled*: cartilage; *cross-hatched*: perichondral bone; *black*: endochondral bone; *white*: vascular and marrow cavities (v. Eggeling, 1938).

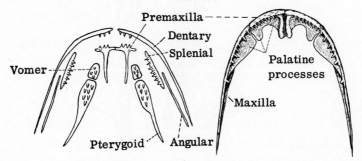

Figure 80.   *a,* Early ossification in the oral region of salamander larvae (*Triturus vulgaris,* St. 23). *b,* Comparatively late ossification in the oral region of frogs (*Rana temporaria,* St. 34) (Erdmann 1933).

refers to the position of the nephric blastema cords between the somites and the lateral plates of early embryos. Its use is particularly adequate since as well as the *nephric organs* the *adrenal cortex* and the *gonadal medulla* also develop from this same preprimordium.

The nephric blastema cells which invaginate alongside the first prospective somites are carried into the head region (Figs. 44, 46). It is for the high position thus attained that the uppermost part of the system often is called the *head kidney*. More usually it is known as the pronephros.

a. The Pronephros is short, extending in salamanders over two, and in frogs over three segments (Figs. 81, 83). The attachment to the corresponding somites is early lost (Fig. 54), while open connections are maintained with the lateral mesoderm. During the neurula period they become funnel-shaped, ciliated *nephrostomes,* leading from

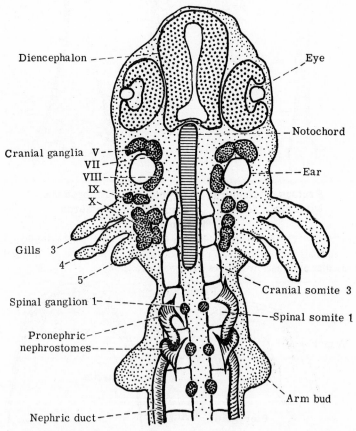

Figure 81.   Salamander embryo (*Taricha torosa*, St. 23). Frontal section of head and upper body, disclosing prevalence of segmental organization; × 47.

the upper celomic cavities into the urinary tubules. The free, distal ends of these two or three tubules soon unite into a single *nephric duct* which grows down along the ventrolateral edge of the intermediate mesoderm (Fig. 59), until it reaches the cloacal level. The progress of these developments is partly recognizable from the outside, since pronephros and nephric duct produce a gradually elongating ridge in early tailbud embryos (Figs. 42, 43; St. 16–21).

In *frog embryos* up to stage 21 the first nephrostome lies at the level of the second myotome and the third visceral arch. In the larva of stage 25 it has withdrawn to the upper limit of the third myotome, so that the three nephrostomes now occupy only the space of two somites (Fig. 83). During later larval life, the openings of the first two, or all three, fuse. At the climax of metamorphosis the pronephros regresses and disappears. In salamanders *(Taricha)* the nephrostomes lie ventral to the fourth and fifth myotomes (Fig. 81). The excretory function necessitates a large surface development. Thus the tubules grow excessively in length and become pleated and piled; but they leave wide interspaces which become filled by the sinusoids of expanding branches of the inferior cardinal vein (Fig. 82).

Figures 59, 81, and 83 present only simplified versions of the ac-

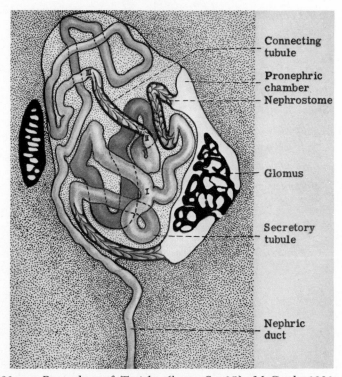

Connecting
tubule

Pronephric
chamber
Nephrostome

Glomus

Secretory
tubule

Nephric
duct

Figure 82.   Pronephros of *Taricha* (larva, St. 25). McCurdy 1931; × 120.
Fine stipple, Lacunae, filled with blood from the inferior cardinal vein.

tually highly complicated arrangements in the pronephroi. Figure 82
is a reconstruction of the true conditions existing in larvae of stage 25.
The tubular units are called *nephrons*. Each one begins proximally
with a *ciliated nephrostome* that leads into the wide *urinary* or *excretory tubule*. The two or three then combine into a common *collecting
tubule* of similar structure, which becomes distally a short, ciliated *connecting piece* with the *nephric duct*. The latter continues its downgrowth toward the hindgut which is broadly attached to the dorsal
body wall. The nephric ducts of both sides turn at nearly right angles
when they reach its level. By receiving them, this part of the endodermal tube becomes a *cloaca*, that is, a common receptacle and pas-
sageway for intestinal and urinary wastes. The connection is established
in salamanders of stage 22 at the sixteenth spinal segment. In frogs
of stage 20 the entrance first lies ventral to the tenth muscle segment
(myotome), but later it moves up to the ninth.

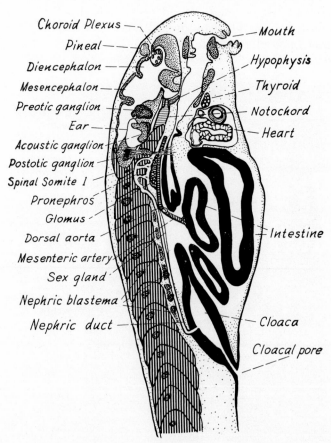

Figure 83.   Larva of *Rana sylvatica* (St. 25); parasagittal section, showing the
relative metameric arrangement of muscles, nervous, and nephric elements; × 28.

The excretory functions of the walls of the nephrons are supplemented by those of the peritoneum and the *pronephric glomus*. The body cavity becomes an almost closed chamber alongside each kidney. Where it borders on the dorsal aorta, a congeries of arterioles forms the large glomus (Fig. 82). It releases wastes into the *pronephric chamber* to be drained off through the nephrostomes.

b. The Mesonephros develops from the intermediate mesoderm between pronephros and cloaca. In frogs the fourth to the ninth spinal segments contribute, but the fifth to the eighth are mostly involved (Figs. 83, 84). The mesenteric artery serves as a convenient landmark, its root lying between the upper ends of the mesonephric bodies.

Beginning in *frog embryos* of stage 21 the nephric blastema becomes separated from the lateral mesoderm plates by the medial movement of the cardinal veins and their eventual fusion in a single, axially located caval vein (Figs. 85, 86*a, b*). The detached nephric blastema cords, each more or less distinctly separated into four to six segmental patches (Fig. 84), are carried along by the veins. Finally they become located between the dorsal aspects of the nephric ducts and the caval vein. This peculiar disruption of the original continuity between lateral plates and intermediate mesoderm explains one characteristic difference in the development of pronephros and mesonephros. Whereas in the former the *nephrostomes* arise from persisting segmental connections, in the mesonephros they appear as primordial condensations at some distance from the peritoneum. Only after secondary ventral migration

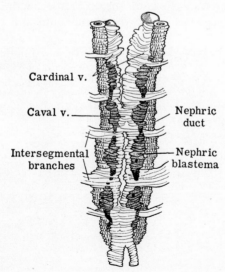

Cardinal v.

Caval v.

Nephric duct

Intersegmental branches

Nephric blastema

Figure 84.   Frog embryo (St. 22); dorsal aspect of the reconstruction of nephric blastema, nephric ducts, and cardinal veins at the level of the 4th to the 9th somites (Van Geertruyden 1948). The cardinal veins are fusing into a median caval vein; × 66.

along the lateral walls of the caval vein are the contacts with the peritoneum again established (Fig. 88). Like rope skippers, the mesonephric blastema cords step over the in-sweeping cardinal veins, to regain their foothold on the peritoneum, after the vessels have passed.

In *salamanders* the cardinal veins do not move as single large tubes toward the axial position; but the formation of the caval vein is preceded by the development of a subcardinal plexus of venous branches and anastomoses. The caval arises by gradual enlargement of the central channel of this plexus. Hence there remains the possibility of persisting contacts between intermediate and lateral mesodermal blastemas. Nevertheless the later development shows that usually the nephrons develop as in frogs, their nephrostomes establishing only secondarily contacts with the peritoneum. Only in the upper region of the mesonephros of *Ambystoma* some peritoneal funnels may develop from persisting primary connections. The conditions in the salamanders resemble those still existing in the higher vertebrates.

The differentiation of *nephrons* from the nephric blastema begins toward the end of larval stage 25 (Fig. 83). A set of primary tubules forms where the blastema is in direct contact with the nephric duct (Fig. 86*b*). In fact this contact is an important prerequisite for differentiation. If experimentally the downgrowth of a duct from the pronephric into the mesonephric region is prevented, the differentiation of nephrons on this side is either rudimentary or entirely missing.

A typical *nephron* of the mesonephros (Fig. 87) consists of a renal corpuscle, a nephrostome, and a convoluted nephric tubule. Such nephrons are found in the kidneys of salamanders. In frogs, the primordial nephrostome separates early from the remainder of the nephron. While it attaches in typical fashion to the peritoneum and transforms into a

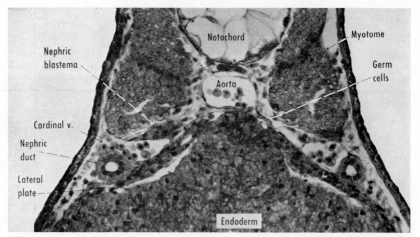

Figure 85.   *Rana sylvatica*, embryo (St. 21/22). Cross section at level of the 6th spinal somite. Mesonephric blastema on the left side of the figure is being separated from the lateral plate by the medial advance of the cardinal vein; × 150.

a

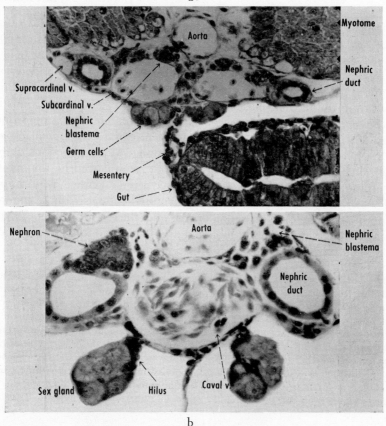

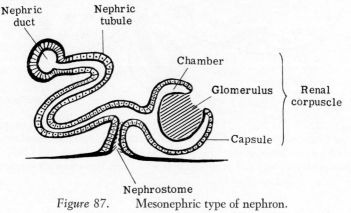

b

Figure 86.   Frog embryos, cross sections at the level of the 5th spinal somites. *a,* Stage 23/24; germ cells at dorsal root of mesentery divided into left and right strands. The original cardinal veins have separated into supracardinal and subcardinal branches; the latter are to form the caval vein (cf. *b*). The nephric blastema is divided into lateral condensations, the primordia of primary nephrons, and median remnants; × 250. *b,* Stage 25; primordial sex glands with medullary blastema beginning to invade at the hilus; on left side part of a primary nephron penetrating wall of nephric duct; × 375.

Figure 87.   Mesonephric type of nephron.

145

peritoneal funnel, its distal end establishes contacts with one of the large venous lacunae and thus opens directly into the blood vascular system. Figure 88 presents three stages of this development and at the same time shows the successive addition of secondary and tertiary nephrons to the primary element. Each new generation of nephrons arises from the median blastema remnant. This results in the formation of the *composite nephrons,* the functional units of adult frog kidneys (Fig. 5). Each *renal corpuscle* consists of a *capsule* (of Bowman) and an arterial *glomerulus.* They represent miniature reproductions of pronephric chamber and glomus. This analogy is enhanced by the similarity of the ciliated neck of the convoluted tubule with a nephrostome (Fig. 88). The distal parts of the convoluted tubules form a common collecting tubule (Fig. 5) that opens into the nephric duct. At this level the latter may now be renamed a *mesonephric duct,* even though it originated by downgrowth from the pronephros.

In *salamanders* the mesonephric bodies are much longer than those of frogs. They differentiate into distinct upper and lower parts (Fig. 89). The former, running alongside the sex glands, are also known as the sex parts. The latter, more voluminous, may then be called urinary parts, even though they are not the exclusive source of urine production. The sex part contains only single, primary nephrons, which in the male sex are partly connected with the testes. The urinary parts are composed of units of compound nephrons, each containing four elements. The nephrostomes leading from the body cavity into each urinary tubule persist usually throughout lifetime. However, in the male the nephrostomes of the sex kidney detach from the tubules and regress at puberty (third year in *Taricha*).

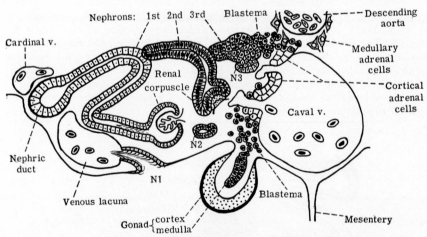

Figure 88.   Derivatives of the mesonephric blastema: three generations of nephrons (eventually four), adrenal cortical cords, and gonadal medullary cords. It is a peculiarity of anurans that the primordia of the nephrostomes (N3) separate from the nephrons (N2) and make contacts with the celom and with venous lacunae (N1).

Also, in the male only, the collecting tubules of the urinary part project as long ducts which unite into a single short ureter (Fig. 89). These differentiations seem to foreshadow the separate formation of a third kidney, the metanephros of the amniote vertebrates.

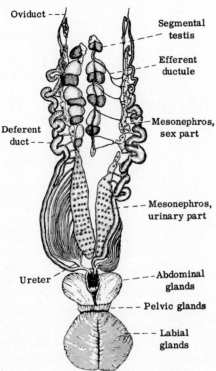

Figure 89. Urogenital organs of an adult male salamander (*Taricha torosa*) (partly after McCurdy). In most amphibians the segmental character of the gonads is less obvious; × 1.5.

Chapter 10

Metamorphosis. II

7. ADRENAL GLANDS

While urinary nephrons differentiate along the nephric duct, adrenal tissue develops from the same blastemic cords at the border of the caval vein. The cells that directly adhere to the dorsal or dorsolateral wall of the vein differentiate into a peculiar type of cords which resemble immature nephric tubules. Obviously these strings of *adreno-cortical cells* are modified nephrons (Fig. 88). Even in small larvae (*Rana*, St. 25) they accumulate lipoid inclusions which give a characteristic histochemical reaction with osmium tetroxide (Fig. 90). Later these cords are invaded by an ectodermal type of cells which derive from ganglia situated along the descending aorta (Fig. 88). These *sympathoblasts*, though rather irregularly distributed between the cortical cells, are called *adrenomedullary cells*, because they are homologous with the elements that occupy the center of the mammalian adrenal gland. The mixed cords remain permanently attached to the veins that drain from the kidneys into the caval vein. However, as more urinary tubules are formed from the blastemic remnants, the adrenals are carried ventrally and then laterally to the midventral position which they occupy on the kidneys of adult frogs (Figs. 91, 5).

It is of interest that the relative number of nephric blastema cells which are to participate in the production of adrenal or urinary nephrons can be modified by hormonal factors. The addition of 1 or 2 mg. of estradiol (female sex hormone) per liter of aquarium water causes a more than ten-fold increase of the adrenals

148

Fig. 90

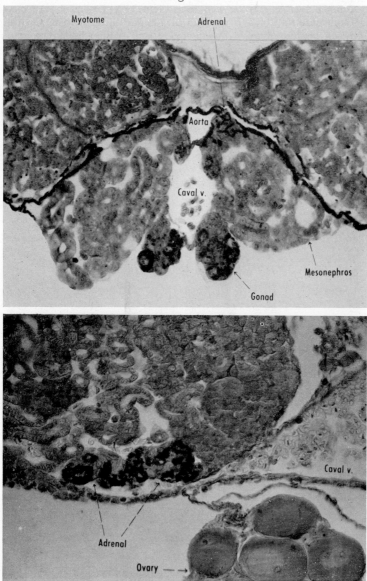

Fig. 91

Figure 90.   Rana sylvatica, larva, stage 25a, cross section: *mesonephros* with convoluted primary and secondary tubules; *indifferent gonads* with enlarging medullary cords; adrenals in original position, at dorsolateral wall of caval vein. Lipoids of adrenal cortex and dissolving yolk platelets of the gonia are blackened by osmic acid fixation (Segal 1953); × 200.

Figure 91.   R. pipiens, metamorphosing female (St. 33). Cross section showing the adrenal descended to the ventral surface of the mesonephros; cortex blackened by osmium deposits (Chang and Witschi 1955); × 200.

of the exposed tadpoles, and a more than proportional reduction of the urinary kidney components. As may be seen from Figure 92, the entire blastema of segment 4 and almost all of 5 is used up in adrenal differentiation. On the other hand, early hypophysectomy, with subsequent lack of the adrenotrophic hormone, is followed by a reduction of adrenal size (Fig. 93). The combination of the two experiments, diagrammatically represented in Figure 93, shows further that estradiol acts not directly, but only by way of the hypophysis. Consequently, both reduction and increase of the adrenal are under the direct control of the adrenotrophic (corticotrophic) hormone. This then is an instance of very *precocious control of a developmental process by hormones* produced in a relatively distant organ.

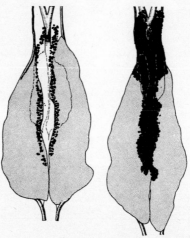

Figure 92.   Kidneys (gray) and adrenals (black) of R. *temporaria,* at metamorphosis (St. 33). *a,* Normal; *b,* raised in estradiol, 1 mg./liter (Witschi 1953); × 18.

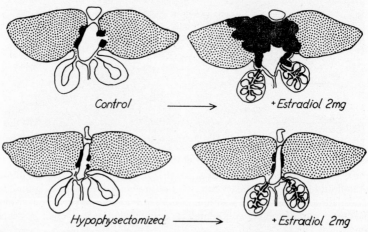

Figure 93.   Graphic presentation of the effects of hypophysectomy and high estradiol treatment on adrenal development and sex reversal in genetically female frog larvae (Chang and Witschi 1955).

8. SEX GLANDS

a. Elementary Organization.   The sex glands of amphibians, and of all higher vertebrates, are composed of three major elements: *cortex, medulla,* and *germ cells.* The first two are somatic tissues, the third represents the germ plasm of the species. The following descriptions are generally based on the conditions existing in frogs.

The *cortex* arises as a peritoneal fold along the inner edge of the upper part of the mesonephric body (Figs. 88, 94).

The *medulla* derives from the mesonephric blastema in the form of a quasi-segmental series of cords (Fig. 94). In the frog they form mostly at the level of the fifth and sixth spinal segments. Their original number of 10 to 12 becomes reduced by regression at the upper and lower ends to about 4, 5, or 6 (Fig. 96a). In the course of development the cords differentiate into tubular structures, forming seminal tubules, rete, and efferent ductules. This tendency is in line with the contention that the medullary cords are a type of modified nephrons.

The *germ cells* first are closely associated with the endoderm. In frogs of advanced tailbud stages they are contained in a high *dorsal crest of the endoderm* (Fig. 85). They become pinched off by the advance of the lateral plates which join to form the intestinal mesentery. When this is accomplished the germ cells lie as a long strand at the dorsal root of the mesentery, between the cardinal veins (Fig. 95). Displaced by the new caval vein, they move laterally into projecting peritoneal *gonadal folds* (Fig. 86a, b).

b. The Indifferent Gonad.   The narrow *hilus* or attachment ligament of these folds soon admits also some blastema cells from the intermediate mesoderm (Figs. 86b, 96). Their condensation into about six definite *medullary cords* starts within the gonad cavity. Growth of

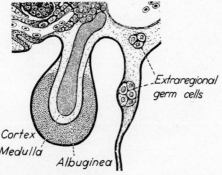

Figure 94.   Diagram representing the composition of the indifferent sex gland of two main parts: cortex and medulla (Witschi 1914). The interspace, the primary gonad cavity or albuginea, contains mesenchyme and blood vessels. Occasionally groups of extraregional, "lost" germ cells are seen in the mesentery (those shown in this diagram are relatively too large; see Fig. 97). They remain sexually undifferentiated.

these cords progresses by mitosis and continued absorption of more blastema cells. The appearance and expansion of the *gonad cavity* parallels the disappearance of the yolk platelets in the gonia. Following their immigration into the gonadal fold, the germ cells have become encapsulated in *follicle cells.*

Thus in the indifferent gonad of the frog (Fig. 96) the *cortex* consists of the peritoneum, the gonia, and the follicle cells. It is separated from the compact *medullary cords* by a *gonad cavity* that is filled with a loose mesenchyme; in the latter spread the *blood vessels* which supply the organ.

c. Sex Differentiation. The differentiation of *ovaries and testes* occurs during the second larval period.

In *female larvae* the general topography of the gonad remains unchanged. The **cortex** *plays the leading role* in the differentiation of the ovary. It thickens by rapid mitotic multiplication of the germ cells which now become *ovogonia.* Already in young larvae (St. 26) some transform into *ovocytes,* while the residual ovogonia continue multiplying (Fig. 97a). The follicle cells keep on multiplying and furnish the growing ovocytes with an investing envelope, the *granulosa* (Figs. 10–12). The early start of ovocyte maturation is characteristic for nearly all vertebrates and assists in the identification of the sex during embryonic stages. The medullary cords remain relatively undeveloped. Their hilar stalk stops growing, but persists as a vestigial *rete of the*

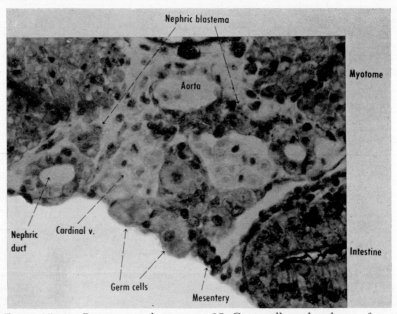

Figure 95. *Rana aurora,* larva, stage 25. Germ cells at dorsal root of mesentery; subcardinal veins nearing each other; nephric blastema in the space between veins, aorta, and nephric ducts; × 250.

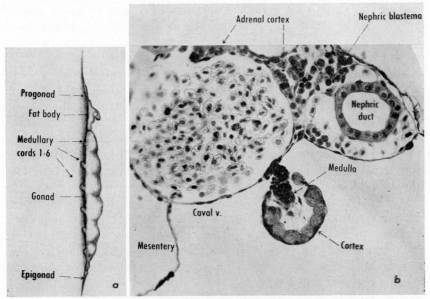

Figure 96.   R. *sylvatica* (St. 25b). The indifferent sex gland. *a,* Total gonad with fat body; × 55; *b,* cross section (Witschi 1929); × 240.

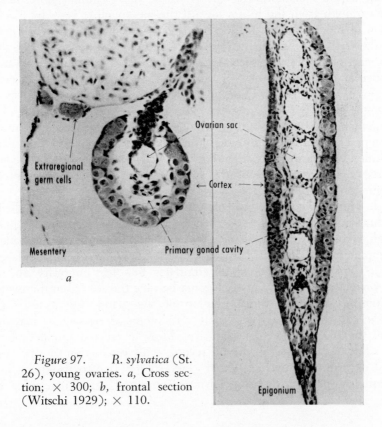

Figure 97.   R. *sylvatica* (St. 26), young ovaries. *a,* Cross section; × 300; *b,* frontal section (Witschi 1929); × 110.

ovary. The part in the center of the gland becomes vesicular and develops into an *ovarial sac.* It pushes the mesenchyme and blood vessels
of the primary gonad cavity toward the cortex, its ovocytes, and growing
eggs. Each ovary contains a series of about six ovarial sacs (Fig. 97*b*).
By the time of metamorphosis they begin to invest the largest eggs with
a second envelope, the theca. Between theca and granulosa lies a thin
mesenchyme layer with a network of arterioles that supply the growing
ovocytes (Fig. 10).

   *In the differentiation of the testis of male larvae the accent lies on
the* **medulla.** Very early the medullary cords begin to swell and attract
the germ cells. Singly or in clusters the gonia and follicle cells cross
the gonad cavity and embed themselves in the medullary cords (Fig.
98*a, b*). This further increases their volume and leads to the fusion
of four to six cords into a single medullary body. The cortex becomes
reduced to a thin *peritoneal membrane.* Directly under it lies the
mesenchyme of the former gonad cavity. It becomes now a second
covering layer of the testicle, the *albuginea,* and contains the major
blood vessels of the sex gland. The distribution patterns of the blood
vessels—superficial in the testis and central in the ovary—are characteristics which become noticeable immediately after sex differentiation.
Even before metamorphosis the stalks of the medullary cords resume
their growth from the hilum toward the mesonephric body by incorporation of more blastema cells. They are to become the *efferent ductules*
of the testis, but establish connections with the kidney tubules only by
the end of the first or second year. At the time of metamorphosis the
testicular medulla consists of vesicular *seminal tubules* and a central
strand of rete blastema (Fig. 98*c*). The former contain all the spermatogonia and their follicle cells. The latter is the primordium of the
testicular network or rete, which considerably later develops into the
system of ductules that collect the mature sperms of all the seminal
tubules. All the relationships that thus become established between the
parts of the testis and of the mesonephros have been presented in
Figure 5 (p. 16).

   d. Hermaphrodism.   Interestingly, in amphibians not all individuals have ovaries or testes, but *hermaphrodites* occur at a relatively
high frequency. Embryologically they arise through side by side development of both the cortical and the medullary components (Fig.
99). Quite often a gonad differentiates first like an ovary and only
at some later stage a number of gonia become transferred to the medulla,
initiating an actual transformation of the gland into a testis (Fig.
100*a*). If this reversal starts late and progresses slowly, it may reach
into the period of sexual maturity. Thus in frogs a number of cases
of adult hermaphrodism are on record, with production of ripe sperms
and eggs in the same sex gland (Fig. 100*b*). In two instances, it was
possible to perform the artificial insemination of eggs with sperms from

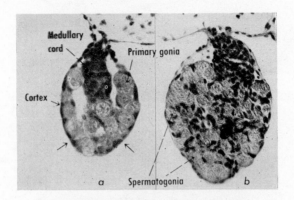

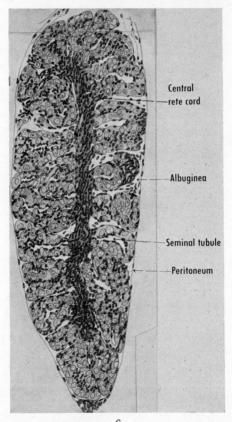

Figure 98.   Testicular development in frogs. *a,* First transfer of germ cells from the cortex to the medulla (St. 25b); × 266; *b,* all germ cells (spermatogonia) are in the medulla (St. 26); × 200; *c,* differentiation of seminal tubules and a central rete cord; frontal section; × 150 (St. 33).

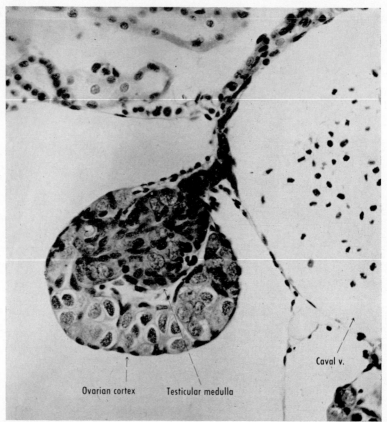

Figure 99. R. *sylvatica* (St. 26b); cross section through ovotestis of juvenile hermaphrodite; × 330.

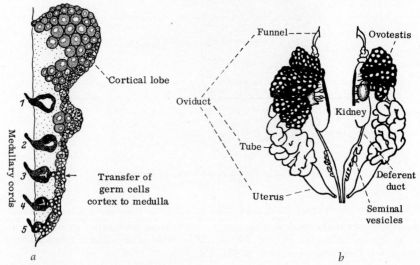

a   *b*

Figure 100.   Hermaphrodite gonads. *a,* Sagittal section through gonad of a metamorphosing toad; a purely cortical lobe at upper end is followed by two ovarian segments and three with progressively testicular character. *b,* Adult hermaphrodite of the frog.

the same individual. These are the only known cases of self-fertile hermaphrodites among quadruped vertebrates. The offspring proved as viable as those from ordinary male-female combinations (Fig. 101). Hermaphrodism is a primitive type of sex distribution. It is found more often among some of the fishes and it is prevalent in ascidians.

Figure 102 shows side by side the urogenital systems of three young frogs, preserved two or three months after metamorphosis. At that time the ovaries of all females (*a*) are many times as large as the testes of *directly differentiating* males (*b*). It is remarkable that testes of hermaphrodites usually are more than normal size. In the pictured case (*c*) the right gonad is in full transformation from an ovary into a testis, the process being more advanced in the lower than the upper parts. On the left side the reversal is near completion and only the irregular shape and large size of the testis still indicate the past history of *indirect differentiation*. The three diagrams of Figure 103 review and summarize the characteristic features of sex differentiation.

e. Gonaducts.   The male germ cells are transported from the testis to the sex part of the mesonephros by way of the *efferent ductules* (Figs. 5, 89, 103*a*). From here on they use the *nephric (mesonephric) duct* for their descent to the cloaca. In the adult this duct thus has the double functions of an ureter and a *seminal deferent duct*. In frogs the free segment below the kidneys usually develops lateral pockets, the *seminal vesicles* (Figs. 100*b*, 102*b*, *c*), which in some species become quite voluminous. In salamanders the duct enlarges in its full length (Fig. 89) and, like the vesicles of the frogs, serves as a storage organ for sperms.

In females, at the time of ovulation, the eggs fall into the body cavity. They are, however, soon propelled by ciliated bands of the

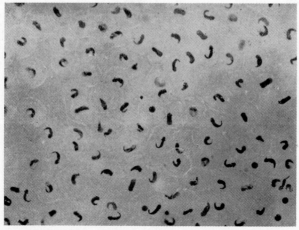

Figure 101.   Uniparental offspring of a hermaphrodite *Rana temporaria*, six days old. Note that only a very few eggs remained unfertilized.

peritoneal epithelium toward the funnels (ostia) of the *oviducts* (Fig.
100*b*), which lie attached to the pericard in the uppermost recesses of
the body cavity. The oviduct arises as a derivative of the pronephros.
In both salamanders and frogs the nephrostomes extend their ciliated
epithelia over a part of the surface of the pronephric body until a
continuous ciliated stripe is established, the *oviducal field*. By thickening
and outpocketing this epithelium first produces the *funnel part* of the
oviduct. At the beginning there may be up to three ostia (mouth
openings), though the one corresponding to the last nephron normally
prevails. In salamanders, where oviduct formation starts early in the
second larval period, the down-growing tip joins the nephric duct a
short distance below the pronephric body. It becomes imbedded laterally in the wall of the duct which itself had developed by downgrowth
from the pronephros a few days or weeks earlier. It is still a debated
question, to what extent cells of the primary nephric duct may become
incorporated in the rapidly lengthening oviduct. Only the relatively
short tip is attached; the duct becomes independent as soon as formed.
In the frogs the downgrowth of the oviduct starts late. At metamorphosis, when the pronephric bodies and ducts rapidly degenerate, the
oviducal field alone survives. In the following downgrowth the tip of

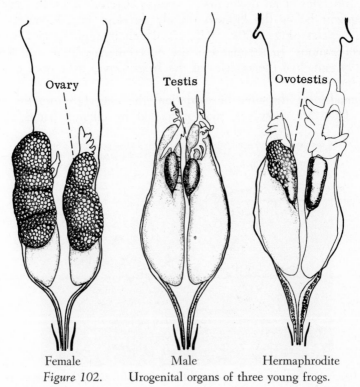

| | Ovary | Testis | Ovotestis |

Female   Male   Hermaphrodite
Figure 102.   Urogenital organs of three young frogs.

the oviduct takes a course parallel to the mesonephric duct, but without ever establishing a connection.

In hermaphrodites, oviducts and seminal ducts with seminal vesicles are both maintained as long as the gonads contain appreciable amounts of ovarian and testicular tissue (Figs. 100b, 102c). In males the development of the oviducts sooner or later lags and even complete regression may occur. More frequently some vestiges are retained (Fig. 89); they are particularly large in the males of the common leopard frog.

From the walls of the endodermal cloaca of salamanders sprout three sets of tubular glands, which are designated as *abdominal, pelvic,* and *labial glands.* Under the influence of the hormones of the mature testes they grow very voluminous and are responsible for the conspicuous labial swelling that characterizes the male (Fig. 89). They remain rudimentary in the female. These glands are the primitive homologue of the glands of the urogenital sinus of mammals and, hence, of the prostate glands.

f. Genic Sex Determination.   The fact that in many animals a fairly constant 1:1 ratio of sex distribution is maintained indicates that a hereditary mechanism of the type of mendelian back-crosses must be involved in sex determination. Furthermore, a complete genetic formula should express the existing constitutional bisexuality of every individual, which manifests itself in the described hermaphrodite traits and in the capacity for sex reversal. Such considerations lead to the assumption that one sex is homozygous for at least one male determin-

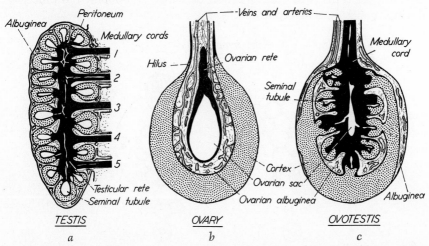

Figure 103.   Diagrams of the composition of the sex glands of frogs and the higher vertebrates. Stippled are the germ cell carrying tissues, black the medullary cord components. The distribution of the blood vessels is indicated. *a,* Sagittal section through testis; *b,* cross section through ovary; *c,* cross section through hermaphrodite gland.

ing (M) and one female determining (F) factor, which may be expressed in the constitutional formula MMFF. The other sex then has to be heterozygous for one or the other of these factors. If this is the female determining one, the formula becomes MMFf. To make this an adequately working mechanism one has further to assume that sex actually is determined by a sort of balance between male and female factors, or their derivatives, as expressed in the following quantitative series:

$$FF > MM > Ff$$

Under such assumptions MMFF represents the female formula, MMFf the male one. Conventionally chromosomes carrying the F factors are designated as X chromosomes; those with f are the Y chromosomes. The M factors are located in Z chromosomes.

Several types of breeding experiments support the above assumptions for the case of the frog. The most direct test involves the crossings of one of the already mentioned hermaphrodites with a normal male and a normal female. The results are diagrammatically represented in Figure 104. They prove that the male is chromosomally of the XY type, the female XX. The hermaphrodite reveals itself as a genetic female and, in spite of sex reversal, the male part of the gonad has remained homozygous and monogametic. This is a remarkable result, for it proves that testicular differentiation, spermatogenesis, and insemination may proceed with female as well as with male chromosomal constitution. This raises the question of which developmental processes the sex genes actually control.

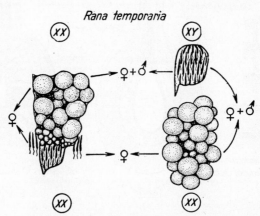

Figure 104. Diagram illustrating the four possible combinations of eggs and sperms from a hermaphrodite, a normal male, and a normal female. Symbols between the arrowheads indicate the sex distribution in the offspring groups (♀ female; ♂ male). Encircled are given the sex chromosome constitutions of the parents.

g. **Concept of Cortical and Medullary Inductors of Sexual Differentiation.**   As may be seen from Figures 99 and 100, germ cells of any animal differentiate in the female sense if located in the cortex, and in the male sense if in the medulla. Breeding tests as well as chromosomal investigations prove that within one hermaphrodite, the genes and the chromosomes of cortical germ cells are the same as those of medullary germ cells (Fig. 104). This leads to the conclusion that irrespective of genetic constitution, *the cortex acts as a feminizing inductor,* causing undifferentiated gonia within its range of influence to differentiate into eggs; and that conversely *the medulla is a masculinizing inductor,* leading the development of germ cells toward spermatogenesis. Gonia transplanted into other body regions, as well as gonia that failed to reach the genital folds during the migration phase, remain permanently undifferentiated (Figs. 94, 97a). The further analysis of the inductors makes it almost certain that the *follicle cell* is the specific element which produces the active agent, presumably a chemical substance. Similarly in the medulla a large cell type can be singled out as the most likely producer of the masculinizing inductor substance. This special medullary cell seems to be identical with the *interstitial cell type* of the adult testis. At the present it seems improbable that the inductive substances are identical with the sex hormones which the same cells secrete at the adult level, e.g., estradiol or testosterone. Therefore, tentatively, the names *corticin* and *medullarin* have been proposed for them.

It is now clear that *the genes F and M must control the activation of the inductor system and the production of the inductive substances.* In general, quantitative superiority of one or the other type of genes determines the prevalent or *epistatic sex.* The suppressed or *hypostatic sex,* being also represented by inductor primordia, is, however, not without possibilities of realization. If, for instance, in a genetically male toad, the medullary parts are surgically removed, the remaining cortical rudiment will fully develop and produce fertilizable eggs (Harms, Ponse). On the other hand, the cortex of larval female frogs can be destroyed selectively by heat treatments, whereupon the medullary rudiments differentiate into typical testes (Witschi). In either experiment the genetically hypostatic sex becomes dominant, after destruction of the inductor system of the epistatic sex.

h. **Antagonism between the Inductors.**   The just mentioned experiments also furnish proof that unisexuality of an individual, technically called *gonochorism* (sex-separation), results from an inhibition of one inductor system by the other. By the method of parabiosis (Fig. 105) it is possible to demonstrate interesting differences in the range of this inhibition, according to amphibian species and races. As indicated in the diagrams (Fig. 106), *cortex inhibition by the medulla*

a   *b*   *c*

Figure 105.   Parabiosis in amphibians. *a,* Pair of frog embryos (St. 19),
twelve hours after grafting operation. A lightly pigmented palustris embryo was
joined with a dark sylvatica; only extensively fused embryos will remain united;
× 10. *b* and *c,* Pairs of *Taricha torosa,* the California newt, before and after metamorphosis.

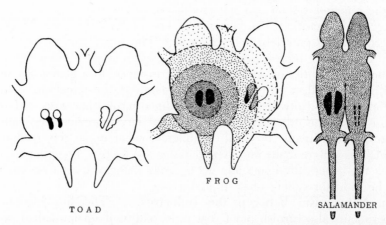

Figure 106.   Graphic presentation of the results of heterosexual parabiosis
in different types of amphibians. In *salamanders* the presence of testes inhibits the
cortical (ovarian) development in the female twin. In *frogs* the inhibition is of
same type but less severe. In *toads* the ovaries of the female develop normally. Density of stipples indicates the distribution and concentration of the inhibiting agent
in the twin system.

is localized within the gonads in toads, it spreads with a dilution gradient in frogs, but is blood-carried and evenly distributed everywhere in most salamanders and particularly in *Taricha*. In the latter species the antagonism is to some degree mutual, but although the inhibition of testicular differentiation is of minor degree and temporary, ovary formation is completely suppressed. In the medulla of inhibited females attempts at compensatory testicular differentiation have been noticed (Witschi and McCurdy). The case of parabiosis in *Taricha* shows clearly that *the inhibitor principles are chemical substances*, somewhat resembling antibodies. They have no similarity to the inductors of primary sex differentiation, corticin or medullarin, and do not occur in hermaphrodite species.

  i. Hormonal Sex Reversal.   The experimental administration of hormones of the adult sex glands, estrogens of the ovaries or androgens of the testes, often has a remarkable effect on the course of sex differentiation. As little as 0.01 microgram of methyltestosterone added per liter of aquarium water is sufficient to completely masculinize all female *Ranidae* raised in this solution. In species with homozygous males, such as the salamander *Pleurodeles* and the toadlike *Xenopus*, the genetic male may be induced to develop like a female by the addition of 25 micrograms of estradiol per liter to the water. In both species the treated animals are easily raised to sexual maturity and the feminized genetic males can be bred with normal males. Their offspring consists entirely of males (Gallien; Chang and Witschi), which proves again that environmental and experimental sex reversal leaves the genic and chromosomal constitution unchanged. It also means that there exists no antagonism between F and M genes and therefore no genic balance in the strict sense. The quantitative variations of the genes control the intensity of the inductor systems. The competition arises at the time of gonad formation and between inductors, not genes.

  The *mode of action of the sex hormones* is still under investigation. However, it is already evident that they produce effects by suppressing either the cortical or the medullary system. In principle they work like temperature or surgery in the first-mentioned experiments on sex reversal (p. 161), and like the antagonistic principles in salamander parabiosis. At any rate they act as inhibitors, and not like inductors of positive differentiation.

Chapter 11

Metamorphosis. III

9. SKIN AND SKIN GLANDS

In early embryos the skin consists only of *ectodermal cells.* In frogs, a *peridermal surface layer* covers the *basal layer,* the true and persisting epidermis. The latter is continuous with the neural crest, and the *placodes* appear in it as distinct thickenings. In salamanders the periderm is less developed and has a more transient character. It covers the placodes and seems altogether to be of protective nature. Shortly before hatching, some epidermal cells enlarge, and coarse granules appear in their lightly staining cytoplasm. These *granular cells* (of Leydig) remain small in frog larvae, but become a prominent element of the larval skin of salamanders (Fig. 68). *Hatching glands* develop in epidermal pads on the front of tailbud embryos; they secrete an enzyme which dissolves the jelly envelopes. Microcephalic and headless embryos lack these glands and cannot hatch. In frog larvae, the epidermis becomes thick. Many of its cells contain heavy fibrillar structures, anchored at the basement membrane, which resemble coarse neurofibrils, but apparently have only mechanical functions.

Beginning in tailbud embryos, scattered *mesenchyme cells* accumulate beneath the basal membrane of the epidermis and form a fibrous *cutis layer* (corium). However, it remains unimportant during the larval period.

Metamorphosis involves a number of radical changes in the histologic character of the skin. The epidermis becomes much thinner and

164

simplified. Periderm, granular cells, and intracellular fibrils disappear. A stratified epidermis forms, with a basal layer of germinative cells and a few layers of cuboidal cells which, toward the surface, become squamous and cornified. From now on, the surface layers are periodically shed, the first molt occurring during the early stages of metamorphosis. Starting at about stage 26, epidermal buds grow into the corium and give origin to *alveolar skin glands*. One distinguishes mucous and granular types, though they are closely related. Both open to the outside and release substances which in some species are quite toxic. They keep the skin moist and fit for respiration. Generally distributed over the entire skin, they also occur closely massed in patches and bands, as in the *parotic glands* of salamanders and in the dorsolateral folds of frogs. The smooth muscles which surround the glands are derived from the ectoderm. The corium becomes thicker through increase of the fibrous tissue and expansion of the embedded skin glands.

10. PIGMENT CELLS

Amphibian chromatophores fall into at least three classes: *melanophores* with black or brown melanin granules, *lipophores* with yellow or red pigments, and *guanophores* with guanin crystals. The last ones reflect the full spectrum and, in combination with turbid and colored media, are responsible for silvery white or for blue-green and metallic yellow colors. In larvae and adults, the pigment cells are found in the skin as epidermal and corial chromatophores, in the perineural sheath around the central nervous system, in the celomic epithelium, and in the sheaths around many blood vessels. With their dendritic processes, they resemble nerve cells. They arise from the neural ectoderm (cf. fate maps, Fig. 44). As prospective pigment cells they are concentrated in the neural folds and the neural crest of early embryos, indistinguishable from prospective ganglia and sheath cells (Fig. 55). When the gillbuds begin to form (St. 19), most crest cells have moved away from the dorsal surface of the neural tube; the melanophores, now recognizable by short dendrites and numbers of melanin granules, lie scattered in the mesenchyme of the dorsal parts of the body. In cross sections through slightly older salamander embryos, the distribution of the melanophores indicates the two main paths of migration which lead laterally and medially along the myotomes (Fig. 68).

Excision of parts of the neural folds of salamanders, as in the experiment of DuShane (Fig. 107a), results in larvae that are deficient in pigment of the trunk region (Fig. 107b). Substitution in neurulae of *Taricha* of the same parts by transplanted neural folds of *Ambystoma tigrinum* gives larvae with large patches of *Ambystoma* melanophores. At metamorphosis most amphibians acquire entirely new color patterns (cf. Fig. 42). In the above experiment *Taricha* assumes, even on its ventral side, the typical colors and color patterns of the adult *Amby-*

stoma (Fig. 108*d*). This leads to the conclusion that the color patterns of larvae and adults are partly determined by the innate constitution of the chromatophores. However, structure and chemical nature of the invaded tissues are not without modifying influence. Since *melanin* is the oxidation product of *tyrosine* or some similar *chromogen* within the melanophore, it is likely that in many instances the host tissues supply the oxidizing enzymes, such as *tyrosinase*.

Even the fully pigmented chromatophore has a capacity for ameboid movements. But the more extensive migrations are executed at the primordial colorless stage. The uncolored ventral skin of *Ambystoma* larvae already contains the chromatophore cells which, after metamorphosis, produce the black and yellow or black and blue pigment patterns of the adult.

Development and display of the chromatophores are often controlled by hormones. The *melanophorotrophic hormone,* which is produced and released by the hypophysis, particularly its intermediate lobe (Fig. 119), is the best investigated one. It causes the epidermal melanophores to expand, so that its concentration in the blood determines lightness or darkness of the skin. Some amphibians, e.g., *Xenopus,* turn pale in total darkness, but become almost black after blinding. In full daylight frogs are darker on black than on light backgrounds. Color adaptations that

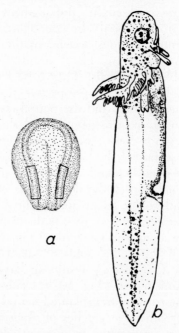

Figure. 107.   Origin of melanophores. *a,* Removal of neural folds of neurula at stage 15; *b* resulting larva (St. 25) lacks dark pigment in corresponding body region (redrawn after DuShane 1943).

follow initial visual stimulation furnish proof that the activity of the
hypophysis may be influenced by way of the central nervous system.
After complete hypophysectomy, amphibians turn extremely pale, owing
to contraction of the epidermal melanophores (Fig. 108a, b). The
lightest larvae are those that had the hypophyseal placode removed at
the tailbud stage. Their melanophores are not only in the contracted
phase, but they are poor in melanin granules and their number is far
below that of normal controls. On the other hand, continued daily injections of the melanophorotrophic hormone into normal or hypophysectomized larvae and adults cause a maximal increase of the melanophores, in size, expansion, and number (Fig. 108c); the entire animals
turn very dark. In hypophysectomized larvae melanophore contraction
is accompanied by guanophore expansion as early as at stage 23. This
is probably the first recognizable endocrine reaction during embryogenesis. Slight fluctuations in hormone concentration in the blood immediately find expression in the pigmentary picture. This is well
illustrated by parabiotic triple chains of *Taricha* (Fig. 109). As a
consequence of the employed grafting technique, only the first member
has a hypophysis. Each of the three has a heart and a nearly closed
circulatory system. Only a small amount of blood is exchanged through
anastomosing arterioles and capillaries. The condition of the melanophores indicates a step-wise reduction of hormone concentrations from
the first to the third parabiont.

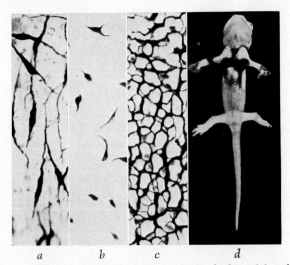

a   b   c   d

Figure 108.   Epidermal melanophores of the back skin of frog larvae. *a*, control; *b*, after hypophysectomy; *c*, after excess stimulation with melanophorotrophic
hormone; × 200 (Bruner, Chang, Witschi). *d*, Partial replacement of neural folds
in *Taricha* with folds of *Ambystoma* at stage 15 is followed by development of
Ambystoma color pattern in some areas of *Triturus* skin (DuShane 1943).

The effects of *sex hormones* on the development of *adult and nuptial colorations* have so far received but little attention. However, it is known that testicular hormones cause the seasonal blackening of the throat of male tree frogs, a reaction which resembles that produced by melanophorotrophin, except that it is strictly localized.

11. LATERAL LINE ORGANS

In the organization of the aquatic vertebrates, the lateral line organs are almost as characteristic a feature as the gills. They are permanent structures in the fishes, but absent in the amniotes. Among the amphibians, they occur in all larval forms, and persist to some extent in most adult salamanders and in *Xenopus*. In frogs and toads, they disappear during metamorphosis.

The lateral line organs are closely related to the ear. Functionally they take a position between the tactile and the auditory senses, perceiving movements of the water as produced by the approach of solid objects. The main structural difference arises from the fact that lateral line organs retain a superifical position in the epidermis while the acoustic organ invaginates and sinks below the body surface. The distribution of the organs extends from the rostral to the caudal ends of the larvae (Fig. 42, St. 29). Each sensory unit is a little corpuscle

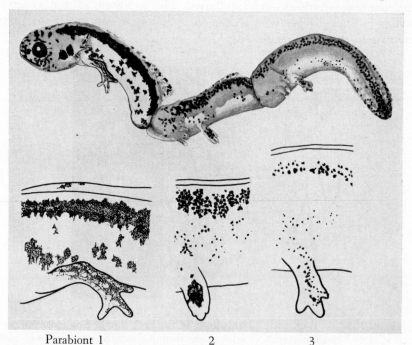

Parabiont 1   2   3

Figure 109.   Parabiotic chain of salamander larvae (*Taricha torosa*) grafted together at stage 17; two months after the operation. Only the first member has a hypophysis. Detail drawings below show melanophores fully expanded in the first, partially expanded in the second, and unexpanded in the third parabiont.

embedded in the epidermis (Figs. 68, 110*a*), with sensory *hair cells* covered by a jelly-like protruding *cupula*. Deflections of the cupula evoke the impulses that are transmitted by the *lateral line nerves* to the *preotic* or the *postotic ganglia* and through *dorsal root nerves* to the *acoustico-lateral area* of the oblong medulla. In frogs, at the time of metamorphosis, this entire complex degenerates, central as well as peripheral parts.

The lateral line system arises, together with the otocyst, from the *dorsolateral series of placodes* (Fig. 53). At the stage of the closed neurula (St. 16), three lateral line placodes (VII, IX, X) and an otic placode are quite distinctly separated from each other. At the first tailbud stage, the former begin to grow out in various directions, giving rise to the lateral line nerves as well as the sensory and supporting cells of the sensory corpuscles. Therefore, the entire organ system that extends from the nose to the tip of the tail arises from a single primordium and is not composed of segmental contributions. Harrison traced the outgrowing lateral lines in frog chimeras composed of a darkly pigmented head grafted on the body of a light embryo. Stone, in an analogous experiment, transplanted a dyed piece of postotic ectoderm, including the placodes IX and X, to its normal position in an unstained embryo. After establishment of such a graft, the outgrowth of stained processes can be observed in the living embryo (Fig. 110*b*, *c*). The growing cords are seen to break up into small clusters of cells, the lateral line organs, which remain connected with the postotic ganglion by fine subepidermal nerve fibers.

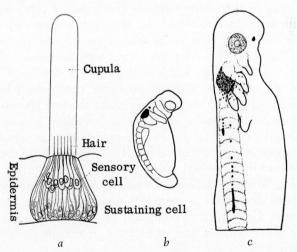

Figure 110.   Amphibian lateral line organs. *a*, Prototype of a lateral line organ (Dijkgraaf 1952). *b*, Salamander embryo, stage 18, dorsolateral placode vitally stained. *c*, Same embryo at stage 22 with downgrowing lateral lines and a number of lateral line organs (after Stone from Hamburger 1947).

12. STATO-ACOUSTIC ORGANS

Of sensory organs of the dorsolateral placode system, only those deriving from its central part persist in metamorphosed frogs and the higher tetrapods. The *static organ,* with utricle and semicircular canals, has remained essentially unchanged from the fishes to birds and mammals. Evolutionary progress is more apparent in the *acoustic sense organ,* which in fishes is represented only by the small *saccule* but in mammals attains a state of high complexity. The following description is mainly based on the development of these organs in frogs.

The *otic vesicle* or *otocyst* forms in late neurula and early tailbud embryos (St. 16–17) by invagination of the *otic placode* (Fig. 53, 54). At stage 18 it is a hollow sphere with two distinct prominences: one is a remnant of the attachment of the placode to the neural layer of the skin; the other, near the top of the vesicle, is the rudiment of the *endolymphatic diverticulum.* Neuroblasts separating from the medial wall of the vesicle aggregate into a club-shaped mass which becomes the *acoustic ganglion.* In hatching larvae (St. 21–24) nerve fibers grow from the acoustic ganglion into the rhombencephalon, forming the *roots of the eighth nerve.*

About the time of closure of the gill sacs (St. 24–25) the *saccule* appears as a small lobe at the ventral pole of the otocyst. The much larger remainder is of irregular shape, with depressions and septums indicating the beginning of the formation of the semicircular canals (Fig. 111a, b). At stage 26 *semicircular canals* and *utricle* are well differentiated (Fig. 111c, d). The *endolymphatic duct* opens into the saccule near its connection with the utricle. The entire organ has now reached a stage which corresponds to the terminal condition in fishes.

Being filled with a clear fluid the *otic cyst* is often called the *endolymphatic organ* or, in view of its relative complexity, the *membranous labyrinth* (Fig. 111e, f). Also, becoming well enclosed within a cartilaginous *otic capsule* (Fig. 113), it is known as the *inner ear*—in distinction to the auxiliary middle and outer ear parts, which develop from the first and second visceral arches and the first pharyngeal pouch.

An excessive enlargement of the *endolymphatic sacs* is peculiar to the amphibians (Fig. 111e, f). In salamanders they are confined to the extradural space of the cranial cavity (Fig. 112a), but in the frogs they also extend into the vertebral canal. Left and right sacs fuse extensively (Fig. 112b). Nothing definite is known about the functional significance of these sacs which permanently retain their communication with the labyrinths. Calcareous deposits are most notable in the *chalk sacs* around the spinal ganglia and, as *otoliths,* in various parts of the auditory vesicles.

Although the sense of hearing is already well developed in fishes, the evolution of the cochlea, the receptive organ of the mammals,

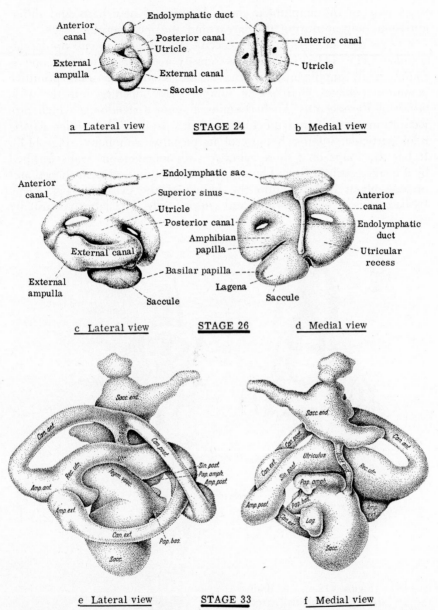

Figure 111.   Development of the left membranous labyrinth (inner ear) of the frog (*Rana temporaria;* Birkmann 1940). *Amp. ant.,* Anterior ampulla; *Amp. ext.,* external (horizontal) ampulla; *Amp. post.,* posterior ampulla; *Can. ant.,* anterior canal; *Can. ext., external* (horizontal or lateral) canal; *Can. post.,* posterior canal; *Duct. end.,* endolymphatic duct; *Lag.,* lagena; *Pap. amph.,* amphibian papilla; *Pap. bas.,* basilar papilla; *Rec. utr.,* utricular recess; *Sacc.,* sacculus; *Sacc. end.,* endolymphatic sac; *Sin. post.,* posterior sinus; *Sin. sup.,* superior sinus; *Utr.,* utricle; *a–d* × 62.5; *e, f* × 25.

starts only in the amphibian class. A series of new parts and differentiations appear during the larval and the metamorphic stages.

a. Two new diverticula of the saccule, the *amphibian and the basilar papillae* (Fig. 111e, f), serve as sensory receptors. The first one is found in all amphibians, but the second is absent in some primitive perennibranchiates. Both are of tubular shape, opening into the wide cavity of the sacculus. Each contains a *sensory membrane* which projects from its wall into the lumen of the papilla. The *basilar papilla* is of particular interest because of its primitive simplicity (Fig. 114). It has the shape of a short cylinder with membranous walls fortified by a heavy cartilage ring. The sensory membrane is crescent-shaped and projects about half-way into the lumen of the cylinder (Fig. 115). Its base consists of *supporting* and *sensory cells*. The latter are usually

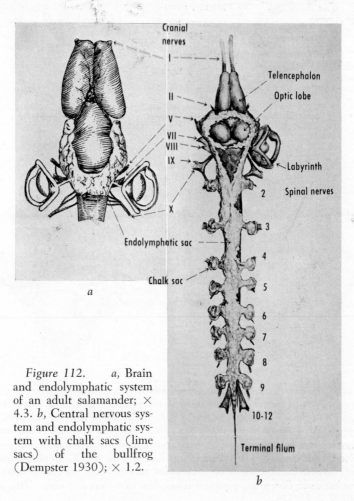

Figure 112. a, Brain and endolymphatic system of an adult salamander; × 4.3. *b,* Central nervous system and endolymphatic system with chalk sacs (lime sacs) of the bullfrog (Dempster 1930); × 1.2.

designated as *hair cells*. The free spreading part of the membrane is of gelatinous consistency; this is the *tectorial membrane*. The *sensory cilia* of the hair cells are arranged in the fashion of hairs in a wet paint brush. The cones thus formed are embedded in the clear substance of the tectorial membrane. From the supporting cells project long bundles of fibers which, fanning out toward the fortified free edge of the membrane, obviously serve as a stiffening and supporting element. In principle the sensory membrane is built like a series of fused

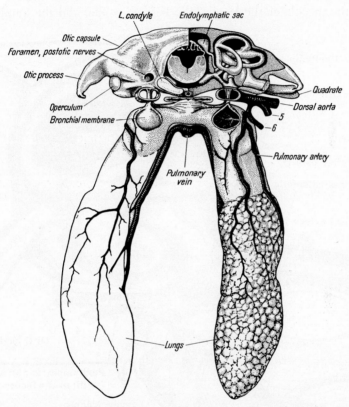

Figure 113.   Frog larva (*Rana catesbeiana*) in metamorphosis (St. 31). Rear view of skull and dorsal view of lungs; pharnyx cut transversely at level of the glottis; right bronchial membrane removed. Left dorsal aorta removed except short piece with bronchial columella; right side showing position of bronchial columella relative to fifth and sixth aortic arches and pulmonary artery; on right side posterior parts of chondrocranium and otic capsule removed to expose membranous labyrinth (stippled) and perilymphatic duct (hatched). From round window (attachment of bronchial columella) a short limb of the perilymphatic duct ascends dorsofrontally to the basilar papilla; a long limb first leads dorsomedially then branches: *medially* to the intracranial perilymphatic sac; *laterally* along amphibian papilla, utricle, and saccule to the wide perilymphatic cistern between saccule and oval window (Witschi 1949); × 9.

lateral line organs (Fig. 110a), the gelatinous cupulae becoming the
elements of the tectorial membrane.

b. The root of the *acoustic nerve* early divides into a dorsal and a
ventral portion, the ganglion into dorsoposterior and ventro-anterior
masses. From the latter emerges the *anterior branch* of the *peripheral
acoustic nerve,* which supplies the sensory crests in the ampullae of the
anterior and the horizontal semicircular canals, and the sensory maculae
of utricle and saccule. The *posterior branch,* issuing from the dorsoposterior ganglion mass, supplies the sensory crest of the posterior ampulla, the macula of the lagena, the basilar papilla, and the amphibian

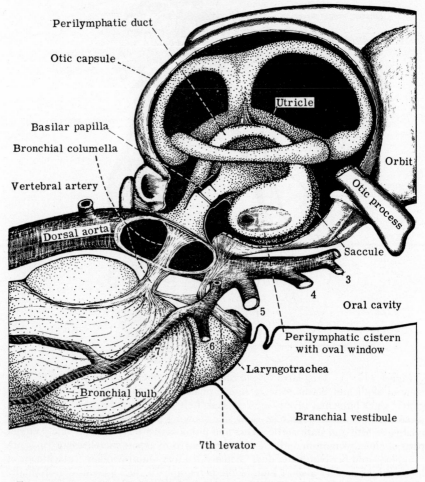

Figure 114. Larval ear of the bull frog (St. 31). An opening was cut into
the lateral wall of the dorsal aorta to expose fully the bronchial columella. The
lateral half of the otic capsule was removed to show the arrangement of the endolymphatic and perilymphatic systems. In the basilar papilla the sensory membrane
protrudes from the dorsal wall into its lumen; × 20.

papilla. The crests are receptor organs of the static sense while the papillae are acoustic receptors. The functional significance of the three maculae is still in doubt.

c. The *oval window* is common to amphibians and higher vertebrates. It is a membrane-covered opening in the lateral wall of the cartilaginous otic capsule, which becomes nearly closed by an independent cartilage, the *operculum* (Figs. 73, 74, 75, 113). In frogs, this lid first appears in larvae of stage 28.

d. The *perilymphatic duct* (Figs. 113, 114) arises in the space between the labyrinth and the otic capsule, through involution of some of the filling mesenchyme. Starting at the oval window, it circles the sacculus dorsocaudally, contacts the amphibian papilla, and turns toward the median wall of the auditory capsule. It then enters the cranial cavity through the *perilymphatic foramen* and expands into a *perilymphatic sac* (Fig. 113). This represents the final condition attained by primitive perennibranchiates (*Proteus, Necturus*). In all amphibians with a basilar papilla, a further branch of the duct develops with a second prolapse into or through the wall of the otic capsule. This ventral opening, covered by an elastic membrane, is the *round window*. From it ascends a terminal limb of the perilymphatic duct which ends at the *basilar membrane* (Figs. 113, 114).

Where the perilymphatic duct contacts the auditory papillae thin

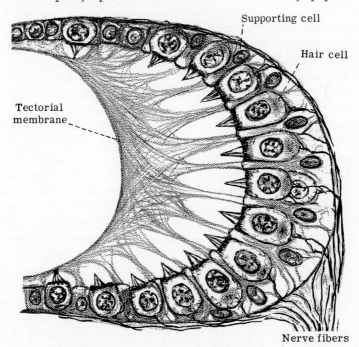

Figure 115.   Sensory membrane from the basilar papilla of a tree frog (*Hyla crucifer*); × 666.

vestibular membranes (of Reissner) are formed which, according to their origin, consist of a perilymphatic and an endolymphatic layer (Fig. 114). Probably the vestibular membranes have little influence on sound transmission, but they may be important as barriers to chemical exchange between endolymph and perilymph.

e. The *bronchial columella* connects the round window with bronchus and lung sac of the same side of the body (Figs. 73, 113, 114). When fully developed, as in larvae of stages 26 to 31, the columella starts from the center of the round window, pierces the dorsal aorta, and then fastens to the bronchus. Here it divides into three portions. One spreads as a fibrous layer over the upper surface of the bronchus and the larynx. The other two form a ring on the surface of the bronchus, holding the thin *bronchial membrane* (Figs. 65, 73, 114).

The columella differentiates at the time of closure of the gill sacs (St. 25). It originates as a condensation of fibers from the mesodermal sheath that surrounds the branchial vestibule and fastens it to the base of the skull. At stage 25 this bundle of fibers is still on the medial side of the dorsal aorta. Subsequently the aorta shifts inward and engulfs the columella, enclosing it in an endothelial sheath. This arrangement is maintained from stage 26 until the end of metamorphosis.

The anatomic structure of the acoustic apparatus indicates that *in frog larvae the lungs serve as ear drums*. The columellae transmit pressure changes, including sound vibrations, across the dorsal aortae to the round windows. From here pressure is conducted by the perilymphatic fluid to the auditory papillae. The oval windows at the ends of the perilymphatic ducts serve as relief valves.

At the height of metamorphosis when the frogs get ready to climb on land, the part of the lumen of the dorsal aorta at the inner side of the columella shrinks. Soon (St. 32) the columella lies again at the medial side of the aorta where it disintegrates (Figs. 74, 75). Bronchi and aortae shift away from the round windows which now border on the lymph sacs under the base of the skull.

f. The *tympanic organ*, consisting of auditory tube, tympanic cavity, and tympanic membrane, is a new accessory by which the ear becomes adapted for the hearing of air-borne sound. None of the salamanders, and not all anurans, have acquired it. Embryologically it arises from the dorsal part of the first pharyngeal pouch. In tailbud embryos of stage 19 (Fig. 58) this pouch shows the primary position between the first and the second visceral arches (Fig. 58). After hatching (St. 21–25), in frog embryos its dorsal and ventral recesses become separated through the development of a joint between the quadrate and the hyoid cartilages (Fig. 65). In older larvae, the recesses project peripherally toward the larval skin, while the middle part of the pouch remains on the oral side of the quadrate and hyoid cartilages. The ventral pouch produces no important derivative. The dorsal part grows very long and becomes the rudiment of the tympanic organ. In larvae its terminal knob is fastened to the subderma and the rostral quadrate near the nose. The thread-like connection with the pharynx follows the surface of the quadrate (Figs. 65, 73). Throughout the larval period the organ retains this rudimentary condition. It becomes reactivated during metamorphosis.

Laterally over the terminal knob of the pharyngeal recess appears a disc-shaped mesenchymal condensation, the rudiment of tympanic ring and tympanic membrane (Fig. 73). Attached to the quadrate it is carried caudally when the mouth assumes its adult size. At the same time the endodermal rudiment transforms into a funnel-shaped *tympanic cavity* and short *auditory tube* (Fig. 74). The opening of the latter into the pharynx moves first to the front of the otic capsule, then ventrally under it. Concurrently the very large *tympanic ring* (Fig. 75) and *tympanic membrane* differentiate. The latter consists of endodermal, mesodermal, and epidermal layers. It forms a part of the body surface of the metamorphosed frog.

g. The *tympanic columella* is derived from the proximal hyoid cartilage (Figs. 73–75). It takes shape late in the larval period as a mesenchymal condensation in front of the operculum and becomes cartilaginous while growing toward the otic process. During metamorphosis there forms a second mesenchymal condensation, the *plectrum*. At stage 32 it lies within a notch of the tympanic ring and above an indentation of the endodermal epithelium. At the end of metamorphosis the columellar connection between tympanic membrane and operculum is complete.

The changes of the ear during metamorphosis of the frog may be summarized as follows. The tympanic organs and the tympanic columellae replace functionally the lung sacs and the bronchial columellae as sound-receiving and transmitting mechanical auxiliaries of the ear. The round and the oval windows exchange their relative roles, the former becoming the relief valve of the perilymphatic duct. Except for the partial ossification of the otic capsule, the central part of the ear remains unchanged. It must be concluded that for sound perception in the basilar and amphibian papillae it is of little or no importance whether the vibrations of the perilymphatic fluid are started at the round or at the oval window.

The condition in larval frogs resembles that of teleosts in which swim bladders are connected to the inner ears by means of Weber ossicles. However, this resemblance is of the nature of a functional analogy and not a morphologic homology.

13. EYE AND CORNEAL REFLEX

The basic structure of the eye develops during the tailbud stages. This part of its history will first be reviewed, to be followed by a short account of the changes during metamorphosis.

The locations of the primordia of *optic cup* and *lens* at the open

neurula stage are indicated in Figure 117*f*. After closure of the neural
folds a pair of *optic bulbs* arise as evaginations of the forebrain and
establish contacts with the basal layer of the epidermis (Fig. 116, St.
16). Through apical invagination during the early tailbud stages each
bulb transforms into an *optic cup* (Fig. 116, St. 18, 19, 20). As a consequence it differentiates into an inner *nervous layer* and an outer
pigment layer. Closely attached to each other they form *retina* and *iris*
of the eye (St. 20 to 25). The development and closure of the choroid
fissure will be described in connection with the human eye where this
is a more prominent feature.

The basal epidermis adjacent to the retina becomes a thick *lens
placode*. Adhering to the retina, it soon assumes the shape of a cup. Its
hollow is filled with loose *periderm cells,* some of which become enclosed in the vesicular primitive lens (Fig. 116, St. 20, 22). However,

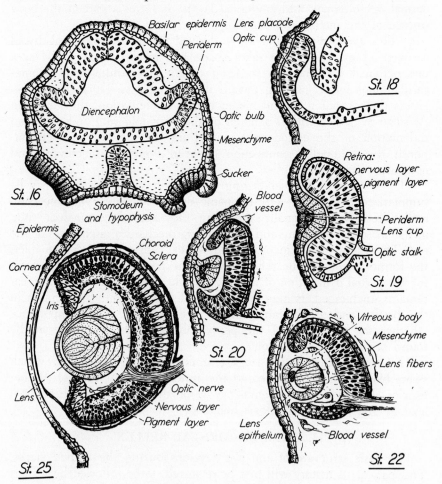

Figure 116.   Eye development in frogs from stage 16 to stage 25.

they degenerate later, and the permanent lens is entirely a derivative
of the basal epidermis (Fig. 116, St. 25). In subsequent stages of lens
development the outer half of the vesicle differentiates into a cap of
cuboid cells, the *lens epithelium,* while the inner half forms rapidly
lengthening *fiber cells.* The boundary region is the site of rapid proliferation. New fiber cells, growing toward the inner pole, repeatedly
spread as new layers over the inner lens surface. They meet at a central
stem or suture line (St. 25) that grows longer as the lens increases
in size.

Beginning about stage 20 the contact between lens and retina becomes loosened through the secretion of the gelatinous *vitreous body*
by cells of both retina and lens. The abundance of this secretion is an
important factor in the control of the size and histologic differentiation
of the eyeball. The formation of the *posterior eye chamber* is immediately followed by an invasion of blood vessels, the *hyaloid arteries
and veins.*

The *histologic differentiation of the retina* occurs during the stages
20 to 25. In the cells of the thin pigment layer appear increasing numbers of *melanin granules.* The neuroblasts of the thick nervous layer
differentiate into sensory *rods* and *cones* and *neurons.* The nuclei of
the latter aggregate in *nuclear layers* which alternate with *plexiform
fibrillar layers.* Outgrowing nerve fibers enter the *optic stalk* which
thereby becomes a sheath of the *optic nerve.*

During the same period the ectodermal eye bulb acquires also two
mesodermal coats, through the condensation of surrounding mesenchyme cells. The pigment layer first becomes covered by the loose-
celled *choroid,* which contains also the plexus of blood vessels formed
by the branching *ophthalmic artery.* This again becomes surrounded by
the much more compact *sclera.* At the edge of the iris the latter continues free from the eyeball, thus creating an *anterior eye chamber*
filled with watery fluid, the *aqueous humor.* At metamorphosis this
free part of the sclera attaches itself to the covering epidermis furnishing the deep fibrous layer of the *cornea.* Even earlier, starting about
stage 22, pigment granules and mucus cells have disappeared from
the epidermis above pupil and iris of the eye bulb. When at stage
25 the larva assumes free swimming habits and starts feeding, the eye
has attained a functional level (Fig. 116). However, throughout metamorphosis the ganglion cells of the *retina,* and the nerve fibers in the
optic nerve, continue increasing their number. This is possibly the most
important though not the only aspect of metamorphic changes in the
eye. *Lens* and *cornea* pass through transformations by which their
optical qualities become adapted to the new environmental conditions.
At the same time some new auxiliary structures are acquired, particularly *lacrimal glands* and *eyelids* (Fig. 42, St. 29–33). They protect the
eye from dirt and injury. The *upper lids* are slightly elevated walls.

The *lower lids,* mainly a growth of the skin, become doubly pleated, the inner folds forming the semitransparent *nictitating membranes.*

The *corneal reflex,* which results in the withdrawal of the bulb into the orbit through contraction of the retractor muscle and subsequent closure of the lids, is released by mechanical stimuli applied to the cornea or to the neighboring skin; it appears in larvae of stage 30. Kollros has shown that its onset depends not so much of the anatomical perfection of the optical apparatus as on the maturity of correlating brain centers. In frogs, this is closely linked with the hormonal conditions of metamorphosis; hypophysectomized specimens never develop the reflex. Quite to the contrary, in urodeles it does become established in hypophysectomized larvae at about the same time as in metamorphosing controls.

14. CENTRAL NERVOUS SYSTEM

The primitive brain of the early tailbud embryos (Figs. 58, 59, St. 18, 19) consists of three vesicles, *prosencephalon, mesencephalon,* and *rhombencephalon.* At stage 20 the *nasal placodes* deepen and establish contacts with the lateral walls of the prosencephalon, which presently begin to thicken. Strong bundles of nerve fibers issuing from the *nasal pits* then grow into the sides of the brain which now rise as heavy cushions (Fig. 118a). These elevations transform rapidly into a pair of

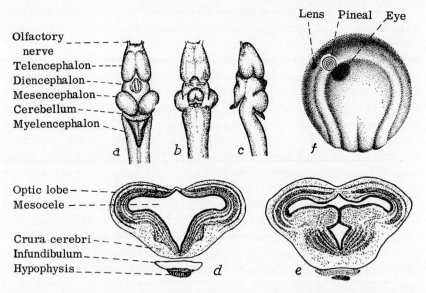

Figure 117.   *a, b, c,* Brain of toad (*Bufo americana,* St. 33) at end of metamorphosis; dorsal, ventral, and left lateral views; *d, e,* cross sections, midbrains of a *R. pipiens* larva (St. 29) and a metamorphosed frog (St. 33) (B. M. Allen 1924). *f,* Open neurula (St. 13); on left side the areas of prospective lens, pineal, and eye are indicated (after Spemann and Van de Kamer).

telencephalic hemispheres (Fig. 118*b*). Larvae at stage 25 have a relatively large head as a consequence of the development of the branchial apparatus. The nasal organs, carried far rostrally, remain connected with the brain by lengthening *olfactory nerves* (Fig. 112). Also the telencephalic vesicles themselves follow the forward trend and soon grow far beyond the *terminal lamina*, the former rostral end of the brain (Fig. 117*a, b, c*). Thus, the early history of the *telencephalon* in amphibians characterizes it as a nose brain or *rhinencephalon*.

The *eyes* show similarly close relationships with the remaining prosencephalic stem, the *diencephalon*, but even more with the *mesen-*

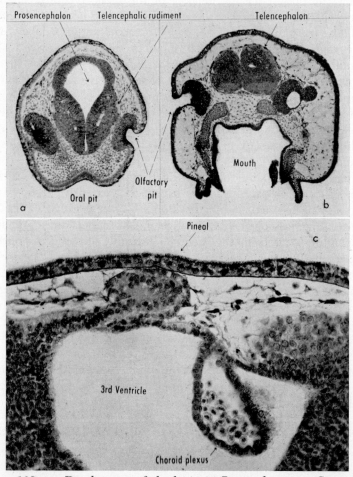

Figure 118.   Development of the brain in *Rana sylvatica. a,* Stage 21–22, cross section through forehead; olfactory nerve in contact with rudiment of telencephalon; × 45; *b,* larva stage 25 with inner choanae. Cross section through nose, telencephalic hemispheres, and right quadrato-mandibular joint; × 45; *c,* larva stage 25; sagittal section through roof of diencephalon with pineal organ (epiphysis); × 185.

cephalon, where the optic nerves end in the *optic lobes* (Fig. 117*a–e*). No satisfactory embryologic explanation has been found for the remarkable crossing of the optic nerves in the *optic chiasma.*

The third of the large cranial sensory organs, the *ear,* has its central terminus in the *acoustico-lateral area* of the upper dorsal part of the *rhombencephalon.* At the larval stage this is the common center also for the lateral line organs. The roof of the uppermost part of the rhombencephalon differentiates as a crosswise lamella, the rudimentary amphibian *cerebellum* (Fig. 117*a, c*). The by far the largest part of the rhombencephalon is now called *myelencephalon* or *oblong medulla.*

Below the optic chiasma the floor of the diencephalon deepens into a funnel-shaped pocket, the *infundibulum.* Its tip becomes the *nervous part of the hypophysis* (Fig. 58, 117*b, c*) or its posterior lobe. At stage 18 the roof of the diencephalon shows a small outgrowth which at later tailbud stages forms the *pineal organ* or *epiphysis.* In some reptiles and fishes it has the organization of a primitive eye bulb and stalk. In amphibians it has only the general appearance of a very rudimentary eye (Fig. 118*c*). It arises from paired preprimordia which at the open neurula stage lie on the neural folds between the optic preprimordia and the lens placodes (Fig. 117*f*). They fuse at the time of closure of the neural folds.

In view of the many fundamental functional changes occurring in metamorphosing frogs, one might expect that extensive reconstructions should also be effected within the *brain.* This is, however, not actually the case. The loss of the lateral line organs entails the regression of corresponding centers in the medulla; probably also the disappearance of the giant *Mauthner cells* is correlated to the same change. Resorption of the several *spinal ganglia* and shortening of the spinal cord accompany the loss of the tail (Fig. 70). The progressive changes are even less impressive. The *mesencephalon* gains in substance while its ventricle becomes narrower (Fig. 117*d, e*). This is in part the result of a considerable enlargement of the cells of the mesencephalic nucleus of a branch of the fifth cranial nerve. But also the *optic tectum* becomes more massive, while at the same time its stratification gets more distinct. Obviously this development is related to the above mentioned resumed growth of the retina and the optic nerve.

15. EXTENSION AND REDUCTION OF THE LARVAL PERIOD

The length of the larval period of North American frogs varies from two weeks to three years. In species like *Rana clamitans* and *R. catesbiana* (the bullfrog), an extensive growth period follows the attainment of stage 25. The buds of the hindlimbs remain stationary oval knobs for months or even years, while the body length doubles or triples. Since limb development in these species reflects the condition of the hypophysis-thyroid system, prolongation of the larval period indicates a low level of endocrine activity.

On the other hand, the secondary larval period (incipient metamorphosis) is reduced or nearly abolished in some tropical frogs. In the Caribbean tree frog, *Eleutherodactylus nubicola,* the formation of gills and other larval organs is completely suppressed. Of visceral arches, only those that produce permanent adult structures develop. In the vascular system the only primitive character is a transitory dorsal anastomosis between the carotid and the systemic arches. It disappears during the transformation of the embryo into the adult form. Metamorphic changes are very few and development seems even more nearly direct than that of amniotes.

16. ENDOCRINE GLANDS OF THE PHARYNGEAL REGION, AND THE HORMONAL CONTROL OF AMPHIBIAN METAMORPHOSIS

It is the distinguishing feature of metamorphosis that within a short period a multitude of not interdependent changes are precipitated— some constructive, others regressive. The problem of their temporal correlation was elucidated by Gudernatsch who, in 1912, showed that precocious metamorphosis may be induced by the feeding of thyroid glands to frog larvae. In quick succession, other discoveries followed which now present a well integrated picture of endocrine control of amphibian metamorphosis. The removal of the hypophysis from small tadpoles (Figs. 83, 119) or of the hypophyseal placode at stages 16 to 18 (Figs. 116, 58) results in the arrest or incomplete development of the thyroid glands (Fig. 120) and prevents metamorphosis. The larvae continue to grow, and eventually even surpass the length of normal metamorphosing tadpoles; but they retain permanently an organization which corresponds to the larval stage 25. Virtually the same results are obtained if, after the method of B. M. Allen, the tadpoles are fully deprived of thyroids by extirpation of the primordia of the glands in early tailbud embryos (Fig. 58, St. 18). The *permanent larvae* resulting from such operations metamorphose readily

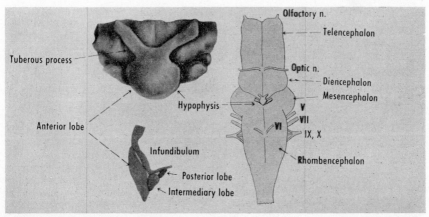

Figure 119.   Hypophysis of frog tadpole. Right: Ventral view of the brain, showing attachment of the gland to the tip of the diencephalic infundibulum. Upper left: Hypophysis attached to the infundibular process. Lower left: Sagittal section V to X cranial nerves (P. E. Smith 1920).

after administration of thyroid substance. *These experiments prove that the thyroid is directly in control of metamorphosis, but is itself governed by the hypophysis.* For many years it had been known that the thyroid is very rich in iodine, and when Swingle treated normal and thyroid-deprived tadpoles with weak solutions of elemental iodine, metamorphosis was induced much as by the feeding of thyroid. On the other hand, tadpoles reared in water and on food without traces of iodine retain short limb buds and do not metamorphose.

Finally the chemists joined this research project. Kendall extracted and crystallized an active principle of the gland and gave it the name *thyroxin.* In 1927, Harington solved the problem of its chemical constitution and synthesis. The molecule contains four iodine atoms.

$$HO \cdot C \overset{\overset{\displaystyle I}{C} = \overset{\displaystyle H}{C}}{\underset{\underset{\displaystyle I}{C} - \underset{\displaystyle H}{C}}{}} C \cdot O \cdot C \overset{\overset{\displaystyle I}{C} = \overset{\displaystyle H}{C}}{\underset{\underset{\displaystyle I}{C} - \underset{\displaystyle H}{C}}{}} C \cdot CH_2 \overset{COOH}{\underset{NH_2}{CH}}$$

Thyroxin

In the thyroid gland thyroxin and its precursor diiodotyrosin are stored bound to proteins. However, the large molecular thyroglobulin has to be broken down to be released into the blood stream. It is not certain whether in the blood it circulates as free thyroxin or as a polypeptide.

Thyroxin and the thyroid-stimulating principle of the hypophysis, *thyrotrophin,* are *morphogenic substances,* i.e., they induce changes of morphologic nature. Being produced and released by glands of internal secretion (endocrine glands), and spread by the blood stream, they are at the same time typical representatives of the class of substances called *hormones.*

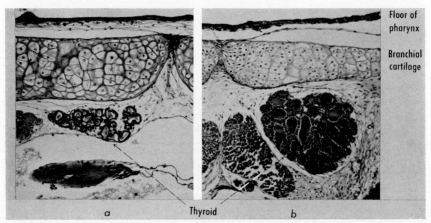

Figure 120.   Sections through thyroids of *Rana sylvatica. a,* Gland of early hypophysectomized non-metamorphosing larva, little colloid. *b,* Normal gland with much colloid, at time of metamorphosis (St. 33); × 80.

Hypophysis and thyroid both arise in the oral region. The *hypophyseal primordium* becomes recognizable in neurulae as an ectodermal placode, situated between the frontal neural fold (terminal lamina) and the oral field (Figs. 42, 53; St. 13–17). Laterally it is bounded by swellings which are the primordia of the first visceral arch and the adhesive organs. For some time, the placode and the oral field form a common, triangular depression (St. 15–17). Later, the placode lies inside, between the projecting foregut and the forebrain (Figs. 58, 83).

Embryologically, the hypophysis is a part of the neural system. Its development resembles that of composite sense organs, especially the eye. One component arises from the infundibulum of the diencephalon, the other from the hypophyseal placode. Where the two primordia come into contact, the infundibulum contributes the *posterior lobe* of the gland. The placode material divides into a large *anterior lobe* with a pair of *tuberous processes* and a smaller *intermediate lobe*. With regard to the difference of origin, one may distinguish *buccal* and *nervous* parts (Fig. 119).

At stage 25, the intermediate lobe still consists of a compact mass of evenly distributed cells; while in the anterior lobe a differentiation of trabeculae has taken place, which are made up of two or three distinct types of cells: chromophobes, acidophiles, and basophiles. The last type probably includes the producers of the *thyroid-stimulating hormone* which at this stage begins to activate the thyroid glands.

The *primordium of the thyroid* becomes noticeable between stages 17 and 18 as a small solid bud growing from the endodermal floor of the foregut (Fig. 58). Later, it detaches and glides down along the ventral surface of the copula. It divides into a pair of separated bodies that become attached to the hypobranchial plates (Fig. 65). They reach this position at stage 24 and maintain it throughout the remainder of the larval period. During metamorphosis they take their final location between the fifth and sixth branchial processes of the pharyngeal cartilage (Figs. 75, 76). Up to stage 24, the thyroid rudiment consists of primitive endoderm cells filled with coarse yolk granules. Then they group themselves into globular bodies or small follicles and become richly supplied by blood vessels. After closure of the gill sacs (St. 25), droplets of colloid appear within the follicles.

Up to this stage the thyroids of normal and of hypophysectomized larvae develop exactly alike (by self-differentiation). Later growth and function depend on hypophyseal stimulation. In hypophysectomized larvae, the glands remain small and inactive (Fig. 120a). The follicles contain only negligible amounts of colloid. Quite to the contrary, in normal larvae, the follicles acquire thicker walls, accumulate increasing amounts of colloid, and the entire glands grow at an accelerated rate (Figs. 120a). A similar development is induced in hypophysectomized larvae by the injection of *thyrotrophic hormone;* the latter may be extracted from hypophysis glands of any vertebrate species. As a consequence of increased functional demands during metamorphosis, there occurs a temporary partial depletion of the follicles with some shrinkage.

The beginning of stage 25 marks, in many respects, an important turning point in the course of anuran development. Up to this stage, growth and energy expenses were met out of the reserves contained in the egg. At stage 24, some food is taken into the stomach, but it does not enter the small intestine before the yolk has completely disappeared from its endodermal walls. In spite of an increase in gross body weight, the total nitrogen content steadily decreases until the establishment of true feeding at stage 25. At this time, the limb buds make their appearance. They grow into olive-shaped, slightly flattened rudiments, in normal as well as in hypophysectomized larvae. However, in completely hypophysectomized or thyroidectomized frog larvae, development does not proceed beyond the bud condition. In such operated animals the addition of minute amounts of thyroxin to the water will cause differentiation and functional growth of the legs. Solutions of 1:1,000,000,-000 are slightly effective, while full metamorphosis requires ten times higher concentrations.

In conclusion, histologic as well as experimental evidence indicates that, in frogs, hypophysis and thyroid glands become hormonally active immediately after disappearance of the yolk reserves, i.e., when the larvae begin to feed. This is about the same stage at which larval tissues become responsive to administrations of thyroxin.

In *salamanders,* the period of incipient metamorphosis is not hormone-controlled. Arms and legs develop by self-differentiation up to stage 29 and thyroidectomy or hypophysectomy affects their proportions only in a minor way. This difference between frogs and salamanders reveals the importance of the constitutional or *intrinsic tissue factors* in hormone-controlled reactions. Inherent differences exist also among areas and tissues of single individuals. A most striking example is that of the larval skin of the frog. In the tail region it reacts to thyroxin with degeneration, and in the body region, by thickening and continued differentiation (Fig. 42, St. 31–33). Pieces which were exchanged by transplantation at early stages behave during metamorphosis in accordance with the place of origin and without regard to their actual environment. In the first case (salamander versus frog) the difference in intrinsic capacities has a genetic foundation, while in the second example (body skin versus tail skin) the different capacities are acquired during ontogenesis, by genetically identical tissues.

The experiments with hormones and hormone glands raise again the question of the *relative importance of extrinsic and intrinsic factors* as determiners of embryonic differentiation. As in previous discussions on the primary organizers and on the determinations in limb development, it must be answered in favor of the latter. Thyroxin, like the inductors of the early embryonic epoch, acts as an *activator,* but only if it comes in contact with responsive tissues. *Responsiveness* and determination of the *specificity of reaction* are intrinsic tissue factors.

In addition to the thyroids, the pharyngeal endoderm gives origin also to parathyroid, thymus, and ultimobranchial bodies. After separating from the third and fourth pouches, the two pairs of *parathyroids* become attached to the ventral roots of the fourth and fifth visceral arches (Figs. 65, 67). The *ultimobranchial bodies* arise from the deeper parts of the vestigial sixth pouches. In urodeles, only the left one persists. *Xenopus* does not seem to have any. After metamorphosis the parathyroid and ultimobranchial bodies lie near the lower lateral surface of the thyroids (Fig. 76). The *thymus* of frogs consists of a single pair of large bodies which originate as buds from the dorsal walls of the second pair of pouches. In salamanders, three pairs of buds arise from the third, fourth, and fifth pouches. In all instances, the thymic buds soon become infiltrated by lymphatic elements which eventually seem to destroy and replace the endodermal primordia.

Chapter 12

Metabolism of

Amphibian Development

The amphibian egg, as it leaves the ovary, contains all the necessary food materials for the support of embryonic development up to the stage of the free swimming larvae (St. 25). During cleavage all reserves become so distributed that most cells receive an adequate share for sustenance until completion of histologic differentiation. This situation has greatly facilitated experimental work in amphibian embryogenesis. Even isolated parts of the germs can be maintained in vitro, i.e., in adjusted saline solutions, without need for added nutritious supplies. When at stage 25 or shortly later the yolk platelets disappear and all supply stores are exhausted, feeding becomes an urgent necessity.

1. COMPOSITION OF THE EGG AND CHANGES DURING DEVELOPMENT

At the time of ovulation, a frog's egg of 1.9 mm. diameter weighs close to 4 mg. and is made up of the following major constituents:

Proteins	1.375 mg.	34.5%
Fats	0.300 mg.	7.5%
Carbohydrates	0.125 mg.	3.0%
Water	2.100 mg.	52.5%
Minerals and Others	0.100 mg.	2.5%
TOTAL	4.000 mg.	100.0%

These weights and percentages are only approximations, based on data contributed by diverse investigators. Very little is known about individual and specific variations.

Following laying and after fertilization, the eggs take up considerable amounts of water, gaining in volume even before the first cleavage division. Krogh reports a 15 per cent increase during the first few hours and a further 5 per cent up to gastrulation (St. 8). At early stages, including the open neurulae (St. 13), much water is contained in the central cavities—blastocele, gastrocele, archenteron; but this is mostly expelled during late neurulation. The intracellular water increase is slower and more steady. It results in a fall of the density from 1.105 at the time of fertilization to 1.007 at stage 25. A comparison of stages 1 and 25 (Fig. 42) brings out the fact that the volume increases several times (est. six- to ten-fold) before the start of feeding. This is an interesting illustration of the limited value and often misleading character of unanalyzed statistical data on "growth." In the present case dimensional growth is combined with morphologic differentiation but with a steady loss in dry weight.

Water intake is related to changes in the *osmotic pressure condition*. The ovarial egg is isotonic with the serum of adult frogs which is about equivalent to the pressure of 120 mM. NaCl (millimolar salt) solution. It was formerly believed that the deposited egg became isotonic with pond water, which is as low as 12 mM. However the investigations of Krogh established definitely that the lowest value, as reached by early gastrulae (St. 8), is only about 80 mM. From this stage on, the further intake of water is more than compensated for by the liberation of osmotically active compounds from the storage materials. Gradually the osmotic pressure in the tissues increases until it reaches again the adult level of 120 mM.

In spite of their high osmotic quality, the germs of amphibia thrive in ordinary and even in distilled water better than in isotonic salt or sugar solutions. This is true also if jelly and vitelline membranes have been removed. Only if large wounds are exposed, as in the culture in vitro of fragments of embryos, it has been found advantageous to shift to salt solutions. The most frequently used Holtfreter solution (NaCl 350 mg., KCl 5 mg., $CaCl_2$ 10 mg., $NaHCO_3$ 20 mg., water 100 cc.) has an osmotic pressure equivalent of 60 mM. and in most instances is used in further diluted form. Obviously the embryonic cell is protected against damage from the habitual environmental osmotic conditions and, to some degree, the functions of its membrane have become adapted to and dependent upon them.

Before feeding, the embryos not only do not gain, but in fact they *expend* considerable fractions of their own substance. At stage 25, when the yolk and other forms of reserves are nearly exhausted, about two-thirds have become converted into organized body tissues and fluids. Roughly one-third have become degraded into energy-poor wastes and eliminated as undesirable by-products of the energy metabolism. To be more specific, the *nitrogen* determinations by Wills show that about 0.500 mg. (36%) of the original 1.375 mg. protein disappear; waste nitrogen is excreted as ammonia and urea. Similarly Savage concludes that at least one-third of the total *carbohydrate* becomes oxidized, i.e., about 0.040 mg. Regarding *fat* metabolism the opinions are still greatly at variance. Certainly it becomes an important metabolite following hatching (stage 23), but whether it is used as a source of energy during early embryogenesis remains doubtful. Fat is partly present as a constituent of the *phospholipids,* which can be expected to play an important role in the energy metabolism of early larvae.

The *changes in protein content* during the development of the individual must follow the shape of the nitrogen curve shown in Figure 121, because nitrogen, as a rule, accounts for 16 per cent of the weight of simple proteins and protein complexes of conjugated proteins. Nitrogen values are conveniently determined by the micro-Kjeldahl method. In *Rana pipiens, five periods* become distinguishable (Fig. 121). During

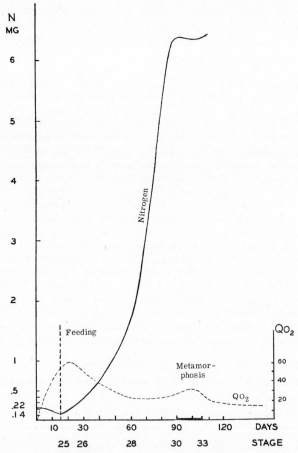

Figure 121.   Graph showing changes of *nitrogen content* during development of *R. pipiens* from fertilization to end of metamorphosis (full line), and of *metabolic rate* (QO₂, broken line). Climactic metamorphosis (stages 30 to 33) occurred in the first half of the fourth month; (from data by Wills 1936).

the *first,* which comprises the non-feeding stages 1 to early 25, the nitrogen falls off from 220 μg. to 140 μg. The loss of about one-third indicates that during this time protein is used up in the maintenance of the life functions. Wills finds smaller values for salamanders, as follows:

SPECIES	ORIGINAL NITROGEN	LOST DURING STAGES 1–25
Rana pipiens	220 μg.	80 μg. or 36%
Triturus torosus	275 μg.	65 μg. or 24%
Ambystoma tigrinum	290 μg.	60 μg. or 21%
A. maculatum	440 μg.	20 μg. or 5%

The very small nitrogen loss in the last species—the one with the largest eggs—suggests that more fat or carbohydrate may be oxidized instead of protein.

The *second period,* starting with feeding at stage 25 and lasting to the end of stage 27, shows the most rapid relative increase in nitrogen. While the rate from 30 to 60 days is $\times$ 5 it drops to $\times$ 3 for the next interval of 30 days. The latter, carrying up to the beginning of metamorphosis, represents the *third period* and is characterized by the biggest absolute growth of the nitrogen value. During the *fourth or metamorphic period* (Stages 30–33) the animals are fasting and consequently lose weight. However, the nitrogen loss, as indicated by the curve, is small, suggesting that in the breakdown of larval organs like the tail, parts of the digestive tube, gills and others, the proteins which become free are carefully conserved and used again in the construction of new parts of the postmetamorphic bodies.

The *fifth period* follows completion of metamorphosis; only its initial stage, showing resumption of nitrogen accumulation, is included in the curve (Fig. 121).

2. TEMPERATURE FACTORS OF GROWTH AND DIFFERENTIATION

The body temperature of amphibian embryos and larvae is identical with that of the ambient water. Therefore speed and to a certain degree also the type of development depend greatly on external temperature conditions. Within what may be called the *optimal range,* acceleration and delay agree with van't Hoff's temperature rule for enzymatic reactions. The speed of development doubles or triples if the temperature is raised by 10° C. This rule applies not only to short periods or single stages, but even to the entire length of development from fertilization to metamorphosis (St. 1 to 31, Fig. 122). For early breeders, mainly the brown frogs (*Rana sylvatica, R. temporaria*), this optimal range extends from about 15° to 21° C. For green frogs (*R. esculenta, R. pipiens*), which reproduce later in the season, minimums and maximums are from 5° to 7° higher. The adaptation to average environmental temperatures is carried even further, inasmuch as the optimal range shifts also with the progress of developmental stages. The brown frogs thrive best at temperatures below 18° C. before stage 25, and above 18° C. afterwards. The change seems related to the disappearance of the yolk which occurs at the critical stage.

Above and below the optimal range, development proceeds slower than expected. Within the range of 15° and 21° C. the temperature quotient Q_{10} equals 2.65. If it remained unchanged, the velocity of development (V) should rise as indicated by the exponential curve in

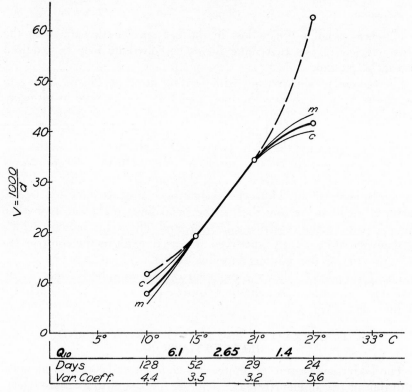

Q_{10}		6.1	2.65	1.4	
Days	128	52	29	24	
Var. Coeff.	4.4	3.5	3.2	5.6	

Figure 122.   Effect of temperature on speed and character of development in the frog R. *temporaria,* based on four lots obtained from eggs of identical parentage. The *velocity (V) of the entire development from fertilization to near-completion of metamorphosis (St. 31)* is the reciprocal of the required time in days (*d*); for convenience this value is multiplied by 1000; therefore $V = \dfrac{1000}{d}$. The average number of days decreases as the temperature rises. The calculated *temperature coefficients,* Q_{10}, for the intervals 10°–15°, 15°–21°, 21°–27° C. are given in heavy print. Also listed are the *variation coefficients* for each of the four lots; they are a relative expression of individual variation, in each lot. Broken line: Expected time curve calculated on a constant $Q_{10} = 2.65$. Heavy solid line: Actually observed time curve. *m–m,* Time curve of strongly catabolic processes (e.g., medullary development in sex glands; *c–c,* time curve of strongly anabolic processes (e.g., cortical development in sex glands) (Witschi 1942).

Figure 122 (broken line). Instead, the actual temperature curve (heavy line) straightens out at the low end and reflexes above. In other words, at extreme high or low temperatures development proceeds more slowly than expected and eventually comes to a standstill. The temperature inhibition of the involved enzyme systems also shows qualitative differences which account for the observed disharmonious development. In general, *at low temperatures differentiation is more retarded than growth,* while at high temperatures the reverse relationship obtains. At stage 31 animals from low temperature cultures are heavier, have shorter gills and legs, and less differentiated kidneys than those from high temperature lots. Obviously some components of the developmental process which are well synchronized at the optimal range, are falling out of step. The situation is graphically illustrated in Figure 122 by the curves m-m and c-c which apply specifically to the case of sex development. At high temperatures medullary development (m) is relatively less impaired than cortical (c) which leads to the complete masculinization of genetically female frog larvae. At the other end, cold favors ovarial differentiation of the sex glands of genetic males, because the cortical component is less retarded than the medullary. The resulting sex reversals serve as striking illustrations of the *partial dissociation of harmonious but complex developmental processes* which may occur under the influence of unusual environmental conditions.

Another significant feature of development under extreme temperature conditions is an *increased variability.* The *variability coefficients* given in Figure 122 are a measure of individual scattering around the average length of the larval period. The two middle temperature groups (15° C. and 21° C.) near the lower and upper limits of the optimal range show the least amount of scattering. In comparison, the cold and heat cultures exhibit sharply increased irregularities in achieving metamorphosis. Apparently minor constitutional differences among larvae of same parentage become enhanced under extreme environmental conditions.

3. RESPIRATORY METABOLISM

Materials stored in the egg are either used for the *construction* of the differentiated organs and tissues that make up the embryo, or spent in the process of *energy production* through enzymatic combustion. The egg developing into a larva (St. 1–25) can be considered as a thermal machine that is driven by the energy derived from the oxidation of up to 0.5 mg. protein, 0.04 mg. carbohydrate, and traces of fat. The energies set free in complete combustion of these materials are of the following order, if expressed in gram calories (cal.):

Protein	4.3 cal. per mg.,		therefore	2.15 cal. per 0.5	mg.
Carbohydrate	4.2 " " "	"		0.17 " " 0.04	"
Fat	9.3 " " "			?	(traces)

Calorimetric studies by Gayda on the development of a toad reveal total heat productions of 0.12 calories up to stage 21 (hatching) and 67 calories up to metamorphosis (St. 31). From his data one can further calculate a total that lies between 1.6 and 1.9 calories up to stage 25 (beginning of feeding). This value compares favorably with the 2.3 calories arrived at for *Rana* in the above deductions; for it must be remembered that *Rana* has larger eggs, embryos, and larvae than the toad.

The small total of barely over 2 gram calories—reduced by unavoidable scattering losses—operates the entire mitotic processes, the morphogenic movements of gastrulation and neurulation, the muscular contractions (starting about stage 18) and many other activities, including morphologic differentiation up to the stage of feeding.

Warburg's respiration manometer technique and other methods of microrespirometry make it possible to study many aspects of the metabolism of embryos, tissues, and even of single cells with high accuracy. The *rate of respiratory metabolism* can be determined in terms of mm.^{3} of oxygen consumed per hour per individual. This *respiratory rate* (RR) increases with the age and the growth of the embryo (Fig. 123 light curve; compare with nitrogen curve, Fig. 121). More interesting in an analytical sense are rates in reference to a constant base.

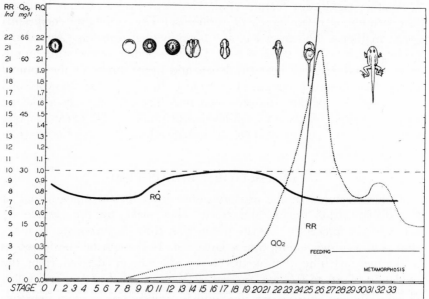

Figure 123.   Respiratory metabolism of developing frogs. Abscissa: Developmental stages from fertilization to completion of metamorphosis; important stages pictured in upper field of the graph. Ordinates: Respiratory rates per individual (RR, light curve), respiratory rates per milligram nitrogen (QO₂ stippled curve), and respiratory quotients (RQ, heavy curve) (Bruner, Failer, and Witschi).

Sometimes the milligram of living or of dry weight of the animal is chosen, but in work with embryos, the milligram of nitrogen, as determined by the Kjeldahl method, is the most meaningful reference base. One thus obtains an oxygen quotient (QO_2) which indicates the number of mm.[3] consumed per milligram of nitrogen per hour. Figure 121 shows the QO_2 curve (broken line) for *Rana pipiens* over an abscissa of chronologic time (days), and Figure 123 the same (dotted line) over a biologic abscissa, i.e., in relation to developmental stages.

The fertilized egg, like a lighted woodpile, first "burns" mostly locally, and the rate of oxidation increases as activation spreads throughout the entire germ. The slow rise at the beginning is more drawn out in large eggs than in small ones of the same species. The curve reaches its high peak when the yolk is used up at larval stage 25. The respiratory rate QO_2 is now 65 mm.[3]O_2/mg.N/hour, which is about four times that of older larvae (St. 28, 29) and five times that of young frogs. The second, smaller elevation of the curves at the height of metamorphosis results from hormonal stimulation of oxidations by the thyroid. The spectacular first rise is still unaccounted for. It coincides with the period of *liquefaction of the yolk,* which conceivably may be accompanied by liberation of quantities of a *respiratory enzyme.* The peak builds up when muscle contractions first occur (St. 18–20), the heart begins to beat, and circulation is established. The crest is reached when feeding and digestion become instituted, i.e., at the inception of the period with the maximal growth rate. While in itself destructive (catabolic), the high energy production sustains the assimilative (anabolic) processes, particularly protein synthesis, that result in true growth of specialized cells and tissues.

A more nearly qualitative analysis of the metabolic processes is possible by the study of *respiratory quotients.* In normal, aerobic respiration the relative amounts of oxygen consumed and carbon dioxide eliminated change characteristically with the chemical nature of the metabolized materials. As a consequence, the respiratory quotient $RQ = \dfrac{\text{volume } CO_2}{\text{volume } O_2}$ provides some guiding information about the nature of the transformations actually in progress within an intact egg. In the oxidation of carbohydrates the volumes of the two gases are equal:

$$C_6H_{12}O_6 + 6\,O_2 \rightarrow 6\,CO_2 + 6\,H_2O$$
$$\text{Glucose}$$

therefore
$$RQ = \frac{6\,CO_2}{6\,O_2} = 1$$

On the other hand, relatively more oxygen is needed to burn fats and oils as, for instance, in the oxidation of triolein:

$$C_{57}H_{104}O_6 + 80\ O_2 \rightarrow 57\ CO_2 + 52\ H_2O$$
Triolein

therefore $$RQ = \frac{57\ CO_2}{80\ O_2} = 0.71$$

The oxidation of proteins, depending on initial composition and nature of the end products (e.g., ammonia, urea, or uric acid), gives various quotients that fall between those of sugars and fats.

In Figure 123 the heavy line represents the values of the respiratory quotient. In conformity with the above statements one might be led to assume that up to gastrulation (St. 1 to 9) and again after the hatching of the larvae (St. 22) fat is the major metabolite; on the other hand carbohydrate would seem to be burned during the later gastrula, primitive streak, neurula, and tailbud stages (St. 9 to 21). However, the chemical transformations in an organism run a more complex course and must also be studied by direct analysis. The available data show that relatively little fat, but much protein, is catabolized during pre-hatching stages.

Special caution in the interpretation of RQ values is demanded by the conditions attending the glycogen metabolism. Embryos have the faculty to build up new glycogen reserves (*glyconeogenesis*) not only from sugars but also from fats and proteins. The latter being poor in oxygen, an oxygen deficit results which is covered from the general oxygen intake. Therefore, the overall RQ value is lowered. On the other hand glycogen, when drawn upon as an energy reserve (i.e., in *glycogenolysis*), does not always completely oxidize, but under special conditions forms lactic acid. This is true when oxygen is partly or fully withheld (anaerobiosis), and to some degree occurs even under aerobic conditions. Acting on bound carbon dioxide, which in amphibian eggs and embryos often is present in considerable quantity, the lactic acid can liberate some so-called *extra* CO_2. This again modifies the RQ values, but now increasing them.

With highly refined methods Brachet, Needham and Boell, and Barth and Gregg were able to measure *regional differences* in QO_2 and RQ values of amphibian gastrulae. Whatever differences in rates otherwise might exist, they are overshadowed and obscured by those arising from the distribution pattern of relatively inert materials, mainly yolk. Barth finds the following relative regional rates in early gastrulae: animal pole 28, dorsal lip 22, ventral lip 15, vegetal pole 4. These rates indicate oxygen consumption per hour per 100 mg. dry weight and cannot be directly compared with values in Figure 123. Highly suggestive are certain differences of respiratory quotients. Brachet calculates an RQ of 1.02 for dorsal lip material of early gastrulae (St. 8), when in ventral epidermis it is only 0.72. This contrast gains importance in combination with the fact that ribonucleoprotein—a suspected organizer substance—is twice as concentrated in the dorsal lip as in the remainder of the embryo. One must not, however, forget that on the RQ curve the gastrulation stages occupy the segment of transition from 0.7 to 1.0 (Fig. 123). Therefore the dorsal lip is merely heading the shift toward carbohydrate metabolism which soon becomes the characteristic of the entire germ.

In summary, the regional determinations reveal the existence of an *axial metabolic gradient* between animal and vegetal pole and the development of a *dorsoventral gradient* at early gastrulation stages.

Section Five

Fishes

Chapter 13

Primitive and

Specialized Traits of Development

The fishes are a large and very heterogeneous class comprising several distinct developmental types. The eggs of lampreys, garpikes, and lung-fishes resemble those of amphibians in size, composition, and the mode of cleavage. Those of the more prevalent bony fishes (teleosts) are larger and highly specialized, through adaptation to particular nutritional arrangements. As a consequence, their development shows many peculiarities, even at late stages. Selachian development, though starting from eggs with even bigger yolk reserves, is less aberrant than that of the teleosts. Many of its adaptational features even present striking evolutionary parallels to distinctive traits in the development of birds and placental mammals.

As a rule the development of fishes ends at a stage that corresponds to the 25th of the amphibian series (Figs. 42, 43). Metamorphic processes by which specialized immature larvae transform into strikingly different adult forms occur in several species. Best known are the cases of *Ammocoetes*, which becomes a lamprey, and of the planktonic *Leptocephalus*, changing into the fresh-water eel. However, the likeness to amphibian metamorphosis is at best only remote, since the adult is still a fish, whose structure resembles that of a tadpole at stage 25.

198

Though fish embryology is a vast and fascinating field of biology, it has not contributed very extensively to the development of the terminology and the basic concepts of vertebrate embryology. For this reason and because study material of the less aberrant species is difficult to obtain, the fishes are placed here after the amphibian chapter. Also, for purely didactic reasons, the presentation is restricted to the selachian and teleost types. They are the numerically prevalent and also the most interesting variants from the prototype of primitive vertebrate development, as represented by amphibians up to their first larval stage.

The development of *discogastrulae* from meroblastic eggs was described above (p. 74 ff., Fig. 34). The gastrula of the trout is about 2 mm. in diameter (Fig. 140, St. 12), which is only one-seventh the circumference of the egg. In selachians, in spite of the extraordinary size of the eggs, up to 10 cm. (cf. table 3), the blastodiscs and gastrulae are scarcely larger than in teleosts. After the cleavage stage the undivided yolk gradually becomes covered with a *yolk-sac epithelium*. In Figure 124, the progress of *epiboly and embryo formation in the trout* is graphically represented by superimposing outline drawings of six consecutive stages. The area of the prospective yolk-sac epithelium at stage 12 is indicated by stippling. Curves marked by arrows show the direction taken by three points chosen in the germ wall of stage 13. The two dorsolateral marks eventually become incorporated in the embryo, at different levels, while the ventrolateral mark moves with the yolk-sac epithelium and finally comes to lie near the closing blastopore. Corresponding left and right parts of the germ wall, meeting dorsally,

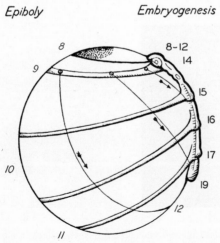

Epiboly   *Embryogenesis*

Figure 124.   Diagram illustrating the heterochrony between embryo formation (stages in vertical numbers) and closure of the blastopore (stages in slanting numbers) (based on figures by His, Kopsch and Pasteels). Only the first series is generally applicable.

furnish the materials for the left and right halves of the embryonic body.

Such convergent movements of blastemic cell masses, which result in the joining of the material halves of a body or of organs, are designated as *concrescence*. They are more extensive in the fishes than in amphibians.

In species with large eggs, the embryo of the first tailbud stage (St. 18) is shorter than half the circumference of the egg. As a consequence, the blastopore either closes on the dorsocaudal side (Figs. 124, 140) or it separates into two: *embryonic and vitelline blastopores,* of which only the latter proceeds toward the extreme end of the yolk mass (Fig. 134). Such a subdivision of the blastopore occurs only in a few teleosts, while it is characteristic for all selachians and myxinoid cyclostomes. Although the closure of the blastopore is delayed in respect to the progress of embryo formation (Fig. 124), the blastopore lips are no longer strictly equivalent to those of a bilaminar gastrula; for even as early as stage 9 (St. 13 of embryogenesis) they start to produce also a third germ layer, the mesodermal sheet of the yolk sac.

When fully formed, the yolk sac of teleosts remains broadly attached to the ventral surface of the body (Fig. 141). In selachians its connection with the embryo becomes a long and thin *yolk stalk* (Fig. 134).

A. SELACHIANS

Gastrulation and embryo formation in selachians are notable for their adaptation to the large size of the eggs. Few exact measurements of eggs at the time of ovulation are available, but in the more common

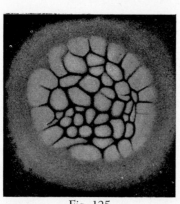
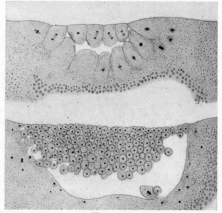

Fig. 125   Fig. 126

Figure 125.   Cleavage, 64 cells (St. 6), in the shark *Scyllium;* surface view of the cellular germ. Closed cells in center (blastomeres), open cells at periphery (blastocones) (Rückert 1899).
Figure 126.   Sections through blastula of selachians at stage 6 and stage 7 with rapidly widening cleavage cavity (blastocele) (Rückert 1899).

species they have diameters between 10 and 30 mm. At the animal pole, an accumulation of clear cytoplasm forms a *germinal area* about 2 mm. in diameter. It is the site of the early developmental processes.

Cleavage results in closed and open cells, blastomeres and blastocones (Figs. 125, 126, 127a). Gradually the entire germinal area becomes a mass of small cells and the germ assumes the aspect of a blob of cultured tissue, up to one millimeter in diameter, embedded in the large sphere of nutrient egg yolk (Figs. 126, 128a). Its surface is formed by an epithelium of cuboidal cells towards the outside; the inside, derived from the blastocones, is a syncytial film, applied to the cup-shaped depression in the vitellus. Between these surface layers and above the blastocele are large numbers of round blastemic cells. It is obvious that each of the three cell types of this *blastula* represents an adaptation to the immediate environmental conditions.

As the cells get smaller, the germ flattens, spreading over a larger surface (Fig. 127a, b). Its ventral half, which contains the larger number of round cells, becomes a two-layered thin disc, with a cleft-like blastocele separating *epiblast* and *hypoblast* (Fig. 128). Events take a somewhat different course in the dorsal half. The rim of the blastodisc seems more solidly anchored at the surface of the egg so that the spreading surface epithelium soon juts out as a crescent-shaped lip (Figs. 127, 128). As a consequence of its mode of formation this lip is double-layered, the under side originating from the surface of the blastula by *invagination*. It is now clear that the result of these changes is a *disc gastrula* (Fig. 129). The ventral half of the blastopore lip is directly attached to the yolk mass which serves as an *archenteric plug*. The dorsal half hangs free over a crescent-shaped *archenteric cavity* (Fig. 143). The larger part of the hypoblast consists of a syncytium with large nuclei and round or spindle-shaped blastema cells. This

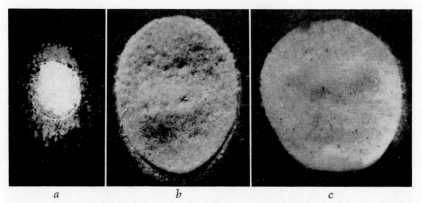

a   b   c

Figure 127.   Surface views of three germs of *Scyllium canicula. a,* Blastula (St. 7); *b,* gastrula (St. 11); *c,* primitive streak stage (St. 12) (Vandebroek 1936; × 18).

vitelline hypoblast goes almost in its entirety into the formation of the endodermal yolk-sac epithelium. The narrow sickle-shaped *embryonic hypoblast* of the under side of the free lip consists of prospective embryonic endoderm, prechordal mesoderm, and the tip of the prospective notochord (Fig. 143).

Maps of areas of prospective differentiation of the surface parts at various stages have been worked out by Vandebroek, with the aid of color marks (Fig. 130). During the blastula and early gastrula stages not only the prospective ectoderm but also the entire mesoderm and a good part of the prospective embryonic endoderm lie at the surface of the germ (Fig. 130, St. 10). At completion of gastrulation (Fig. 130, St. 11) the endoderm and parts of the mesoderm have disappeared by invagination, as described above. This marks also the end of the two-layered stages. From here on epiboly and invagination will be coupled with the formation of the third germ layer.

The *primitive streak stage* (St. 12, Figs. 127c, 131a) is externally characterized by a distinct nodal swelling in the middle of the dorsal lip. The thickening continues laterally, tapering off to the left and right. The lateral welts are the primitive folds. The swellings are caused by the accumulation of the mesodermal blastema in the lips.

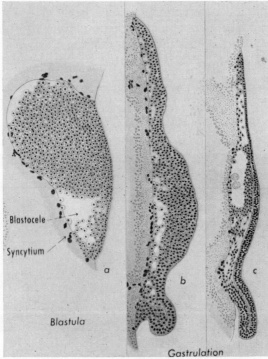

Figure 128.   Gastrulation in selachians; *a,* stage 8; *b,* stage 9; *c,* stage 10 (Rückert 1899).

Already at this stage mesodermal wedges begin to grow into the cleft (blastocele) between the epiblastic and hypoblastic layers (Figs. 129, 131a). The fate map (Fig. 130, St. 12, 12a) shows that the notochordal blastema has shifted from the surface into the node of the blastopore lip.

The next following stages are externally remarkable for the extensive neural development, wherefore the embryos of the entire phase are called *neurulae* (St. 13–17, Fig. 134). At stage 13 the prosencephalic neural plate rises above the general level of the blastoderm. The mesencephalic, rhombencephalic, and upper spinal sections are presently added (St. 14). At stage 15 the neural folds meet and fuse in the lower rhombencephalic and the cervical region. The upper *neuropore* closes

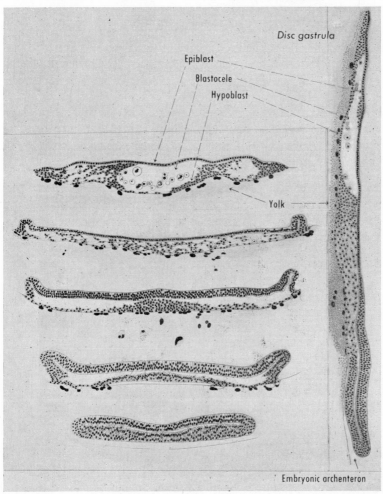

Figure 129. Selachian disc gastrulae (St. 11); five cross sections and one sagittal section. The cross sections are placed at about corresponding levels along the longitudinal section (Rückert 1899).

at stage 16 and the lower at stage 17. A comparison of the *fate maps* (Fig. 130) with the outline drawings of some of these stages (Fig. 134) reveals the generally convergent character of the movements of the neural blastema and of the adjacent epidermis. The latter finally completely covers the neural tube.

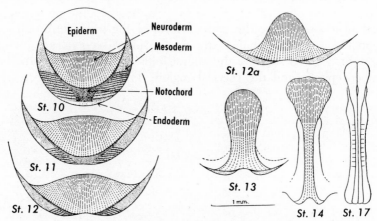

Figure 130. Maps of areas of prospective differentiation in selachian embryos of stages 10–17. *Darkest stipple:* prechordal mesoderm plate; *cross lines:* first 10 somites (Vandebroek 1936).

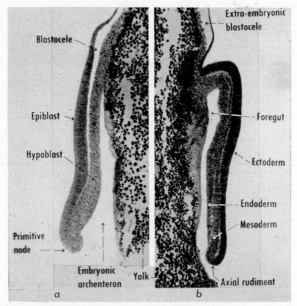

Figure 131. *Squalus acanthias,* shark; *a,* primitive streak stage (St. 12), sagittal section through the embryonic part of the blastoderm; × 70. *b,* Early neurula stage (St. 13); third layer formation. Prechordal plate fused with roof of foregut; × 35.

The neurula stages are equally important also in regard to *meso-dermal* and *endodermal development*. Specific variations occur, regarding the time of segregation of *prechordal mesoderm* and the *tip of the notochord* from the roof of the endoderm. In *Squalus*, separation begins immediately at the primitive streak stage (Fig. 131), while in *Scyllium* the mesodermal head plate first becomes incorporated in the endodermal roof of the foregut (Fig. 132). In both species the prechordal plates remain attached to the pharynx, at least superficially, throughout the neurula stages. Following stage 12 mesoderm formation issues from the blastopore lips, which are the equivalent of the primitive folds of corresponding amphibian stages. The fate maps (Fig. 130) illustrate stepwise the concrescence of the prospective *somitic mesoderm* and its gradual disappearance from the surface. Parasagittal sections (St. 14, Fig. 133*b*) show that it grows from the under edge of the lip into the space between epiblast and hypoblast. The same mode prevails until closure of the blastopore (St. 17, Fig. 135). In whole mounts (Fig. 133*a*) it can be seen that the somitic cords are continuous with the prechordal mesoderm. Somites, presomites, and

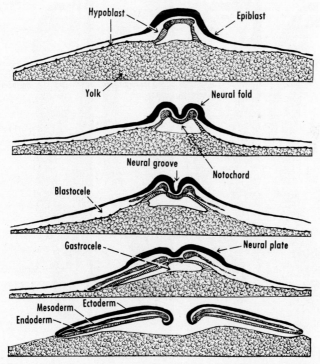

Figure 132. Cross sections through stage 13 of *Scyllium canicula;* prechordal plate and tip of notochord temporarily from the roof of the archenteron. *Black:* Neuroderm and epiderm; *gray:* mesoderm; *white hatched:* notochord; *black hatched:* embryonic endoderm; *foam:* yolk and yolk-sac endoderm; × 44.

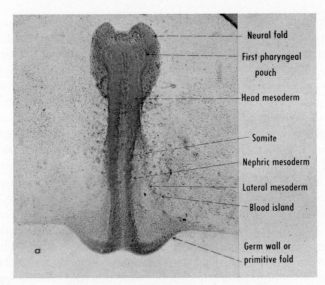

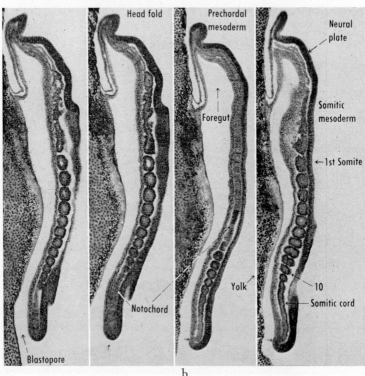

Figure 133.   *Squalus acanthias,* open neurula (St. 14), 10 to 11 free somites. *a,* Whole mount, dorsal aspect. *b,* Four sagittal sections, slightly oblique, so
that the root of the notochord shows in the second, the top in the third section; arrows point at mesoderm proliferating zone; × 15.

prechordal mesoderm all exhibit a tendency toward cavitation (Fig. 133b).

The *notochord* does not form through concrescence of paired pre-primordia but, like the neural floorplate, it proliferates from the median primitive node, the *axial rudiment* (Figs. 131–135).

The relative importance of *invagination* and of *mitotic cell proliferation* is not easily evaluated. Both processes are involved in the formation of the embryo. Migration and rearrangement of blastemic cells are conspicuous factors during the gastrulation and neurulation stages, but lose importance with the progress of time. Mitotic figures are frequently found in all parts of early embryos, with the exception of the notochord. Here mitoses are restricted to a short zone in the blastopore lip, the root of the notochord. However, growth of the axial organ is not merely by terminal proliferation but largely, at later stages, through vesicular transformation and water intake of its cells.

The ventral half of the blastoderm spreads rapidly to cover the entire yolk mass. Its progress is illustrated in Figure 134. At the time when embryo formation enters the primitive streak stage, a mesodermal layer begins to grow in also from the lip of the yolk blastopore (Figs. 129, 134a). Consequently the yolk sac early becomes three-layered, which is important in connection with the development of the circulatory system (see p. 212). At stage 17 the *embryonic blastopore* separates from the *vitelline blastopore*. While the former closes at stage 18, the latter takes much longer time to grow over the entire yolk; it closes only after the nearly fully differentiated embryo has become set off by a *yolk stalk* from the large *yolk sac* (Figs. 134, 139).

The *tailbud stages* (St. 18–24, Fig. 136) start with the closure of the embryonic blastopore (St. 18, Fig. 134d). At stage 17 (Fig. 134c) the vitelline blastopore is still continuous with the embryonic blastopore. But in short succession the latter becomes pinched off and closed. Since the neural groove runs around the end of the notochord into the blastopore, the final closure of the neural folds and the lips of the embryonic blastopore results in the formation of a patent *neurenteric canal*. This occurs at the stage of about 30 somites (St. 19, Fig. 137a) and the lumen remains pervious until 50 somites (St. 21, Fig. 137b). It then regresses (St. 22, Fig. 137c) and disappears while the last somites form (over 80 in most species).

A prevailingly *epithelial character of the tailbud* is characteristic for the selachians. The relationships so clearly seen here between the neural and endodermal tubes and the notochord are obscured in amphibian and amniote embryos by the development of extensive blastemic proliferation cones. In the selachian tailbud embryos the root of the notochord first is inserted in the floorplate of the neural tube where it turns into the neurenteric canal (St. 19–22, Fig. 137); later it remains attached to the caudal end of the neural tube. The region of fusion is the *axial rudiment*. The ephemeral neurenteric canal of the

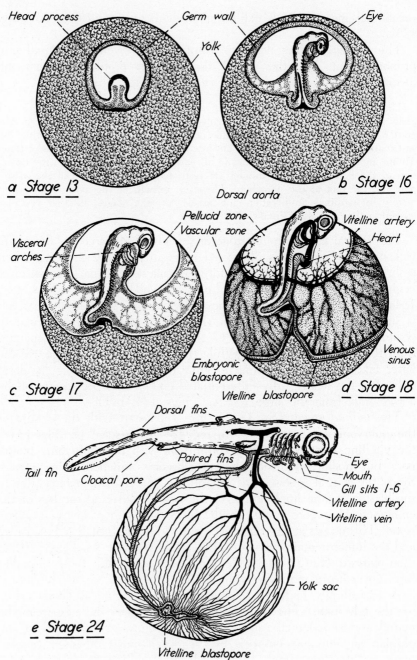

Figure 134. Selachian development. In most species the yolk mass is relatively larger than indicated in these figures. The distribution of the angioblastema
is represented by stippling; arteries black, veins hatched. *a, Early neurula,* beginning head fold (St. 13). *b, Neurula,* about 16 somites; spreading vascular zone
(St. 16). *c, Neurula,* about 22 somites; lower neural folds closing, beginning sep-

selachians is the homologue of the blind tailgut of amphibian and other
vertebrate embryos.

When the *cloaca* first becomes recognizable as a part of the closing
blastopore, it lies approximately at the level of the twentieth somite.

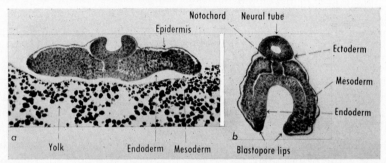

Figure 135.   *Squalus acanthias*. Mesoderm formation from blastopore lips;
cross sections through the lower body regions of neurulae. *a*, Stage 16, *neurula* of
16 somites; *b*, stage 17, *neurula* of 22 somites, closing embryonic blastopore; × 50.

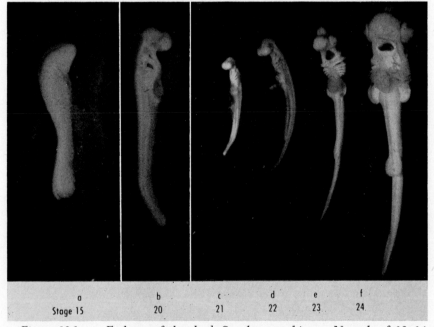

Figure 136.   Embryos of the shark *Squalus acanthias*. *a*, *Neurula* of 13–14
somites, with upper and lower neuropores; × 13. *b*, *Tailbud embryo* of 40 somites,
with open gill clefts; × 6.5. *c–f*, *Tailbud* stages with 50 to 800 somites; × 2.4.

aration of embryonic and vitelline blastopores (St. 17). *d*, *Tailbud embryo* of
about 30 somites; embryonic blastopore closing, connecting with vitelline blastopore. Two aortic arches, primitive heart, circulation starting; vitelline arteries
invade pellucid zone (St. 18). *e*, *Embryo* with external gills, primitive paired
appendages, and large yolk sac (St. 24).

Later it is carried caudally, and at the time of the formation of the last somite (total about 80) it has reached its final position at the level of the fortieth somite. The cloacal membrane ruptures in embryos of stage 24, after the kidneys have attained an advanced and probably functional state of development (Fig. 136*f*).

The *segmental structure* (metamery) of the vertebrate body is more clearly exhibited in the selachians than in the higher orders and classes. The study of selachian embryos has contributed particularly to the understanding of the composition of the *vertebrate head*. In embryos, segments appear as a series of somites and visceral arches that are continuous with somites and visceral mesoderm of the trunk. Most selachians have seven distinctly recognizable head segments, though some archaic species of sharks have more (*Heptanchus* 9; *Clamydoselachus* 8, Fig. 138). The visceral arches are arranged much as in amphibians: the first is the mandibular, the second the hyoid arch, and the following ones are branchial arches (5 to 7). All pharyngeal pouches break through in open clefts. The first one remains small but in many species it is temporarily provided with gill filaments, like the branchial clefts. All visceral arches with the exception of the last one (which is fused to the wall of the trunk) are supplied by separate aortic arches. In the later stages the mandibular and partly the hyoid vessels lose their direct

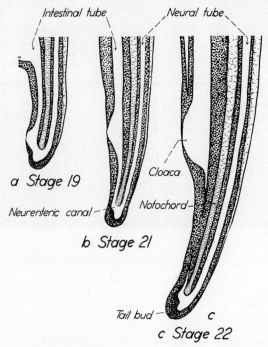

Figure 137.   *Squalus acanthias.* Sagittal sections through lower body and tail of three tailbud embryos; the *neurenteric canal* at stages 19 and 21, and its rupture and regression at stage 22.

connections with the ventral aortic trunk and receive oxygenated blood from the first branchial arch system.

The development of the *circulatory system* shows an interesting division of embryonic and extra-embryonic processes. Vandebroek's fate maps show neither the location of the lateral (visceral) mesoderm nor the angioblastema. In the early gastrula (Fig. 130a) evidently they lie at the periphery of the entire disc, except in the dorsal region where the embryonic endoderm comes to the surface. The approximate location of the prospective angioblastema at stage 13 is indicated by

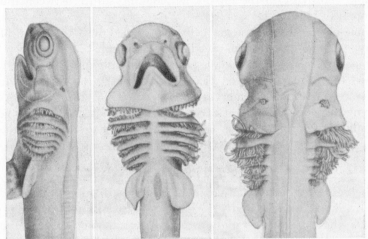

Figure 138.   *Chlamydoselachus* (St. 22–23); primitive shark with eight visceral arches, seven open gill slits, the first one reduced to a small spiracle (Dean 1937).

Figure 139.   Embryos of the skate, *Raia binoculata*, removed from shells. The younger ones with external gills, stages 24 and 25; × .5.

stippling in Figure 134*a*. At stage 15 the extra-embryonic mesoderm belt appears mottled, which is the expression of the differentiation of numerous *blood islands,* consisting each of only a small number of angioblastema cells (Fig. 133*a*). At the end of the neurula stage, the angioblastema accumulates along the inner and the outer edges of the belt. As early as stage 18 it becomes clear that in the inner circle the main stems of the *vitelline arteries* are differentiating while the outer circle, close to the blastopore, forms a terminal *venous sinus* (Fig. 134*b, d*). On their way toward the embryo body, left and right *vitelline veins* fuse in the rapidly lengthening suture between the two blastopores (Figs. 134*d, e,* 139).

Some of the angioblastema cells are carried into the body of the embryo. They give origin to the endotheliums of the *heart* and the *blood vessels of the embryo.* During the embryonic phase, *erythropoiesis,* the formation of red blood cells, seems to be restricted to the yolk sac. In *Squalus* embryos of stage 19 (7 to 8 mm.), with pharyngeal pouches and oral cavity still closed, heart and blood vessels are only blastemic primordia. But at stage 20 (9 to 10 mm.), the gill clefts open (Fig. 136*b*) and circulation becomes established.

B. TELEOSTS

The course of teleost development after gastrulation (St. 12–35) is outlined in Figures 140 and 141. The prospective significance of various parts of the epiblast of *Fundulus* and *Salmo* having been ascertained by the study of the movements of artificial color marks, Oppenheimer and Pasteels constructed *fate maps of early gastrulae* which differ in one important detail. This is the presence, at stage 10, of some endoderm in the surface layer of *Fundulus,* but not of the trout (Fig. 142*a, b*). The former is therefore very similar to the shark of the same stage (Fig. 130*a*). This endodermal crescent is rolled under and becomes a part of the hypoblast before the end of gastrulation. But neither *Fundulus* nor the trout forms an overhanging free blastopore lip. The embryonic archenteron is reduced to a very small vesicle under the dorsal lip of the blastopore (Fig. 144*a*). Thus the invagination movements of gastrulation are greatly reduced in *Fundulus* and practically abolished in *Salmo.* The prospective mesoderm never becomes a part of the hypoblast.

The evolution of the gastrulae accompanying the accumulation of great masses of yolk is illustrated by the comparative series of types assembled in Figure 143. The relatively inert yolk protrudes through the blastopore of amphibian gastrulae and keeps that of the fishes wide open. It forms *yolk plugs* which reduce the *archenteric cavities* to small spaces beneath the embryonic parts of the blastodiscs. This gives the germ the shape which is well characterized by the name *disc gastrula.* Another concurrent change seems to result from the reduced speed of

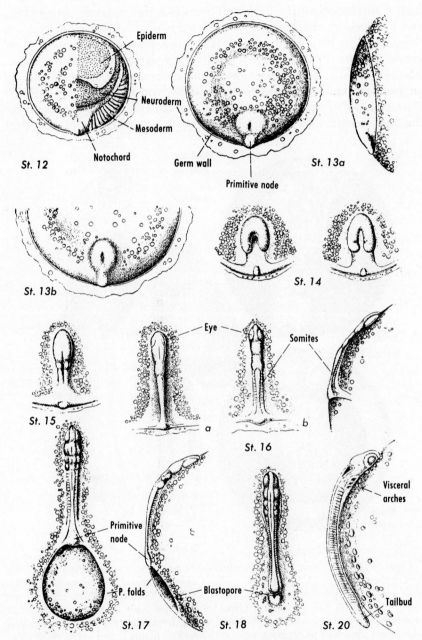

Figure 140.   Trout (*Salmo fario*), stages of early development (12–20) (after Kopsch, from Hertwig). On right half of stage 12, prospective areas of primordial differentiation (after Pasteels). × 14.

invagination. In the ascidian gastrula the prospective mesoderm is a part of the hypoblast. In the amphibians it is incompletely invaginated, and in sharks at the most some small parts of the head mesoderm are rolled in. Finally in the teleosts *the entire prospective mesoderm remains in the epiblast.* These differences have far-reaching consequences. While hypoblastic mesoderm differentiates through folding off from the endoderm, the epiblastic mesoderm moves merely into the blastopore lip, from where it enters directly the blastocele (postgastrulation invagination). The changes in the gastrulation process thus

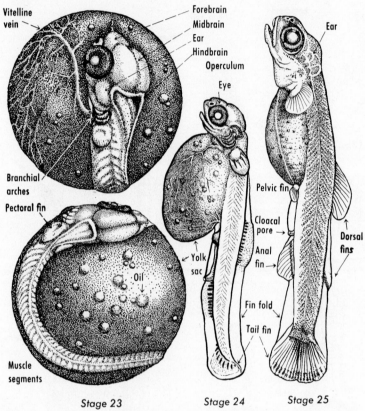

Figure 141. Trout (*Salmo gairdnerii irideus*), stages of advanced embryonic development. *Stage 23* (10 mm.), embryo closely applied to the surface of the large yolk sac. Egg shell was removed. Four branchial arches with gillbuds are partly covered by the operculum (hyoid arch); flat buds of pectoral fins; small prosencephalon; large mesencephalon (paired hemispheres); rhombencephalon with broad, thin roof plate; nose, eye (with chorioid fissure), and ear in close series at side of the head. At this stage the blood from the yolk-sac epithelium is returned by way of the left vitelline vein. *Stage 24,* hatching trout (15 mm.) with buds of pelvic fins and more advanced pectoral and unpaired fins (continuous fin fold). *Stage 25,* 20 mm., fry with vanishing yolk sac; all fins (including adipose fin) differentiated, separated; operculum completely covers gills.

lead to a new manner of mesoderm formation, one that is widely operative in all higher vertebrates.

In teleosts the differentiation of the hypoblast into prospective *embryonic endoderm* and prospective *yolk-sac endoderm* is as distinct as in
selachians. The latter consists almost entirely of syncytial cells while

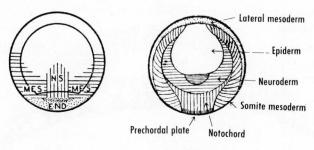

a *Fundulus*   b *Salmo*

Figure 142.   Fate maps of teleost gastrulae at about stage 10. *a, Fundulus*
(Oppenheimer 1936); NS, prospective neural system; MES, mesoderm; END,
endoderm. The prospective notochord is indicated by dark stipple, the epidermis is
left white. *b, Salmo* (Pasteels 1936).

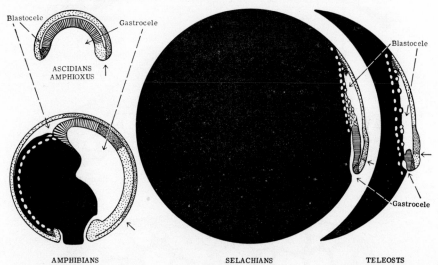

Figure 143.   Comparative diagrams of gastrulae, illustrating the effect of
accumulation of large yolk masses (black). Arrows point at the axial rudiment,
located where neuroderm and notochord meet. Prospective areas of differentiation:
epidermis (light stipple), neuroderm (denser stipple), notochord (light stipple),
prechordal plate and ventral mesenchyme (darkest stipple), gut (hatched), endodermal yolk-sac epithelium (white dots). Note changing shapes of blastocele and
gastrocele; in the selachians and teleosts the gastrocele is reduced to a narrow space
between yolk and gut endoderm, while beneath the yolk-sac epithelium its place is
taken by the uncleaved yolk mass (black). All gastrulae are so oriented that the main
axis of the embryo approaches the vertical position.

the embryonic part lies in the blastemic thickening along the dorsal blastopore lip (Fig. 144a). Though a free blastoporal lip is not formed, sagittal sections disclose a *vestigial archenteric cavity* or gastrocele between the dorsal germ wall and the underlying yolk.

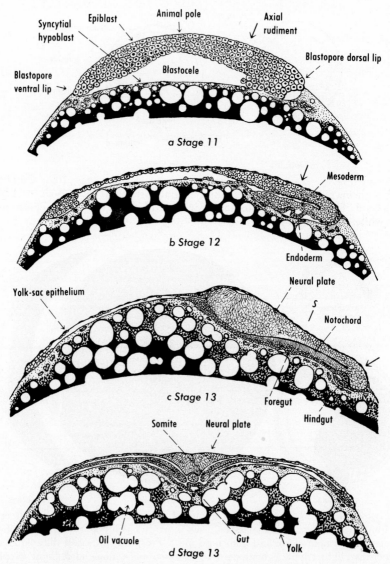

Figure 144. *Salmo fario,* trout. *a,* Gastrula, sagittal section; the small cavity under the dorsal blastopore lip is a rudimentary gastrocele. *b,* Primitive streak stage, sagittal section, showing start of formation of the third germ layer. *c,* Early neurula, embryo of 1.7 mm. with first somite formation; sagittal section. *d,* Cross section through same stage, at level marked S in figure *c;* arrows point to border of prospective ectoderm and mesoderm (axial rudiment in the sagittal plane). × 45.

At the *late gastrula stage* (St. 11, Fig. 144*a*) the blastocele is still fairly spacious, the vitelline hypoblast is syncytial, and the epiblast is everywhere several cells deep. Examination of the sagittal section reveals little differentiation in the dorsal lip. However, comparison with Pasteels' fate maps and with sections through more advanced stages discloses that the roof of the small gastrocele consists of blastemic endoderm, which is followed by prechordal plate (Fig. 143, teleosts).

At the *primitive streak stage* (St. 12) differentiation has made considerable progress (Fig. 144*b*). The primitive node is an evenly rounded knob and projects slightly from the germ wall (Fig. 140, St. 12). The surface of the blastoderm has become a thin *periderm layer*. Beneath it, the *extra-embryonic ectoderm* is only a single cell deep. In the embryonic region the prospective *neural plate* remains thick and continues without recognizable limit (arrow) into the superficial part of the notochordal blastema. As the sagittal section shows, *notochord formation* is direct, by ingrowth from the primitive node, not by separation from the roof of the gastrocele. The *embryonic endoderm* has become a thin epithelium, rostrally fused with the axial mesoderm of the *prechordal plate*, and caudally in contact with the periderm. One or two transverse folds belong to the foregut region and probably correspond to the first and second pairs of *pharyngeal pouches*.

At the *early neurula* stage (St. 13), the time of first somite formation (Figs. 144*c*, *d*), a new crosswise fold is present in the endoderm. It has a considerable lateral extension and in the center expands into a lens-shaped vesicle, the *hindgut* (formerly described as Kupffer's vesicle). From this stage on, the embryonic endoderm elongates mainly by growth of the midgut region. *Mesoderm formation* is now in progress along the entire circumference of the blastoderm. As the yolk-sac epithelium advances over the surface of the yolk sphere (Fig. 124), the germ wall is constantly proliferating, adding to the ectodermal and endodermal membranes also a mesodermal layer. In *Fundulus,* a species with relatively small eggs (2 mm. diameter), migration of superficial cells around the blastopore lip into the proliferating zone has been seen to contribute to this growth; though probably the major factor is the active mitotic cell multiplication which still occurs everywhere, except in the histologically differentiated notochord.

Some students of early stages of embryo formation in bony fishes have claimed movement and rearrangement of the cells to be the only important factors of morphogenesis. Proliferation should not occur, and the total volume of cellular tissue not increase before the tailbud stage is attained. However, exact measurements to support such statements are difficult to make. Moreover, all embryonic tissues lose weight rapidly through metabolic activity, if cut off from yolk and outside nutrition. Therefore, mere maintenance of weight and volume during an active phase of normal embryogenesis actually involves true growth in cell numbers, cell nuclei, nucleoproteins, and other important components of living tissues.

Salmon and trout furnished the material on which Wilhelm His made the observations that led to the classic *concept of concrescence* (1874, 1876). At the time he had no presentiment of its universal applicability to all vertebrates. To the contrary, he believed that the lamprey, the chick and other vertebrate groups were quite different developmental types. The principle of identity of the process of embryo formation in all vertebrates was brought to light only through the construction of fate maps, half a century later.

The teleost type of concrescence differs from the selachian in the formation of the *terminal knob*. Whereas in selachians the germ walls swing in, with redundant curves, meeting first at an obtuse and later at an acute angle (Fig. 134*a, b*), in teleosts the entire germ ring remains almost exactly circular. The terminal knob thus receives a constant flow of blastemic material from both sides. Its center part consists first of notochordal and later of neural and notochordal material, the axial rudiment (Figs. 144, 145). The laterally incoming blastema first collects, swelling the knob from both sides, and then transforms into somitic blastema cords and somites (Fig. 145). There is little or no upward pushing of these materials; each part differentiates at its station, while later arriving cells are added at lower levels (Fig. 124).

After closure of the blastopore, the terminal knob of the dorsal germ wall becomes the *tailbud* (St. 18) which presently begins to elongate in the space between yolk sac and egg shell (Fig. 141, St. 23). The

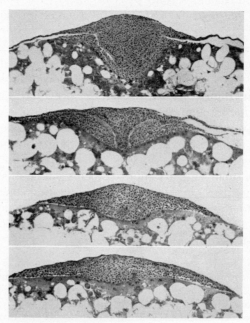

Figure 145.   *Salmo fario,* trout, neurula, 1.7 mm., stage 13. Four cross sections, of which the lowest passes through the germinal wall and the terminal knob, the top section through the brain. Second section: contracting neural plate, notochord, and lateral mesodermal masses. Third section: beginning differentiation. × 70.

lower segments of the trunk and the tail are thus formed and are pressed flat against the surface of the yolk, while the head frees itself very slowly, by folding off from the yolk. Until the time of hatching, the egg shell retains a spherical shape. The *hatching trout* (St. 24, Fig. 141) has partly differentiated pectoral fins, but the pelvic fins are only primordial buds. The large yolk sac impedes the swimming movements and forces the *fry* to spend most of its time at the bottom of the waters, near the spawning grounds.

In the bony fishes *organogenesis* is of a singularly specialized type. The flat shape of the embryonic body and its close adherence to the syncytium-covered yolk mass is probably causally linked with the late development of the extra-embryonic circulation. The developing organs appear dorsoventrally compressed; neural folds are barely indicated (Figs. 140, 144, 145). The entire neural plate transforms into a massive neural cord which only secondarily acquires a central canal. The eye bulbs and the lenses also start from solid primordia.

Vascular development in the extra-embryonic region is much retarded. At stage 12 the angioblastema is restricted almost entirely to the prospective embryonic region, particularly along the dorsal germ wall. Consequently it becomes transported into the embryonic body, and early angiogenesis occurs within the embryo alone. The yolk sac becomes vascularized later, by veins growing out from the embryonic body (Fig. 146). The yolk-sac epithelium temporarily assumes some importance as a respiratory organ. When the gills are still short, a fine network of venules develops over the surface of the yolk sac, facilitating the gaseous exchange between blood and water. In *viviparous species,* this respiratory function becomes more specialized. A collar-shaped extension rises from the upper margins of yolk sac and pericardial sac; in some species it envelops the entire head (Fig. 147*a*). This formation closely resembles the chorio-amniotic fold of the higher vertebrates, except for its peculiar, rich venous blood supply (Fig. 147*b*).

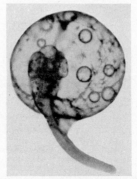

Figure 146.   *Fundulus heteroclitus,* embryo (St. 22) with blood vessels spreading in the vitelline area (Phot. J. Oppenheimer); × 15.

The *resorption of the yolk sac* is completed long after hatching, and after the full development of paired fins, opercular gill covers, pigmentation, and other adult characters (Fig. 141). The organization of the young fish is now of a similar type to that of amphibian larvae of stage 25. In contrast to the latter, the fish lacks the potentiality of metamorphosis and thus has now reached its final stage of development.

Twinning is a relatively frequent abnormality in teleosts. In trout hatcheries thousands of double-headed embryos and hundreds of triplets have been collected. Multiplicity of the upper parts (anadidymus) is far more frequent than doubling of the lower parts (katadidymus) or of the entire axis (anakatadidymus). In a material of 3652 twin and triplet trout embryos, Lynn found only three each of the last two types. Apparently the proportions depend on some specific factors. A female of the viviparous *Gambusia* gave birth to the twins of Figure 148*b* and *c* together with 33 normal litter mates. The chances of such an occurrence would be extremely small on the basis of the trout statistics.

It has long been realized that the development of the monsters starts from *multiple centers in the germ wall*. In the case of triplets (Fig. 148*a*) three primitive nodes must have formed instead of one. The closer together the nodes, and the shorter the stretch of germ wall between them, the sooner (in terms of somites) the embryonic axes must meet. Siamese twins with separate heads and tails (Fig. 148*b*), and united only by some ventral organs, originate from nodes at opposite sides of the germ disc. In some instances both embryos are nearly perfect (identical twins).

Double development was experimentally induced in the trout by the transplantation of a small part of primitive node tissue into the ventral blastopore lip (Fig. 149). This gives proof of the competence of the ventral rim to produce an embryo in lieu of simple yolk-sac epithelium; but it does not reveal the primary cause of spontaneous twin development. From the fact that the experimentally induced secondary embryo usually has a defective forehead one must conclude that the causes

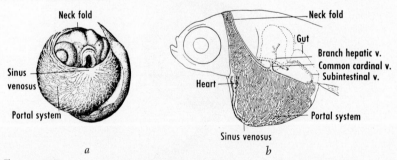

Figure 147.   *a,* Viviparous teleost *Poeciliopsis infans.* Head nearly enclosed by a pericardial sac; × 12. *b,* Viviparous teleost *Lebistes reticulatus.* Diagram of portal system in yolk sac and pericardial sac of 7.5 mm. embryo (C. L. Turner 1940).

of natural twinning operate at an earlier stage, i.e., before the formation of the primitive node; for natural twins of the trout, with rare exceptions, have complete heads (Fig. 148a).

The interpretation of twins with fused heads and separate tails (Fig. 148c) is quite uncertain. Most likely the initial centers were so close together that nodes fused, with primary axes meeting head on or at a

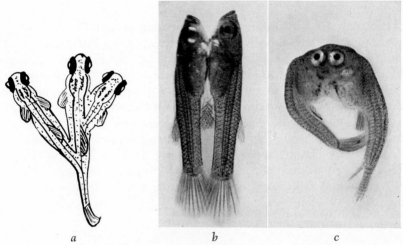

a   *b*   *c*

Figure 148.   Multiple embryo formation in teleosts. *a*, Triplet trout (Lynn 1949). *b* and *c*, Newborn twins of *Gambusia holbrooki.*

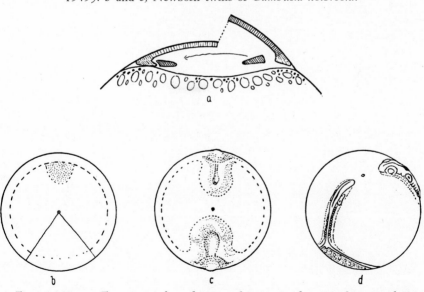

b   *c*   *d*

Figure 149.   Experimental production of twins in the trout by transplantation of a piece of inductive tissue from the dorsal to the ventral lip of the disc gastrula (Luther 1935). *a–d*, Sequence of operation (*a*) and resulting stages of normal and induced embryo formation.

widely open angle. In the later development, the axes project into the germ walls, one to the left, the other to the right. Thus, it is assumed that each body and tail developed from only one half of the germ wall, and therefore without concrescence. This interpretation is the more permissible as it had already been shown by some early work of T. H. Morgan—later repeatedly confirmed—that after destruction of one half of the blastopore lip, the other half is capable of producing a nearly complete body.

This analysis of twinning has an important bearing on the proper understanding of the process of concrescence. Direct microscopic study shows that the fusing blastoporal lips are *blastemic* in appearance, not preformed left and right halves of the embryo (Fig. 145). But now it is further established that this blastema is not even predetermined. The *fate maps* express only what every part contributes to embryo formation in a normal course of development, not a fixed rigid pattern of differentiation. The relationship between *prospective fate* and total potentiality or *competence* of embryonic blastemas is a problem that has already been discussed in connection with amphibian development (pp. 93–101), and which will pose itself again during consideration of avian and mammalian development.

Birds

Chapter 14

Presomite Stages

The chick has been the favored material of embryologic investigation for more than two centuries. The era of scientific embryology opened when Fabricius ab Aquapendente published his book on the formation of the egg and the chick. Two hundred years later, Wolff (1759), Pander (1817), and von Baer (1828), elaborating the germ-layer concept, still based their presentations mostly on the study of developing hen's eggs. In the course of time many beautifully illustrated monographs have been devoted to the accurate and detailed description of the ontogeny of this one species.

The ready availability of live material throughout the year and the many technical advantages which it offers for experimental work will always secure for the egg of the domestic chicken, and also that of the duck, a preferred place in the laboratory.

1. GENERAL

The physiologic zero, below which the hen's egg will not start developing, is near 28° C. At 40° C. embryos progress almost twice as fast as at 35° C.; but normal development over several days or the entire incubation period can be expected only if the temperature is close to 37.5° C. (99.5° Fahrenheit; Fig. 150). In small songbirds the optimal temperature is about 2 degrees lower. Thus the incubating temperature is from 2 to 4 degrees below adult body temperature, depending on the size of the species. The capacity to regulate the body temperature and maintain it near the optimal level is acquired only toward the end of the incubation period. Even after hatching the young birds need protection against extreme temperature variations.

The main steps in the evolution of incubation, from the viewpoint of both maternal behavior and embryonic adaptations, are indicated by the reproductive habits of the primitive *megapods*. Some of these tropical birds simply bury their large eggs in sand. Development proceeds at the average environmental temperature of about 28° C. Other species build large hills of earth and vegetable matter, into which they lay their eggs. The heat of fermentation may raise the temperature as much as 4 to 5 degrees above that of the surrounding air. However, in these birds development takes its normal course also at temperatures considerably below those required by the chick. The hatching young, like those of reptiles, need no assistance from the parents.

Unincubated chicken eggs may be stored at 10° C. about two weeks without apparent loss of viability. At this temperature their development is at a standstill.

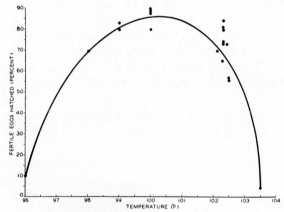

Figure 150.   Incubation temperature and hatchability of fertile eggs of the domestic chicken (after Barott 1937).

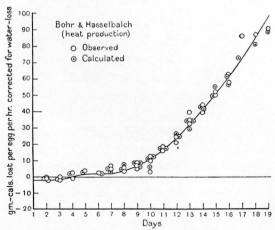

Figure 151.   Heat production by hen's egg during incubation (from Needham 1931).

During a third and fourth week, storage becomes increasingly harmful, and after one month, the ability to hatch is destroyed. In songbirds which begin incubating immediately after laying of the first egg, even a few days' storage is fatal.

During incubation, development depends on extraneous heat supply. Nevertheless, the energy balance is always positive. Incubation raises the temperature of the egg to the level which is most favorable for the orderly progress of biologic oxidations. Calorimetric determinations prove that the developing egg produces and eliminates heat in ever increasing amounts (Fig. 243). Toward the end the incubator temperature may be lowered by as much as 3° C. without ill effects. By hatching time, about one fourth of the original chemical energy content of the egg has been lost as heat; approximately one half is now invested in the tissues of the chick and one fourth remains in the form of yolk within the yolk sac. At hatching the latter is withdrawn into the body cavity. When pulmonary respiration and free muscular activity become established, the total metabolism rises three- to four-fold and is maintained at that level after hatching for at least four days, even if the chick is kept without food. On the other hand, metabolism declines immediately and steadily if the yolk sac is surgically removed (Byerly).

While the hatched chick still lives off its yolk stores, fat metabolism is predominant, and the low respiratory quotient (RQ 0.71, after Byerly) is the same as during the prehatching period. After intake of

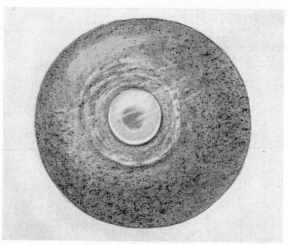

Figure 152.   Sparrow, unincubated egg (St. 8, disc gastrula); shell and albumen removed; polar view (cf. sagittal section, Fig. 35c); the dark pellucid area in center of disc indicates the extent of the subgerminal cavity (gastrocele). The germ wall (white) is thickest along the dorsal (lower) circumference. Spreading of the blastoderm causes formation of concentric folds on the yolk. Yolk and blastoderm are enclosed in transparent vitelline membrane; × 6.

food, an immediate rise of the quotient indicates a change to carbohydrate metabolism.

Most species have a fairly constant hatching age (Table 8). Therefore, it is
possible to express developmental stages in hours and days of incubation. Such
time-tables are practical, but do not obviate the necessity of supplementary characterization. In order to facilitate comparison with similar stages of other vertebrate
classes, the same numeral classification is applied as in the previous description
of amphibians and fishes.

2. POLARITY AND ORGANIZATION CENTER

The main or *polar axis* of eggs can always be ascertained, even in
the earliest ovocytes. It is determined by the relative positions of nucleus and central body. In the full-grown egg the distribution of the
white yolk (Fig. 17), the location of the pronucleus, and the center
of the blastoderm serve as landmarks in the recognition of the animal-
vegetal axis (Fig. 35). In the upper oviduct, the formation of the
chalazae emphasizes the existence of another axis which, as seen by

Table 8

Egg Size and Hatching Condition of Some Birds

SPECIES	EGG WEIGHT Grams	HATCHING AGE Days
NEST QUITTERS		
Contour feathers—down; open eyes		
Megapodius, var. sp. (mound birds)	100–250	60–90
Casuarius sp. (casowary)	780	56
Struthio camelus (ostrich)	1500	42
Meleagris gallopavo (dom. turkey)	85	28
Gallus domesticus (leghorn chicken)	58	21
Phasianus colchicus (pheasant)	30	24
Anas platyrhynchos (duck)	60	27
PRIMITIVE NEST SITTERS		
Down; open eyes		
Aquila chrysaetos (eagle)	150	40
Accipiter nisus (hawk)	21	34
Larus argentatus (herring gull)	97	27
SPECIALIZED NEST SITTERS		
Incomplete down or naked; closed eyes		
Agapornis taranta (Ethiopian love bird)	4.2	24
Melopsittacus undulatus (Australian love bird)	2.3	17
Corvus corax (raven)	30.0	20
Sturnus vulgaris (starling)	6.5	13
Agelaius phoeniceus (redwing blackbird)	3.75	13
Passer domesticus (sparrow)	2.8	13
Troglodytes aedon (wren)	1.3	12
Vermivora pinus (warbler)	1.5	10
Vermivora luciae (warbler)	1.0	10 (?)

von Baer more than a century ago, stands at right angles to the polar axis. The remarkable fact that with respect to this *chalazal axis* the blastodisc always is found in an equatorial position, is explained by a further observation of von Baer, namely that the hen's egg is not exactly spherical. The polar axis is the shortest, the chalazal the longest. In the pigeon, Bartelmez finds a difference of 10 per cent. It develops during ovogenesis and is recognizable even in fairly small ovocytes. The large ovarian follicles are pedunculate, with the egg nucleus (animal pole) situated at the base of the stalk.

Von Baer reported also that the *longitudinal axis of the blastoderm* more often than expected lies crosswise to the chalazal axis. Furthermore the embryo of one or two days' incubation usually turns its left side to the blunt end of the shell, i.e., toward the air chamber (Fig. 153). Extensive checking by Lutz shows that about two thirds of the embryos of chicks and ducks conform to this *rule of von Baer*.

Bartelmez is inclined to assume that all three axes are determined already in the ovulating egg, and that exceptional positions of embryos result from imperfect orientation of the eggs while entering the oviducts. Such evidence would seem to indicate that the orientation of the embryos is rigidly predetermined. It was therefore a great surprise when Morita and Lutz found that unincubated blastodiscs (St. 7, 8) if split into two, three, or four pieces are capable of producing several embryos (Fig. 154*b, c*). Ventral as well as dorsal parts of the blastodisc can furnish entire embryos by self-differentiation. Obviously the orientation of the embryonic axes is not rigidly predetermined. Moreover, in the intact disc the dominant organization center inhibits all

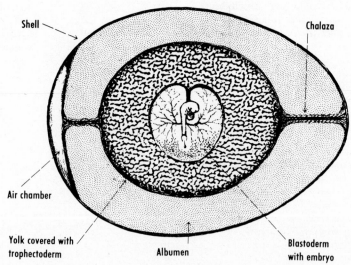

Figure 153.   Typical orientation of a 2-day embryo in accordance with the rule of Carl Ernst von Baer.

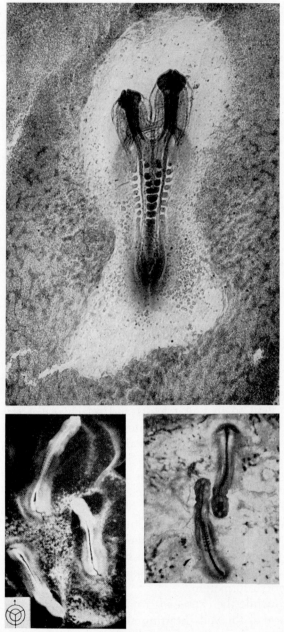

Figure 154.   Twinning in the chick. *Above:* Case of spontaneous twinning; bifurcation of pellucid area still indicates double initiation of embryo formation. *Lower left:* Triplets obtained by splitting of an unincubated blastoderm (St. 7 or 8) in three parts; diagram in lower left shows original main axis and cuts (Lutz 1949). *Lower right:* Normal and accessory embryos, the latter induced by implantation of dead brain substance from a 14-day chick (Morita 1936).

other potential centers. There can indeed be no doubt but that such *inhibitions,* and *antagonisms between competing inductor systems,* play an important role in the harmonious development of organisms.

The extensive literature on spontaneous *twinning in birds* is testimony to the frequent failures of the control mechanism of physiologic dominance. The case shown in Figure 154*a* is a perfect structural counterpart of the amphibian twins derived from overripe eggs (Fig. 50), and the fate map for frog twins (Fig. 52) is essentially adequate also for this double-headed chick embryo. A number of experimental factors increase the incidence of twinning, among them cooling before laying, local or general restriction of oxygen supply, and shaking.

The limits and relationships between *self-differentiation* and *induction* are less well known than in amphibians. Waddington has been able to give evidence of induction, though the necessity of working with blastodiscs cultured in vitro is unfavorable for this type of investigations. He distinguishes two levels, speaking of *evocation* if the reaction is only an unorganized growth, but of *individuation* if the result is a morphologically integrated whole or a part of a unit.

3. GASTRULA TO PRIMITIVE STREAK STAGE: INCUBATION AGE 0 to 14 HOURS (ST. 8–12)

The disc gastrula of unincubated eggs (Fig. 35) is bounded by a *germ wall* which is thickest dorsally and flattens out left and right toward the ventral rim (St. 8, Fig. 152). It is clearly visible in good surface views. In sagittal sections the rounded dorsal and wedgelike ventral blastoporal lips are in marked contrast (Fig. 35*c*). This germ wall is equivalent to that of teleosts and selachians of stage 8. As in the latter, the dorsal part contributes to embryo formation through concrescence, while the ventral remainder becomes a yolk-sac blastopore. However, concrescence of the left and right dorsal germ walls proceeds more rapidly in birds than in fishes. At 11 to 13 hours of incubation it is completed, and the result is a full-length *primitive streak* (St. 11, 12, Figs. 155*a*, 158). Sections show that at ten hours the primitive streak retains the essential character of the germ wall, being still a region of fusion of epiblast and hypoblast (Figs. 155*b*, *c*). In contrast to the events in the fishes, concrescence and complete closure of the embryonic blastopore, *precede* differentiation of the third layer and embryo formation.

In the meanwhile the *extra-embryonic part of the rim* spreads rapidly over the surface of the yolk. Starting about the fifth hour of incubation (discs of 2 mm.), the epibolic growth of the epiblast soon outdistances that of the other parts of the disc. A crescent-shaped zone of *overgrowth* appears, first at the ventral circumference. As it widens, it also advances dorsally. At ten hours (largest diameter about 4.5 mm.) a belt of trophectoderm forms an opaque zone about 1 mm. wide around the embryonic shield (pellucid zone, germ wall, and streak; see Fig. 155). Thus a round *yolk-sac blastopore* with separate epiblastic and hypoblastic borders has arisen, and has become independent of the *primitive streak,* the equivalent of an embryonic blastopore.

Between the tenth and the sixteenth hours, the primitive streak doubles its length. The upper end thickens and becomes the *primitive node.* Invagination movements through the center of the streak are initiated and gradually become more intensive. Consequently a central depression, the *primitive groove,* appears, with a *primitive pit* at its upper end (St. 12, 13*a*, Figs. 156, 157). While the node shifts into the center of the originally circular pellucid area, the lower end of the streak grows until the near-maximal length of about 2 mm. is attained.

Tracing the migrations of a number of marked areas, one observes

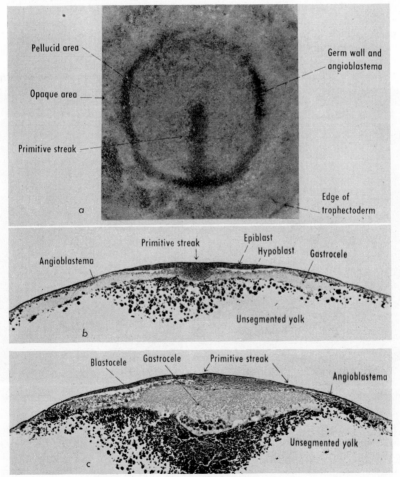

Figure 155. Blastoderm, stage 11; nearly complete primitive streak; 11 hours incubated. *a,* Chick, whole mount. *b,* Sparrow, cross section through lower half; *c,* sagittal section; × 33.

that the top of the primitive streak arises by a rushing together of prospective notochord, the middle part by concrescence and upward stretching of dorsal lip, and the lower part by concrescence and downward
movement of lateral sections of the blastopore lips (Fig. 158). Concurrently, the pellucid area expands and becomes pear-shaped, indicating
that the subgerminal cavity expands with the growth of the embryonic
rudiment (Figs. 156, 157, 161). The lower end of the streak remains
more or less distinctly bifurcated, bordering on, or partly enclosing,
the *cloacal membrane* which forms by the end of this period.

The interrelationship of all these changes, and the direction and extent of the
morphogenic movements, become easily comprehensible if successive stages are
superimposed, as in Figure 158. While the diameter of the blastoderm increases
from about 1.5 to 4 or 5 mm. (first ten hours of incubation), the mid-dorsal germ
wall (mark 1) advances toward the center of the disc. Since the mark stands at
the place of the prospective prechordal plate it is topped by the notochordal
material, which now concentrates axially and thus contributes to the lengthening
of the streak at its upper end. At the same time, parts of the wall to the left

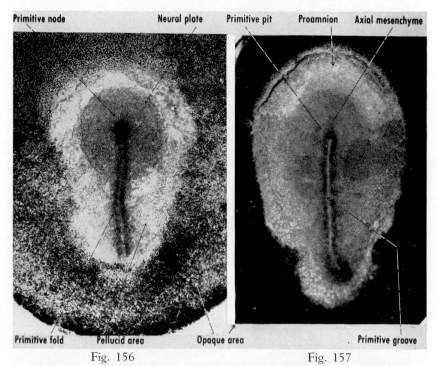

Fig. 156   Fig. 157

Figure 156.   Primitive streak stage (St. 12); chick, 13 hours incubated.
Lower end of streak detaching from opaque area. Primitive groove (beginning
mesoderm formation). Neuroderm a thick plate around upper half of streak; × 16.
   Figure 157.   Early neurula (St. 13a), chick, 17 hours incubated. Lower
primitive streak surrounded by extension of pellucid zone. Mesoderm layer spreads
laterally into opaque zone and upward beyond level of the primitive node; prechordal plate (axial mesenchyme) invaginated; × 16.

and to the right follow the centrifugal (epibolic) movement of the rim, but also approach each other until they meet along the dorsal midline. The path travelled by mark 2 is indicated by a fine straight line. More lateral parts of the germ wall (mark 3) have also moved downward, and now lie close to the lower end of the short streak.

After the eleventh hour, streak formation continues. The lateral ends of the embryogenic germ wall (mark 3) travel the longest surface distance and at 17 hours form the terminal part of the streak. Beginning mesoderm formation carries marks 1 and 2 through the primitive streak into the blastocelic cleft between epiblast and hypoblast. A broken line in Figure 158 indicates the course taken by mark 2 up to the seventeenth hour, while traveling beneath the epiblast. Mark 1 also invaginates and then completes its upward movement; at 17 hours it lies at the tip of the axial mesoderm.

Since the *hypoblast,* which in the gastrula attaches to the prechordal plate, is to form the oral part of the embryonic foregut, it moves up relatively faster than mark 1 of the composite Figure 158. Such outdistancing of the epiblast by the hypoblast has been observed by Spratt in blastoderms cultured in vitro (see also Fig. 164). The advance of the upper streak causes some compression in the pellucid area. In the

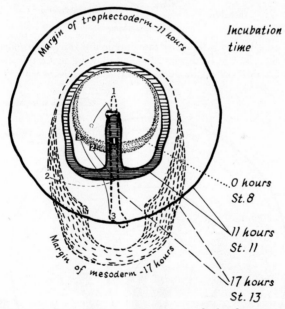

Figure 158.   Outlines of three stages of streak development, superimposed. *Stippled:* Germ wall of the unincubated discogastrula (St. 8); *full lines:* primitive streak, germ wall and edge of trophectoderm at 11 hours incubation (St. 11); *broken lines:* primitive streak, pellucid area, and vascular area at 17 hours incubation (St. 13). *Marks 1, 2, and 3:* Three points at start of incubation (*white*) and after 17 hours incubation (*black*). At the end, 1 and 2 are invaginated and lie at the periphery of the mesodermal layer; 3 lies at the surface in the lower streak; o, on border of prospective neural and notochordal areas, moves into the primitive node (axial rudiment); × 12.5.

epiblast it is absorbed by the thickening which attends the now progressing differentiation of the neuroderm. In the hypoblast, the pressure against the unyielding yolk wall causes the formation of a ruff
of little folds (Fig. 155*a, c*). In whole mounts it becomes visible as
an opaque crescent (Figs. 157, 161). Later it smoothens, and disappears again when the foregut begins to rise (Fig. 168).

An interpretation of gastrula and early primitive streak blastoderms
in terms of areas of prospective differentiation is presented in the *fate
maps* of Figures 159 and 160. The prospective endoderm, being iden-

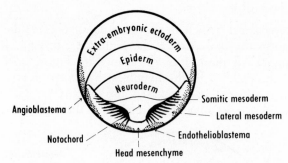

Figure 159.   Map of prospective fate of epiblastic areas; blastodisc of the unincubated avian egg (St. 8). In this and in the following figure the stippled areas of
angioblastema are not part of the epiblast, but lie directly beneath it.

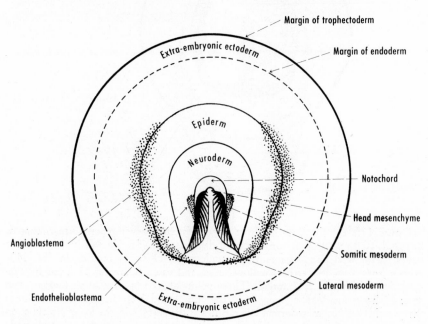

Figure 160.   Map of prospective fate of the epiblast at stage 10 (10 hours incubated). *Stippled:* Angioblastema, beneath the epiblast.

tical with the hypoblast, is not visible in these surface diagrams. However, the angioblastema is perceptible through the transparent epiblasts.

4. NEURULATION
AND DIFFERENTIATION OF GERM LAYERS AT THE PRESOMITE STAGE: INCUBATION AGE 12 TO 20 HOURS (ST. 13)

a. Description. Neurulation slightly overlaps streak formation. It begins at stage 12 when the ectoderm of the pellucid zone visibly segregates into a peripheral, thin *epidermis* and a central *neural plate* (Figs. 155b, c, 156). Epiderm and neuroderm are clearly delimited in the region above the primitive streak, but their boundaries remain rather indefinite along the left and right of the upper primitive streak. The lower end of the plate eventually becomes recognizable near the center of the streak (Figs. 156, 157, 161a, 167a). The extra-embryonic epiblast, beginning at the inner boundary of the opaque zone and assuming mainly a role in the development of the respiratory supply system, is now designated as *trophectoderm;* the extra-embryonic hypoblast becomes the *yolk-sac endoderm.*

Soon after the eleventh hour, the *mesodermal layer* begins to proliferate from the deep lateral borders of the streak. Wedging its way between epiblast and hypoblast, it spreads through the blastocelic cleft (Fig. 161b). After the seventeenth hour it extends laterally and caudally through the pellucid and the vascular areas (Figs. 157, 161a, c). About the same time, a condensation appears in front of the primitive node. This is the beginning development of *prechordal plate, parachordal mesenchyme,* and *notochord* (Fig. 162). The mesoderm advances more slowly in the frontal than in the lateral direction, and for some time the upper part of the pellucid zone remains two-layered (diploblastic). However, during the second day also this so-called *proamniotic region* becomes supplied with mesoderm. The diagrams of Figure 163 summarize the process of mesoderm formation from the primitive streak. During invagination the left and right halves of the superficial mesoblastic plate first fuse, but immediately become reflexed, so that most cells remain on the original sides.

The *primitive node* starts as an aggregation of blastemic cells of axial mesoderm. But during the early neurula stage this blastema disappears from the surface by invagination and the node acquires a superficial layer of neural blastema (Fig. 158o). Thus the frontal rim of the primitive pit is now actually a fold in which a neural surface layer meets with a notochordal middle layer. It is at once the lower end of the prospective neural floor plate and of the notochord; an *axial rudiment.* During the following stages of the neurulation phase (St. 14–17), it descends through the primitive groove laying down the *neural floor plate* between the concrescing left and right basal plates of the neuroderm. At the same time the deeper part of the rudiment produces the

a

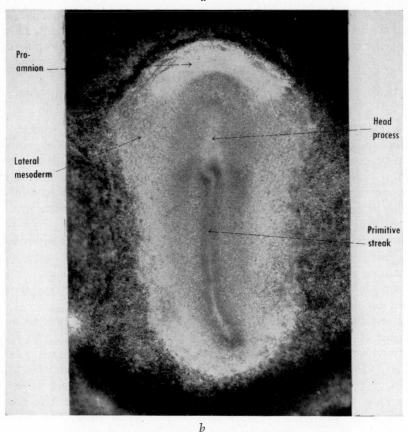

b

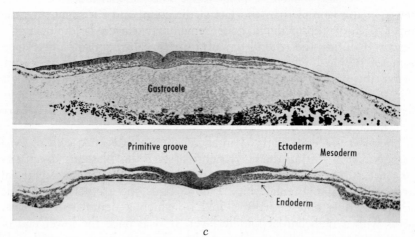

c

Figure 161. Neurulae with chorda process. *a,* Chick, 18 hours incubated
(St. 13b); × 25. *b,* Sparrow, 16 hours incubated (St. 13a); cross section; third
germ layer formation; the mesoderm extends through the larger part of the pellucid
area with periphery apposed to ectoderm; × 50. *c,* Chick, 18 hours incubated (St.
13b); cross section. The mesoderm extends through the pellucid and the opaque
areas; × 50.

notochord, placing it between the separating halves of the somitic blastema, the *somitic cords.*

Toward the twentieth hour of incubation, the *head process* becomes established (Fig. 162). The neural plate above the primitive streak has further gained in length but lost in width, and a *head fold* becomes noticeable. It arises as the combined result of a slight elevation of the upper neural plate and the formation of an undercutting crescentic furrow in front of head mesenchyme and foregut rudiment. These developments mark the beginning of the *folding-off process,* through which the embryo eventually becomes free from the yolk sac.

The origin of the *angioblastema* is not yet completely cleared up. The available facts indicate that in the gastrula the large primordial cells are located in the germ wall along the line of fusion of epiblast and hypoblast (Fig. 159). This location is analogous to that in the amphibian blastula (cf. Fig. 57), and the neurula of the shark (cf. Fig. 134*a*). During primitive streak formation, some angioblastema cells move along with the streak material. They give rise to the endothelia of the heart and of the embryonic blood vessels (endothelioblastema).

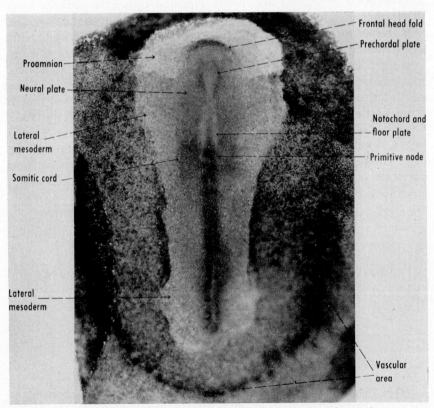

Proamnion

Neural plate

Lateral mesoderm

Somitic cord

Lateral mesoderm

Frontal head fold

Prechordal plate

Notochord and floor plate

Primitive node

Vascular area

Figure 162. Chick, presomite neurula (head process stage), 20 hours incubated (St. 13c); × 22.5.

The remainder scatter along the inner margin of the opaque zone, adhering to the endoderm. Slowly, and at a distance, they follow the centrifugal growth of the yolk-sac epithelium (Fig. 160). After the fourteenth hour of incubation this vitelline angioblastema becomes covered by the outgrowing mesodermal layer (Fig. 161c). In whole mounts the darkly staining blastema becomes visible as a mottled, oval zone about the tenth hour. By the twentieth hour, when the blood islands begin to differentiate, it forms a distinct *vascular area* which encloses the pear-shaped pellucid zone (Fig. 162).

It is a characteristic feature of early avian development that *no part of the prospective mesoderm ever becomes included in the hypoblast.* Even in the head region where the prechordal plate and the tip of the notochord are fastened to the prospective foregut, mesoderm does not arise from the hypoblast. This is in striking contrast to the conditions found in amphibians (Fig. 40). The hypoblast of the avian discogastrula consists, therefore, entirely of prospective endoderm. Between the tenth and the eighteenth hours of incubation, it differentiates into a thin membranous *endoderm of the pellucid area* and a thick *yolk-sac endoderm* of cuboid and partly syncytial cells (Fig. 161c). From the former will arise the *gut* and other permanent endodermal organs.

b. Experimental Analysis of Prospective Fate and Morphogenic Competence of Presomite Blastoderms. The approach of the embryo for operative purposes requires some technical preparations which, fortunately, are facilitated by the gravitational conditions within the egg. The yolk sphere, restrained only by the elastic chalazae and fibroid layers of the albumen (Fig. 17), ascends to near the top of the shell. Often it is advantageous to start operations by withdrawing 1 or 2 ml. of albumen through a small drill hole near the pointed end of the egg. This causes the formation of a little air space under the highest curvature of the shell. If now with the help of a file or a dental drill a

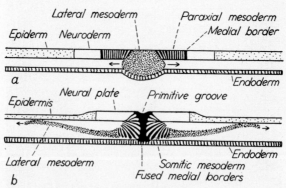

Figure 163. Diagrams illustrating the mode of invagination of mesoblast and of mesoderm formation: *a,* primitive streak stage (St. 11–12, cf. Fig. 155*b*); *b,* early neurula stage (St. 13, cf. Fig. 161*b*).

window of about 1.5 cm. clearance is opened, the embryo immediately becomes exposed. After removal of the covering albumen the blastodisc still lies protected under a tough vitelline membrane. Neutral red or Nile blue marks can be applied across this membrane and also minor surgical interventions may be performed without necessitating its removal. Before replacing the egg in the incubator the window is sealed with a cover glass or a piece of cellophane.

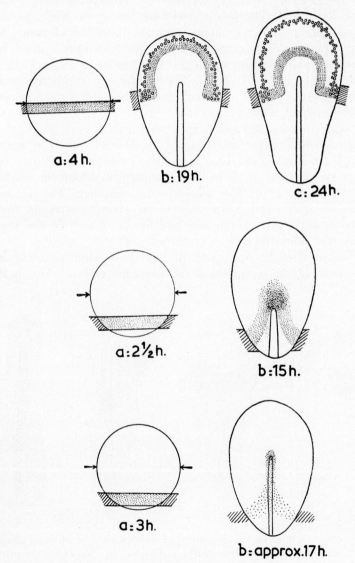

Figure 164. Three examples of movement of Nile blue sulfate marks placed on blastodiscs during the early hours of incubation. Separation of epiblastic and hypoblastic marks in the first case (Malan 1953).

Color marks are applied with thin glass needles, dipped in a solution of the dye in agar, and dried. They are placed on the cleaned vitelline membrane with gentle pressure toward the blastoderm, and removed after less than half a minute. The dye quickly penetrates, staining not only the epiblast but even more densely the hypoblast cells. It attaches itself to some mitochondrial granules.

Malan's series of three gastrulae stained at stage 9, with cross bars at various levels (Fig. 164), shows that the embryo is formed mostly from the dorsal half. The subequatorial bar lies at the border of neuroderm and epiderm. After 19 hours, with the formation of neural folds, the epiblastic mark separates from the simultaneously stained hypoblast cells, the latter piling up in the folds near the edge of the subgerminal cavity (Fig. 164, 24h.). The second and third cases provide the characteristic picture of streak formation with attending movements as described above (Fig. 158).

The same staining method is applicable also at later stages. An interesting coloring effect was obtained by Wetzel, when at stage 12 he placed a mark of Nile blue across the primitive streak just below the primitive pit (Fig. 165). In the subsequent development, forebrain, midbrain, and the entire floor plate remain unstained. The dye is carried into the lateral and dorsal walls of the rhombencephalon and the spinal cord; some gets invaginated and finally is seen in the somites. Caudally, the primitive node is unstained and now lies below the blue mark, proving that the upper one-third of the original primitive streak becomes used in the formation of the 13-somite embryo. This is also a

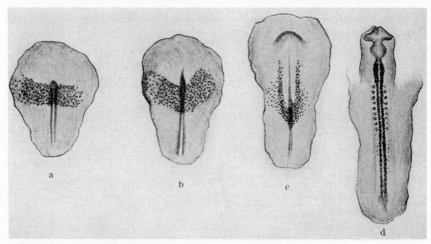

Figure 165.   Tracing the movement of various parts of an early chick embryo by means of Nile blue sulfate marks. *a,* Original location below the primitive node (St. 12); *b* and *c,* intermediate stages; *d,* distribution after 28 hours (St. 15): unstained are forebrain, midbrain, and floorplate of rhombencephalon and spinal cord (Wetzel 1929).

striking demonstration of the *independent origin of the neural floor plate of rhombencephalon and spinal cord, from the axial rudiment.*

Evidence to the same effect is also contributed by Wolff's experiments on localized *irradiation defects.* His instrumental setup (Fig. 166*a*) permits focusing a small beam of x-rays on any desired part of a chick blastoderm. Beams as small as 0.3 mm. diameter have been employed; they may be given any desired shape (Fig. 166*c*). Interpreting the remarkable results one must take into consideration that radiation kills tissues only after a delay of hours, and that secondary effects, healing and restitutions, may occur if the defects are relatively small. The two cases in Figure 166 show that administration of a lethal dose to the primitive node causes degeneration of the axial rudiment within about eight hours. Temporarily also neural differentiation is more or less completely interrupted (Fig. 166*b, d*), which must be ascribed to local irradiation damage. Later, when tube formation is resumed, the floor plate is always missing. Where both notochord and neural tube are much reduced or absent, the left and right somites remain unseparated median blocks. Cross sections at this level (Fig. 166*e*) resemble those through acephalic amphibian embryos without notochords (Fig. 56). At lower levels the somites are paired again, left and right somitic cords being kept apart by the neural tube. The radiation experiment reveals a high *specificity of the axial rudiment,* which is not regenerated from either neural plate or primitive groove material.

Surgical intervention in blastoderms within the egg is fraught with

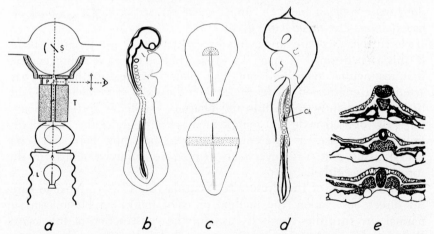

Figure 166. Exposure of the primitive node at stage 12 or 13 to high doses of x-rays (Wolff 1936). *a,* Experimental arrangement (*S,* anticathode, *P,* observation mirror, *T,* perforated lead shield, *L,* candling lamp); *b,* embryo that was irradiated locally at stage 12 (upper *c*); *d,* embryo that was irradiated at stage 13 (lower *c*); *e,* cross sections through lower body region, showing absence of neural floor plate, absence of notochord and often failure of somitic mesoderm to separate in the midplane (axial syndrome); partly redrawn.

difficulties, because even slight wounds result in rents and large gaping holes. The blastoderm seems tightly stretched within the zone of junction, like a drum head. Nevertheless, Wetzel used methods of transection and extirpation to advantage in testing the capacity for self-differentiation of upper and lower areas of primitive streak and neurula blastoderms. The three cases presented in Figure 167 illustrate the effect of transection directly *above the primitive node*. The operations were performed at stages 12, 13, and 14. In every case the upper and lower parts differentiate essentially as they would have normally. The head pieces are complete, with notochord and floor plate stopping at the level of the cut. The lower pieces likewise are provided with neural tubes, floor plates, notochords, and paired somites. In the cases A and C the upper part of the streak splits along the primitive groove. The cross section of A shows that in such cases the neural and somitic elements differentiate in half-embryo fashion. The axial rudiment adheres undivided to one or the other side and consequently only one notochord forms (cross section, Fig. 167).

If the germ is transected just *below the node*, the outcome is quite different, even though all areas prove capable of self-differentiation (Fig. 168D). The lower part lacks neural floor plate and notochord. With the node, the axial rudiment becomes confined to the head piece. For a while it continues proliferating and produces an axial process that projects into the hole. It consists of neural material, neural floor plate, notochord, and a few very small somites. From these observations Wetzel draws the conclusions that *the primitive node has not the function of an inductor,* and that *at the streak stage, regional determinations are already in effect.*

He further ascertains his points by *extirpation of the primitive node.* If this is performed at stage 12 (Fig. 168E), the developing embryo acquires neither notochord nor floor plate, thus exhibiting the characteristic combination of deficiencies of the *axial syndrome.* The midbrain consequently opens into the pharynx (see cross section). Sometimes the excised node was reimplanted laterally under the blastoderm. In successful cases it differentiated into a short notochord and some neural tissue, but was never seen to produce inductive effects in the surrounding epithelia.

c. Fate Maps of the Presomite Neurula (St. 13).   Next to careful direct observation, the method of color marks on blastoderms in normal site furnishes the best basis for the construction of fate maps. But also the transection experiments are helpful, since at the neurula stage, all basic determinations are completed and the germ has become a mosaic of almost non-regulating preprimordia.

The maps proposed by various investigators vary greatly. Those presented here (Fig. 169) are based on reevaluation of basic facts and compromise between conflicting interpretations. Some authors have suggested that possibly, in unin-

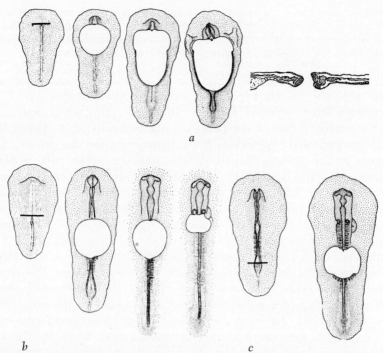

Figure 167.   Testing developmental potencies in the primitive streak of the chick by the method of transection (Wetzel 1936). Embryos transected above the primitive node: *a*, at stage 12; *b*, at stage 13; *c*, at stage 14. The cut (black line) widens into a gaping hole. Upper and lower parts of resulting embryos are essentially normal.

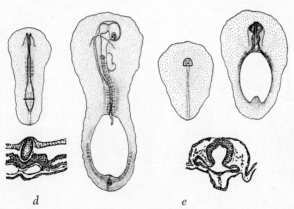

Figure 168.   *d*, Transection below primitive node (St. 14); the axial rudiment grows out into a tail-like structure, consisting mainly of neural floor plate and notochord; the lower part exhibits the deficiencies of the axial syndrome. *e*, Surgical elimination of primitive node at stage 12 results in total absence of floor plate and notochord (Wetzel 1936).

cubated gastrulae (St. 8), a narrow strip of endoderm may reach the surface in the dorsal germ wall. It would later be carried to where the primitive pit forms. Such a condition indeed exists in reptiles. However, it seems fairly definitely established that in birds the endoderm is entirely restricted to the hypoblast.

Compared with stage 10 (Fig. 160), the surface map of the presomite neurula (St. 13, Fig. 169a) shows two major differences. First, one notes a lengthening of the primitive streak, particularly downward into the extended part of the pellucid area. Secondly, it is evident that the larger part of the mesoderm has disappeared from the surface. The addition to the primitive streak differs from the upper part in being bordered by prospective *lateral mesoderm* only. The entire *somitic area* invaginates through the upper half of the streak. At the present stage the upper somitic cords are already in the middle layer and prepare to constrict off the first segments (Fig. 169b). The lower parts are concentrated in the primitive folds or lie in the surface sheet. The prospective tail somites occupy the lowest edge of the area, concentrating toward the border with the prospective neuroderm. The center of the streak toward which the lower ends of the somitic and neural areas are converging may be designated as the *locus of the prospective tailbud*. It should, however, be understood that the prospective tailbud blastemas have not yet reached this location. Only by the end of the second day of incubation (St. 17) will the following meet here and contribute to the formation of the *tailbud*: the axial rudiment,

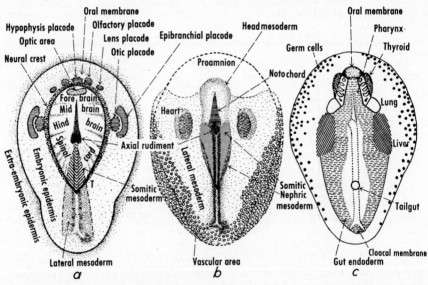

Figure 169. Fate maps of the three blastoderm layers at the presomite stage (St. 13): a, top layer, b, middle layer, c, lowest layer. (These maps and the Figs. 159, 160 are largely based on work by Wetzel, Gräper, Waddington, Pasteels, Willier, Rawles, Rudnick and Spratt.)

the lower corners of the neural plates, and the last invaginated inner edges of the lower somitic areas (Fig. 169a, T). The endodermal rudiment, the *prospective tailgut,* is probably already in place (circle in Fig. 169c). The streak endoderm above this area represents prospective roof of the intestines, and below it, the connecting lamella between tailgut and cloacal membrane. The endoderm adheres still broadly to the streak blastema (white area in Fig. 169c).

At the top of the streak, the *notochordal blastema* is completely invaginated, and the node is covered with neuroderm. The *axial rudiment* (black) has started its downward movement.

A study of the fate maps of the three separated blastoderm layers proves that in essential traits, this stage of bird development corresponds to the early amphibian neurula (Figs. 40d, 44g). The comparison may be facilitated by assuming that an amphibian neurula is slit open, ventrally, from the oral to the cloacal membranes, spread out, and flattened. In the chick, the margin of the embryonic disc along the edge of the pellucid area is the prospective ventral midline; consequently, in the maps, the preprimordia of ventral organs (e.g., heart, liver, thyroid) appear as widely separated paired areas.

d. Culture "in Vitro." Since in the egg the embryo is at best accessible from the surface only, methods of culture in vitro promise more freedom of choice in experimental procedures. Strangeways, Fell, and Waddington developed a method of culturing entire blastoderms in a watch glass, on clotted media made up by equal parts of chicken blood plasma and embryo extract. They were able to keep embryos alive up to three days. However, such embryos reached at best the stage of 20 somites (normally the 40-hour condition) and a length of 2 mm. (instead of 5.3 in normal 40-hour chicks). Thus the rates of differentiation and of linear growth were reduced to about half of the normal. Even though the type of differentiation appears grossly normal, the fact that development is so limited makes it necessary to use caution in the interpretation of observations made on cultured embryos. Having made those reservations, it must, however, be emphasized that the "in vitro" method is a remarkable success, opening up entirely new avenues for the study of the process of early development. How close reactions may be to those observed in embryos "in ovo" is illustrated by experiments of transection, as performed by Spratt and by Waddington (Figs. 170, 171, compare with Figs. 168d and 167c). Waddington, like Wetzel, comments on the fact that in the lower fragment the neural system usually is relatively more defective than the somites. After removal of the primitive node from a stage 13 blastoderm, he obtained a reaction remarkably similar to Wolff's irradiation effect (Fig. 166).

Two advantages resulting from this method are the possibility of studying the progress of development continuously in transmitted light, under the high power microscope, and the easy access to the embryo from the hypoblastic as well as the epiblastic side.

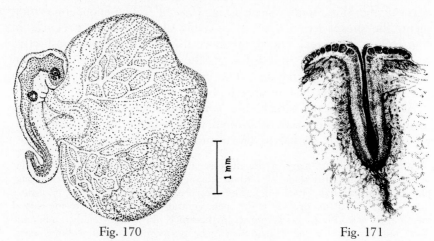

Fig. 170   Fig. 171

Figure 170.   Side view of an incomplete embryo grown from the upper portion of a blastoderm (stage 13), after 55 hours cultivation on a pure albumen extract, saline, and agar medium (Spratt 1947).

Figure 171.   Incomplete embryo from the lower portion of a stage 14 blastoderm grown on the surface of a clot made up by equal parts of fowl blood plasma and embryo extract (Waddington 1952).

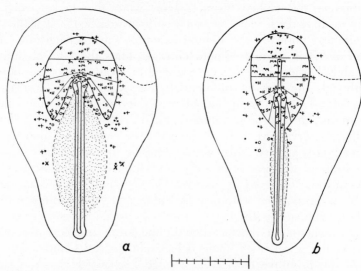

Figure 172.   Chick blastoderms marked with carbon particles. *a*, Primitive streak (St. 12). *b*, Presomite neurula (St. 13b). Signs indicate the prospective fate: finely stippled, areas of epiblastic (non-invaginated) mesoderm; F, forebrain; M, midbrain; H, hindbrain; S, spinal cord; +, epidermis (Spratt 1952).

Spratt found also that on explanted blastoderms, freed of the vitelline membrane, *blood-carbon particles* will adhere solidly to surface cells and, if invaginated through the streak, become incorporated into the cells. They provide much more durable marks than vital dyes and have permitted drafting of fate maps for explanted blastoderms which prove somewhat different from those previously obtained (Fig. 172).

Furthermore, isolated blastoderms are particularly well suited for studies on nutrition, respiration, and enzymatic conditions during early embryogenesis.

e. Chorio-allantoic Transplants.   Better survival of embryonic tissues than "in vitro" may be obtained by grafting. Various sites on young or adult chicks have been tried, but for delicate early blastoderms the best living conditions were found on the chorio-allantoic membrane of eggs, beginning the second week of incubation. Willier transplanted entire blastoderms, while Rawles investigated systematically the morphogenic potentialities of presomite stages by serial transplantation of as many as 18 fragments (Fig. 173a). These pieces may

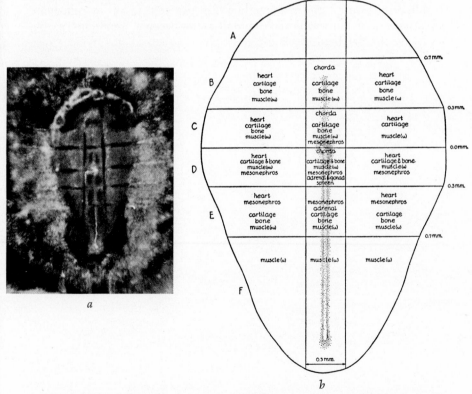

Figure 173.   Localization of organ-forming areas in the chick blastoderm (St. 13) by means of a chorio-allantoic graft: *a,* blastoderm prepared for isolation of pieces; *b,* map listing obtained types of mesodermal differentiations (Rawles 1936).

be left at the implantation site for ten days or even longer. During this time they become differentiated cytologically and histologically, though organ formation is very incomplete. Rawles suggests that mechanical conditions, associated with restrictions in space, might be the limiting factor. In general one notices the beginnings of more than the expected differentiations, but finally the result falls short of that indicated by the fate maps. In the tabulation of mesodermal derivatives (Fig. 173*b*) the spread of "heart" formation is indeed impressive; yet actually no organized hearts, but mostly myocardial nodules, are formed. The method seems best suited to the study of organ differentiation at fairly advanced stages.

f. **Disaggregation and Transplantation by the Vascular Route.** Embryonic tissues may be caused to fall apart into single cells by mechanical grinding or by treatment with alkaline media. Weiss and Andres have shown that such disaggregated cells, injected into extraembryonic veins of a chick embryo of 3 days or older, may settle and become established at various embryonic and extra-embryonic sites and develop into cell clusters, tissues, or fragments of organs of various levels of differentiation. This new method for the testing of morphogenic potentialities of embryonic cells promises to become important particularly also in the field of cancer research.

Chapter 15

Neurula Stages

1. ONE- TO FOUR-SOMITE NEURULAE: INCUBATION AGE 21–24 HOURS (ST. 14)

a. General Survey. In the frequently investigated forms, such as chick, turkey, duck, and various songbirds, somites appear after the twentieth hour at the rate of about one per hour, until the end of the second day. At the beginning of the second day, the center of the upper half of the pellucid area is occupied by the head rudiment (Fig. 175). As many as six pairs of somites contribute to the occipital part of the head, but the first and second disperse early, adding to the general head mesenchyme. In Figure 175 only the second of these *otic somites* is still recognizable. Therefore, the end of the head lies below the fourth and last of the completely free *occipital somites* of the embryo. Frontally, the folding-off process has continued, so that the rostral one-fourth of the head projects above the proamniotic area (Fig. 176a, p, s).

b. The Nervous System exhibits various steps of early differentiation. At the two-somite stage the neural folds are still far apart but at three somites they close in over the midbrain, forming a first short piece of *neural tube* (comp. Fig. 174A and B). At the end of the first day (Figs. 175, 176), the neural plate below the last somite is wide open and lancet-shaped; its notched end is above the middle of the primitive streak. It is broadest at the level of the primitive node (Fig. 176g). From here to its end it is two-pronged, since primitive groove and folds still are formed by a narrow strip of superficial mesoderm. Above the node the neural plate becomes narrower; its edges rise dorsally and

249

form *neural folds* (Fig. 176*e*). The entire *rhombencephalic part* of the primitive brain is a dorsally open trough. The *mesencephalon* and the lower part of the short *prosencephalon* form a nearly straight tube closed dorsally by apposition rather than fusion of left and right neural folds (Fig. 176*b–d*). The frontal part of the prosencephalon, which bends ventrally and covers the upper end of the foregut, is still open (Fig.

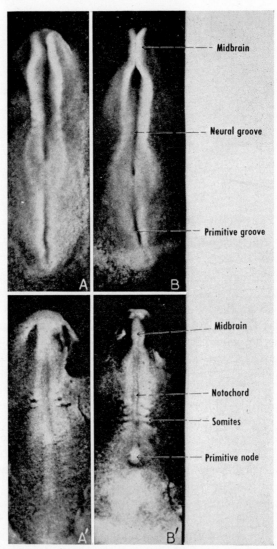

Figure 174.   Dorsal and ventral surface views of two chick embryos at the end of the first day of incubation (St. 14); *A*, with open neural plate and two somites; *B*, with partly closed neural tube (midbrain) and three somites (Streeter 1933); × 15.

176a). The short neural tube thus has an *upper* as well as a *lower neuro-pore* (Fig. 176b).

c. The Foregut has by this time grown into a dorsoventrally compressed pocket (cf. Figs. 175 and 176a–d). It opens into the gastrocele through the *intestinal portal* (Figs. 174, 175). Ventrally below the forebrain, the floor of the gut is intimately applied to the epidermis in the *oral membrane*.

d. The Mesoderm becomes the site of many important differentiations. With the completion of invagination of the notochordal blastema the external elevation of the primitive node disappears. The shallow primitive pit (Fig. 306g, h) now connects with the neural groove (floor plate) as well as with the primitive groove. However, the blastema of the *notochord* forms a knob that protrudes into the gastrocele, in front and slightly to the right of the primitive pit (Figs. 174B', 176g). Comparison of Figures 162 and 175 shows that during the last four hours of the first day, notochord and prechordal plate gain rapidly in length (from 0.6 to 2.75 mm.). The notochord grows mainly at its lower end, through proliferating activity—in the primitive node. The sagittal and serial cross sections (Fig. 176) clearly expose its close embryologic and topographic relationship to the neural floor plate. While the *somitic blastema cords* are segmenting above, they gain in total length at the expense of the upper primitive streak region. During the last four hours of the first day the streak decreases from its original length of 2.2 mm. to about 1.2 mm. The *lateral plates* above the first somite level are partly split into *somatic and splanchnic* sheets, applied to the ectodermal and endodermal layers respectively (Fig. 176). They enclose the primitive *celomic cavities*. The parts of the splanchnopleures that border on the foregut in the region of the intestinal portal begin to thicken and become primordia of the *myocardia* (Fig. 176d). A number of delicate angioblastema cells between these myocardial plates and the foregut endoderm begin to arrange themselves into small vesicles, the primitive *endocardial tubes*. The *vascular area* assumes a spotted appearance through condensation of numerous *blood islands*. The mesoderm-free proamniotic area lies directly in front of the celomic sacs and beneath the free part of the head.

2. FIVE- TO TWELVE-SOMITE NEURULAE: INCUBATION AGE 25 TO 32 HOURS (ST. 15)

a. General Survey. The 12-somite stage is the last one with almost perfectly symmetric arrangements (Figs. 177, 178). The head is folded off down to the level of the mesencephalon. Although all previously differentiated parts of the embryos keep enlarging by general growth, the most characteristic gain in length derives from the addition of new segments. Comparative measurements show that after the twenty-fourth hour, the embryo gained at twice the rate below the mesencephalic border that it did above (Table 10). To the four occipital somites, present at the end of the first day, eight have been added that belong to the upper neck region. Table 9 presents a survey of the metamery of the chick, to which frequent reference will be made during following descriptions. The primitive streak is reduced to less than half its original length. The lower tip of the neural plate and the locus of the tail-bud have moved deep into the extension of the pellucid area. The latter lies now about 3 mm. below its location in the early primitive streak.

b. Nervous System. The *upper neuropore* is reduced to pinhole size, or closed. At its lower end, the long neural tube opens through a funnel-shaped *lower neuropore* into the rhomboid sinus, i.e., the field of the remnant neural plate, walled by neural folds. In the head region the tube is superficially segmented by constrictions which chiefly involve the lateral walls. From the sides of the *prosencephalon* emerge large *optic vesicles*. A pair of thickened and slightly bulging areas in

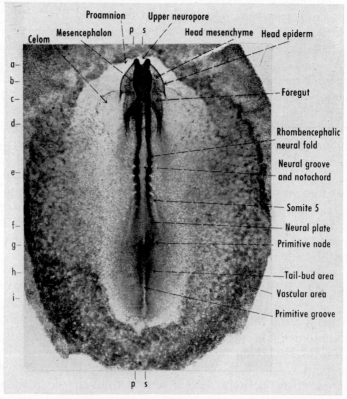

Figure 175.   Chick, 24 hours incubated (St. 14); four free occipital somites; the condensation in front of the first is the dispersing last otic somite. Whole mount; × 16.

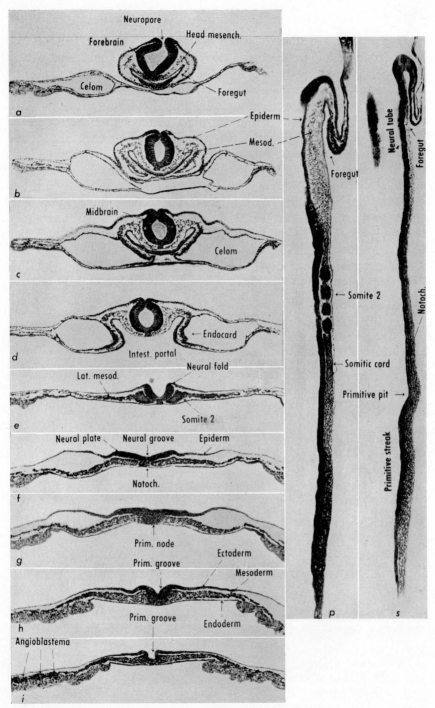

Figure 176. Chick (St. 14), 24 hours incubated; four somites. *a–i*, Nine cross sections; *p*, parasagittal, *s*, sagittal sections. Section planes indicated along the margins of Fig. 175; × 36.

front represent a first step in the development of the *telencephalon*. The second vesicle or *mesencephalon* shows slight dorsolateral distentions which are the primordial *optic bulbs*. A true metameric segmentation is found in the *rhombencephalon*. The first and largest swelling is of a composite nature; from its upper and dorsal wall arises the *cerebellum* (metencephalon), while the remainder becomes the *trigeminal rhombomere*. The second segment is not connected with any of the primordial ganglia. It is followed by the *facial rhombomere* with its pair of facial ganglia, and by the *acoustic (otic) rhombomere*. The thick and slightly concave *otic placodes* (Fig. 178*d*) are connected with this section of the brain tube by cell bridges which later develop into ganglia and acoustic nerves. Further below, at least one more distinct rhombomere is recognizable, the *glossopharyngeal segment*. The vagus region is a fairly smooth tube.

The ganglia and sensory fibers of the *cranial nerves* originate from

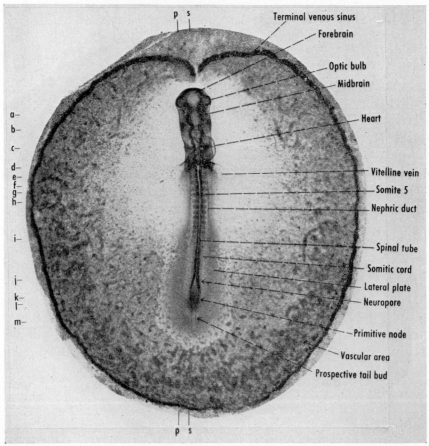

Figure 177.   Chick (St. 15), 32 hours incubated; 12 somites. Whole mount; × 12.

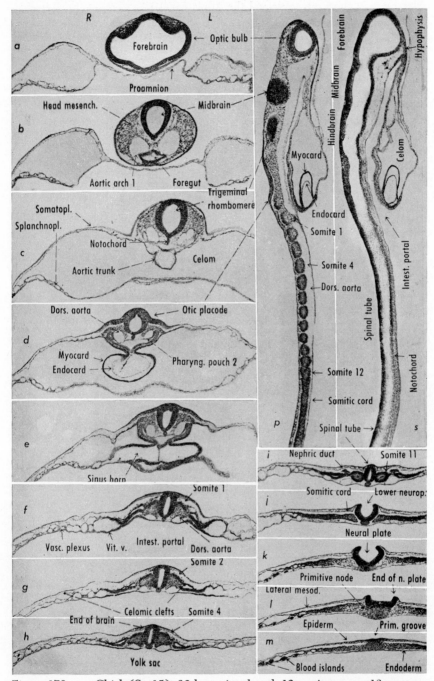

Figure 178.   Chick (St. 15), 32 hours incubated; 12 somites; *a–m*, 13 cross sections; *p*, parasagittal and *s*, sagittal sections. Planes indicated on Fig. 177; × 32.

Table 9

Metamery in the Embryonic and the Adult Chick

NERVES	ORIGIN: CR.	DL.	EB.	VR.	ARTERIES	SOMITES	SEG.	AXIAL SKELETON
	V		V		I ao.			
	VII	VIII	VII	VI	II ao.	(1)		
	IX		IX	VI	III ao.	(2)		
	X		X	XII	IV ao.	1		
Cranial nerves V–XII	X		X	XII	(V) ao.	2		} occiput
	X		X	XII	VI ao.	3		
	XI			XII	pul. a.	4		
	XI			1		5	1	1 — atlas
	XI			2		6	2	2 — axis
	3			3		7	3	3
	4			4		8	4	4
	5			5		9	5	5
	6			6		10	6	6
	7			7		11	7	7
Cervical nerves 1–15	8			8		12	8	8 — 14 cervical vertebrae
	9			9		13	9	9
	10			10		14	10	10
	11			11		15	11	11
	12			12		16	12	12
	13			13		17	13	13
	14			14		18	14	14
	15			15		19	15	15
Brachial plexus	16			16	p. scl. a.	20	16	16 — 7 true ribs, thoracic vertebrae
	17			17		21	17	17
	18			18		22	18	18
Thoracic nerves 16–22	19			19	mesent. a.	23	19	19
	20			20		24	20	20
	21			21		25	21	21
	22			22		26	22	22
	23			23		27	23	23
Crural plexus	24			24	femoral a.	28	24	24 — 8 lumbar vertebrae
	25	furcalis		25		29	25	25
Lumbar nerves 23–30	26			26		30	26	26
	27			27	sciatic a.	31	27	27
	28			28		32	28	28
Sciatic plexus	29			29		33	29	29
	30			30		34	30	30 — 6 sacral vertebrae
	31			31		35	31	31
Pudendal plexus (30) 31–35	32			32		36	32	32
	33			33		37	33	33
	34			34		38	34	34
	35			35		39	35	35
	36			36		40	36	36
Caudal nerves 36–39	37			37		41	37	37 — (5 free) 6 caudal vertebrae
	38			38		42	38	38
	39			39		43	39	39
	40					44	40	40
	41					45	41	41
						46	42	42
						47	43	43
						48	44	44 — pygostyle ca. 6 fused vertebrae
						49	45	45
						50	46	46
						51	47	47
						52	48	
						53		

Axial skeleton bracket groupings: 14 cervical vertebrae (seg. 1–14); 7 true ribs, thoracic vertebrae; 8 lumbar vertebrae; 6 sacral vertebrae; 21–36: synsacrum; pygostyle ca. 6 fused vertebrae, (5 free) 6 caudal vertebrae.

The visceral arches are given the same order numbers as the aortic arches. The first two somites (otic somites) disperse early and are separately numbered.

a. artery; *ao.* aortic arch; *Cr.* neural crest (dorsal roots); *Dl.* dorsolateral placodes; *Eb.* epibranchial placodes; *mesent. a.* mesenteric artery (changes its position during development); *pul. a.* pulmonary artery; *p. scl. a.* primary subclavian artery; *seg.* body segments (same order numbers as spinal nerves); *Vr.* ventral roots.

neural crest and placode cells, i.e., from parts of the primitive neuro-derm, not included in the tubular central organ. At the present stage, most neural crest cells have left their original superficial location and actively migrate through spaces between epidermis and neural tube. Distinct condensations forming dorsal root ganglia for the fifth, ninth, and tenth cranial nerves are recognizable in whole mounts and in sections (Figs. 177, 178c, f, g). As in all amniotes, the acousticolateralis group consists only of the *otic placodes.* At the present stage they are shallow depressions at the level of the corresponding rhombomere (Figs. 177, 178d). *Hypophyseal, olfactory, lens,* and at least three pairs of *epibranchial placodes* appear as slight thickenings in the head ectoderm.

c. Endoderm. The *foregut* opens into the gastrocele through the *intestinal portal* at the level of the second somite, between the sinus limbs of the heart. Two pairs of lateral extensions are the primitive first and second *pharyngeal pouches.* A slight depression in the floor between them is the primordium of the *thyroid gland* (Fig. 178s).

d. Mesoderm. The *paraxial mesoderm* (epimere) consists of 12 pairs of somites and the somitic blastema cords. The first and partly also the second somites are breaking up, adding material to the head mesenchyme (Fig. 178p).

The *intermediate mesoderm* (mesomere) is visible as a pair of slender cords of nephrogenic blastema running between somites and lateral mesoderm (Figs. 177, 178g–i). Primordia of nephric ducts arise from the lateral edges of the cords (Fig. 178i).

In the *lateral mesoderm* (hypomere), the celomic cavities are greatly enlarged. They communicate with each other ventral to the heart and extend upward alongside and to the front of the head, where the am-

Table 10

Changes in Length during Neurulation of Neural System (Prospective or Differentiated) and Primitive Streak

	STAGE 12 P. streak	STAGE 14 4 somites	STAGE 15 13 somites	STAGE 17 26 somites
Neural tube	mm.	mm.	mm.	mm.
Mesencephalon + prosencephalon	0.5	0.7	0.9	1.4
Rhombencephalon + spinal tube	1.2	2.5	4.1	5.7
Total	1.7	3.2	5.0	7.1
Primitive streak				
Above tailbud locus	1.3	0.8	0.33	0.0
Below tailbud locus	1.0	0.6	0.46	0.2
Total	2.3	1.4	0.8	0.2

niotic folds begin to rise (Fig. 178*a–d*). From the base of this bicornuate amnopericardial sac, small celomic diverticula also enter the lateral plates of the occipital and cervical region (Fig. 178*f–i*). In the extra-embryonic area the celomic sacs spread as a system of fine clefts. Through these developments the lateral mesoderm of the pellucid area has largely become split into a *somatic* and a *splanchnic layer.*

The *primitive heart* lies ventrally beneath the gut, at the rhomb-encephalic level. Its early history is illustrated by the Figures 159, 160, 169*b*, 176*d*, 178*c–e*. Starting from the prospective endothelioblas-tema, a pair of endothelial condensations between gut and splanchnic mesoderm first become visible at the four-somite stage. During the early hours of the second day they become tubular hearts and immediately begin to fuse. This union progresses along the ventral surface of the foregut, following the downward movement of the intestinal portal. The bending of the ventricular loop serves as evidence that the tubular heart grows faster than the foregut.

Only the endothelia or inner linings of the circulatory organs are derived from the angioblastema. The enveloping sheaths are simulta-neous contributions of the splanchnic mesoderm that furnishes also the muscle layer of the heart (myocardium). Ventrally, the left and right celomic sacs become confluent; but dorsally they remain separated by the dorsal mesocardium (Fig. 178*d*). At 32 hours the heart consists of a pair of *sino-atrial limbs* originating from the vitelline veins, a *ventricular loop* bent far to right, and a short *aortic bulb* and *aortic trunk segment* (Figs. 177, 178*e, d, c*) which leads into the paired *ventral aortas*. A first pair of *aortic arches* circle around the foregut and con-nect the ventral with the *dorsal aortas*. The latter descend left and right of the notochord, and end in the plexus of blood islands below the last pair of somites.

At 32 hours, the heart and the major blood vessels contain no blood cells. Circulation is not yet established, though irregular fibrillations which start as early as the nine-somite stage in the bulboventricular region produce stirring movements in the fluids within and outside the vessels.

In the *vascular area,* a dense network of richly anastomosing blood vessels and blood islands leads peripherally into a *terminal sinus* (Fig. 177). Other primitive vessels establish connections with the sinus horns of the heart through *vitelline veins.* A further consolidation of vascular elements appears along the shelf between primary and secondary parts of the pellucid area. It approaches the lower ends of the dorsal aortas and prepares for the development of the *vitelline arterial plexus.*

Close examination shows that the vitelline vascular plexus is made up of blister-like small cysts and short tubes which contain *immature blood cells* and aggregations of *hemoblasts.* Apparently the endothelia of the peripheral vessels, as well as all blood cells, develop from the angioblastema of the vascular area. On the other hand, the embryonic vascular material seems to be purely an endothelioblastema.

3. THIRTEEN- TO NINETEEN-SOMITE NEURULAE: INCUBATION AGE 33 TO 40 HOURS (ST. 16)

This stage is characterized by the development of the *full series of cervical somites,* and preparation of the vascular system to the point where regular circulation will soon become possible. Figure 179, by Duval, illustrates adequately the rich development of the *extra-embryonic vascular plexuses,* with easily recognizable venous and arterial main stems. The chorio-amniotic fold grows as a hood over the top of the head. The otic placodes have become deep cups. The head has started to bend and rotate.

Although the neck of the domestic fowl has only 14 vertebrae, one usually accredits 15 nerves and hence 15 somites to this territory (cf. Table 9).

4. TWENTY- TO TWENTY-SIX-SOMITE NEURULAE: INCUBATION AGE 40 TO 48 HOURS (ST. 17)

a. **Extra-embryonic Membranes.** By the end of the second day about half of the yolk sphere is covered by extra-embryonic membranes. The *vitelline blastopore,* formed by the edge of the *trophectoderm,* is

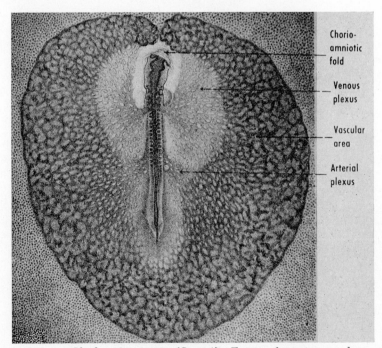

Figure 179. Chick, 18 somites (St. 16). Extra-embryonic vascular system (Duval 1889).

even slightly below the equator, and the *endodermal yolk-sac epithelium* ends near the equator; but the *mesodermal layer* lags, covering a zone around the animal pole only about 15 mm. in diameter (Fig. 153). The extent of the extra-embryonic mesoderm is nearly identical with that of the vascular area which is bounded by the terminal venous sinus. The relative tardiness of the mesoderm is obviously caused by its indirect mode of formation. From the original location in the epiblast it passes through the primitive streak before spreading out.

The free head of the embryo rises partly above the general surface of the egg, but mainly lies in a depression of the yolk sac (Fig. 180).

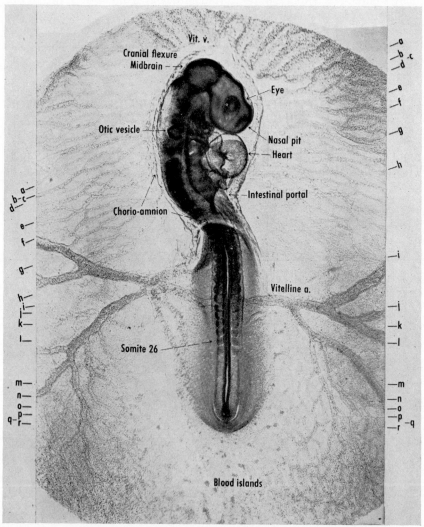

Figure 180.   Chick (St. 17), 48 hours incubated; 26 somites. Embryo and parts of extra-embryonic membranes; × 16.

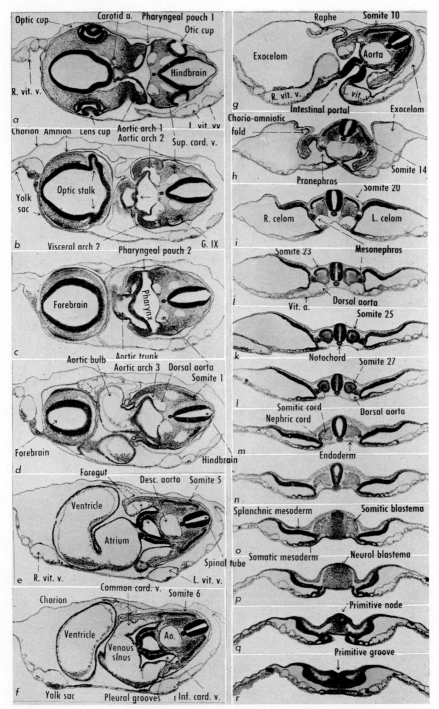

Figure 181. Two-day chick embryo of 26 to 27 somites (St. 17); head more bent than in Fig. 180; *a–r*, 18 cross sections (levels indicated in Fig. 180); × 25.

261

Up to the middle of the second day this hollow is located in the two-layered proamniotic region, and its sharp edge, which early begins to grow over the forehead, consists of trophectoderm only. The rising *chorio-amniotic fold* retains this single-layered condition only during a few hours; in the second half of the day, the expanding celomic sacs enter and provide an inner mesodermal lining (Fig. 181*b, d*). The frontal downgrowth is restricted and ends over the upper cephalic region. From here on, chorion and amnion formation progresses by concrescence of the lateral folds. A suture, the *chorio-amniotic raphe*, forms where they meet (Fig. 181*c–g*). At the end of the second day, the fold covers the entire head, the heart, and part of the neck region (Fig. 180). Its lateral horns reach the level of the twentieth somites.

b. General Morphology.   Chick embryos of 26 somites mark the end of the neurulation phase. They still have a small vestige of the primitive streak (Figs. 180, 181*r;* Table 10). During the last hours of the second day the series of *seven thoracic somites* separate from the somitic cords. The head is entirely free, and the cervical region is partially folded off from the yolk sac. Above the thorax, the embryo has rotated, so that the left side of the head now rests on the yolk sac. The longitudinal axis bends dorsally in the lower cervical region, and ventrally in the upper cervical and mesencephalic parts. Thus a *cranial flexure* develops at the level of the midbrain, and a *cervical flexure* in the rhombencephalon. The concavity of these flexures holds the heart (Fig. 180).

Though development proceeds by terminal addition of body segments, growth is by no means localized but is a very general property of embryonic tissues. While between stages 12 and 18 the primitive streak becomes used up in the production of body segments, the head and all organized segments steadily continue growing (Table 10). Mitotic activity is a fairly general quality of all embryonic cells, even though the rate of cell division shows some regional variation.

c. Nervous System.   All five major divisions of the brain are recognizable on whole mounts and in sections. The *telencephalon* (cerebrum) makes its appearance in the form of slight bulges in the lateral walls of the upper prosencephalon beneath the *nasal placodes* (Fig. 181*b–d*). The *diencephalon* is still the major part of the forebrain. Its optic vesicles have become *optic cups* by a process of invagination. This hollow is largely occupied by the *lens sac*, derivative of the lens placode (Fig. 181 *a*). The *olfactory and hypophyseal placodes* are well defined primordia. The *mesencephalon* has become the site of the cranial flexure through the disproportionate growth of its dorsal walls. In the rhombencephalon a swelling of the upper dorsolateral walls prepares for the separation of the *metencephalon* (cerebellum) from the *myelencephalon* (medulla oblongata). The *otic cups* are open to the outside, resembling the lens sacs (Fig. 181*a*). The primitive ganglia of the trigeminal, facial, and glossopharyngeal nerves are prominent cell aggregations. In the lower *rhombencephalic* and in the *spinal region,* one observes various stages of early differentiation of neural crest materials. The entire neural tube is histologically and cytologically still quite indifferent (Fig. 182).

In the chick, the *lower neuropore* closes at about the 22-somite stage; in sparrows, considerably earlier, at 11 to 12 somites. At two days, the neural tube is connected with the primitive streak by a short solid cord of neural blastema (Figs. 180, 181).

d. Endodermal Development. The foregut is a closed tube down to the level of the seventh cervical somite. Three pairs of lateral expansions, *pharyngeal pouches,* meet with corresponding epidermal depressions, forming three pairs of narrow *visceral membranes* (Fig. 181a, c). Those of the first pair are partly perforated; their rupture precedes that of the *oral membrane* by about eight hours. The first and second pharyngeal pouches meet ventrally in a shallow depression, the center of the cup-shaped *primordium of the thyroid.* Between the upper and the lower intestinal portals, the roof of the *midgut* forms a long and narrow groove; the lateral walls spread far apart, ventrally, and serve as a broad attachment for the yolk sac (Fig. 182, 185).

e. The Paraxial Mesoderm shows a striking progression of histologic differentiation in the caudocranial direction. The somitic blastema cords (Fig. 181m, n, o) are of an undifferentiated mesenchymal structure, somewhat looser than primitive streak blastema (Fig. 181q, r). As the upper ends of these cords condense and divide into somites, the cells along the surface arrange themselves in columnar epithelia (Figs. 181n, 182). The epithelial shell of each of the last three somites is open on the side where the nephric blastema is attached (Figs. 181k, l, 182). Above the twenty-fifth somite, and in older embryos,

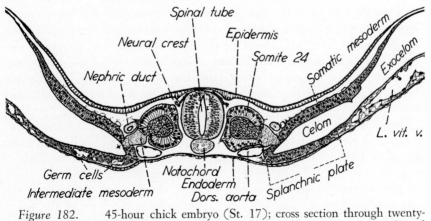

Figure 182. 45-hour chick embryo (St. 17); cross section through twenty-fourth somite level (Witschi 1935); +, attachment of nephric cord to lateral mesoderm marks the border between splanchnopleure and somatopleure; × 60.

the epithelia of the ventromedial surface progressively reassume the mesenchymal character (Figs. 181*d–j*; 185). Jointly with the core of the somites they begin to proliferate, supplying the *axial mesenchyme* that fills the spaces between the organs in the upper half of embryos of this age. Much of it accumulates around the notochord and spinal cord, and later gives origin to the vertebral skeleton. The entire part of a somite which undergoes the mesenchymal transformation is given the name of *sclerotome.* The epithelial remnant further differentiates into the *dermatome,* which lies directly beneath the epidermis, and the *myotome,* which gradually proliferates from the edges of the epithelial cup. In the course of a few hours every individual somite passes through the same changes as those which appear here in a caudocranial progression.

In the head region, the original first and second somites have dispersed entirely into mesenchyme (Fig. 181*b, c*). The four *occipital somites* differentiate essentially like those of neck and thorax. With the separation of the twenty-sixth somite from the somitic blastema cords, the *series of seven thoracic segments becomes complete* (see Table 9).

f. The Intermediate Mesoderm is inconspicuous, and histologically very incompletely differentiated. Above the sixth segment its cells have dispersed, contributing to the mesenchyme of the region. Elements of a *pronephros* are found from the seventh (third cervical) to the sixteenth (twelfth cervical) segments. Their arrangement is segmental and they are given the order numbers of the accompanying somites. The first five pairs (seventh to eleventh segments) are mere vestiges. They consist of isolated short tubules and glomeruli. The latter are little bags of thickened and folded peritoneum enclosing a few mesenchymal cells. The relatively best developed pronephric units are found in the twelfth and the thirteenth segments. Each consists of a glomerulus, a *nephrostome,* and a convoluted *nephric tubule.* The nephrostomes form at the juncture of a nephron with the lateral mesoderm, as funnel-shaped openings into the celomic cavity (Fig. 181*h*). No glomeruli have yet arisen in the fourteenth to the sixteenth segments, though tubules are present. Since the pronephros forms and regresses in craniocaudal order, the first five elements are already degenerating, while the last three have not yet reached their maximal development.

Tubules above the twelfth somite end blindly in the mesenchyme. Further down, the terminal pieces turn caudally and each joins with the next lower one. Thus, on each side, several units contribute a segmental piece to the formation of a common outlet, the *nephric duct.* At the present stage, the paired nephric ducts reach down into the *mesonephric region* (Fig. 182) ending blindly at the level of the twenty-seventh somite. The *mesonephros* is still at a blastemic stage.

g. The Lateral Mesoderm shows indications of further differentiation. In the head region it becomes divided into *visceral segments,* through the development of the pharyngeal pouches. The *mandibular, hyoid,* and *first branchial arches* now are well established and separated from each other; but below the third pouch, segmentation is still indistinct.

The *embryonic celom* prepares for subdivision into the three major body cavities. In connection with the folding-off process in the upper body region, the lateral body walls swing in ventrally and thereby cause the formation of a pair of celomic diverticula between themselves and the dorsal mesocardium. These are the *pleural grooves,* which communicate ventrally with the large *pericardial cavity* (Fig. 181*e*) and caudally, above the lateral mesocardia, with the paired *abdominal* or *peritoneal sacs* (Figs. 181*f*, 182).

h. The Circulatory Organs form a closed, functioning system, whose rapid development during the last half of the second day passes through the following major phases. Some channels of the vitelline arterial plexuses of the previous stage (Fig. 179) become patent and circulation is initiated at the time when the twenty-second somite appears. The attachment of the vitelline network to the dorsal aortas becomes rapidly reduced to one single vessel on each side, at the level of the twenty-second somite. Through these *vitelline arteries* the larger part of the blood carried by the dorsal aortas pours into the network of vessels of yolk sac and then collects in the *terminal sinus* or drains directly through the many branches of the *vitelline veins.* In the extra-embryonic venous system, two main stems have developed which start from the ends of the terminal sinus above the head of the embryo (Figs. 177, 179, 180, 183). On their way toward the heart, these primitive *superior vitelline veins* originally followed the border of the proamnion. In general, they still maintain the original course at the end of the second day, though small branches now spread into the enclosed region which in the meantime has become invaded by mesoderm (Fig. 183). Near the terminal sinus, the left and right systems communicate through anastomoses between such branches. Firmly attached to the surface of the yolk sac, the vitelline veins descend into the hollow in which the head of the embryo lies, and then return the blood to the heart, in front of the upper intestinal portal (Fig. 181*a–g*). The blood of the middle and lower parts of the vascular area is collected by freely anastomosing branches of the superior vitelline veins (Fig. 183). The blood islands and primary plexuses of the lower vascular area still serve as the common source for the formation of arterial and venous vessels and capillaries (Fig. 183).

The heart (Figs. 183, 180, 181*d–f*) is a coiled single tube, indistinctly subdivided into four segments by crosswise constrictions. A shallow sino-atrial groove indicates the beginning differentiation of *venous sinus* and *atrium.* Two deeper circular constrictions mark the borders of the *ventricle* with the atrium and with the *aortic bulb*. From the short *aortic trunk* rise three pairs of *aortic arches* which lead the blood through the first three visceral arches into the *dorsal aortas*. The dorsal root of the third arch lies at the level of the first somite. Between the second and the fifteenth somites, the formerly independent left and right aortas are now fused into a single *descending aorta*. The *carotid arteries* arise from the highest point of the first aortic arches. They supply the upper head region through a finely branching capillary plexus. The returning blood collects in the *upper cardinal veins*. The arterial supply of the lower embryonic body is not yet abundant, and, accordingly, the *lower cardinal veins* are rather small. They unite

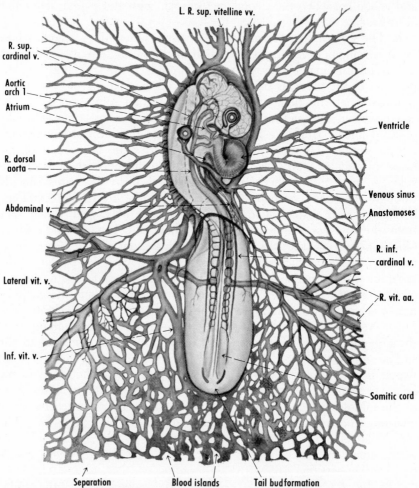

Figure 183. Circulatory system of chick embryo, two days old (St. 17); *R. vit. aa.*, right vitelline arteries; *Inf. vit. v.*, inferior vitelline vein. *Separation* of arterial and venous vessels is in progress but *anastomoses* between fairly large branches persist for some time. × 15.

with the upper branches into *common cardinal veins,* which by way of the lateral mesocardia join the vitelline veins in the *venous sinus* (Fig. 181f). Before this juncture, the common cardinals also receive the short *abdominal veins* from the ventrolateral body walls, which are the homologues of the abdominal veins of amphibians. In birds and the other amniota, they also serve later as *allantoic veins.*

The system of cardinal and abdominal veins, which collect the blood in the somatopleure, arises through branching from the vitelline veins. Their early formation prevents the complete separation of the splanchnic from the somatic mesoderm. The persisting connections, which contain the common cardinal veins, are the *lateral mesocardia* (Fig. 181f). They are to play an important role in the separation of the body cavities.

Chapter 16

The Tailbud Stages

1. FORMATION AND NATURE OF THE TAILBUD

The data presented in Table 10 show that in the course of neurulation the primitive streak steadily shortens and finally disappears. The part above the tailbud locus regresses through invagination in a regular, craniocaudal sequence. The lower part recedes more slowly, finally getting covered with epidermis (Fig. 184).

The *tailbud blastema* is made up mainly by the lower remnants of the neural and somitic areas; its core encloses also the axial rudiment, which continues to contribute notochord and neural floor plate (Fig. 184). If by transection below the node the axial rudiment is removed, a tailbud forms nevertheless, and its growth is normal, except for the absence of the axial elements. The intermediate and lateral mesoderm, as well as the endoderm, contribute only slightly to the composition of the bud blastema. Moreover, at 30 somites, when the bud has gained definite shape, the long somitic cords already contain the material for about another ten somites. Obviously the preprimordia of the body, including the entire sacral region, are laid out before the tailbud begins to proliferate.

The formation of the *hindgut* accompanies that of the tailbud (Fig. 184). At the last neurula stage, the gut endoderm is attached to the epidermis immediately below the streak in a narrow transverse zone that becomes now the *cloacal membrane*. During the formation of the tailbud appears an undercutting groove through which the lower end of the body becomes lifted off the yolk sac. This process also involves the endoderm. A floor of the *hindgut* is formed by the tucked-in endoderm from below the cloacal membrane. The hindgut assumes the shape of a short, dorsoventrally compressed pouch. It opens into the gastrocele through the *inferior intestinal portal*. The upper limit of the hindgut is marked by a recess in its dorsal wall, which is the *tailgut*. It forms where the endoderm is firmly attached to the tailbud (cf. Fig. 169c). For some time, the tip will still follow the downgrowth of the tailbud; this appendix reaches maximal length during the third day of incubation.

The *change in mesoderm formation* from primitive streak invagination to tailbud proliferation has been the subject of many discussions and speculations. As in amphibians it is associated with a shift from trunk to tail production. The neural tube now extends by solid terminal growth and subsequent cavitation. Probably also the somitic cords develop, as in the amphibians, by continued abortive invagination movements, though the process has not been thoroughly studied.

2. CHARACTERIZATION OF STAGES 18 TO 24

The tailbud phase brings to a close the development by segmental proliferation. The speed of somite formation gradually declines and ends in the course of the fourth day of incubation. Consequently the seven stages of this period are best defined by the character of the somites added and by their number in the chick. Certain externally visible changes in other organ systems also are useful in making the definitions more precise. In the following list consideration is given to the developmental status of the visceral arches, the paired appendages, and the extra-embryonic membranes.

STAGE 18: Separation of upper *lumbar somites* (27–30); three *visceral arches* and grooves (or clefts). First appearance of distinct *wing and leg rudiments* as blastemic concentrations in the lateral body walls (Fig. 184a); wingbud at level of fourteenth to twentieth somites; legs from twenty-fifth to the somitic cords. *Amnion* headfold descends to about the twentieth somite. Tailfold rising above tip of tailbud (Fig. 184a). *Age* up to 56 hours.

STAGE 19: *Lumbar series of somites* completed (31–33). *Limb buds* form noticeable elevations; wingbuds slightly ahead of legbuds. *Amnion* folds converging. *Age* up to 60 hours.

STAGE 20: Formation of upper sacral somites (34–36). *Limb buds* (Fig. 186); *visceral arch four* is formed. Chorio-amniotic folds near closure above the lumbar region. *Age* up to 66 hours.

STAGE 21: *Sacral series of somites completed* (37–39). Figure 188. Limb buds (Figs. 186, 189). Distinct *maxillary process* of first arch. *Fourth visceral arch and groove* well recognizable. *Chorio-amniotic pore* closing (chorio-amniotic connection persisting) (Fig. 188). Allantois a small pouch. *Age* up to three days.

STAGE 22: *Formation of upper caudal somites* (40–42). *Legbuds* getting longer than *wingbuds* (Fig. 186). *Maxillary process* of same length as mandibulary. Opercular fold rising on second arch. *Allantoic vesicle begins to protrude. Age* up to 78 hours.

STAGE 23: *Caudal series of somites completed* (43–45). Limb buds (Fig. 186). *Age* up to 84 hours.

STAGE 24: Last somites (pygostyle) forming, not always clearly separated. *Limb buds* (Fig. 186): wings alongside seventeenth to twentieth somite; legs from twenty-seventh to thirty-third somite. Allantoic stalk and vesicle protrude from body of the embryo, turning to the right. *Age* up to 92 hours.

Wings and legs develop very much in the same way throughout the tailbud stages. They arise from preprimordia which Rudnik was able to locate first in presomite neurulae (St. 13), lateral to the primitive streaks. At that time prospective wing and leg of the same side lie close together, possibly in one continuous band. The fact that this extends even into the pellucid area below the streak suggests that the lower

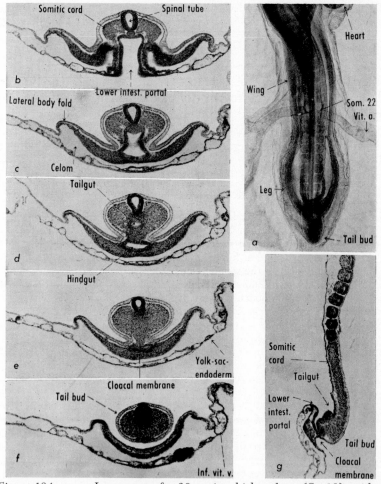

Figure 184.   *a,* Lower part of a 30-somite chick embryo (St. 18), with tail-bud; × 12. *b–f,* Cross sections through a similar embryo at levels indicated in *a;* × 35. *g,* Parasagittal section through the lower part of a sparrow embryo of similar stage; × 32.

part (prospective legs) derives from mesoderm invaginated through the lower half of the streak. At any rate, at stage 18 the limb buds arise as condensations of the lateral plates. The longitudinal orientation of the first ridges is maintained later by the base of the buds. This dimension is usually called the width of the bud. Its length is the distance from the base to the apex. Throughout the tailbud stages the width exceeds the length. At stage 25, i.e., in fully developed embryos, the buds are about equally long and wide (Fig. 186). During the second day the wing is slightly larger than the legbud, but the relationship becomes reversed early in the third day.

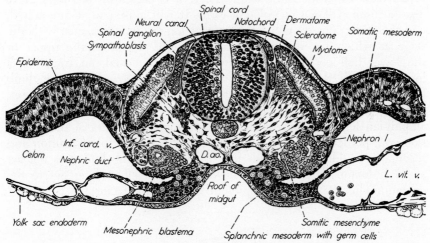

Figure 185.   Cross section through twenty-second somite of a 50-hour embryo (St. 18) of the blackbird (*Agelaius*) (Witschi 1935); × 120.

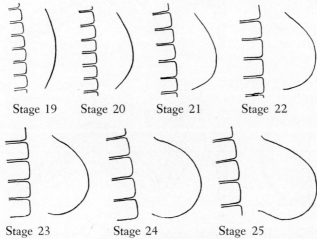

Stage 19   Stage 20   Stage 21   Stage 22

Stage 23   Stage 24   Stage 25

Figure 186.   Stages of limb-bud development during the fourth day (Saunders 1948).

The *capacity for self-differentiation of early limb buds* and of their prospective preprimordia has been thoroughly tested by many investigators. The most successful methods employed were isolation in tissue culture (Strangeways and Fell), and transplantation into the celom of another embryo three days old or slightly older (Hamburger, Rudnick). All experiments give evidence of a high degree of determination, even as early as the first neurula stage (St. 13). Wing and leg character are from the beginning immutable. It is possible that even the three major axes are determined that early.

An important role of the *apical epidermis* of the limb buds was revealed by experiments of Saunders. If it is peeled off at stages 21 to 24, the limb will not completely form. It will appear as if amputated, and the stump (base) will be shorter or longer, in accordance with the stage at which the operation was performed. If either the upper or the lower half of the cap of a wingbud is removed, an upper or a lower sector of the wing will be missing (Fig. 187). The avian limb buds thus exhibit not only an extreme example of *mosaic development,* but also the *near-absence of the faculty of restitution.* In comparison, amphibian leg development shows a considerable lability of determination and, particularly in salamanders, a high capacity for restitution and regeneration. The apical epidermis of the avian limb bud does not act as an inductor—determinations having been in effect long before the operation—but it seems to represent a necessary factor for continued

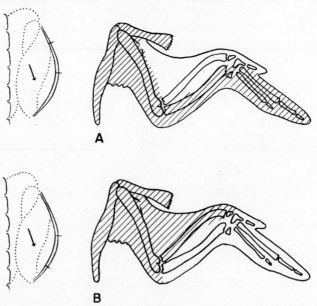

A

B

Figure 187.   Role of apical epidermis in the development of the wing (Saunders 1948). Removal of indicated piece at stage 20 (buds at left) results in absence of white area in the developing wings.

development of the subjacent mesodermal blastema of the bud. Sections show that the apex consists of columnar cells which rise in a high lamella (Figs. 189, 192).

3. THE TAILBUD EMBRYO OF 39 OR 40 SOMITES: INCUBATION AGE 3 DAYS (ST. 21-22)

a. **Extra-embryonic Membranes.**   By the end of the third day, all the four extra-embryonic membranes which are characteristic for avian development have made their appearance. *Trophectoderm* and *yolk-sac endoderm* cover nearly three fourths of the surface of the yolk sphere. The mesodermal zone has an average diameter of about 20 mm. Through splitting of the mesoderm into splanchnic and somatic layers, with consequent expansion of the exocelom (Fig. 182), the trophoblast changes into a double system of envelopes. The inner membrane, consisting of endoderm and splanchnic mesoderm, becomes the *yolk sac;* the outer layer, made up of trophectoderm and somatic mesoderm, gives origin to both *chorion* and *amnion.* The yolk sac is well supplied with blood vessels (vitelline veins and arteries, Fig. 188*b*), while chorion and amnion are not vascularized (Fig. 188*a*). This distribution arises as an immediate consequence of the location of the primitive angioblast between mesoderm and endoderm.

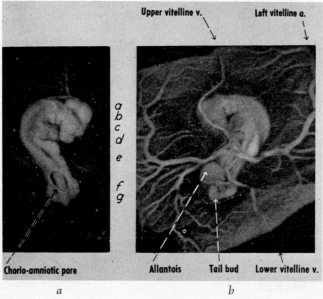

Figure 188.   Sparrow embryo, tailbud stage, near end of third day of incubation (St. 21). *a,* View across the chorion; in the chorio-amniotic pore four to five pairs of somites are still directly visible. *b,* View across the yolk-sac epithelium; the ventral edge of the amnion (umbilicus) is visible; caudally it covers part of the allantois; × 8.

Early in the third day, a semicircular *chorio-amniotic fold* rises in
the clear zone below the tailbud. Gradually it covers the caudal part
of the embryo. When upper and lower folds meet, an oval *chorio-
amniotic pore* forms over the lower back of the embryo (Fig. 188*a*). In
34-somite embryos (total length 7 mm.) this opening extends from the
twenty-second to the thirty-third somite. Its longitudinal diameter
measures 1 mm. During the second half of the third day, the pore
becomes rapidly smaller, and closes about the 40-somite stage, by formation of a thick plug of trophectoderm. Closure occurs at the level of
the twenty-ninth somite. The *chorio-amniotic raphe* finally reaches from
the fifteenth to the thirty-fourth somite, passing through the *chorio-
amniotic stalk* (Fig. 189*f*, *g*). From it, the amnion spreads around the
embryo to the ventral rim of the somatopleure of the embryonic body

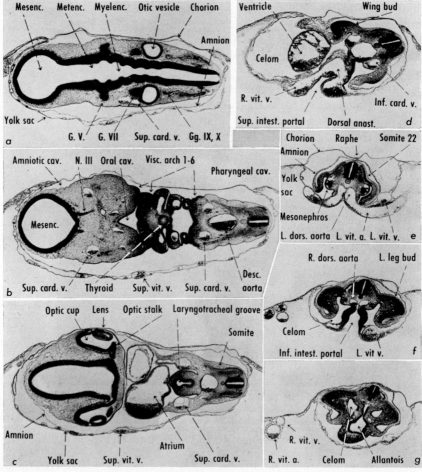

Figure 189.   Chick embryo, 39 somites (St. 21), 72 hours incubated. 7 Sections
at levels indicated in Fig. 188; × 16.

(Fig. 189*d–g*). The oval attachment line becomes the border of the *umbilicus* (Fig. 188*b*).

The *allantois,* fourth of the fetal membranes, arises during the third day, from the floor of the hindgut (Figs. 188*b*, 189*g*). It is a urinary bladder, still contained within the embryo, but preparing to grow through the umbilicus into the extra-embryonic celom. Its wall, like that of the yolk sac, is made up of an inner endodermal epithelium and an outer layer of splanchnic mesoderm.

Four *extra-embryonic cavities* arise together with the extra-embryonic membranes. The *amniotic cavity* is entirely walled by ectoderm; it contains the amniotic fluid. The *yolk-sac cavity,* still open on the vegetal pole side, is endoderm-lined and filled with yolk. The small *allantoic cavity* is likewise endodermal, but filled with allantoic fluid. This fluid is excreted by the kidneys, and consequently is the urine of the embryo. The extra-embryonic part of the celom, or exocelom, goes also under the designation of *chorionic cavity;* it lies within the mesoderm and contains the chorionic fluid.

b. General Morphology. The major changes in body shape that occur in the course of the third day are related to the rapid growth of the head, the proliferation of the tailbud, and the progressive detachment of the body from the yolk. The upper intestinal portal now lies at the sixteenth somite and the lower portal at the twenty-ninth. This permits the sinistral rotation of head and cervical region, and also of the free sacrocaudal end of the body. Even the thoracolumbar trunk, which is still firmly attached to the yolk, tilts slightly to the left (Figs. 188, 189). The increased ventral flexion in the cervical region brings the rhombencephalon into a transverse position above the aortic arches. The *cranial flexure* has become a sharp angle and brings the forehead to rest against the heart. The wing and limb buds are easily recognizable prominences.

During the third day many organs begin to differentiate which gain characteristic shape and appreciable size only at the fourth day. Therefore, in connection with the following descriptions, reference should be made to Fig. 197, which represents a reconstruction of the 100 hour embryo. It shows the organized structures that develop from the rudiments of the third day.

c. Nervous System. The telencephalic rudiments begin to assume hemispheric shape. Their proximity with the *olfactory cups* is plainly visible in Figure 188*a*. The eyes are large, but histologically little differentiated (Fig. 189*c*). Since the *two-layered retina* arises from the transformation of the optic vesicle through invagination from the ventrodistal side, it has temporarily the shape of a spoon. But soon the edges of the bowl grow ventrally around the attachment of the stalk. At the end of the third day the *cup* is complete except for a narrow cleft, which extends from the stalk to the ventral rim; this is the *choroid fissure.* The opening of the cup holds the flat and hollow lens.

The *hypophyseal* and *olfactory placodes* are cup-shaped depressions, and the *lens* and *ear placodes* have become closed vesicles, completely detached from the surface ectoderm. Sections cutting frontally through the hindbrain give a good picture of the segmental character of this region (Fig. 189*a*). The cranial and upper spinal *ganglia* exhibit various stages of histologic differentiation; some are connected with the central nervous system by bundles of primitive nerve fibers. In the medulla and the spinal cord, a *mantle layer* becomes distinguishable with histologically differentiated neurons. Axons begin to grow out, initiating the formation of peripheral motor nerves. Some darkly staining neuroblasts aggregate along the dorsolateral surfaces of the dorsal aortas, forming a pair of *primary trunks of sympathetic ganglia* (Figs. 185, 194).

d. Endodermal Organs.   The *oral membrane ruptures* early in the third day. Since it was not located at the end of the foregut, but on the ventral side, the oral cavity extends rostrally into a small pouch, the *preoral gut.* The first two *pharyngeal pouches* open to the outside through narrow slits or pores, and the closing membrane of the third pouch is very thin. The fourth pouch also reaches the epidermis; it has a caudal recess, the common vestige of the fifth and sixth pouches. The primordium of the *thyroid* gland projects out from the floor of the pharynx. It has the shape of a short tube or flask that opens at the ventral confluence of the first and second pouches. Below the last pair of pouches, the pharynx is laterally compressed. Its narrow ventral part becomes the *laryngotracheal groove,* and ends in a pair of small sacs, the *lung buds.* The dorsal, *esophageal part* leads into a short, slightly extended *stomach.* The foregut ends with the *duodenal segment* at the upper intestinal portal. It is encircled by the left and right vitelline veins, and their dorsal and ventral anastomoses (Fig. 189*d*). In front of the gut, i.e., on its ventral surface, the vitelline veins form a common wide duct, the venous meatus, which opens into the venous sinus of the heart. It is here that the *hepatopancreatic system* develops. At the present stage it consists of a small *dorsal pancreatic,* and two larger *ventral hepatic evaginations* of the duodenal gut. The latter grow dorsally and ventrally around the ring formed by the vitelline veins. According to their position, one distinguishes a dorsocranial diverticulum and a ventrocaudal diverticulum. Both branch out into an anastomosing system of *hepatic cords,* which enclose the venous meatus, and even part of the venous sinus, like a loosely woven basket. The cords also push toward the lumen of the meatus and thus become covered with venous endothelium. Through these developments, the peripheral meatus becomes transformed into a labyrinth of sinusoid recesses and passages.

The *hindgut* receives the nephric ducts, and thus becomes a *cloaca.* The *allantois,* which projects from its floor, is an endodermal pocket, about 0.5 mm. deep, surrounded by a thick, richly vascularized layer of splanchnic mesoderm. From its place of origin, it turns upward and to the right. Still mainly confined to the lower right body cavity, it also protrudes slightly into the extra-embryonic celom (Figs. 188*b*, 189*g*). The lateral and caudal mesoderm of the allantoic neck fuses broadly with the somatopleure, through which the primitive allantoic arteries descend. The *tailgut* is in process of disintegration. At this stage it usually consists of a fairly well preserved terminal vesicle and a cord of degenerating endodermal cells, invaded by phagocytes. In the chick and many other birds (duck, pheasant, redwing) degeneration and phagocytosis are not restricted to the tailgut, but extend also to the dorsocaudal cloaca up to the level of the thirty-third somite. Temporarily, a wide gaping hole forms around the place where the tailgut had been attached. It closes again during the latter part of the fourth day. This temporary cloacal window varies in size according to species; it is especially large in the common fowl, but apparently does not occur in the ostrich, the tern, and the sparrow.

e. Paraxial Mesoderm.   It has already been mentioned that not more than one or two of the present 40 somites may have arisen from the tailbud. This conclusion gains support from observations made on the "tailless" chicken (Du Toit and Zwilling). The tail rudiment of embryos of this peculiar "rumpless" breed degenerates during the third and fourth days of incubation. Adult specimens have 35 vertebrae. This agrees with the contention that the tailbud normally produces only the somites below the sacral series (Table 9).

In the cervical and occipital regions, histologic differentiation has progressed further. The dermatomes are actively proliferating mesenchyme, which initiates the formation of the corium layer of the skin (Figs. 185, 189*c, d*). Many cells of the myotomes are transforming into cross-striated muscle fibers.

f. Intermediate Mesoderm.   The *pronephros* is near the end of its development. Some segments have fully differentiated glomeruli, supplied with small arteries. Their tubules are in communication with the cloaca by way of the *nephric ducts*. Since the *vesica* (allantois) contains some fluid, a degree of excretory function seems to have become established. Possibly only water is passed at this early stage. The first pronephric element is now located at the ventromedial edge of the ninth myotome. It consists, on each side, of a short unconnected tubule. The next two segments are also isolated, but in addition to tubules, they have vestigial glomeruli. The fourth to the seventh segments (twelfth to fifteenth somites) are fairly complete in composition, and connect with the nephric duct. The eighth segment is transitional, showing some mesonephric features.

The *mesonephros*, therefore, begins at the level of the sixteenth somite. Mesonephric tubules in various stages of histologic differentiation are found as far as the twenty-seventh somite (Figs. 185, 194). From here on, cords of mesonephric blastema run alongside the nephric ducts, tapering off toward the thirty-third somite. The *nephric ducts* open into the cloaca just below the thirty-sixth somite. The most obvious structural differences between pronephros and mesonephros are the absence in the latter of nephrostomes and the inclusion of the glomeruli in *renal corpuscles*. Transitional conditions with regard to these two characters occur in the first few mesonephric nephrons.

g. Lateral Mesoderm.   During the third day of incubation the primordia of wings and legs make their appearance. In fact, slight swellings in the somatopleures between the fifteenth and eighteenth somite levels are noticeable even in serial sections of embryos from the end of the second day. One day later the wingbuds are considerable aggregations of blastema cells covered with epidermis, and reach from the fifteenth to the twentieth somites. The hind legs have a slightly later start, but by the end of the day, they equal the wingbuds in size. They are located ventrolateral to somites 26 to 32. Processes growing out from the ventral edge of the somites reach the base of the four buds, but do not enter (Fig. 189*d–g*). All four buds are abundantly vascularized but not yet innervated.

h. Circulatory System.   In the course of the preceding development, the heart has shifted from the upper rhombencephalic into the cervical region. This movement is accompanied by a *change of aortic arches,* lower ones being added as the highest two regress. At the present stage, the first arch has become discontinuous. Its ventral root persists as a part of the *ventral carotid artery.* The second arch is slightly reduced. The *third one is now the largest of the series.* A pair of fourth arches become added toward the end of the third day (at the 36-somite stage). The fifth and sixth arches and the pulmonary vessels, while not individually differentiated, are contained in the *vascular plexus* of this region.

The *vascularization of the wingbuds* was studied in great detail by Evans. Early in the third day, the *abdominal veins,* branches of the common cardinals, ascend through the lateral body walls, up from the region where the wingbuds begin to form (Fig. 183). Here they emerge from a meshwork of small vessels, the *primary body wall plexus.* Into this plexus grow arterioles from the nearby descending aorta, and venules from the inferior cardinal veins, at the level of somites 15 to 19. These *primitive subclavian vessels* increase rapidly in number. At first they are irregularly arranged. Toward the end of the third day, a semblance of segmental arrangement is attained, because the arterial branches that originate near the roots of the dorsal intersegmental arteries enlarge while the remainder regress. As a consequence of its mode of origin, the wing plexus drains through the cardinal as well as the abdominal veins.

In the buds of the hind legs, a *plexus* similar to that in the wings develops. The *sciatic and the allantoic arteries* have common roots, and it was mentioned that in the broad umbilical adhesion the latter cross over from the somatopleure to the allantois.

Important changes in the *venous system of the yolk sac* occur toward the end of the third day. The terminal sinus drains mainly through an *upper* and a *lower vitelline vein,* both of which are branches of the *left* main stem of vitelline veins. The lower branch is a new vessel while the upper one is derived directly from the left member of the pair of primitive superior vitelline veins (cf. Figs. 183 and 188*b*). The right member persists only as a small branch of the right lateral vein. The new *lateral branches of the vitelline veins* closely follow the ramifications of the left and right *vitelline arteries.* They collect much blood directly from the arterial capillary plexuses, though some of their branches originate from the terminal sinus (cf. Fig. 200). The lowest ramifications of left and right vitelline veins form an anastomosing plexus covering the yolk sac around the caudal umbilical fold as well as the urinary vesica (allantois) and the ventral surface of the cloaca.

The formation of dorsal and ventral *anastomoses between the left and right vitelline veins* was mentioned in connection with the hepato-pancreatic development. The vitelline as well as the cardinal veins empty into the *venous sinus.* Only the small and short *pulmonary vein* opens directly into the atrium.

The *tubular heart* is now strongly bent so that the ventricular loop forms its lowest, and the atrium its highest apex.

4. THE COMPLETE EMBRYO: INCUBATION AGE 4 DAYS (ST. 25)

a. General Morphology. Though physiologically not practicing branchial respiration, the embryo has acquired the structural type of young fishes and amphibian larvae of stage 25 (Fig. 190). The *visceral arches* have attained the peak of their primitive development. The *mandibular arch* is sharply bent, with *maxillary* and *mandibular processes.* The *hyoid arch* is equally prominent; the opercular fold, rising from its lower edge, partly covers the third arch (Fig. 192*b*); dorsally above its base is located the otic vesicle. Of *branchial arches,* the third and the fourth are easily visible; the fifth remains rudimentary and the small sixth lies hidden under the *cervical fold* which rises from the upper cardiac swelling. *Ephemeral gill buds* are noticed most often on the second and the third visceral arches. Though physiologically useless, they are of interest from the viewpoint of vertebrate evolution.

The curved *tail* contains about 12 somites. The *paired appendages* are flat paddles, fully as long as wide, and are distinctly reminiscent of paired fins of fish embryos (cf. Figs. 190, 136, and 141).

b. Rotation. The embryo, now nearly free from the yolk sac, has turned completely on its left side. The tubular *yolk stalk* is its only persisting attachment. It originates from the midgut. Entering the *umbilicus,* it turns left, and widens into the yolk sac (Fig. 192*e, f*). The *allantoic vesicle* protrudes through the umbilicus into the extra-embryonic celom (chorionic cavity). Turning to the right, it reaches the chorion, and thus approaches the shell membrane (Figs. 190, 197).

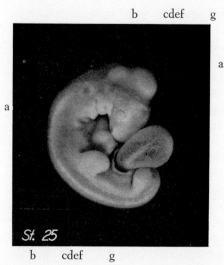

Figure 190.   Sparrow embryo, about 50 somites, four days incubated; it has completely turned on its left side; allantois, protruding through the right half of the umbilicus, with right allantoic artery; × 9.

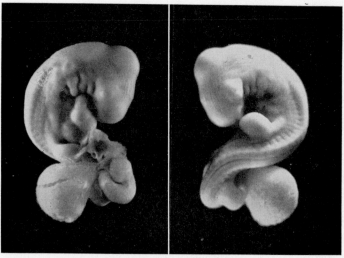

Figure 191.   Embryo of the redwing blackbird (*Agelaius phoeniceus*), incubated four days at higher than optimal temperature. *Malposition:* Yolk sac as well as allantois turned to the right. Body twisted below the twentieth somite; × 9.

The mechanism of normal sinistral rotation of the embryo is easily upset by environmental factors, especially by high incubation temperatures. Up to the beginning of the third day, dextral rotation may produce almost a mirror image of the normal arrangements. However, after the appearance of the tailbud, the outgrowing lower part of the body rotates sinistrally. Consequently, by the end of the fourth day the back has become twisted into a double coil, and both yolk stalk and allantois are bent to the right (Fig. 191). A comparison with normal embryos shows that the asymmetry of the heart is not affected by dextral rotation of the upper body. In either case, the aortic bulb lies on the right side. Abnormally turned embryos suffer a high mortality between the third and the fifth day of incubation. Those surviving often are unable to hatch because of *malposition;* the tip of the beak usually comes to lie under the left instead of the right wing.

c. Nervous System.   The *brain* (Figs. 197, 238*a, b*) has attained a stage of development which may be characterized as the primitive vertebrate type. Its general morphology resembles that of adult amphibia and of fully developed mammalian embryos, particularly in the prevalence of the brain stem and the small size of cerebrum and cerebellum. It differs from the former by the still relatively undeveloped condition of the telencephalon, which is not yet connected with the olfactory organs, and from the latter, by the very large size of the eyeballs and the mesencephalic optic lobes. This comparison refers only to the gross appearance. In regard to histologic differentiation and functional capacity, the brain of the amphibian larva of stage 25 has advanced far beyond that of the four-day chick embryo.

The five major parts of the brain are easily recognizable, even in total views of embryos (Fig. 190). The *telencephalon* or *cerebrum,* which arose as a pair of evaginations from the prosencephalon, has attained a considerable size (Fig. 192*d, e*). Its cavities, the first and second ventricles, communicate through a wide foramen with the central cavity of the brain. The *terminal lamina* serves at the same time as a frontal wall of the third ventricle and a link between the hemispheres. In the *diencephalon* starts the differentiation into *thalamus, hypothalamus,* and *metathalamus* (Fig. 238*a, b*). The tube-shaped *epiphysis* projects from its dorsal roof, while its floor deepens into the *infundibulum.* The *basal plates* arise as a pair of distinct swellings at the left and the right of the floor of the diencephalon; they continue through the cervical flexure of the mesencephalon into the rhombencephalon, and enter the spinal cord.

In the base of the *mesencephalon* are two lens-shaped thickenings which contain ganglia cells of the third or oculomotor nerve (Figs. 192*c*, 197). The *optic lobes* are now conspicuous prominences.

The rhombencephalon is divided into *cerebellum* or metencephalon, and *oblong medulla* or myelencephalon (Fig. 190). In sections (Fig. 192*a*), its neuromeric construction is still recognizable. The first segment is conspicuous because of the size and massive development of its walls; it includes the primordia of pons and cerebellum. The roof plate of the medulla is very broad and thin, the floor plate narrow. The lateral walls are thick and longitudinally subdivided by the *limiting sulcus* into dorsolateral or *alar plates* and ventrolateral or *basal plates* (Fig. 192*b*).

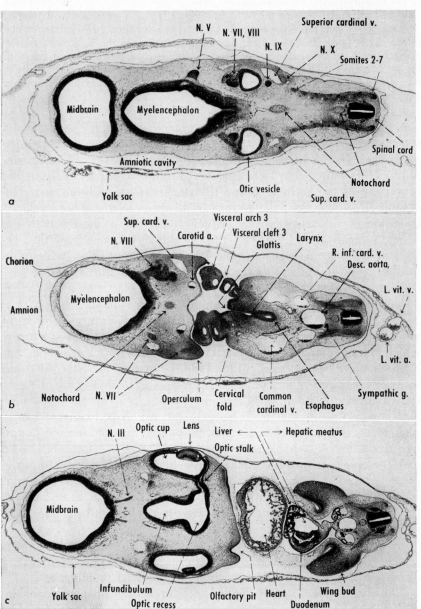

Figure 192. Chick embryo, 96 hours incubation, about 52 somites (St. 25). Approximate direction of sections indicated in Fig. 190; ×18.

The *spinal cord* is a smooth tube, gradually tapering off toward the tip of the tail (Fig. 197). It terminates as a small fibrous remnant in connection with the notochord. The neural cavity vanishes below the last recognizable somite. The tail region of the cord is still gaining slightly during the fifth day.

The *olfactory pits* have gained in depth through the elevation of surrounding tissues. Thus, the sensory epithelia which alone are derived from the olfactory placodes become removed from the surface

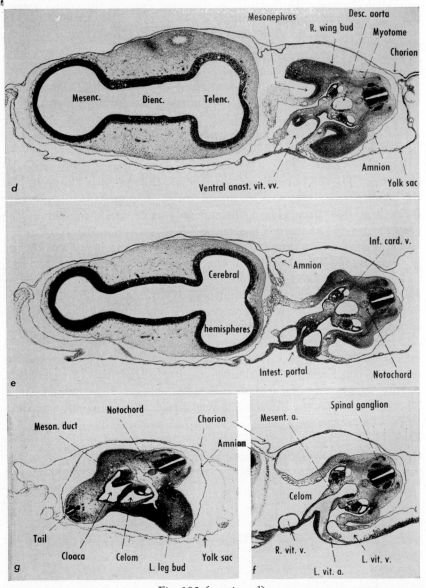

Fig. 192 (*continued*)

of the body and *vestibular parts* are added. From the sensory epithelia arise the *olfactory nerves,* growing toward the frontal and ventral surface of the hemispheres of the cerebrum. At four days they have not yet entered the substance of the brain.

The *eyes* show a beginning of histologic differentiation (Fig. 192c). The deeper part of the lens sac has become very thick; its slender cells are transforming into *lens fibers.* The surface part retains the low epithelial character. In the cells of the outer layer of the retina appear the first *melanin granules,* while in the inner layer, which is four to five times thicker, neurons with long nerve fibers have made their appearance. The latter converge toward the optic stalk, through which some reach the base of the diencephalon. From this stage on, the two parts of the retina are distinguished as *pigment epithelium* and *nervous layer.* The choroid fissure has become very narrow, but between its bordering edges it holds the *hyaloid artery,* which spreads along the inside of the retina. Other branches of the *ophthalmic artery* run over its surface and initiate the formation of a *choroid plexus.*

The *ear vesicles* (Figs. 190, 192a, 197) have lost contact with the epidermis. The endolymphatic ducts have shifted from the apical to the median side. The vesicles are of irregular shape, though not subdivided at this stage. From their ventromedial walls proliferate the *acoustic ganglia* and *acoustic nerves.*

The *buccal hypophysis* is a deep narrow pouch. Its apex touches the infundibulum of the brain and the tip of the notochord (Fig. 197).

The *cranial ganglia* are of diverse origin (Table 11, Fig. 197). The *root ganglia* of the seventh, ninth, and tenth nerves arise from the neural crests, the *trunk ganglia* from the epibranchial placodes. The *trigeminal (semilunar) ganglion,* forming in the region where the epibranchial series of placodes separates from the dorsal crest, belongs mainly in the class of crest ganglia. However, the neuroblasts of its ventral process seem to be derived from placodal thickenings which, on the second day of incubation, appear along the mandibular arch. These swellings resemble the placode above the hyomandibular cleft,

Table 11

Origin of the Cranial Ganglia from Neural Crests and Placodes

ORIGIN	TRIGEMINAL N. V.	FACIAL N. VII	ACOUSTIC N. VIII	GLOSSO-PHARYNGEAL N. IX	VAGUS N. X
Neural crest	semilunar	facial root	—	superior	jugular
Dorsolateral placodes	—	—	acoustic	—	—
Epibranchial placodes	contributions to semilunar	geniculate	—	petrosal	nodose

from which the *geniculate ganglion* arises. The *petrosal ganglion* forms in connection with the second cleft, the complex *nodose ganglion* in connection with the third, fourth, and fifth visceral grooves. The *acoustic ganglion* takes a special position. Since lateral line organs do not form, even at the embryonic stage, it is the only survivor of the dorsolateral placode series, which is so extensive in fishes and amphibians.

The *spinal ganglia* take their origin entirely from the neural crest. The first two are not connected with the corresponding spinal nerves, but become a part of the *vagus-accessorius complex* of cranial nerves (Fig. 197). Consequently the first and second cervical nerves have ventral roots only. The series of caudal ganglia is incomplete, in number as well as in histologic differentiation.

The *ventral* roots of most *cranial and spinal nerves* are well recognizable. Many motor fibers are in contact with muscle plates and follow their outgrowing buds and divisions. The roots of the four occipital segments combine in the formation of the purely motor *hypoglossal nerve* (Fig. 197; Table 9). Usually, sensory fibers from the cranial and spinal ganglia combine with the bundles of motor fibers from ventral roots to form mixed peripheral nerves. Some spinal nerves have reached the base of the wing and leg buds (Fig. 192c, d); these early connections are the beginning of the formation of *brachial and lumbosacral plexuses* (Table 9, Fig. 197).

The *sympathetic trunks* consist of two chains of ganglionic condensations, segmentally arranged dorsolaterally along the wall of the descending aorta (Fig. 192). The ganglia are linked longitudinally by a pair of strands of nerve fibers, and each connects with the spinal nerve of its segment by a *communicant branch*. In the mesonephric region, below the mesenteric artery, some sympathetic neuroblasts migrate ventrally, left and right of the aorta, and establish contacts with the adrenocortical blastema, as early as the middle of the fourth day (Fig. 194). In embryos of 100 hours this material segregates into *adrenomedullary cells* which attach themselves to the adrenocortical cords, and *cells of the aortic plexus* (Fig. 195).

The *cranial division* of the autonomic system likewise assumes definite shape. As the vagus nerve grows toward the stomach, it is followed and partly preceded by parasympathetic neuroblasts which later spread in the splanchnic mesenchyme of esophagus, heart, stomach and upper intestine. Definite visceral ganglia and plexuses form between the eighth and the tenth days.

The *parasympathetic outflow of the pudendal plexus* (sacral nerves) is just beginning to supply the viscera of the lower abdomen.

The *derivation of the elements of the autonomic system* (sympathetic and parasympathetic) has been the subject of many old controversies. Recent discussions were mainly focussed on the alternatives of origin from either neural crest or neural tube. From the patient observations and experiments particularly of Kuntz,

Yntema and collaborators a double origin seems to evolve as the final solution. The preganglionic fibers, which leave the brain or spinal cord through the ventral motor roots, arise from cell bodies within the tubular nervous system. In their development these central elements are closely associated with the motor neurons. However, all peripheral ganglia and the postganglionic nerve fibers seem to derive more or less directly from dorsal crest cells. The sympathoblasts leave the dorsal crest together with the neuroblasts of the dorsal root ganglia of cranial and spinal nerves, immediately before and during the closure of the neural tube.

d. Endodermal Organs.   The *pharynx* is that of a branchiate animal. Three pairs of pouches actually open to the outside, the first one through a fine dorsal pore, the next two through clefts. The fourth pharyngeal pouch meets the superficial branchial groove which corresponds to a fourth cleft, but does not break open. The endodermal epithelium has a tendency to grow out through the slits, displacing and undergrowing the epidermis until it reaches the surface of the body. Irregular protuberances which appear on the outer surface of the second and third visceral arches of chick embryos have been recognized by Boyden as vestigial gills. They are of common occurrence at the end of the fourth day. In the chick, the fifth pouch is a small groove in the frontolateral wall of the sixth pouch; in hawk embryos it is slightly better developed, but in the passerines it is barely recognizable. The sixth pouch also is much reduced in all birds; together with the fifth it assumes the character of an accessory of the fourth pouch.

The *primordium of the thyroid* is a globule with walls of high columnar epithelium enclosing a tiny central lumen. Though detached from the pharyngeal epithelium, it still maintains its position beneath the second pharyngeal pouches (Fig. 197).

The lower part of the pharyngotracheal groove of the previous day has separated from the *esophagus* and forms the tubular *trachea*. The surrounding splanchnic mesenchyme proliferates and produces massive, bifurcating ridges, along the ventral and the left and right sides of the endodermal esophagus. This is the origin of the *mesodermal primordia of the lungs* and the *pleuroperitoneal folds*. Into their core extend the *endodermal lungbuds* which by lengthening become the *primary bronchi*—one on each side of the esophagus. The bronchi actually take a dorsocaudal course. Their bulbous ends project into the pleuroperitoneal cavity, approaching the mesonephric bodies (Fig. 197).

Growth and differentiation of the *hepatopancreatic system* become greatly accelerated during the fourth day, so that the development of duodenum and upper small intestine makes considerable progress. The main body of the *liver* lies in the right celomic cavity, while the stomach is bent to the left. The shape of the liver changes in conformity with the development of new vascular channels, described below. The *dorsal pancreas* is a fairly large body with many budding tubules. From the hepatic duct arise as two new short evaginations the *ventral pancreatic*

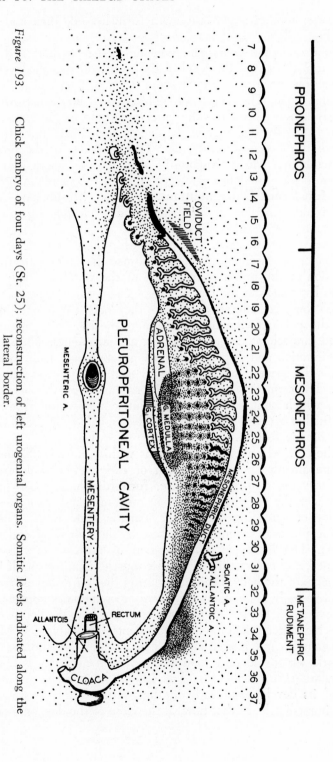

Figure 193. Chick embryo of four days (St. 25); reconstruction of left urogenital organs. Somitic levels indicated along the lateral border.

primordia; another larger outgrowth furnishes *bile duct* and *gall bladder* (Fig. 197).

The endodermal *yolk stalk,* now reduced to a short and flat duct,
opens into the gut at the level of the twenty-first to the twenty-fourth
somites. The opening is a cleft about 0.5 mm. long and not more than
0.05 mm. wide. The *allantois* is differentiated into a narrow stalk and
a nearly spherical vesicle. The latter is located in the extra-embryonic
celom. Below the openings of the mesonephric ducts, the left and right
walls of the *cloaca* grow together. This prepares for the formation of
the membrane, which temporarily separates the cloaca into urodeum
and bursal sac. The latter extends to the *cloacal membrane* (Fig. 197).

e. Mesodermal Differentiations.   AXIAL MESODERM.   The *notochord* is differentiated in full length and is passing through a period
of stretching by vesiculation of its cells.

PARAXIAL MESODERM.   The relationship of the somitic series to the
body regions is indicated in Table 9. Since the somites are the clearest
expression of the primitive metamery of the vertebrate body, they are
used as landmarks in the description of embryonic development. In the
form of compact, cube-shaped bodies they persist now only in the tail.
From the pelvic to the brachial regions they are histologically differentiated into sclerotomes, dermatomes, and myotomes. The *sclerotomes,*
by proliferation and dispersal, produce an abundant, loose mesenchyme
that fills the spaces lateral and ventral to the spinal cord and the notochord. Their proximal parts remain separated by the intersegmental
spaces, which contain the intersegmental arteries and veins, and become further divided into upper and lower halves by the development
of *sclerotomic* fissures.

In the cervical region condensations within the scleroblastemic mesenchyme already show the pattern of early vertebral differentiation.
The *dermatomes* likewise disperse, furnishing a mesenchymal *corial
layer* under the dorsal epidermis. Dermatomes and *myotomes* show a
tendency of spreading toward the somatic body walls. The ventral
myotome processes extend to the base of the paired appendages (Fig.
192*d–f*). The histologic differentiation of muscle fibers has greatly
progressed, and contractility of somitic muscles manifests itself in spastic
movements of the body, beginning during the fourth day of incubation.
The terms *body segment* or *metamere* are sometimes applied to designate topographic levels after the somites proper have disappeared through
progressive differentiation (for equivalents see Table 9). Myotomes,
spinal ganglia, and intersegmental blood vessels are the most helpful
landmarks for the identification of erstwhile somitic levels (Fig. 197).

INTERMEDIATE MESODERM (Fig. 193). The *pronephros* reached the
peak of its development early in the fourth day. Regressive changes
follow immediately, so that now, at the close of the day, only occasional

isolated remnants of tubules may be found, embedded in the mesenchyme of the sixth to the thirteenth somites. Glomerular vestiges occur
regularly at the level of the twelfth to the sixteenth somites. In one
typical case (Fig. 193) the twelfth glomerulus is enclosed in a cyst
which has lost continuity with the celom; the thirteenth maintains
connection through a narrow canal; the fourteenth, fifteenth, and sixteenth still protrude normally into the upper body cavity. The pronephric duct begins at the level of the fourteenth somite, but a lumen
exists only along the sixteenth, the last of the pronephric somites.

The *mesonephros* consists of an uper and a lower division. Above
the root of the mesenteric (vitelline) artery (in the chick somites 16
to 22) it is made up of about ten elements, *single nephrons,* each
composed of a *renal corpuscle* and a *urinary tubule.* The latter opens
into the *nephric duct.* Below the mesenteric artery follows a series of
multiple units, each one composed of two to five, but most often four
single nephrons (corpuscles and tubules). The elements of a unit
form in lateromedial progression (Figs. 185, 194). Each unit establishes
a separate contact with the mesonephric duct. The latter is no longer
a cylindrical tube. In cross sections, it appears of irregular shape because it sends out processes which meet the individual urinary tubules
(Fig. 195). Gradually elongating, this outgrowth of the duct becomes
a *collecting tubule* which receives all urinary tubules (two to five)
of the unit. The arrangement of these units is not in agreement with

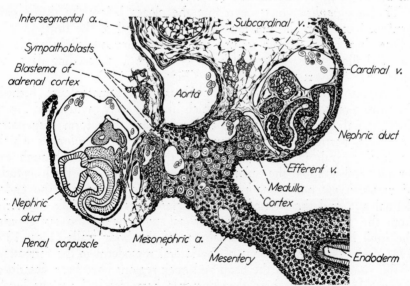

Figure 194.   Redwing blackbird, embryo middle of fourth day (St. 25). Part
of cross section located between somites 21 and 22 (below mesenteric artery). The
large round cells at the dorsal root of the mesentery are primordial germ cells. Succession of three nephrons in right mesonephros (Witschi 1935); × 160.

somitic segmentation; usually two or three mesonephric units correspond to the length of one somite (Fig. 196).

The *glomeruli* of the upper mesonephros and also those of the
ventral renal corpuscles at the level of the twenty-second and twenty-
third somites are vascularized and the anatomic picture suggests that
these elements are now actually functioning. Boyden added experimental proof to this interpretation. Cautery, followed by obstruction
of the lower mesonephric ducts, causes an extreme dilatation of the
upper ducts and the kidney tubules. This condition is known as *hydronephrosis*. The fluid which accumulates in the tubular system probably
comes from the renal capillaries, passing through the glomerular
endothelia. On the other hand, in the absence of pressure by mesonephric excretions, the allantois fails to grow to normal size. It has
further been shown that trypan blue and several other dyes and chemicals, if introduced into the circulation of chick embryos, are eliminated
through the mesonephros from the fourth day on. Finally, chemical
evidence of nitrogenous excretion (uric acid) has been obtained in
chicks of the fifth day of incubation. Thus it seems well established
that secretory activities of the pronephros begin during the third and
those of the mesonephros on the fourth day.

However, the largest part of the lower mesonephros has not attained
this functional state. It exhibits all developmental stages, beginning
with the condition of primitive blastemic cords at the level of the
thirtieth and thirty-first somites (Fig. 193).

The *mesonephric ducts* open into the cloaca below the thirty-sixth
somites, just as on the previous day. At the level of the thirty-fourth,
where they bend sharply toward the cloaca, they are slightly dilated
and a shallow recess indicates the place where in succeeding days the
metanephric diverticulum will arise (Figs. 193, 197).

LATERAL MESODERM. Splanchnopleure and somatopleure furnish
the thin, serous *celomic epithelia* which line the body cavities and invest
the internal organs. By folding and stretching they form *suspensory
ligaments*, particularly the *mesenteries*, and *septal membranes* which
eventually result in the subdivision of the body cavity. Through extensive proliferation the splanchnopleure produces the thick *mantle
of mesenchyme and smooth musculature* which surrounds the endodermal gut, and the striated heart muscles (Figs. 185, 192). Similarly
from the somatopleure arise the *cortical epithelia of the sex glands*,
the *limb buds*, and some *mesenchyme* of the body walls (Figs. 185,
192, 194). The contributions of the lateral mesoderm to the formation
of the *visceral arches* in the head and neck regions have been described
before. At four days these developments have reached various levels
of differentiation and only a few will be more fully described.

The *celomic body cavity* is still one continuous space, but its imminent subdivision into pericardial, pleural, and peritoneal (abdominal)

sacs is indicated by the broadening of the *lateral mesocardia,* the rise of the *transverse septum,* and the formation of *pleuroperitoneal folds.* The last named arise as caudal extensions of the mesodermal lung primordia, as mentioned above.

Up to the middle of the second day the heart tube was attached to the esophagus by means of an intact median *mesocardium;* but in embryos of 16 to 17 somites this ligament became perforate, and later it disappeared over the entire length of the ventricle. Consequently, the heart of the four-day embryo is suspended only by its upper and lower ends. The small *atrial mesocardium* serves also as a bridge by which the pulmonary vein reaches the heart.

The *buds of the wings and legs* have grown into prominent paddle-shaped appendages (Fig. 190), occupying the somite levels 17 to 20 and 27 to 34 respectively. Their histologic differentiation has barely started; the light center areas noticeable in the photographs of sections (Fig. 192*d, g*) represent *skeletomuscular condensations,* surrounded by vascular plexuses.

f. Primordia of Adrenals and Sex Glands.   Between the twentieth and the twenty-seventh somites the mesonephric blastema is not entirely used up in the formation of kidney tubules and renal corpuscles. On either side, a *blastemic remnant* extends along the ventromedial edge of the kidney. Occasionally vestigial nephrostomes become recognizable and short nephric tubules appear within the blastemic aggregation, testifying to the true nephric nature of this remnant. It is partly separated from the kidney by a mesenchymal shelf which completes the capsule enveloping the mesonephric body. In this partition run the mesonephric arteries that supply the glomeruli, and the efferent veins which drain the kidney toward the subcardinal veins (Figs. 194–196). The main stems of the efferent veins finally break through the blastemic cord and divide it into a dorsal and a ventral strand. The former furnishes the material for the *adrenal cortex,* the latter for the *medulla of the sex gland* (Figs. 194, 195). The line of division, however, is somewhat slanting so that the upper end of the cord contributes almost entirely to the formation of adrenal cortex. In four-day embryos, the blastema of adrenal cortex extends from the twentieth to the twenty-fourth somite, that of gonadal medulla from the twenty-second to the twenty-sixth (Fig. 193). With the adrenal cortical rudiment there are now associated some migrating cells of the sympathetic nervous system that later become the *medullary part of the adrenal gland* (Figs. 194, 195).

The *gonadal medulla* connects with the neighboring renal corpuscles through short blastemic cords, the *primordial efferent ductules* of the sex glands (Figs. 195, 196).

The medullary blastema is only one of three major components of the *primordial sex glands* which become organized during the fourth day. Of the other two, the *gonadal cortex* is a band of specialized celomic epithelium which covers the distal surface of the medulla. It is not as well developed on the right as on the left side (Figs. 195, 196).

The third and most important element, the *primordial germ cells,* migrate into the gonadal region from the yolk-sac epithelium. After having reached the dorsal root of the mesentery, they distribute themselves asymmetrically, favoring the gonad primordium of the left side (Figs. 194, 196). At the end of the fourth day, the left gonad contains from three to ten times as many germ cells as the right one (Table 12). As they arrive in the gonad primordia, the germ cells become imbedded in either the cortex or the medulla. For a while, some remain also in the mesenchyme-filled interspace which is the *primitive albuginea.* Counts reveal that the difference between left and right gonads is mainly the consequence of deficient development of the right cortex. In some species, especially hawks, asymmetry is less pronounced.

g. Circulatory System.   In chick embryos of four days, the primitive circulatory system reaches the peak of its development (Fig. 197). Its fundamental features are identical with those of the frog larva with external gills (Fig. 63).

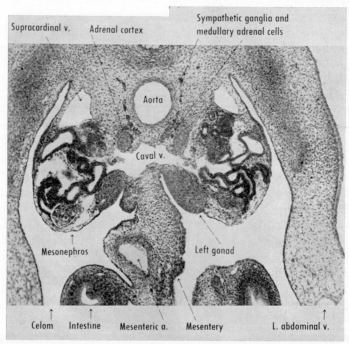

Figure 195.   Sparrow embryo early in fifth day (St. 26); cross section passing through upper gonad region (below root of mesenteric artery). Left gonad larger than right, consists of cortical and medullary components; the medulla is separated from the adrenal blastema by efferent veins of the mesonephros. Groups of sympathoblasts associate with the cortical cells; × 80.

The *heart* is still of the single tube type, though the approaching separation of the left and right atrial chambers is indicated by the ingrowth of a sickle-shaped ridge from the dorsal wall of the atrium. This primordial *atrial septum* is placed between the openings of the venous sinus and the pulmonary vein, so that the latter lies to its left, and the former to its right.

Of the *aortic arches,* the third and fourth are the main channels that convey the blood to the *dorsal aortas* (Fig. 197). The ventral roots of the first and second arches persist, and form the *ventral carotids;* they supply the floor of the mouth, and the mandibular and maxillary rudiments. The fifth aortic arches are short and thin vessels, which arise from, and return to, the sixth arches. In passerines they are even more rudimentary than in the chick, being represented by only a few irregular capillaries that are not shown in Figure 197. Each sixth arch gives off a branch to the lung and thus is subdivided in two sections. The ventral part serves as a root of the *pulmonary artery;* the dorsal part is the *arterial duct.* Late in the fourth day the arterial ducts are still small and open into the dorsal root of the fourth arches, or directly into the dorsal aortas. Each primitive pulmonary plexus drains through a *pulmonary vein.* Left and right veins unite into a short common vessel which descends through the mesocardium to the atrium of the heart. With the exception of this last segment of the pulmonary veins,

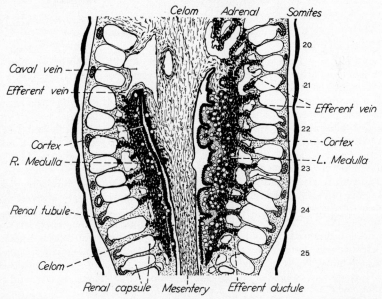

Figure 196.   Sparrow embryo, early in fifth day (St. 26). Frontal sections through gonadal region. Caval vein cut where it passes around mesenteric artery. The medullary parts of both gonads connect with renal capsules by blastema cords (glomeruli omitted). Germ cells represented by white dots (Witschi 1935); × 66.

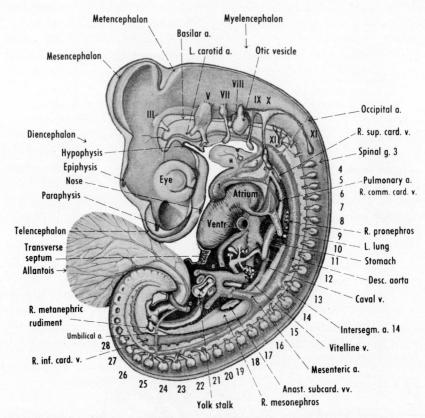

Figure 197. Redwing blackbird embryo (St. 25–26), slightly over four days (100 hours) incubated. Dissection, and reconstruction from sagittal sections; × 19. Metamorphic changes starting in the vascular system.

M, Mandible and tongue, with carotid and thyroid. 3, 4, Pharyngeal pouches; *T*, aortic trunk; *Ventr.*, ventricle of heart; crescent-shaped small atrial septum visible through semitransparent wall of atrium; from the sixth aortic arch branches the pulmonary artery; pulmonary vein returns to left side of atrium; *R. sup. card. v.*, right superior cardinal vein; *R. inf. card. v.*, right inferior cardinal vein. Left common cardinal vein is cut off at entrance into the venous sinus; left abdominal (allantoic) vein resected between *a–a'*. The occipital artery (first intersegmental a.) marks limit of head and body. The fourteenth intersegmental is also the root of the primary subclavian artery; similarly the femoral artery arises from the 23rd, the sciatic and allantoic arteries from the 25th intersegmentals. The mesenteric artery branches into left and right vitelline arteries. The vitelline vein collects from right and left stems, the latter with large upper, median, and lower roots. *Anast. subcard. vv.*, Anastomosis of left and right subcardinal veins (origin of inferior caval vein). III–XII, Roots and ganglia of cranial nerves; 4–28, spinal ganglia, nerves, and body segments; first and second cervical nerves have only ventral roots.

Ventral to segments 13 and 14 the intestine forms the duodenal loop; into it open the ducts of dorsal and ventral pancreatic lobes and the hepatic duct, which receives a third pancreatic and the bile duct.

the entire system of aortic arches and pulmonary vessels is paired and its left and right sides are equally developed.

The paired *dorsal aortas,* having received the sixth, fourth, and third aortic arches, continue upward as the *dorsal carotid arteries.* Close to the infundibulum of the diencephalon, they divide into several major branches which supply eyes, forebrain, and midbrain. Medial branches from each carotid fuse into a single vessel, the *basilar artery.* Reversing its course, this vessel passes between the roots of the oculomotor nerves and then runs between notochord and hindbrain toward the end of the occipital region. Here, it anastomoses with the first pair of intersegmental arteries. Along its course, the basilar artery gives off numerous lateral and dorsal branches which supply the hindbrain. Below the sixth arches, the dorsal aortas unite into the single *descending aorta.* At the end of the fourth day, fusion is complete down to the thirtieth somites. More caudally, the dorsal aortas run close to each other and are connected by many anastomoses (Fig. 192g).

From the dorsal surface of the aortas, pairs of *dorsal intersegmental arteries* grow into the connective tissue between the somites. The first cervical pair originate from the dorsal aortas below the entrance of the sixth aortic arches. As was mentioned above, these two vessels join the basilar artery (Fig. 197). All other pairs (over 30) arise from the descending aorta. They supply the somites and their derivatives as well as the neural tube (Fig. 194).

Below the nineteenth somite, a pair of primary *subclavian arteries* branch from the dorsal edge of the aorta. They are the only survivors of the series of arteries which at three days supplied the wing buds.

Along the extent of the pronephric and the mesonephric bodies, many small *renal arteries* arise from the ventrolateral walls of the aorta (Fig. 194). They supply the kidneys, particularly the glomeruli of the renal corpuscles (Fig. 194). Their distribution does not follow the order of the somites, but that of the nephric units.

The legbuds are supplied by at least five pairs of segmentally arranged arteries. Largest are the *sciatic arteries* located below the thirtieth somite (twenty-eighth in the sparrow). From them branch off the *allantoic arteries* which run within the body wall ventrally to the allantois (Figs. 192g, 193, 197).

Even while the intestine, at the level of the twenty-second and twenty-third somites, still opens into the yolk sac, a dorsal mesentery has formed in this region. Consequently, the proximal vitelline arteries are fused into a single vessel, the *mesenteric artery* (Fig. 192f); distally, *left* and *right vitelline arteries* are of near equal size. They divide into many branches, supplying the entire vascular network of the yolk sac.

In the *venous system,* splanchnic and somatic channels are largely separated (Fig. 197). The *splanchnic veins* arise from the extra-embryonic *vitelline veins*. On the left side, an upper and a lower branch bring in the blood from the terminal sinus (Fig. 200) while the large lateral branch mainly collects blood from inner districts of the vascular plexus of the yolk sac. On the right side, the upper branch has become very much reduced and is now merely a small tributary of the lateral branch. At four days, the latter is the only fully developed collecting system of the right vitelline vein.

The transverse anastomoses which in the two-day chick joined the vitelline plexuses of both sides around the caudal circumference of the body have become part of the capillary network of the allantois. On the right side, they have lost their attachment, but the left root is now drawn out into a fairly large vessel that runs along the ventral surface of the gut, eventually joining the lower branch of the left vitelline vein. This *subintestinal vein* (Fig. 197) returns the blood from the allantois before this function is taken over by the abdominal veins.

In front of the yolk stalk, a new *ventral anastomosis connects left and right vitelline veins*. From here on, the left vessel conveys the larger volume of blood around the left side of the intestine to the previously formed dorsal anastomosis and over it to the right side of the intestine, where it enters the liver. Passing through the hepatic meatus, and many collateral sinusoids, the blood returns to the venous sinus of the heart (Fig. 197). From the *dorsal anastomosis*, below the dorsal pancreas, a small new vessel grows caudally into the mesentery; this is the primitive *mesenteric vein*.

The *somatic part of the venous system* consists of the cardinal veins and their branches. As in the early stages of embryonic development, one still distinguishes pairs of *upper* and *lower cardinal veins*. The *common cardinals* converge ventrally, and open into the venous sinus (Fig. 197).

Corresponding to the intersegmental arteries, a series of *dorsal intersegmental veins* return the blood from the back of the embryo to the big cardinal trunks. The lower cardinals also receive several small branches from the subclavian and iliac plexuses.

Running along the dorsolateral edge of the kidneys, the lower cardinal veins give off a number of branches which spread into a reticular system of vessels and lacunae between the nephric tubules. From here, efferent venules drain the blood toward the ventromedial edge of the mesonephros. By confluence, they form a pair of longitudinal ducts, the *subcardinal veins*, which, near the upper end of the mesonephric bodies, gradually return to the main trunk of the cardinal veins of their respective sides.

The *abdominal veins* are still connected with the common cardinal veins; but they have also made connections with the rapidly expanding liver and thus return part of their blood to the venous sinus by way of the hepatic meatus. Distally, the branches of the abdominal veins now extend as far as the pelvic region. They not only collect in the lateral body walls, but also have established *contacts with the allantoic plexus*. Moreover, they still receive side branches from the ventral parts of the wing- and legbuds.

Chapter 17

Metamorphosis

Chick Incubation age 4¼ to 7½ days (St. 26–33)

1. GENERAL ASPECTS

a. Dissociation of Morphologic and Physiologic Differentation.
Barely formed, the embryo passes through a period of reconstruction,
in the course of which its original fishlike organization is changed into
that of a terrestrial vertebrate. This phase of avian development bears
so close a resemblance to amphibian metamorphosis that there can be
no doubt about the homology of the morphologic processes. However,
the elaborate reorganization is of no immediate physiologic consequence.
Respiration is neither branchial before metamorphosis nor pulmonary
after its completion, and locomotion is very restricted throughout the
incubation period. Clearly the dissociation of form and function has the
value of an adaptation to the environmental conditions that exist within
the egg shell. But it is none the less remarkable that morphologic recapitulation persists so tenaciously where entire organ complexes have
long lost their specific functional importance.

b. The Metamorphic Period.   In the domestic fowl, the sparrow, and the
redwing, metamorphosis starts at the close of the fourth day, or early in the fifth,
and is completed at eight days. In the turkey, corresponding changes occur about
12 hours later than in the chick. Hawks develop extremely slowly; in laboratory-
incubated eggs, metamorphosis starts near the middle of the eighth day and ends
after the twelfth. Five-day embryos of chicks and passerines show metamor-

phosis in full progress (Fig. 198*a, b*); in external views, the visceral arches and paired appendages are most profoundly involved. Passerine embryos of this period are only about half the linear size of chicks of the same developmental and chronologic age. They are therefore a favorable object for the study of these and later developmental stages by serial sections (Figs. 198, 199).

c. **The Mechanism of Metamorphosis.**   Throughout the neurula and tail-bud stages, self-differentiation was the leading morphogenic principle. Similarly also the metamorphic processes prove to be fully determined by intrinsic factors, i.e., by conditions developing within the transforming tissues, independent of

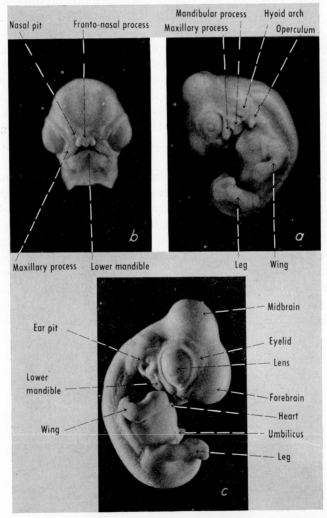

Figure 198.   *a,* Sparrow embryo about the middle of metamorphic period (St. 28), five days incubation (cf. Fig. 206); × 6.6. *b,* Redwing blackbird; head of five-day embryo; stage 29. Ventral view, showing frontonasal, maxillary, and mandibular processes; ×6. *c,* Redwing blackbird, embryo near end of metamorphosis (6½ days incubated; cf. Fig. 206); stage 30; × 6.

outside induction. Direct observations and experiments prove that metamorphosis in birds is independent of thyroid function. Thyroxin, the powerful and often indispensable booster of the metamorphic events in amphibians, has no stimulating effects in birds. Also, the metabolic rate shows no rise during this period that might be comparable to the spurt in metamorphosing amphibians.

2. VISCERAL ARCHES AND FORMATION OF THE FACE

The first visceral arches take a leading part in the construction of the face. Their upper or maxillary processes grow early to considerable length, closely following the ventral circumference of the eyes (Fig. 198a–c). Between their distal ends lies the *frontonasal process*. It arises from the front of the head. During the fifth day it develops five distinct lobes. Three of them grow down medially and two laterally around the olfactory pits. As they fuse with the maxillary process, the olfactory sensory epithelia come to lie in nasal passages with *nares* opening to the outside and *choanae* into the oral cavity. By the end of the sixth day, the frontonasal and maxillary processes are fused and form a short cone, the primitive *upper bill* (Figs. 198c, 206). The lower mandibular processes of both sides meet in the sagittal plane; together they form the lower bill (Fig. 198b).

As one of the first characteristic expressions of beginning metamorphosis, a ridge forms across the first visceral cleft, through fusion of converging processes from the maxillary and the hyoid arches. It separates the open dorsal part of the cleft from the rapidly vanishing ventral section (Fig. 198a). Toward the middle of the fifth day, the tubelike dorsal part also becomes closed; but its external opening persists as a shallow pit, the primitive *acoustic meatus* (Figs. 198c, 206). The second and third visceral clefts close about the middle of the fifth day. The operculum or "collar" of the hyoid arch grows down toward the cardiac swelling. In the course of the fifth and sixth days, it covers all

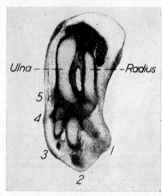

Figure 199.   Pentadactyl upper limb (wing) of sparrow, six days incubated (St. 31); section; note indication of possible digit preceding the one designated as the first; × 25.

branchial arches and grooves. Hidden under it, in the so-called *cervical sinus,* one usually finds some vestigial gills, which attain the peak of their development at the inception of metamorphosis. Through the now occurring lengthening of the neck and the descent of the heart, the closure of the cervical sinus leaves its mark some distance above the chest (Figs. 198c, 206).

3. GLANDULAR DERIVATIVES OF THE PHARYNX

The second pharyngeal pouches disappear completely, while parts of the endodermal epithelia of the regressing third, fourth, and sixth pouches transform into glandular organs. These glands correspond to those described above for amphibians; but they differentiate later, and are differently distributed. At the end of metamorphosis *thymus lobes* grow out of the dorsal recesses of the third and fourth visceral pouches. They do not entirely follow the downward movement of the aortic arches and remain widely distributed along the lateral surface of the upper cardinal (jugular) veins. The ventral recesses of the same pouches become vesicular or compact epithelioid bodies, the primitive *parathyroid glands.* From the combined fifth and sixth pouches, condensations of mesenchymal cells persist, the *ultimobranchial bodies,* which lag in the downward shift, and therefore come into the neighborhood of the thyroid bodies.

The *thyroid* has attached itself to the third aortic arches. Early in the fifth day (Fig. 197), it has the shape of a slightly angular bar, bridging the space between the roots of the left and right ventral carotids. From the central apex, a slender stalk points in the direction of the epithelial thickening on the tongue, which marks the place of its origin. The attachments to the carotids persist throughout metamorphosis, and the thyroid participates in the downward shift of the aortic complex. As the distance between the roots of the carotids grows, the center of the bar narrows and finally breaks. Consequently at the end of metamorphosis, the fetus has paired thyroid bodies. Their histologic differentiation lags. At the start of metamorphosis, each consists of a compact core of blastemic cells, some in mitotic division, and a cuboid surface epithelium. No colloid is formed throughout the metamorphic period, and the histologic picture clearly indicates that secretory activity has not yet started. This striking contrast to the conditions observed in frogs and salamanders serves in itself as proof that metamorphosis in birds is not controlled by thyroid hormones.

4. RESPIRATORY ORGANS

a. Lungs. Even though without respiratory function, the lungs acquire bronchial trees and thereby the basic structure of higher tetrapods. From each primary bronchus arise several successions of *secondary bronchi.* Through this budding process the lungs become a pair of voluminous bodies which protrude from the dorsolateral surface of the pleuroperitoneal folds into the pleural parts of the celomic cavity.

At the end of the sixth day each primary bronchus consists of a free extrapulmonary, and a pulmonary section. From the latter issue about eight blind *secondary bronchi*. Its unbranched end becomes the *abdominal air sac*.

b. Allantois.   At the inception of metamorphosis, the allantois is merely a urinary bladder, protruding into the extra-embryonic celom. In sparrows it has a diameter of about 1 mm., which is one-fourth the length of the embryo (Fig. 190). By the end of the period, the diameter has grown to 15 mm., or nearly twice body length. The distal surface now spreads along the inside of the chorion, to which it becomes attached, forming a *chorio-allantoic membrane* (Fig. 200). Above the back of the fetus, where the allantois meets the chorio-amniotic stalk, it forms two lobes which grow left and right around the large right allantoic vein. Fusing again, the adjacent walls of these lobes form a *septum* through which the allantoic vein descends from the chorio-allantoic membrane to the under side and to the stalk of the allantois (Fig. 200).

The right *allantoic artery* remains small. The left one soon divides into two branches (Fig. 197) which circle around the edge of the

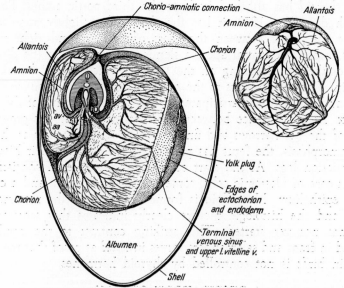

Figure 200.   Sparrow embryo of 5½ days incubation (St. 30), within shell and albumen. The body of the embryo above the yolk stalk is cut away, exposing the lower abdominal cavity. Allantoic vein (*av*), entering umbilicus, runs from right to left body wall, below allantoic and yolk stalk; *aa* allantoic arteries. At upper right a surface view of the chorio-allantoic membrane, with allantoic vessels: veins black, arteries white (Witschi 1949); × 3.5.

allantois ventral to the embryo (Fig. 200). In the chorio-allantoic membrane, they spread into a dense network of capillaries which is drained by the collecting branches of the *allantoic vein*. The respiratory importance of the chorio-allantois is emphasized by its location immediately under the highest part of the egg shell.

5. CIRCULATORY ORGANS

a. **Characteristics of Fetal Circulation.**   In avian as in amphibian metamorphosis, the branchiate single vascular circuit becomes changed into the pulmonate double circuit system. However, in the functional sense the birds maintain a single circuit until hatching time. This is accomplished through the development of *perforations in the atrial septum* and through persistence of the dorsal parts of the sixth aortic arches, the *arterial ducts* (Fig. 201). The pulmonary circuit is almost completely by-passed and remains functionally unimportant, while *the allantoic system develops into the true respiratory organ of the fetal period.*

b. **Heart and Aortic Arches.**   The segregation of the pulmonary circuit starts with the appearance of a sickle-shaped sagittal fold in the roof of the atrium of the heart, even before the fifth day. It is placed between the entrances of the pulmonary vein and the venous sinus (Fig. 197). In the course of the fifth day, this *interatrial septum* grows ventrally toward the atrioventricular canal, separating *left and right atrial* chambers (Fig. 201). The *atrioventricular canal* itself becomes divided by the development of thick pads within its dorsal and ventral walls. These *endocardial cushions* soon meet and partly fuse, establishing separate left and right canals. The division of the ventricle proceeds more slowly. The *interventricular septum* (Fig. 201) is completed during the seventh day. It starts at the endocardial cushions as a sagittally placed lamella, but then twists in such a way that the outlet of the *right ventricular chamber* lies ventral to and above that of the *left chamber* (Fig. 201). Almost simultaneously developing *septums in the aortic bulb and trunk* continue this spiral twist. Thus the passage from the right ventricular chamber next ascends on the left and then enters the left and right sixth aortic arches. The complete spiraling of the right aortic trunk around the left one is facilitated by the early reduction and *disappearance of the left fourth aortic arch*. The outlet from the *left ventricle* is an almost straight tube within the spiraling right vessel. It leads into the upper aortic arches (3 and 4) and the ventral carotids.

The changes within the system of aortic arches follow the type set in anuran metamorphosis but show some characteristic special features. The vestigial fifth arches disappear and the dorsal aortas become interrupted below the third aortic arches. The right *fourth aortic arch* persists to become the *systemic arch* while the left one is lost (Fig. 201).

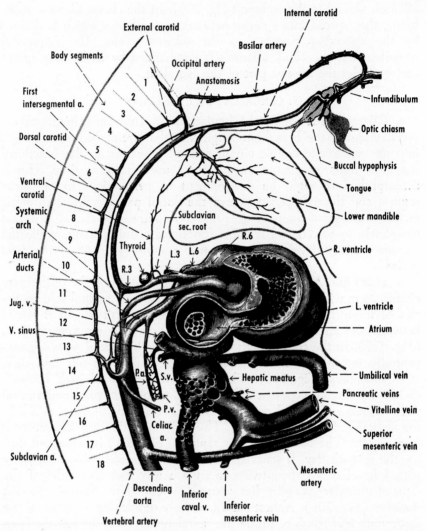

Figure 201. Sparrow, six days incubated. Right lateral view of heart and adjoining vessels toward end of metamorphosis (St. 31). A tangential section has opened right atrium, right atrioventricular canal, and right ventricle. In the atrial cavity the sinus valves, the interatrial septum, and the septal perforations (sieve) become visible. In the walls of the canal are exposed the dorsal and ventral endocardial cushions. The canal projects into the ventricle (primary atrioventricular valve). From the walls of the ventricle rises a framework of muscular lamellae, the muscle sponge. The interventricular septum nears completion, but a passage is still seen connecting the dorsobulbar parts of the ventricular chambers. 3, 6 paired aortic arches; the fourth arch persists only on the right side (systemic arch). *Jug. v.,* jugular vein; *P. a.,* pulmonary artery; *P. v.,* pulmonary vein; *Subclavian sec. root,* secondary root of subclavian artery (primary from the fourteenth intersegmental artery); *S. v.,* subclavian vein; *V. sinus,* venous sinus; × 26.

Both sixth arches are maintained and become capacious *arterial ducts;* together with the right fourth, they supply the descending aorta. The pulmonary arteries remain small and little blood is returned by way of the pulmonary veins to the left atrium of the heart. The resulting unbalance of pressure obviously is the cause for the development of *perforations in the atrial septum* (Fig. 201) which admit blood from the right into the left atrial chamber.

Thus becomes established the particular feature of *fetal circulation.* The blood returning from the body is immediately directed again to the body—either by way of the *perforated atrial septum* or through the *paired arterial ducts.*

c. **Arteries.** Many changes in the arterial system are rather incidental secondary adaptations to local developments, and therefore are specific for avian development only.

The rapid downward shift of the heart and the stretching of the neck are attended by the development of new roots in several distribution systems. The muscles of tongue and face are originally supplied by branches of the *ventral carotids.* As their stems become more and more extended, anastomosing branches from the *dorsal carotids* assume the role of secondary roots. Finally the ventral carotids disappear; the supply branches from the dorsal carotids become the *external carotids.* The roots of these branches also divide the dorsal main vessels into lower *common carotids* and upper *internal carotids* (Fig. 201).

Early in the fifth day the *basilar artery* connects with the dorsal aortas through the pair of intersegmental arteries between the last occipital and the first cervical segments. The roots of these two arteries are at the fork of the dorsal aortas. At 100 hours' incubation they have been pulled slightly downward to about the middle of the first cervical segment. The rapid relative contraction of the descending aorta during metamorphosis brings the fork down to the thirteenth cervical somite, by the end of the sixth day. The first segmental arteries follow this movement; but eventually new roots become established on the dorsal carotids near the ventral surface of the first vertebra. The old roots then quickly disappear, the left one slightly before the right (Fig. 201). The roots of all other intersegmental arteries above the subclavian disappear even earlier. Their peripheral plexuses are now supplied through the *vertebral arteries.* This pair of longitudinal vessels arose from anastomoses between the intersegmental arteries; they run along the lateral surfaces of the vertebral column. Thus, the newly established root at the dorsal carotid supplies three major vessels: *basilar artery, occipital artery,* and *vertebral artery* (Fig. 201).

The third vessel that acquires a new root is the *subclavian artery.* In the latter half of the sixth day, when the heart has moved into the lower cervical region, one of the upper branches of the subclavian plexus establishes contact and anastomoses with the root of the ventral carotid. At the beginning of the seventh day, the primary root of the subclavian artery disappears and is functionally replaced by the *secondary root,* off the carotid artery (Fig. 201).

Allantoic respiration differs from the branchial and pulmonary types in submitting only a fraction of the circulating blood to the process of gaseous exchange. The two *allantoic arteries* are branches of the *sciatic arteries* which themselves receive but a fraction of the entire volume of the arterial circulation. The left one, dividing into two arches, ascends to the chorio-allantoic membrane. The small right artery merely supplies the hilar region and parts of the under surface of the allantois (Figs. 197, 200).

d. Veins.   It was mentioned in the description of the four-day embryo that originally the blood of the allantois drains through the *subintestinal vein,* and that at the end of the day the terminal branches of the *left and right abdominal veins* reach the base of the allantois. Of the three outlets thus established, the subintestinal vein dries up early in the fifth day. In correlation with the prevailingly left-sided arterial supply, the venous plexus of the allantois finally collects into a single *allantoic vein* on the right side. Thus it seems natural that for a while the right abdominal vein swells larger than the left one. However, after a few hours, the transverse anastomosis around the caudal circumference of the allantoic stalk becomes a wide passage (Fig. 200) through which the entire allantoic blood flows over to the *left abdominal vein.* The latter becomes the *intra-embryonic segment of the allantoic vein.*

Simultaneous with these developments in the lower body region, the upper ends of the abdominal veins change their course. First they establish contacts with some liver sinuses (Fig. 197) and then lose their connections with the common cardinal veins. On the sixth day, while the right abdominal disappears, the left one grows into a main tributary to the inferior caval vein. The right allantoic and the left abdominal are now one unit, the *umbilical vein* (Fig. 201).

An important change in the venous system of the lower body region begins with the establishment of an anastomosis between the *subcardinal veins* just below the mesenteric artery (Figs. 195, 196). The upper right subcardinal descending through the caval ligament establishes contacts with the liver sinuses at the beginning of the fifth day (Fig. 197). This new passage is known as the *inferior caval vein.* It conducts the blood from the somatic parts of the lower body, the legs (iliac veins), and the kidneys, to the liver. The upper parts of the inferior cardinal veins disappear completely.

The upper cardinals become the *jugular veins.* They receive the subclavian and vertebral veins as main tributaries. Their last segments, the former common cardinal veins, persist as left and right *superior caval veins.* At the end of the metamorphic period, the venous sinus therefore receives three caval veins. The lower one, while passing through the liver, is swelled by affluence of the umbilical and the *hepatic portal veins.* The venous sinus becomes progressively incorporated into the wall of the right atrium. At the end of the sixth day, its relative shrinkage has brought the ends of the veins close to the slit-shaped *sinus orifice.* This absorption process continues during the first few days after metamorphosis, but in most birds it is never carried to completion. Only the *left superior caval* and its former branch, the *coronary vein,* acquire separate openings into the right atrium. The orifices of the inferior and the right superior caval veins remain in a common depression between persisting *sinus valves* (Fig. 201).

6. ALIMENTARY TRACT

During metamorphosis the main sections of the alimentary tract become well defined and histologically differentiated. The straight *esophagus* leads into a thick-walled *stomach* which curves to the left. Below the pyloric constriction the intestine describes two major loops (Fig. 197). The first one, the *duodenum,* is located between the liver lobes and closely associated with the dorsal and the two ventral pancreatic lobes, receiving their three separate outlets. The liver consists of a smaller left and larger right lobe, the latter with the gall bladder. Each lobe is connected with the duodenum through a bile duct.

The second loop descends toward the umbilicus where the yolk stalk emerges from its ventral wall. The lumen of the stalk is reduced to a very fine vitelline duct, but it widens like a funnel as it approaches the yolk mass (Fig. 200). The yolk-sac epithelium is merely an expanded part of the intestinal wall. Its function is the gradual mobilization and absorption of the yolk. Its inner digestive surface is greatly enlarged by the formation of septums and folds into which penetrate the vitelline arteries and veins (Fig. 222).

At the end of the loop, where the intestine again approaches the dorsal body wall, two *caecal diverticula* grow laterally out of the thickened tube.

During the fifth day the cloaca becomes separated into *bursa* (of Fabricius) and *urodeum.* From the latter projects the allantois. It also receives the nephric ducts. The part of the rectum directly above the urodeum becomes the *coprodeum.* An ectodermal invagination into the bursa becomes the *proctodeum.* It is surrounded by a wall which, ventrally, rises into a primitive *phallic papilla.* The *cloacal membrane* —between proctodeum and bursa—ruptures during the sixth day. However, a newly formed membrane between urodeum and bursa prevents the flow of urine into the amniotic cavity (Figs. 203, 223).

7. EXCRETORY ORGANS

Boyden discovered the interesting fact that local destruction of the tip of the nephric duct late in the second or early in the third day prevents its further formation and downgrowth. At the same time the parts of the nephric blastema that remain without duct, differentiate very incompletely or not at all (Fig. 202). One might be inclined to ascribe to the duct a capacity of *induction* of nephric differentiation. However, its effectiveness is restricted to nephric blastema, i.e., a tissue already of high specialization. Like the apical ectoderm in limb differentiation, the duct acts as a *limiting factor,* in the absence of which differentiation cannot well proceed. But the nature of this relationship is not yet fully clear.

At the end of the embryonic stage the lower body region was still comparatively small, and its differentiation lagging. But during metamorphosis lumbosacral development becomes accelerated, and some pelvic organs like the intestine and the nephric system grow so fast that finally they project into the caudal region (Fig. 203).

The *regression of the pronephros* is nearly complete; only isolated glomeruli may still persist in the upper pleural cavity of young fetuses (Fig. 203D). The *mesonephros* becomes an independent body, and the persisting part of the primitive nephric duct is now a *mesonephric* or *deferent duct*. Degeneration of the slender part of the mesonephros above the mesenteric artery starts from the top. The lower, more complex body (Fig. 193) completes histologic differentiation of all its *compound nephrons*. A considerable excretory activity is indicated by the large number of renal corpuscles, the wide lumen of the collecting and deferent ducts, and the rapid enlargement of the allantoic vesicle.

The *metanephros* is the last to differentiate and the most complex of all nephric bodies. Like collecting tubules of the mesonephros, the *metanephric ducts* or *ureters* originate as outpocketings of the meso-

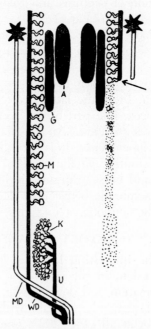

Figure 202.   Developmental relationships in the urogenital system. Organs developing by self-differentiation are shown in black, those which depend on others in thin outline (Gruenwald 1952). *A*, Adrenal, *G*, gonad, *K*, metanephros, *M*, mesonephros, *MD*, oviduct, *U*, ureter, *WD*, nephric duct. Arrow designates place where at an early stage the downgrowing tip of the nephric duct was destroyed.

nephric ducts, one on each side (Figs. 193, 203*A*). They grow into the stroma of the lower *nephric blastema cords*. Instead of the medial, they take an upward direction, following as a whole the dorsolateral surfaces of the mesonephric ducts and bodies. Within one day the unbranched and nearly straight ducts, sheathed and capped with nephrogenic blastema, reach the twentieth body segment, their permanent upper limit (Fig. 203*B*). During the second day of metamorphosis, three distinct lobes are formed in adaptation to space conditions created by the arteries and veins of the pelvic region. Within these lobes gradually appears the characteristic histologic structure of the functioning metanephros. The general downward trend in the development of the

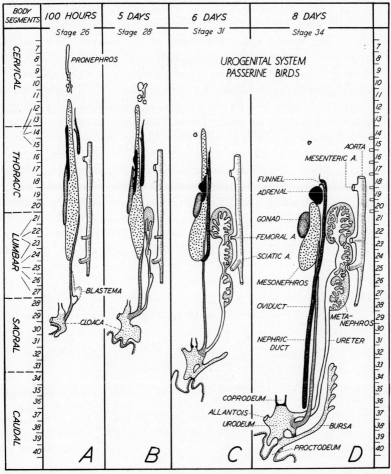

Figure 203.   Development of urogenital organs and cloaca in passerine birds during and following metamorphosis. Reconstructions reveal segmental shifting; size proportions somewhat distorted, because segments are given as if of equal and constant size. (Compare Fig. 193, St. 25.)

urinary system is illustrated in Figure 203. It is mainly the result of reductions in the upper, and compensating additions in the lower regions. Stretching and disproportionate growth of lower parts further accentuate the character of this expansion.

At the beginning the metanephric rudiments are located dorsal to the *inferior cardinal veins*. But toward the end of metamorphosis, these vessels are replaced by a pair of *supracardinal veins* that arise from anastomoses between segmental veins. They carry the blood dorsolaterally around the sciatic arteries. On each side a ventral branch then conveys much of it to the mesonephros while the main course supplies the portal system of the upper metanephric lobe.

8. SEX DIFFERENTIATION

The differentiation of the primitive, indifferent sex glands into ovaries and testes occurs during the metamorphic period (St. 30). It follows similar lines to those in all other terrestrial vertebrates. However, birds offer some special interest because of the extreme *asymmetry of the female sex organs*. The right oviduct is vestigial in all adult females, and the right ovary is reduced or absent in most species. The advantages secured by evolutionary suppression of the primitive duplicity of these organs are obvious. In flying animals, weight reduction is of vital importance. In adult female starlings averaging about 75 gm., the left oviduct, which weighs only 35 mg. during the non-breeding season, increases to more than 4 gm. at the height of the reproductive season. After ovulation, egg and oviduct together weigh from 8 to 10 gm. Moreover, the left ovary increases at this time from 10 mg. to nearly 2 gm. Therefore the total extra load represented by organs of the left side may at times rise to 15 per cent or more of the body weight. Since the eggs mature one by one, at intervals of a full day or more, a single oviduct is sufficient to take care of their delivery and the reduction of the right one relieves the bird of an unnecessary extra load.

Table 12

Right-Left Distribution of Germ Cells during Migration; Embryos of the Chick and of Songbirds

Age	Chick			Songbirds			cf. Fig.	Location
	R	M	L	R	M	L		
2 days	44	—	48	38	—	40	182	Splanchnic plates
Third day	370	—	383	518	—	529	185	Celomic angles
3 days	130	138	171*	341	195	770	194	Root of mesentery
4 days	317	243	509*	424	32	2009	195, 196	Gonad primordia
5½ days, ♀				481	1	1931		Differentiating ovary
5½ days, ♂				1538	—	4573		Differentiating testes

L left side; M medial position in root of mesentery; R right side

* Cited after Vannini.

In most birds, a *gonadal asymmetry* becomes first noticeable in three-day-old embryos. Larger numbers of migrating germ cells move toward the left than toward the right mesonephric fold (Figs. 194–196: Table 12). At four days, the majority of germ cells are implanted either in the *cortex* or in the *medulla* of the *primitive sex glands*. A few stragglers still are in the mesenchyme at the root of the mesentery. Others lie in the narrow space between cortex and medulla, the *albuginea* (Figs. 195, 196). This is called the *indifferent stage* in sex gland development. The data collected in Table 13 disclose that the asymmetric distribution of germ cells is now mostly a deficiency of the right cortex. There is good reason to conclude that the migration of germ cells is directed by chemotropism, and that the cortex of the right gonad exerts relatively little attraction. As a rule, the cortex of the left indifferent gonad contains twice or three times as many germ cells as the medulla. On the right side, the ratio is about the reverse.

Early in the sixth day a change occurs in the proportional distribution of the germ cells. In about half the embryos, the *left gonad* shows a distinct increase in the medulla; this is an expression of beginning *testicular differentiation*. In the other embryos, the gonia become relatively more numerous in the cortex, which is a sure sign of an *ovarian trend of differentiation*. In the case of male differentiation, a secondary migration of germ cells from the cortex to the medulla is involved. But in both sexes, the shift in proportion is mainly a result of mitotic multiplication of the germ cells in one system and degeneration in the other (cf. Table 13). Often a vestigial cortex covers part of the surface ·of the left testis even several days after metamorphosis (Fig. 204). Later it disappears completely.

The *right gonad* with its poorly developed cortex usually follows a

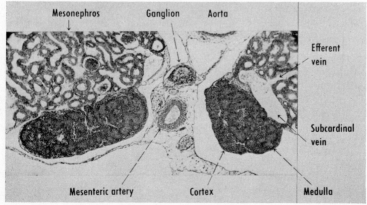

Figure 204.   Sparrow, male embryo, 8 days; stage 34a. Cross section through testes and mesonephric bodies. Left testis (right in figure) with considerable cortical remnant. In both glands the medulla consists almost entirely of seminal tubules; × 60.

testicular course of development in females as well as in males. The cortical rudiment degenerates while the number of medullary germ cells increases (Table 13). Exceptions to this rule do occur and are discussed below.

In the male, the medulla shows early a characteristic differentiation of compact cords in which the germ cells, now spermatogonia, become embedded; these are the *primitive seminal tubules* (Fig. 204).

The development of the *oviducts* during the metamorphic period is indicated in Figures 203A, B, C. Each oviducal field (Fig. 193) deepens into a funnel that slowly lengthens into a narrow tube along the lateral surface of the mesonephric body. Gruenwald has shown that after the interruption of the mesonephric duct the oviduct stops its downgrowth at the same level (Fig. 202). The reason for this seems to be a purely mechanical condition, the tip of the oviduct being caught within the enveloping membranes of the mesonephric duct.

The *adrenal*, which develops in close relationship with the sex glands, becomes a compact body (Fig. 203). Its *cortical part* differentiates into cords that resemble those of the testicular medulla as well as immature nephrons. The *medullary part* becomes more slowly organized. At the present stage it consists of clusters of round or stellate cells on the surface of the compact cortex.

9. PAIRED APPENDAGES

The dorsoventrally compressed, paddle-shaped limb buds transform into primitive *pentadactyl extremities*. Throughout this period they retain the primary orientation, so that the first digits (fingers, toes) and the preaxial (radial, tibial) parts are at the upper edge; the fifth digits and the postaxial (ulnar, fibular) parts at the lower edge. Also, the palmar (plantar) or flexor sides face ventrally, the extensor sides, dorsally. The differentiation into stylopodium, zeugopodium, and autopodium progresses swiftly; digits become visible before the end of the

Table 13

Distribution of Germ Cells in Passerine Birds during the Progress of Sex Differentiation

BIRD	AGE	RIGHT GONAD			MESEN-TERY	LEFT GONAD			SEX
		Cortex	Albuginea	Medulla		Cortex	Albuginea	Medulla	
Passer. domest.	100 hours	28	8	39	11	241	39	128	indiff.
Passer. domest.	102 hours	180	57	187	32	1423	86	500	indiff.
Agelaius phoen.	5½ days	25*	46	410	1	1536	143	252*	early ♀
Agelaius phoen.	5½ days	68*	35	1435	—	1724*	86	2763	early ♂

* Many of these in process of degeneration.

fifth day. The development of the girdle skeletons becomes recognizable, superficially, by the appearance of broad folds around the base of each limb. As in amphibians, the skeletal parts and most of the muscles of the limbs arise from the somatopleure. At four days, one notices a precartilaginous condensation within the blastema of the limb buds. During the fifth day, definite centers of cartilage formation appear, and by the end of the sixth day, a fairly complete cartilaginous skeleton has arisen. In the upper limbs the first, second, and third digits are represented by proximal cartilage pieces and distal blastemic pads (Fig. 199). The fourth and fifth are barely identifiable condensation of tissue. The composition of the lower limbs is very similar at this early stage.

10. TAIL

The tail reaches its greatest length in terms of somites at the end of the fourth day. In the songbirds (Fig. 197) one counts forty fully individualized body segments. Four more are incompletely separated from the tail blastema. Together with the four occipital and two early disappearing metotic segments, this gives a total number of 50 somites for the passerines. In the chick this number is larger by at least three (compare Table 9 and Fig. 203). During the two metamorphic days, the histologic differentiation of the segments at the base of the tail progresses with the formation of muscles and parts of a cartilaginous skeleton. The last spinal ganglion of passerines is found at four days in the thirty-third or thirty-fourth body segment (Fig. 197), at five and at six days in the thirty-seventh. In a chick of five days, it was located in the forty-first segment. The very end of the tail shows regressive changes; the segmental limits become indistinct; beginning fibrotic transformations are the first step toward the development of the vestigial terminal part of the bird tail known as the *pygostyle*.

Chapter 18

Fetuses and Nestling

Birds (St. 34-36). I

Through the process of metamorphosis, the embryo becomes a *fetus*. It is structurally a pulmonate tetrapod, but the functioning of the newly acquired respiratory and locomotor organs is temporarily suspended. This condition persists until hatching.

The course of postmetamorphic development is conveniently divided in three phases, in accordance with the condition of the eyelids. They are present only as rudimentary folds at the start of the fetal period (Fig. 206, 8d). During stage 34 they constantly grow and finally fuse. Stage 35 is characterized by closed eyelids (Figs. 205, 207, 208). Stage 36 begins with the reopening of the lids and lasts until termination of parental care.

1. HATCHING

A fairly close correlation exists between egg size, incubation time, and developmental stage attained at hatching (Table 8). The latter is also related to the extent of parental care and nest building. Most advanced are the *nest quitters* which leave the nest immediately after hatching and secure their own food. The above-mentioned megapods (p. 225) represent an extreme and obviously the most primitive case. Their newly hatched young are relatively large, covered with a plumage

resembling the adult, and are able to fly. The domestic chick, somewhat less mature, still serves as a good representative of the nest quit-
ting (nidifugous) type. At hatching, the chicks are covered with
down. Their wings have a few rows of partly emerged contour feathers,
remiges, and coverts (Fig. 213*b*), but they are not capable of flight for
another week. The young chick receives some protection and guidance
from one or both parents, but picks up its own food.

The least modified of the *nest sitters,* such as the herring gulls, are
nearly as far advanced at hatching as the chick, and it is mainly the fact
that they are regularly fed by their parents that keeps them located at
or near the nests.

The extreme type of *nest sitters* (Table 8), of which the domestic
sparrow is a good example, hatch very precociously, usually about the
thirteenth day of incubation. At this time the sparrow most closely
resembles the incubating chick of 14 or 15 days, but is entirely naked
(Figs. 207, 208). Feather germs which first appear on the eighth day
regress and become dormant on the tenth (Figs. 206, 207). Probably
the suppression of the early down plumage is an adaptation to living
within the nest. The helpless young lie in the depth of the nest, warm-
ing each other, and when necessary they are protected by a parent.
Also, a fluffy down plumage might render cleanliness difficult. Contour feathers of the wings begin to break through on the fourth day
after hatching (Fig. 208); the eyelids open one or two days later. During the first week of development in the nest, the external appearance
of the sparrow keeps pace with the morphologic development of the
chick within its shell, and at the total age of 21 days, the nestling

St. 34   St. 35   St. 36

Figure 205.   Development of the brown leghorn chick during second half
of the incubation period (10 days, stage 34; 16 days, stage 35; and 20 days, stage
36); × ⅔.

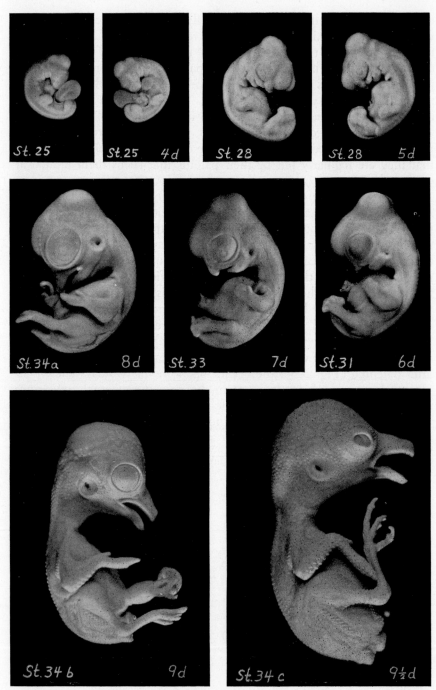

Figure 206.   Standard stages of sparrow development from the age of 4 days
(embryo), through metamorphosis (5 to 7 days), to the first fetal stage at the age
of 8 to 10 days; × 4.5.

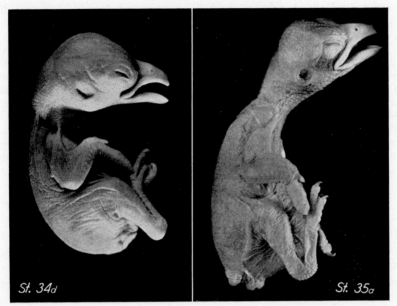

Figure 207.   Standard stages of sparrow development, beginning of the second fetal stage. 10 Days, stage 34d; 13 days, stage 35a (hatching); × 3.

St. 35b   St. 35c

Figure 208.   Standard stages of sparrow development, second fetal stage. 14 Days (1 day after hatching, St. 35b) and 18 days (5 days after hatching, St. 35c); × 1.

sparrow and the hatching chick have attained closely corresponding stages of differentiation. One week later, both are able to fly.

The biologic importance of precocious hatching can be seen in the accompanying reduction of egg size. The eggs of various birds, for which data are available, lose about 40 per cent of their weight during incubation, regardless of its duration (Table 14). Therefore, assuming that a sparrow should hatch on the twentieth day, when it has attained the developmental stage of a hatching leghorn chick, and when it weighs close to 20 gm., the egg would have to carry food material for an additional week and weigh about 30 gm. instead of the actual 3 gm. It is quite evident that eggs of such relative size are impossible and that the evolution of the small birds actually depended on the evolution of precocious hatching.

2. GROWTH

The speed of development—growth as well as morphologic differentiation—is controlled by constitutional factors. Basically, it depends on little-known enzyme systems that are set up during the growth of the ovocytes in the ovaries. The parakeet and the sparrow have eggs of similar size, and both hatch at the same developmental stage; but the former is considerably slower than the latter (Table 8). Hawks proceed at comparatively slow rates. The chicken hatches earlier than any other nest quitters. The songbirds as a group not only have the shortest incubation period, but actually differentiate and grow faster than all others (see p. 227).

During the first nine days of incubation the sparrow and the domestic chicken proceed at nearly equal rate. The same descriptions of timed stages are applicable to both species, except for size and some minor specific differences. The normal stages of sparrow development shown in Figure 206 are also representative of the chicken. However, on the tenth day, the sparrow begins to progress faster, probably in preparation for the approaching hatching process. This spurt is more sustained with respect to internal organs than to external morphology. In outside appearance the 20-day-old nestling sparrow seems only about one day ahead of the chick (compare Figs. 207, 208 with 205); however, on this day its lungs have been functioning for nearly 10 days while those of the chick are just starting. The differentiation of the

Table 14

Average Weights of Unincubated Eggs and Hatching Birds

SPECIES	EGG WEIGHT grams	HATCHING YOUNG grams	WEIGHT LOSS* per cent
White leghorn chicken	58	34	41
Domestic turkey	85	48	44
Herring gull	97	61	37
Sparrow	2.8	1.7	40

* Includes shell and discarded membranes.

Table 15

Size and Weight at Various Stages of the Sparrow and Leghorn Chicken

AGE days	SPARROW LENGTH mm.		WEIGHT gm.	GROWTH RATE	LEGHORN CHICKEN LENGTH mm.		WEIGHT gm.	GROWTH RATE
4	4		.006		8		.073	
		M		× 3.5		M		× 2.3
5	6.5	M	.021		12	M	.170	
		M		× 2.5		M		× 2.1
6	8.5	M	.055		14.5	M	.348	
				× 1.5				× 1.9
7	9.4		.084				.663	
				× 1.4				× 1.7
8	10		.115		20		1.132	
		I		× 1.8				× 1.4
9	13	I	.207				1.585	
		I		× 2.5				× 1.3
10	18	I	.521		30	I	2.035	
		I		1.7		I		× 1.6
11	23	I	.908		34	I	3.267	
				× 1.3		I		× 1.4
12	28		1.163		40	I	4.382	
				× 1.5		I		× 1.4
13	33	H	1.700		49	I	6.283	
				× 2		I		× 1.3
14	37		3.400		56	I	8.283	
				× 1.5		I		× 1.5
15	40		5		64	I	12	
				× 1.6		I		× 1.3
16	43		8		68		16	
				× 1.3				× 1.1
17	52		10				18	
				× 1.3				× 1.2
18	66		13		73		22	
				× 1.2				× 1.1
19	74	E	16		80		24	
				× 1.2				× 1.2
20	81		19		85	E	28	
				× 1.1				× 1.2
21	85		21		86	H	35	
28	90	F	26			F	63	
70	100		28				700	
Adult	100		28		500		2800 (cock)	

E eyelids open; F fledging day; H hatching day; I ingestion of albumen; M metamorphosis.

Data on Leghorn weights mostly from Henderson and Penquite.

circulatory and the urogenital organs is also in advance, by one week or more.

The rise in weight increment during part of the fetal period (table 15, sparrow ninth to eleventh day; chicken eleventh to fifteenth day) is based not•only on growth, but particularly on the ingestion of the egg white after the reopening of the chorio-amniotic canal (Figs. 222, 223).

The nest sitters grow more rapidly than the quitters (Table 15). The chick embryo of four days is about twice as long and 10 to 14 times as heavy as the sparrow embryo; but at the age of 20 days, the differences in size and weight have become only small. At this time, the sparrow attains two-thirds of the adult weight of the species; the chick only 1 per cent. At fledging time the sparrow is practically full grown; the chick approaches full weight only at about 10 months. The growth curves in Figure 209 clearly express the tendency of shortening the growth period in the nest sitters. Sea gulls keep an intermediate position between representatives of the extreme types.

3. NURTURE

Precocious hatching is possible only in combination with caretaking by parents or—as in the case of cowbirds—by foster parents. The nests often are substantially built and adapted to serve not only during incubation, but also later, as nurseries. The parent birds begin bringing in food immediately after the hatch of the first young. In many species in which the female alone incubates, the male comes to the nest to feed the mother, the nestlings, or both.

Often the food collected for the young is entirely different from that consumed by the parents. Exclusive or near-exclusive seed eaters among the finches bring soft insect food to their young. Later when they change over to grain, they may soften

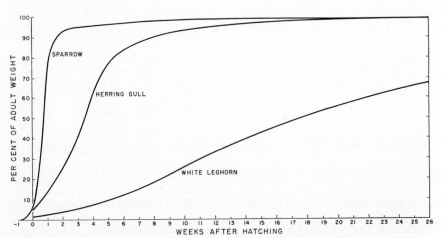

Figure 209.   Characteristic growth curves of nest sitters and nest quitters, during the six months following hatching (data collected with the assistance of W. R. Boss).

and predigest it in their crops and stomachs, and regurgitate into the beaks of the near fledglings.

Young and parent cooperate, often with intricate behavior patterns, in keeping nests clean. The many morphologic, physiologic, and behavioristic adaptations in the young and the parent, which complement each other or unite into single patterns, represent some of the most fascinating features of animal evolution.

4. EXTERNAL APPEARANCE

a. **Bill.** For most birds the bill is an important tool, serving not only in the ordinary role of jaws but also like a human hand in nest building and a variety of other occupations. Immediately following metamorphosis, it grows to a considerable length (St. 31 to 34, Fig. 206). The entire back and the tip of the upper jaw—usually called upper mandible—is formed by the excessive development of the fronto-nasal *premaxillary process*. The part below the external nares and much of the roof of the mouth is derived from the *maxillary processes* of the mandibular arches. The left and right mandibular processes unite in the formation of the *lower mandible*. The center part of the mandibular arch becomes the quadrate which, with joints at both ends, connects upper and lower mandibles. The skeletal parts are largely covered with horny sheaths (Figs. 207, 208).

b. **Eye** (Fig. 206). In the early fetus nearly the entire distal surface of the eyeball is exposed. The lens is visible through the pupillary opening of the iris. A *sclerotic coat* covers much of the peripheral part of the bulb. On the seventh day (St. 33), several *papillae* appear near the central margin of the sclera. With ectodermal thickenings in the covering conjunctiva, they resemble the feather germs which at the same time make their first appearance in certain regions of the skin. After the eighth day, the *circular lid-folds* grow rapidly over the eyeballs. First their advance is concentric and the visible part of the eyeball becomes rapidly smaller. At nine days, the sclera is covered on the lower side while papillae are still visible above. Then separate *upper and lower lids* begin to form; through their growth, the opening becomes oval (Fig. 214), later lens-shaped (Figs. 206, 223; 9½d), and finally it closes (Fig. 207; 10d). The remaining short lids do not actually fuse but are tightly shut, with their edges adhering superficially to each other (Fig. 207; 13d). When they open again later, they expose only the corneal center of the eye bulb; the scleral part remains enclosed in the *lid sac*. The latter is fastened to the bulb and a conjunctival sac persists only under the secondary eyelids.

It is easily seen that the lower lid grows much larger than the upper (Figs. 205; 16d, 20d and 207; 13d). In fact, in sparrows, chicks and most other birds, the eyes are shut by lifting of the lower lid. Simultaneously with the lids arises the *nictitating membrane*. At first, it is merely a crescent-shaped fold of the conjunctiva and the inner rim of the lids (Fig. 214a). Later, it can be pulled over the entire cornea. It becomes almost perfectly transparent and serves for frequent cleansing and lubricating movements. The lids of many birds are closed only during sleep.

c. Ear. The external ear develops from the dorsal part of the first visceral cleft and the first and second visceral arches (St. 28, Fig. 198*a*). In the six-day-old fetus the *external ear duct*, or acoustic meatus, is merely a shallow pit, walled by parts of the mandibular and hyoid arches (St. 32, Fig. 198*c*). During the following days it deepens into a pouch which grows inside, over the tympanic end of the pharyngeal auditory tube. The external meatus remains a narrow cleft until about the eighteenth day. Correspondingly, the sense of hearing of the young nestling sparrows is not very keen. Later, about the time when the eyes reopen, the cleft expands into a wide duct which participates in the formation of the *tympanic membrane*. From the eighth day on, the *external opening* is almost exactly circular (Figs. 206, 214*a*). At the end of stage 35 it becomes shielded by contour feathers (Fig. 205).

d. Wings. It is easy to recognize three rays in the terminal part of the primitive wing of six-day-old fetuses (St. 31, 32; Figs. 198*a*, 206). On sections, one can also identify a fourth digit at the lower or ulnar side of the hand (Fig. 199). But the position of the fifth ray of the pentadactyle prototype remains conjectural, since further but distinct condensations appear on the radial as well as on the ulnar sides. Following metamorphosis, the hand develops into a very characteristic and specialized part of the wing. The metacarpus gradually flexes toward the ulnar side. Hand and lower arm assume the shape of a flat rudder, which later becomes tremendously enlarged through the growth of the flight feathers or *remiges* (Figs. 205–208; 213*b*).

e. Legs. At the end of metamorphosis the primitive leg is similar to the wing. However, the fourth ray is as well developed as the first three. The fifth is missing in all birds (St. 31; Fig. 206). Since the entire body is supported by only two legs, the thigh early turns upward, bringing the knee joint close to the center of the body (Figs. 198*c*, 206). The lower part of the leg becomes jointed in a peculiar way. The proximal ossicles of the tarsus fuse with the large tibia, while the distal ones join with the long second, third, and fourth metatarsals to form a single long bone, the *tarso-metatarsus*, or *shank*. Therefore, ankle and tarsal joints become reduced into a single *intertarsal joint* or *hock*. Usually it is held high above the ground, which is touched only by the toes.

f. Tail. Recent birds have a short but strong tail, containing a skeleton of six distinct *caudal vertebrae* and the *pygostyle*, a bone containing the fused remnants of at least six additional vertebrae. In the adult the main tail feathers, usually six pairs, appear terminally inserted, fastened mainly to the pygostyle. On the other hand, in the possible prototype of the modern bird, *Archaeopteryx*, the tail feathers are segmentally arranged, one pair attached to each caudal vertebra. It is therefore of interest that in fetuses the papillae of the tail feathers still show the ancestral segmental arrangement alongside the caudal vertebrae (Fig. 210). Eight-day old fetuses of sparrows and chicks exhibit this rudimentary "Archaeopteryx tail" at the height of its development (Figs. 206, 220).

g. **Epidermal Differentiations.**   The epidermis produces a variety of specialized structures through cornification of its surface layers. The ends of the toes and sometimes of the fingers are furnished with *claws;* the shanks become covered with *scales;* the *bills* develop horny sheaths; and a plumage variously composed of *filoplumes, down,* and *contour feathers* spreads over the larger part of the body.

The *process of cornification* in its simplest form may be studied in the *bill* of an adult bird (Fig. 211). Sections through the upper part show the premaxillary bone covered by a thin *corium* which contains nerves, blood vessels, and numerous bundles of collagenous fibrils. The *epidermis* is stratified. The *basal layer* is attached to a basement membrane and consists of prismatic cells. Through mitotic activity, it produces and constantly renews the more peripheral layers. By their histochemical reactions, the middle or *granular layer* of cuboidal cells and the peripheral *cornified layer* appear sharply delimited. This is the consequence of the sudden keratinization of the peripherally moving

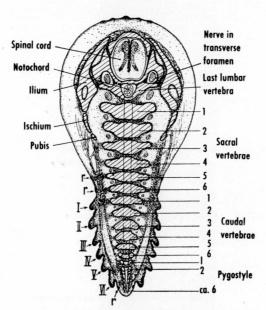

Figure 210.   Fetus of an owl (22 mm.). Cross section through last lumbar vertebra, combined with frontal section through sacrocaudal region; showing segmental arrangement of buds of tail feathers (I–VI); *r,* rudimentary feather germs (Steiner 1938).

cells that now become compressed into scaly platelets. The growth within the epidermis is not only directed toward the surface, but also toward the apex of the bill. Birds kept in captivity with soft food often grow excessively long bills because of insufficient wear.

The *development of feathers* rests on the same principles of epidermal proliferation and cornification. It starts with the differentiation of a mesodermal nutritional supply system, the well vascularized *corium papillae* (Fig. 212). The epidermis thickens slowly, and proliferates the horny parts of the feathers. In brief, the feather arises as a cornified surface structure of the papilla and then becomes independent through degeneration of the distal part of its mesodermal core, the *pulp*. F. R. Lillie, Juhn, and Wang have made a comprehensive study of feather development. The following description is largely based on their work.

Feather papillae appear in definite number and order during the early days of fetal development. They are arranged in *feather tracts* or pterylae, limited areas within the otherwise bare skin, the apterium.

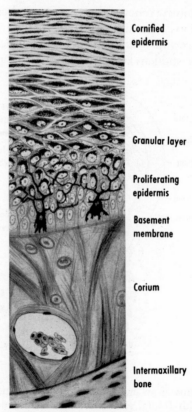

Cornified epidermis

Granular layer

Proliferating epidermis

Basement membrane

Corium

Intermaxillary bone

Figure 211.   Part of section through bill of a sparrow. Two melanophores supply epidermis cells with melanin (Witschi and Woods 1936); × 320.

Each tract begins as a slight general elevation, caused by subepidermal condensation of corium cells (Fig. 206, at 6–7 days). On this ridge rise successive series of lentil-shaped primitive feather papillae (Figs. 206; 8 to 9½ days, 212*a*, 221). As the papillae grow, they project over the surface; but their base also becomes more deeply imbedded in the dermis (Fig. 212*b*, *c*). The follicles produce first *down feathers,* and afterward *contour feathers.* The down may be shed, or for some time carried on the tip of the shaft of the contour feather (Fig. 213). After the tenth day the feather papillae of finches usually disappear in the depth of their follicles. In the sparrow the down generation is

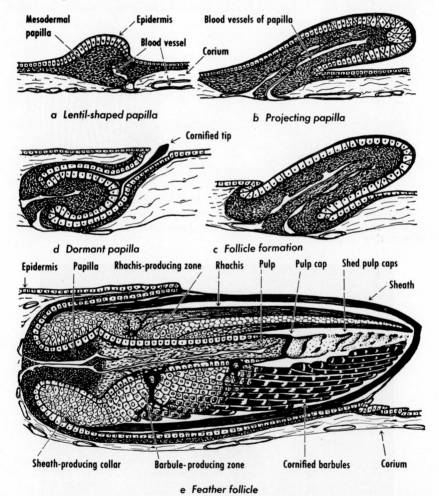

Figure 212.   Stages of feather development (semidiagrammatic). *a–c,* Early stages. *d,* Dormant papilla of sparrow fetus. *e,* Sagittal section, through mature feather germ (more enlarged in width than length); formation of rhachis on outer side, barbs and barbules on inner side. Only three melanophores are shown (actual number 20 to 50 per section).

completely suppressed or reduced to insignificant horny vestiges (Fig. 212*d*). In the redwing blackbird, the robin, the starling, and many other passerines, a few feather germs continue development, while the large majority become dormant, like those of the sparrow. Accordingly, the hatching nestlings have just a few isolated groups of down feathers (Fig. 214*a, b*). Fledging robins still present a fuzzy appearance, with conspicuous tufts of down at the ends of some contours above the eyes and in a few other places.

The epidermis displays a capacity to produce cornified parts of many shapes (Fig. 212*e*). A short collar around the base furnishes the *feather sheath*. From the longer cylinder around the pulp sprout *barbules*,

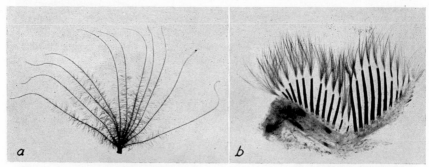

Figure 213.   Feathers of the newly hatched chick (Watterson 1942). *a,* Down feather with calamus; 12 barbs and paired series of barbules; × 3.5. *b,* Wing; flight feathers in sheaths (pin feathers) and down (feathers with down) attached to their tips; × 1.5.

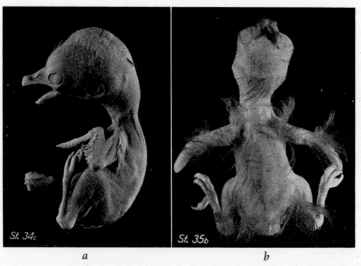

Figure 214.   Redwing blackbird. *a,* Fetus 9¼ days incubation, stage 34c; feather tracts with many dormant and few developed germs; × 2.5. *b,* Newly hatched nestling, stage 35b, with few down feathers, 13½ days old; × 1.5.

barbs, and *rhachis.* The tips of the barbules form at the inner side (toward the body of the bird) directly above the sheath collar. The mid-parts follow as the barbule grows in the apical direction. When a pile of cells reaches a certain length, the tip cornifies. The proximal part of the barbule is added from the lateral rim of the proliferating cylinder. Here also starts the formation of *barbs* which collect the barbules and become attached to the shaft. At the outer side of the papilla of contour feathers, forms the single shaft or *rhachis* with a spongy core of air-filled cells and a compact surface layer (Fig. 212e). The epidermis covering the tip of the pulp also cornifies and produces a series of *pulp caps.*

While *down feathers* have only a single set of barbs and no shaft (Fig. 213), in *contour feathers* barbs follow each other in long series (Fig. 216b, c).

Feather development terminates with the *quill* or *calamus* to which fastens also the base of the feather sheath. During the last stage the pulp recedes and the shortened papilla remains quiescent as long as it is enclosed in the base of the quill. Accidental loss or shedding of the feather during seasonal molting results in reactivation of the papilla. Its regenerative capacity seems unlimited.

Experiments by Wang (cf. Fig. 215) show that after complete extirpation of the papilla a feather does not regenerate. However, if another papilla is transplanted into the empty follicle, it will produce a new feather. If transferred from the saddle track into a breast follicle, it still produces a saddle feather, and if rotated at the time of the operation the regenerated feather shows irregularities that indicate an existing fixation of its symmetry axes. Wang further showed that

Figure 215.   Diagram of feather germ (Wang 1943) showing positions of normal (*h*) and transplanted (*g*) papillae.

transplanted "denuded" papillae, consisting only of the mesodermal core, may become covered with epidermis from the lower part of the empty follicle. Feathers resulting from such an arrangement exhibit the type of the site of implantation, but their orientation depends on that of the implant. Of the two components of the papilla the mesodermal part does not regenerate from extrapapillary corium. The epidermal part can be replaced by epidermis from the basal half of the follicle; but extrafollicular epidermis has no feather-forming capacity. Thus each component carries a set of determinations: the *epidermis* those of feather shape and color pattern, the *mesodermal core* those of feather orientation.

h. Pigmentation.   The variety of the epidermal structures becomes further increased through the addition of pigments. The development of the brown and black melanins is better studied than that of the yellow, orange, or red lipochromes, carotenoids, and more rare dyes. The melanins are formed by special cells which, as Dorris proved, are derived from the neural crest of the central nervous system. These *melanophores* begin their migration during the second day of incubation. They arrive in the territory of prospective wing buds during the first half of the third day of incubation. They are widely distributed

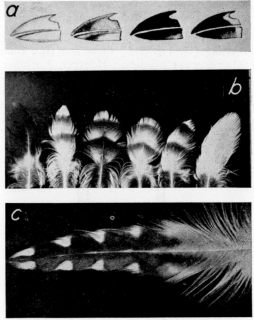

Figure 216.   Melanin reactions. *a,* Bills of castrated sparrow males. Left: Uninjected. Center two: Testosterone injected. Right: One week after last testosterone injection, uncolored base of bill again appearing (Witschi and Woods 1936). *b,* Subtail feathers of Wydah finches; left, cock type, right, hen type; center, four hen feathers, each recording two injections of luteinizing hormone (LH); since the interval was four days, feather growth amounted to 1.1 mm. per day (Witschi 1950). *c,* Saddle feather of brown leghorn cock injected every sixth day with 1.5 mg. of thyroxin (Lillie and Juhn 1932).

in the epidermis of colored breeds and species, several days before horny structures begin to differentiate. They remain colorless up to the stage of cornification. By this time the melanophores are anchored with short dendrites at the basement membrane of the epidermis (Figs. 211, 212e). Much longer processes reach toward the cells of the granular layer into which they inject portions of their pigment. The granules accumulate over the peripheral surface of the nuclei and become imbedded into the keratin substance during cornification.

Formation and delivery of the melanins is often under *hormonal control*. The production of colors that are distinctive of one sex, or of the breeding season (nuptial colors), frequently depends on the appearance of gonadal and hypophyseal sex hormones in the blood stream. As little as 0.25 micrograms of testosterone propionate injected into the breast muscle of a castrate sparrow induces pigment formation in its bill (Fig. 216a). On the other hand in the feathers of weaver finches, pigmentation is induced by small amounts of a hypophyseal gonadotrophic substance (Fig. 216b). Yet not all variations are of a sexual type. The change from juvenile to adult plumages is probably more closely related to modifications in the basic metabolism attending the progress of development. Although experiments have not disclosed the entire control mechanism, it is known that thyroxin has a profound influence on both structure and coloration of feathers (Fig. 216c), and sometimes induces the regeneration of juvenile types of plumage in adult birds.

Experimental induction of pigment reactions has become a valuable tool in the study of bill and feather development. The upper margin of a bar indicates all points of barbs and barbules that receive pigment at approximately the same time. Hence, the distance between the starting lines of two bars, divided by the time elapsed between two injections, expresses the rate of growth of the feather (Fig. 216b, c).

Many factors of pattern formation still defy analysis and interpretation. In some investigations by Willier and Rawles a dominating importance of *genetic constitution* was demonstrated. Melanophores of barred Plymouth Rock transferred to white Leghorn chicks produced barred Leghorn feathers. As expected, transplanted pigment cells maintained the color and pattern characteristics of their genetic type.

5. SKELETON

In embryos of the fifth day, *precartilaginous condensations of mesenchyme* indicate the location and general morphology of the future axial and appendicular skeletal systems. As the lower half of each sclerotome fuses with the upper half of the following one, primitive *vertebral bodies* are formed that *alternate in position with the myotomes*. Chondrification begins immediately and results in the formation of a nearly complete cartilaginous skeleton at eight days. Ossification begins on the eighth day. During the remainder of the fetal period, the *membrane bones* develop much faster than the *cartilage bones*. One distinguishes *perichondrial bone formation*—starting from a surface membrane, the periost—and *endochondrial ossification,* with osteoblasts becoming active within the primordial cartilages. The latter type prevails in the development of the vertebral bodies, the former in the formation of the long bones. The lack of independent epiphyseal centers of ossification in the long bones is a feature shared with amphibians and may be considered primitive. The vertebrae of the sacral and lumbar regions fuse and, absorbing also the last thoracic and the first caudal vertebrae, form the *synsacrum.* To the lateral sides of this large bone are joined the left and right halves of the pelvis which remain widely separated ventrally, except in the ostrich and the nandu.

Another peculiarity of birds is the persistence, and often excessive growth, of *long horns of the hyoid apparatus.* They arise from the cartilages of the third visceral arch. In woodpeckers, in the resting condition, they circle around the occiput and their ends become lodged in cavities of the upper bill. They support the long, flexible tongue which, in some species, can be extended to a length surpassing that of the head.

6. RESPIRATORY ORGANS

a. Lungs. After metamorphosis the lungs follow a course of development which prepares them to become the most efficient respiratory organ found in any terrestrial vertebrates. Two features are almost unique for birds, namely, (1) the transformation of the bronchial tree into a system of *bronchial circuits,* and (2) the differentiation of respiratory sections, the *lungs proper,* and large non-respiratory *air sacs.* On the ninth day of incubation, both particularities are already apparent. Each lung differentiates into two sections of which the upper comprises the *vestibule* with the first four secondary bronchi, while the lower consists of the *mesobronchus* and the remaining secondary bronchi, which may now number twenty or more. All except the most recently formed secondary bronchi have started to branch out again. The new tertiary bronchi or *parabronchi* of the two sections grow toward each other until they meet in an oblique septum across the entire lung (Fig. 217). Here mesenchymal condensation and abundant vascularization precede the *formation of terminal anastomoses between the two sets of parabronchi;* this occurs on the fifteenth day in the chick, but as early as the end of the ninth day of incubation in the sparrow and the redwing blackbird (Fig. 218). In the days that remain until hatching, *air capillaries* arise from the walls of the parabronchi which thereby become spongy hexagonal cylinders. The walls of these cylinders soon become covered with a network of arterioles and venules of the pulmonary vascular system. The finer blood capillaries enter the air capillaries. After hatching, the endodermal epithelium regresses so that the endothelia of the vessels remain the only barrier between the air and the circulating blood.

The *air sacs* (Figs. 217, 219) are the non-respiratory parts of the lungs. Like the secondary and tertiary bronchi, they are directly or indirectly connected with either vestibulum or mesobronchus. The latter group consists of the *abdominal sac* which arises from the end of the mesobronchus, and the *lower thoracic sac,* originating from one of the inferior bronchi. The vestibular group starts from four branches of the superior bronchi. The uppermost one develops into the *cervical sac.* The next two fuse with each other, and with the corresponding diverticulums of the other lung, into the single *interclavicular sac.* The last one becomes the *upper thoracic sac.* In addition to their original connections with the bronchial system, new *recurrent bronchi* or saccobronchi grow out from all air sacs, except the cervical ones, and anastomose extensively with the secondary and parabronchi.

Since the openings of the secondary bronchi into the bronchial tube are provided with constrictor muscles and some of the main passages have valves, the *mechanics of the bird lung* is evidently complicated and adaptable to various

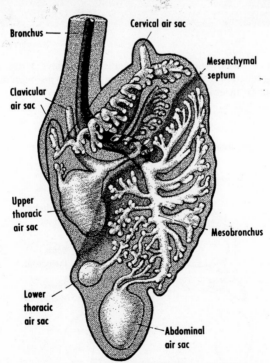

Figure 217.   Lung of the chick, at end of ninth incubation day. From the vestibule of the upper lung (darkly shaded) arise four secondary bronchi; of the last two only the proximal parts are shown. The mesenchymal condensation (septum) between upper and lower sections of the lung is indicated by close stippling.

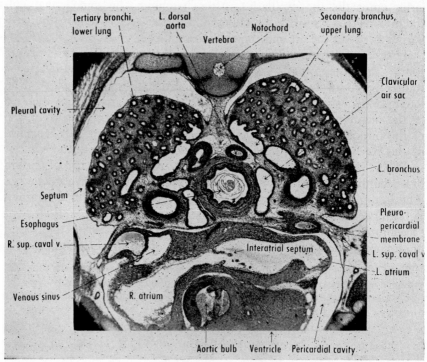

Figure 218.   Redwing (*Agelaius*) fetus of 8⅓ days. Cross section through lungs, showing separation of upper and lower divisions by mesenchymal septum; swallowed albumen in esophagus; × 33.

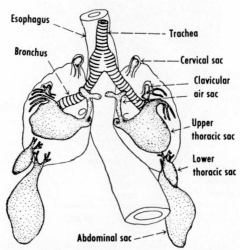

Figure 219.   Chick, fetus 10½ days. Ventral view of lungs with primitive air sacs and recurrent bronchi (Locy and Larsell 1916).

external conditions. Under simplest conditions, in the resting bird, inhalation probably brings the air through the open vestibule and mesobronchus into the abdominal sac. From here it is pressed through the saccobronchi into the inferior bronchi, the system of parabronchi and air capillaries, and out through the superior bronchi into the vestibulum and the vestibular air sacs. The air may be exhaled or passed through the respiratory passages again. In diving birds, the air is probably passed repeatedly between the opposing vestibular and mesobronchial air sacs. This arrangement permits ducks to stay under water as long as 15 minutes without discomfort.

Respiratory movements apparently become initiated immediately after the parabronchi of the upper and lower lung sections have developed into communicating channels. Since air is not available, amniotic fluid is drawn into the lung and the air sacs. At this stage it contains much albumen. Sections through *sparrow lungs* show the hollow spaces filled with thin albumen solutions on the tenth day, and with more concentrated ones on the eleventh. By the end of the twelfth day, the albumen is expelled and replaced by air.

Air is first taken into the lungs one or two days before hatching. Most birds begin then to make faint peeping sounds. In the *chick* they are usually heard on the nineteenth day of incubation, when the bill enters the air chamber. At this time the arterial ducts begin to contract, thereby forcing an increased flow of blood through the pulmonary vessels. On the twentieth day the bill pierces the egg shell and full pulmonary respiration is established before the chick hatches on the twenty-first day.

b. Primitive Forms of Gaseous Exchange.   As long as the bird embryo is small, respiration is accomplished by diffuse gaseous exchange across epidermis, fetal membranes (when present), albumen, and egg shell. This is, of course, a very imperfect method that can satisfy only small total requirements like those of the first-day blastoderms. As early as the second day various methods of stirring and shaking begin to develop which obviously facilitate the exchange of O_2 and CO_2. First the *pulsations of the heart*, starting at about the thirty-third hour of incubation, slightly agitate the celomic fluid.

Stirring becomes more effective following closure of the chorioamniotic pore, when *smooth muscle fibers* develop in the mesodermal surface of the amnion. Their contractions, beginning late in the fourth day, are automatic and myogenic; the amnion acquires no connections with the nervous system. Peristaltic waves running over the amnion produce rocking movements of the embryo about the anchoring umbilical cord; they soon become rhythmical. Candled, intact hens' eggs of five days undergo from 10 to 25 pendulations per minute. The rate is highest between the eighth and the tenth days. In the redwing and other songbirds, frequencies are about double, and maximums are reached during the seventh day. The movements slow down and stop completely before the thirteenth day in the chick, and about the ninth day in the redwing. The phase of acceleration parallels early body growth, while decrease follows the development of the allantois into a respiratory organ. Both relationships point toward a supporting respiratory importance of *amniotic peristalsis.*

A third type of muscular activity seems to start as a sort of *primitive swimming movements of the body.* According to Kuo, they begin about the middle of the fourth day with lifting and bending of the head; a few hours later, the trunk participates in the contractions, curving alternately left and right. After the tenth day, more complex jerking and wriggling movements become substituted; they occur intermittently until the end of the incubation period. It is not probable that these spasmodic movements of the body are primarily respiratory, though possibly the seizures are to some degree linked with conditions created by the metabolic process.

c. Allantois. The allantois is the functional respiratory organ characteristic of the fetal period. After the sixth day it spreads quickly toward the pointed end of the shell (Fig. 200). Since the allantoic vein and the two branches of the left allantoic artery are slow to follow this expansion, the sac forms three lobes that pass between these vessels. Fusing again, they leave *septums* which enclose the arteries and veins that pass between the inner and the outer surfaces of the allantois (Figs. 220–222).

The expansion of the allantois is mechanically supported by the *increase in urine.* Fiske and Boyden determined its volume for the chicken as about 1 cc. at the

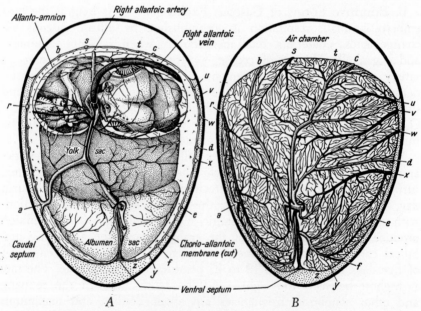

Figure 220. Sparrow, fetus within the egg; 8½ days. *A,* Ventral view after removal of half of the shell. *B,* Removed half of the chorio-allantois. From the umbilicus emerge left and right allantoic arteries and veins. *a–e,* Major branches of the left allantoic artery; *r–z,* major branches of the right allantoic vein. Clusters of crystals in the allantoic cavity indicate deposits of uric acid; (Witschi 1949); × 3.5.

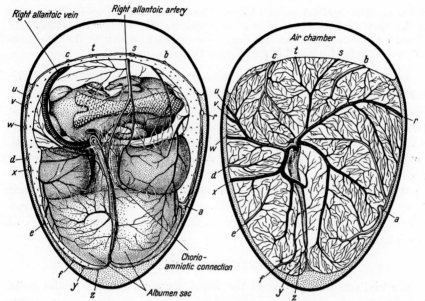

Figure 221.   Sparrow, fetus of 8½ days, within the egg; dorsal views of specimen shown in Fig. 220; × 3.5.

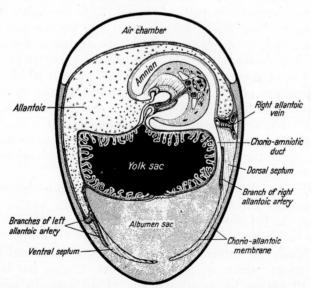

Figure 222.   Sparrow, fetus of 8½ days. Cross section through entire egg. The chorio-amniotic connection has developed a lumen and becomes an albumen duct. Yolk-sac epithelium with numerous septums. Diagrammatically, an entire loop of gut is reconstructed, to show the origins of yolk sac and allantois in the ventral wall of the intestine. From the dorsal aorta, the mesenteric artery descends through the mesentery, giving off left and right vitelline arteries. The small yolk-sac blastopore is closed toward the albumen sac by a remnant of vitelline membrane; × 3.5.

age of six days, and 6.5 cc. at 13 days. The latter amount is about 20 per cent of the entire water content at that stage. During the third week, reabsorption of water proceeds at a higher rate than urine excretion, so that by the nineteenth day very little fluid is found in the allantoic cavity.

At 15 to 16 days (nine in finches) the allantois has reached the maximum possible expansion. It now invests the entire inner surface of the shell membrane. The capillary network is so dense that the potential quantitative limit of gas exchange is reached. From the nineteenth day on, the blood entering the sixth aortic arches becomes increasingly diverted into the pulmonary arteries, and the allantois gradually dries up. A part of its inner wall is carried into the body cavity of the fetus by the yolk sac, to which it had become attached (Fig. 222). The larger portion, however, with the accumulated crystals of uric acid, remains outside, adhering to shell and feathers of the hatching chick.

7. NUTRITIONAL SYSTEM

Material economy is one of the many accomplishments of the avian egg. During the entire incubation period of the chicken, about 8 gm. of *water* is lost by evaporation. Experiments show that this amount may vary according to the relative humidity of the environment. But viability and hatchability suffer by even slight deviations from the optimal relative humidity of 60 per cent. The energy metabolism is maintained largely (over 90 per cent) by the oxidation of about 3 gm. of *fat,* i.e., half of the entire store. This does not involve any decrease in the weight of the egg, since the *metabolic water,* which is one of the end products of the process, compensates almost quantitatively for the loss of fat. Most impressive is the conservation of the *proteins* during their transfer from the external albumen layer and the yolk sac into the body of the fetus, and during their transformation into organized, living tissue. By the twentieth day, only about 4 per cent, i.e., one-fourth of a gram, has been destroyed.

Gradually, weight and volume of the *egg white* become much reduced through dehydration. In the chick the daily loss by transpiration amounts to 0.3 gm. under optimal humidity conditions. This loss in volume is compensated for by formation and expansion of the air chamber. Much more water is absorbed by the yolk sac and the fetus. Thus the white, which at laying was about 33 gm., has become reduced to 10 gm. at the incubation age of 11 days. In view of the established impermeability for colloids of the surface membranes of yolk sac and chorio-allantois, and the near absence of active digestive ferments in the albumen, it is not surprising to find that the egg white is now a very concentrated, viscous solution of proteins which, under the action of Bouin's or Zenker's fixatives, gels into a hard, homogeneous, amber-like mass.

Of particular interest is the *ingestion of the egg white* which, in the chick, occurs mainly between the eleventh and the sixteenth days, and in songbirds from the ninth to the eleventh. Through the development of the allantois, the albumen becomes gradually pushed toward the pointed end of the egg and enclosed in its folds. Thus a hemispheric *albumen sac* is formed under the flattened bottom of the yolk sac (Figs. 220–222). In the course of these developments the *chorio-amniotic connection* (Fig. 200) is drawn over the dorsal side of the yolk sac, so that finally it forms a broad ligament between albumen sac and amnion (Figs. 221, 222). During the ninth day of sparrow development this ligament acquires a central lumen and thus becomes an open *albumen duct* (Fig. 222). The albumen immediately begins to flow through it into the amniotic cavity. At 9½ days the sparrow fetus is deeply imbedded in an albumen mass (Fig. 223*a*). Soon after the opening of the canal, the fetus begins to ingest the mixture of amniotic fluid and albumen (Fig. 223*b*). Since the amnion muscles do not degenerate after cessation of the respiratory movements, it seems not unlikely that their contractions may now help in the transfer of the albumen. Swallowing movements of the fetus probably are the most important mechanical factor in the actual ingestion. In 10- and 11-day sparrow fetuses the albumen fills the intestine down to the coprodeum. At this time, the passage into the urodeum is temporarily closed (Fig. 223*b*). On the eleventh day, even lungs and air sacs are filled with albumen. On the twelfth they are again empty, and air breathing is starting. In stomach and intestine the albumen is rapidly digested and absorbed. Since the amniotic supply is exhausted at the end of the eleventh day, the digestive tract is nearly empty by the latter part of the twelfth day. Before hatching the remnant amniotic fluid is swallowed, and the young bird leaves the shell with a practically dry surface.

The formation of the albumen duct through reopening of the chorio-amniotic connection, with subsequent ingestion of the albumen, has also been observed in hawks and a number of other species and obviously is the common method of albumen absorption in all birds.

The most important store of food is contained in the *yolk sac*. Though the sac is connected with the gut by the yolk stalk, yolk is not transmitted directly into the embryo, but only after digestion and by way of the vitelline veins. The inner, digestive surface of the sac rises in many folds which penetrate deeply into the yolk mass (Fig. 222). Their mesodermal core contains the distal network of the vitelline blood vessels. From here, the vitelline veins carry a steadily swelling stream of metabolites and building materials to the fetus. The contents of the yolk sac are even ample enough to supply the young bird for a short period beyond hatching. Chicks can live at least four days without food intake. Sparrows and other birds hatching from

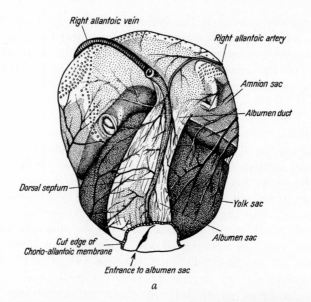

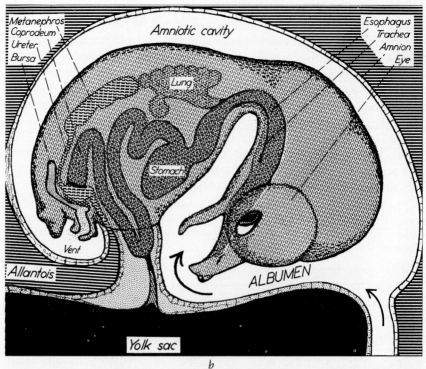

Figure 223.   *a*, Sparrow, fetus of 9½ days; shell and most of the chorio-allantoic membrane removed. The albumen has passed from the albumen sac into
the amnion. Fetus deeply imbedded in albumen; only left eye, top of head, back, and
left wing partly visible; × 3.5. *b*, Sparrow in amnion, at 10 days; digestive tract
and respiratory organs filled with ingested albumen.

small eggs are in more immediate need of food. Usually one finds their stomachs filled with insects even on the first day, and they double their weight within the first 24 hours (Table 15). Nevertheless, even these passerines do not hatch entirely without reserves. About 1½ days before hatching the yolk sac enters through the umbilical opening of the ventral body wall, which subsequently closes. In sparrows, the sac soon disappears completely. But in fowls and many other birds a small vitelline diverticulum persists and eventually becomes a lymphatic organ.

At the fetal stage the esophagus of most birds has already developed the *crop,* a mere extension which later serves as a food storing organ. During the same period the stomach differentiates into *proventricle* and *ventricle.* In the walls of the former arise various types of mucous and digestive glands; the latter becomes the muscle stomach or gizzard.

The differentiation of the hindgut and the cloacal bursa is indicated in Figures 203*a–d* and 223*b.* The *urodeal membrane* opens two or three days before hatching, so that at the very end of the incubation period the urine is voided through the vent, into the amniotic cavity.

8. CIRCULATORY ORGANS

a. **Heart.**   The separation of the ventricular chambers becomes completed through closure of the intraventricular foramen (Fig. 201) during the seventh day (sparrow). The perforations in the interatrial septum close at the approach of hatching, through endocardial growth. In hatching sparrows (13 days old) only a single pore is still open; it disappears soon after.

b. **Arteries and Veins.**   The primary roots of the basilar and vertebral arteries, of the external carotids, and of the subclavian arteries disappear completely during the fetal period (Fig. 201).

All the special arrangements of the fetal stage which serve the substitution of allantoic for pulmonary respiration regress toward the approach of hatching time and then disappear. The *arterial ducts* of the sixth aortic arches shrink, while the *pulmonary arteries and veins* pass more blood; at hatching they become occluded and disappear. Thereby the right fourth aortic or *systemic arch* becomes the sole root of the descending aorta. Simultaneously with the arterial ducts, the *allantoic arteries* also disappear; at hatching, their proximal stems within the body are much reduced in size and contain stagnant blood (Figs. 226, 227), while the large peripheral distribution system dries up. Later, the stems degenerate into fibrous ligaments or disappear entirely. The allantoic part of the *umbilical vein* disappears while the proximal part, between umbilicus and liver, persists as a small vessel, reassuming the name of *abdominal vein.*

The *vitelline arteries and veins* regress more slowly and disappear only days after hatching, together with the yolk sac. The *mesenteric arteries and veins* expand, as the intestinal tube assumes its trophic functions.

c. Lymphatic System. Morphology and function of the lymphatic system of the birds hold a position between the amphibian and mammalian types. Pulsating *lymph hearts*—present in the former, but absent in the latter—form and function in the chick during the fetal period, but disappear within about one month after hatching. *Valves*

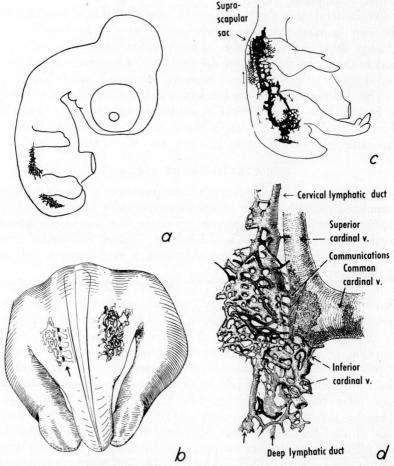

Figure 224.   Lymphatic system of chicks. *a*, Embryo of 5½ days incubation. Primary superficial lymphatic plexuses, before circulation; × 3.6. *b*, Embryo of 6 days incubation, dorsal view of tail region; lymph heart plexuses and connections with the intersegmental coccygeal veins (arrow); × 12. *c*. Fetus of 9 days. Superficial parts of lymphatic system of the right side. Arrows indicate direction of circulation; × 3.6. *d*, Embryo of 6 days. Lateral view of right jugular lymphatic plexus. Five connections with the cardinal veins are visible; arrow indicates ducts connecting superficial lymphatics with the jugular plexus (E. L. and E. R. Clark 1912, 1915, 1920). × 33.

and lymph nodes in the lymphatic ducts, a characteristic of the mammalian system, form in small numbers mainly after the disappearance of the hearts. In the duck, the ostrich, and a few other species, lymph hearts persist in the adult.

The development of the *superficial lymphatic plexuses* in the chick has been studied by C. and E. Clark. They appear in the course of the fifth day in the form of strands of endothelial cells and small vessels, as evaginations from branches of the venous system. The plexuses which give rise to the single pair of *lymph hearts* of the chick develop in connection with four to five coccygeal intersegmental veins (Fig. 224a, b). Pulsations begin late in the seventh day when the lymph flow, back to the venous system, is established (Fig. 224c, d). Many of the original connections with the veins disappear early, but the superficial lymph system of the body remains permanently connected only with the coccygeal segmentals and, through the jugular lymphatic plexus, with the superior caval veins. The lymph hearts are connected with the elaborate *allantoic system of lymph capillaries* by means of the *posterior lymph sac.* A finely branching system of lymphatic vessels spreads in the outer, respiratory surface of the allantois as well as in its under side. Since their reduction and disappearance accompanies that of the allantois, it seems likely that the allantoic lymphatic system and the lymph hearts play a role in the recovery of water from the allantoic fluid and in its return into the body circulation.

Chapter 19

Fetuses and Nestling

Birds. II

9. EXCRETORY ORGANS

a. Mesonephros. The differentiation of new nephrons, i.e., renal corpuscles and urinary tubules, came to an end during the metamorphic period. However, the mesonephric bodies continue growing and are the only excreting organs until the eleventh day, when metanephric elements gradually begin to function. Immediately following metamorphosis, the parts above the mesenteric arteries shrink and disappear (Fig. 203c–d). In the passerines the mesonephric bodies reach their largest size at 10 days (Fig. 226). During the eleventh day a sudden change occurs. The glomeruli of the renal corpuscles lose their blood supply, and all urinary tubules that are not connected with the gonadal medullae degenerate (Figs. 203D, 225). Within two days the middle kidneys shrink to about one-fourth of their volume (Figs. 226, 227). At hatching, only the tubules which have become a part of the genital complex persist. Their renal corpuscles also degenerate but more slowly. The mesonephros thus transforms into the *epididymis*. In the chick the mesonephros has a longer active period than in finches. Occlusion of the glomerular arterioles, marking the end of the functional phase, occurs on the nineteenth day of incubation.

b. Metanephros. On the eighth day of incubation the collecting tubules which arose by budding and branching of the metanephric duct are still imbedded in a blastemic cortex, though condensations around their ends indicate the beginning of the differentiation of nephrons (Fig. 203D). During the fetal period renal corpuscles and urinary tubules form in quick succession and make connections with the collecting tubules and ureters. On the eleventh day, arterial circulation becomes established in the first sets of glomeruli, and the ureters open into the urodeum (Figs. 226, 227). Gradually in the chick, but more rapidly in the songbirds, the function of excretion is taken over from the mesonephros.

c. Elimination of Nitrogenous Wastes.   The task of eliminating the wastes that arise from protein metabolism is simplified by the smallness of the quantities involved. The available analytical data, mostly by Fiske and Boyden, and by Needham, refer to the domestic chick. They indicate that about 250 mg. of proteins are destroyed during the entire incubation period. The resulting wastes are mainly *salts of uric acid*, but traces of urea and creatine are also excreted. The total amount of uric acid eliminated up to the day of hatching is near 100 mg., which accounts for combustion of 213 mg. of protein. Uric acid and its salts are of a very low solubility (about 1 part of uric acid in 1500 of water). Between the end of the embryonic period (St. 25) and hatching, the volume of urine excreted by the kidneys totals probably close to 1 liter. Since the allantois never contains more than 7 ml., it is obvious that allantoic reabsorption of water is highly

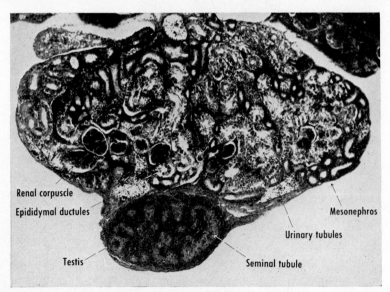

Renal corpuscle

Epididymal ductules

Mesonephros

Urinary tubules

Testis   Seminal tubule

Figure 225.   Redwing, fetus of eleventh day (St. 35a). Cross section through right testis and mesonephros; pyknotic transformation of glomeruli and degeneration of urinary tubules; × 75.

efficient. As a consequence of the increasing concentration, and since the allantoic membrane is impermeable to uric acid, precipitates are formed beginning about the seventh day. After the eleventh, the crystalline materials coalesce into brittle platelets. This relative insolubility of the waste material, and its accumulation outside the body of the fetus, are of vital importance for organisms developing within a closed shell. It is therefore more than a mere coincidence that uric acid is the end product of protein metabolism in bird and reptile and also in insect eggs.

Apparently the swallowing of the egg albumen and its digestion have no influence on the progress of protein catabolism. In the chick, the highest rate per 100 mg. embryo dry weight has been located between the eighth and tenth days, i.e., days before the opening of the albumen duct.

10. SEX ORGANS

a. Testes and Male Gonaducts.   The basic structure of the testes is well established at the beginning of the fetal period (Fig. 204). The

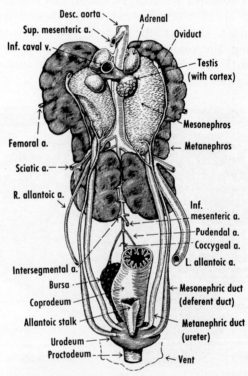

Figure 226.   Redwing (*Agelaius phoeniceus*) fetus, 11 days (St. 35a). Male urogenital organs. Left testis partly covered with cortical remnants; oviducts regressing; the right mesonephric body shows some reduction in size. Lumen of gut filled with albumen (black); × 10.

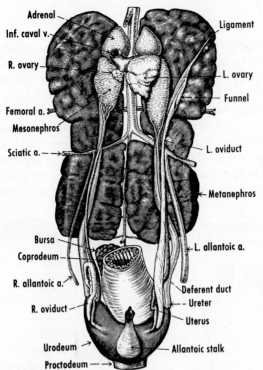

Figure 227.   Redwing, after hatching (St. 35b, 14th day). Female urogenital organs. The presence of a small right ovary is characteristic for this species. Right oviduct in pelvis; left oviduct shows regional differentiation. Mesonephros reduced, metanephros large. Allantoic arteries and allantoic stalk drying up; × 7.

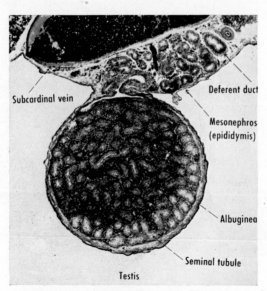

Figure 228.   Sparrow, male, fall of first year. Cross section through left testis and epididymis. Broad hilus with cleft-like antrum, into which opens a seminal tubule, and from which an efferent ductule leads to epididymis; × 50.

345

cortex has disappeared in the right gonad, and is reduced to a nearly sterile remnant in the left (Fig. 226). The medulla consists of twisted and anastomosing seminal tubules, imbedded in a sparse stroma. The latter also encloses blood vessels, nerves, and scattered interstitial cells.

After hatching, both testes are covered by a perfectly smooth *peritoneal epithelium*. At first the subjacent fibrous *albuginea* is very delicate. Later it becomes a thick, elastic capsule (Fig. 228), which expands and thins out when the testes grow large, during the reproductive seasons. Within the walls of the *seminal tubules* are the *spermatogonia* and their nurse cells, the *sustentacular cells*. Maturation with sperm-

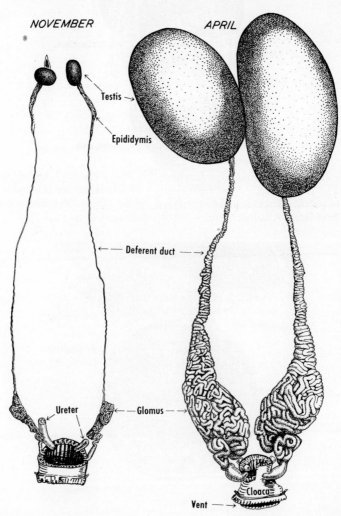

Figure 229.   Adult males of the starling. Testes and genital ducts at the eclipse (November) and the breeding seasons (April). Testicular weight increase 300 fold; × 2.5.

atocyte and sperm formation starts at the approach of the first breeding season. In most species this is toward the end of the first year, but in the herring gull, maturation is attained at the end of the second or third year. Spermatogenesis then proceeds in diurnal waves, mitotic and miotic divisions occurring only at night when the body temperature of sleeping birds falls about 3° C. below that of the daytime.

Originally the testis is broadly attached to the mesonephros (Fig. 204). During the tenth day it becomes partly folded off, but the mesorchium remains rather wide, since it contains a large pocket, the *antrum*

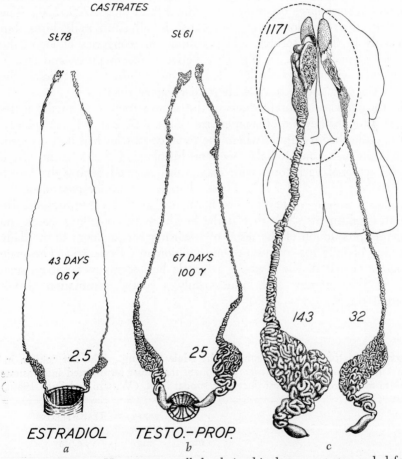

CASTRATES

St.78   St.61   1171

43 DAYS   67 DAYS
0.6 γ   100 γ

143   32

2.5   25

ESTRADIOL   TESTO.-PROP.
a   b   c

Figure 230.   Hormone-controlled relationship between testes and deferent ducts in the starling. *a,* Male castrate, injected with 0.6 μg. estradiol daily (43 times), maintains castrate condition (estradiol without effect); weight of deferent duct 2.5 mg. *b,* Male castrate injected with 100 μg. testosterone propionate daily (67 times); deferent ducts greatly stimulated, weight 25 mg. *c,* Unilaterally castrated male, right testis enlarged to 1.171 gm. during the breeding season; empty left deferent duct weighs 32 mg., the sperm-filled right one 143 mg. (Witschi 1945) × 2.3.

of the testis (Fig. 228). The albuginea is split into two layers, one adhering to the testis and the other to the mesonephric remnant, now called *epididymis*. Both show a number of perforations; through the testicular wall enter many rete tubules, short links between the seminal tubules and the antrum (Fig. 228). The mesonephric side has only about six funnel-shaped outlets, the beginnings of the *efferent ductules* (Fig. 230c). At pre-hatching stages the ductules open into mesonephric renal capsules. Since the latter degenerate following hatching, the efferent ductules finally join directly the *epididymal ductules*. During the breeding season the entire duct system becomes highly distended, since it serves to store large quantities of seminal fluid (Figs. 229, 230). The *deferent ducts* are long and convoluted in all adult male birds, but especially in the passerines, where voluminous congeries of loops, the *seminal glomera* locate in the space between metanephros and cloaca. The ends widen into thick-walled *ampullary ducts* and pierce the lateral sides of the cloaca, as short *ejaculatory ducts*.

In the females, deferent ducts of the same structure as in the males persist, though they are of smaller size (Figs. 227, 231). Their epididymal ductules begin blindly where the renal corpuscles had been located.

In adult males and females, size and histology of the deferent system exhibit seasonal variations, with maximums reached during the breeding season (Figs. 229–231). These changes are under control of the sex glands and mediated by sex hormones, probably *testosterone*. Injection experiments show that at the height of the breeding season the hormone production of the testes of a starling is equivalent to the daily injection of 0.25 mg. of testosterone propionate (Table 16). The male hormone output of the ovary of a female bird seems to be about one-fifth of that amount and induces only a partial stimulation of the deferent ducts.

Table 16

Seasonal Variation of Sex Organs in the Male Starling. The last column indicates the amount of testosterone propionate that must be injected into castrate males to maintain the deferent ducts at a similar level. (Witschi and Fugo 1940.)

SEASON	TESTIS mg.[1]	DEFERENT DUCT mg.[1]	TESTOSTERONE SUBSTITUTION µg/day
Eclipse: September–November	3	3	—
Prenuptial: December	5	3	1
Prenuptial: January	8	6	20
Prenuptial: March	500	20	100
Nuptial: April	1200	200[2]	250

[1] Round weights of fresh organs.

[2] Filled with seminal fluid, which accounts for four-fifths of this weight.

b. Ovaries and Female Gonaducts.   Paired ovaries of equal size develop in only a few species of hawks, belonging to the genera *Circus* and *Accipiter*. In other female birds, the *right ovary* is *smaller* (Fig. 227), and its development deviates from the normal ovarian course. Its primordial cortex is more reduced than the medulla. Consequently a marked tendency toward testicular differentiation is noticed. Primitive seminal cords become organized, and for a while, rete and efferent ductules show a progressive development. The medullary germ cells assume a spermatogonial character. The cortical germ cells, depending on the size of the cortex, either degenerate, remain undifferentiated, or transform into ovocytes. Between hatching and maturity, the right gonad becomes most often a sterile vestige, but in some instances, it forms a persisting testicular, ambisexual, or ovarial rudiment (Fig. 232). Normally, the further development of such rudiments is checked by the presence of the large left ovary. After surgical removal or pathologic destruction of the latter, growth of the right rudiment may be resumed. Through compensatory hypertrophy, it then develops into either a sterile testis, a fertile testis, a hermaphrodite gland, or an ovary, always

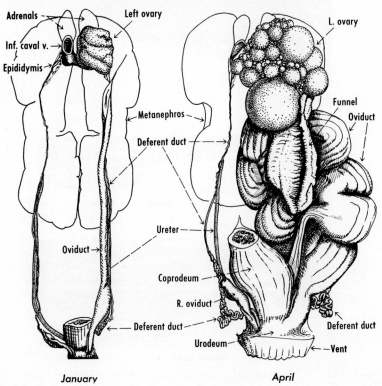

Figure 231.   Adult females of the sparrow. Ovaries and genital ducts at eclipse (January) and beginning breeding season (April) (Witschi and Riley 1940); × 3.3.

in accordance with its initial composition. Mixtures of these types are common. Male secondary sex characters, notably combs and deferent ducts, increase in size following the development of testicular nodules. Studying the spermatogenesis in the compensatory right testicle, R. Miller was able to show that it proceeds without change in the inherited female chromosome pattern.

The *left ovary* spreads as a flat crust over parts of the adrenal, the mesonephros, and the cross-wise anastomosis between the subcardinal veins (Fig. 227). The medullary cords acquire cavities (Fig. 15) which are the homologues of the *ovarial sacs* of amphibian ovaries, but also of the rete tubules and antrums of the bird testes (Fig. 228). The slender blastema strands that link the medulla of indifferent gonads with some mesonephric renal capsules (St. 26; Fig. 196) regress in the course

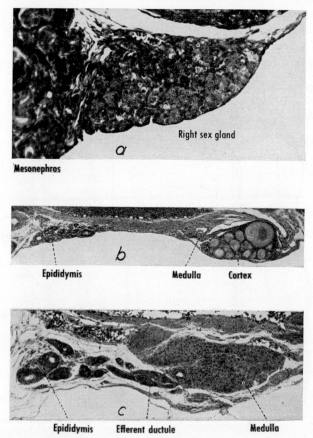

Figure 232.　　Vestigial right gonads of three female birds. *a,* Turkey; fetus of 25 days; this vestige contains many gonia, partly in cortical and partly in medullary position; × 160. *b,* Adult sparrow; right vestige prevailingly of cortical character, with small and medium size ovocytes; × 64. *c,* Adult sparrow; right vestige an entirely medullary remnant; sterile; × 120.

of ovarial differentiation. Hence, at hatching, the homologues of the testicular efferent ductules persist only as mere vestiges, which later may disappear completely.

The *maturation phase* begins very early, usually from two to four days before hatching (Fig. 15; Table 17). Within a few days, all cortical gonia become ovocytes. This change prevents further germ cell multiplication. At the time of hatching, the ovocytes number in the hundred thousands. Only relatively few of them will successfully complete maturation and develop into fertile eggs.

The *oviducts* of males and females first develop symmetrically, and grow at the same rate in both sexes (Table 18). At the end of this *progressive period* (St. 26–34), their *funnels* open above the mesenteric artery and the tubes end near the urodeum (Figs. 202, 203).

Table 17

Time Relationships between Sex Differentiation, Beginning of Ovarial Maturation (Synaptic Ovocyte Formation), Mesonephric Reduction (Cessation of Glomerular Circulation), and Hatching, in Five Species of Birds. (Some data in Tables 17 and 18 from A. J. Stanley.)

SPECIES	SEX DIFFERENTIATION day	OVOCYTE FORMATION day	MESONEPHRIC REDUCTION day	HATCHING AGE day
Domestic sparrow	6	10	11	13
Redwing blackbird	6	10–11	11	13
Domestic chicken	7	16	19	21
Domestic turkey	8	20	22	28
Red-tailed hawk	12	24	28	32
Stage	32	35	35	35 or 36

Table 18

Oviduct Development in Five Species of Birds

SPECIES	PROGRESSIVE PERIOD days	FEMALE: REDUCTION RIGHT DUCT			MALE REDUCTION days
		start day	half length day	vestige day	
Domestic sparrow	5–8	8⅓	9	12	8–(13)*
Redwing blackbird	5–8	8⅓	9½	12	8–(13)
Domestic chicken	5–8½	9	12	16	8½–(15)
Domestic turkey	6–10	11	15	22	10–(16)
Red-tailed hawk	9–18	20	28	32	18–(26)
Stage:	26–34a	34a	34b	35	34–35

* In parenthesis: day when remnants are found in about half of the male fetuses. In this table *days* indicate incubation ages.

Following testis differentiation both *oviducts of the males regress* (St. 34–35). The long tubes below the mesonephric bodies usually disappear within one day (Fig. 226). The funnel segments form vesicular remnants which may persist as long as two weeks.

In the females, the right oviduct stops further growth, while the left one continues and then differentiates into *magnum, isthmus,* and *uterus.* As the fetus grows, the tubal end of the right duct slides downward along the lateral edge of the mesonephros. Even before hatching, the entire duct is withdrawn into the lower pelvis, where it persists as a functionally unimportant rudiment (Figs. 227, 231). The funnel of the left oviduct also descends, but becomes permanently fixed at the surface of the kidney below the left ovary. The time relationships which apply to some of the best known species are summarized in Table 18.

The extreme seasonal changes in size and gross morphology of the adult ovaries and gonaducts are illustrated in Figures 16 and 231.

11. ENDOCRINE SYSTEM

The primordia of the glands of internal secretion originate at early embryonic stages, but become histologically differentiated and functional only after completion of metamorphosis. Removal of the hypophyseal placode of the 12- to 14-somite chick results in characteristic deficiencies during the later fetal period. The operation reveals a dominating role of the hypophysis within the endocrine system, and provides valuable information concerning the functional development of the other glands of internal secretion.

a. **Hypophysis.** The *hypophyseal placode* is identifiable in the 33-hour embryo as a plate of thickened ectoderm between forebrain and oral membrane (Fig. 178s). At four days this plate has become invaginated and transformed into a *slender tube (Rathke's pouch).* Starting from the oral pit, it passes under the primitive optic chiasma and ends at the frontal surface of the diencephalic infundibulum (Fig. 197). Toward the end of metamorphosis, the connection with the roof of the oral cavity narrows, preparatory to its rupture about the ninth day. On

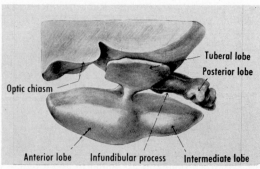

Figure 233.   Hypophysis of 15-day chicken fetus (Atwell 1939); × 30.

the other hand, the body of the hypophysis becomes more massive (Fig. 201). A separation into four parts is already indicated. The distal end, which becomes the *intermediate lobe,* is superficially separated from the main body or *anterior lobe* by a furrow which holds the internal carotids and their anastomosis. From the anterior lobe arise two processes which grow laterally around the infundibulum below the optic chiasma; these are the *tuberal lobes.* In accordance with their early history, these four lobes are collectively called the *buccal hypophysis.* At this time, the *neural hypophysis* or *posterior lobe* also gains definite shape. It arises as an outgrowth from the floor of the infundibulum. *In chicks of the fifteenth day of incubation, the gland has nearly acquired its adult shape* (Fig. 233).

The superficial layers of the posterior lobe are a maze of terminal nerve fibers, which do not enter the intermediate lobe. Possibly vascular connections between hypothalamus and hypophysis may be of importance for the transmission of stimuli from the nervous system to the secretory gland.

Surgical *removal of the hypophyseal placode* (Fig. 234) and consequent absence of the hypophysis has little influence on growth and general differentiation before the end of the second week. The total body weight is below that of normal controls (Fig. 235) because the missing forehead (Fig. 236*b*) represents an important fraction of

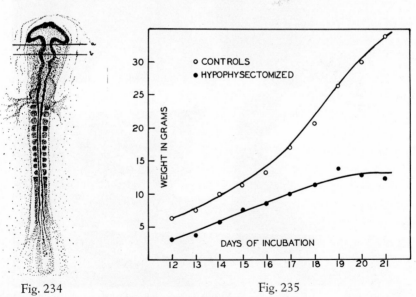

Fig. 234   Fig. 235

Figure 234.   Hypophysectomy in the 32-hour chick embryo: the forehead with olfactory and hypophyseal placodes is removed at the level of *a* (Fugo and Witschi 1938).

Figure 235.   Growth of normal and hypophysectomized fetuses of the chick (Fugo 1940).

the entire fetus. But about the fifteenth day, the growth rate begins to lag, and by the end of the third week, the hypophysectomized chicks are less than half the size of normal, hatching controls.

This experiment proves that at the fetal stage 35, normal growth becomes dependent on the presence of the hypophysis, and that in the chick, elaboration and release of the hypophyseal *growth hormone* or *somatotrophic hormone* (STH) starts about the end of the second week of incubation.

b. Thyroid.   The cords of cuboid cells which form the solid framework of the thyroids at metamorphosis (St. 26–33) gradually become strings of nodules and follicles. In the chick of 10 days (St. 34b), colloid droplets begin to appear in the center of the cell clusters. By the eighteenth day the histologic pattern of the adult thyroid, with

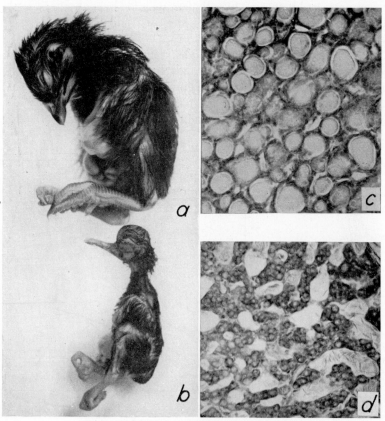

Figure 236.   Effect of hypophysectomy on the development of the chick (Fugo 1940). *a,* Control fetus of 21 days. *b,* Hypophysectomized at 32 hours: fetus at 21 days shows absence of upper bill and eyes, retardation of growth. *c,* Part of thyroid of normal 18-day chicken fetus (Fugo 1940). *d,* Part of thyroid of 18-day chicken fetus, hypophysectomized during second day (Fugo 1940); *c* and *d* × 250.

many colloid-filled follicles of all sizes, is well established (St. 35, Fig. 236c). Also, beginning about the tenth day, iodine gradually becomes concentrated in the two small glands. The actual presence of hormone in fetal chick thyroids of 11 days and older has been demonstrated by feeding experiments, which brought about an acceleration of amphibian metamorphosis.

The *thyroids of hypophysectomized chicks* maintain the primitive framework of cellular cords. Small droplets of colloid appear about the fourteenth day, but from there on the gland remains inactive (Fig. 236c, d). Evidently the hypophysis normally releases a *thyroid stimulating hormone* (TSH) beginning about the tenth day of incubation. However, the initial morphologic differentiation of the thyroid and even the production of small colloid globules are independent of hypophyseal stimulation.

The most important conclusion to be derived from the reported experiments is that of the complete independence of avian metamorphosis from hormonal agents of either the hypophysis or the thyroid gland.

c. Parathyroids, Thymus, and Ultimobranchial Bodies.   Little is known about the functional importance of these pharyngeal glands during the fetal period. In hypophysectomized fetuses their development is not markedly different from that of controls.

d. Islets of Langerhans.   The general outlines of *pancreatic islets* appear even before the 10th day; but the insulin-producing beta cells can be identified only in 12-day fetuses. Clear evidence of insulin production before hatching is not available.

e. Adrenals.   During the fetal stage the previously accumulated and superficially attached medullary cell groups of neural origin break up and become integrated in the framework of mesodermal cortical

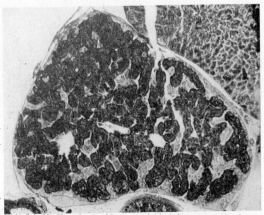

Figure 237.   Adrenal of fledgling redwing blackbird. Cortical cords, with black osmium deposits; medullary cords, lightly stained. × 50.

cells. Thus the checkerboard mixture of these two components, so characteristic for the bird adrenal, becomes established. Even at the fetal stage the cortical cells are rich in lipoid droplets, and the medullary cells give the bichromate reaction, indicating the presence of epinephrine (Fig. 237). In hypophysectomized chicks adrenal development is essentially normal though slightly retarded.

f. **Sex Glands.**   In addition to their production of mature germ cells, the gonads have also *endocrine functions*. It is therefore of interest that in hypophysectomized chick fetuses the testes as well as the ovaries differentiate normally at stage 30, but after stage 34 they grow more slowly than in controls. The differences become evident after the twelfth day. This condition must eventually result in endocrine hypofunction. However, development and differentiation of the oviducts, which at stage 34 have progressed quite far in normal controls (Table 18), follow the typical pattern in hypophysectomized chicks of either sex. The only definite indication of endocrine deficiency at the fetal stage is seen in the small size or absence of ovarial sacs in the medulla of the ovaries. It appears that their formation in normal controls is an indication of the presence of female sex hormones, which are produced in the ovarian cortex.

The injection of androgenic and gynogenic hormones into incubating eggs at certain dosage levels interferes with the normal course of the development of gonads and ducts. Experiments of this type reveal a responsiveness of the early sex organs to these hormones. It remains undecided whether the same or similar hormones also play a role in the course of normal embryonic differentiation.

A comparison of birds and amphibians shows that the primordia of hormone organs make their very first appearance at similar developmental stages; but with the possible exception of the sex glands, they reach a functional level considerably later in the birds than in the amphibians.

12. NERVOUS SYSTEM

a. **Principles of Differention.**   At the end of the embryonic period, the tubular nervous system is laid out in full length and its major subdivisions are easily recognizable. However, histologically it is still very little differentiated. Only on close examination will the stratification of the tubular walls be noticed. Differentiation is most advanced in the rhombencephalon at the level of the otic vesicles (St. 25, Fig. 192*a*). One distinguishes *ependyme, mantle,* and *marginal layer*. The first, bordering the *neural cavity,* is the seat of all mitotic activity. Multiplication of neural cells continues at a high rate through the larger part of the metamorphic period; it then rapidly falls off and comes to an end in the beginning days of the fetal period (St. 34; cf. Fig. 206, 8*d*).

During the metamorphic and fetal periods (St. 26–35) occurs a *secondary differentiation of the nervous system* through the development of sensory and motor centers in the brain and in the spinal cord. At the start of metamorphosis the latter still had a fairly even diameter from the cervical to the sacral region (St. 25, Fig. 239). At its termina-

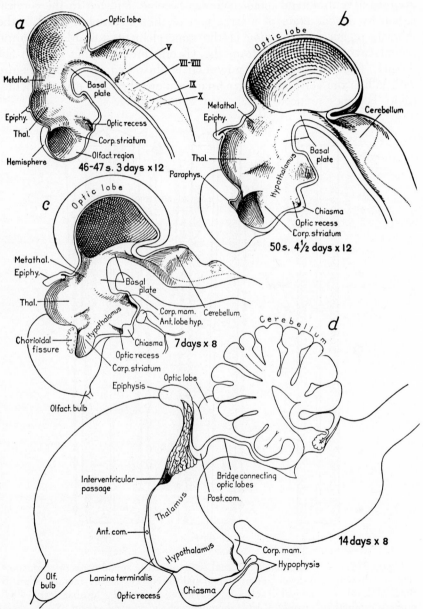

Figure 238.   Development of the brain of the chicken from three days to 14 days incubation. *a*, Stage 23, *b*, stage 26, *c*, stage 33, *d*, stage 35 (Streeter 1933).

tion, the brachial and lumbar regions are marked by considerable swellings (St. 34, Fig. 239). The difference between these and the cervical and thoracic regions is not brought about by uneven cellular multiplication. On the contrary, mitotic proliferation is evenly distributed through the entire length of the spinal cord. But the originally even-sized ventrolateral motor columns become *depleted* in the cervical region *by degeneration* of a large part of their neuroblasts, and in the thoracic region *by migration* of the same elements toward the central neural cavity, where they form the visceral preganglionic column (of Terni). The progress of this migration is illustrated stepwise in Figure 240. When the cells reach their final location, the wide primary neural cavity becomes reduced to a narrow *central canal*.

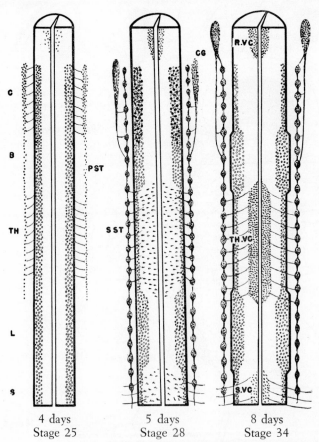

4 days	5 days	8 days
Stage 25	Stage 28	Stage 34

Figure 239.   Diagrammatic frontal sections of the spinal cords of three chick embryos showing the development of regional differences in the motor system. *B*, Brachial level; *C*, cervical level; *CG*, cervical ganglion; *L*, lumbar level; *PST*, primary sympathetic trunk; *R.VC*, rhombencephalic visceral center; *S.VC*, sacral visceral center; *TH*, thoracic center; *TH.VC*, thoracic visceral center (Hamburger and Levi-Montalcini 1950).

Significantly, the cervical neuroblasts degenerate only after they had produced some neurites. It is the general property of nerve cells to be able to grow out into long processes, called *neurites*. Shorter, heavily branching *dendrites* and longer *neuraxons* are distinguished. Physiologically, the latter procure for the nerve cell a new "remote milieu" which may become equally or more important for the existence and differentiation of the cell than even the conditions immediately surrounding the main cell body, the *pericaryon*. Sensory as well as motor cells may degenerate if their neurites fail to establish contacts with the appropriate end-organs, sensory epithelia or muscles.

If at early embryonic stages the peripheral fields are reduced—usually by extirpation of limbs or sense organs—the motor and sensory centers shrink, mostly through degeneration of neurons. If, on the contrary, the peripheral fields are enlarged—by implantation of additional limbs or sense organs near the primary ones—the effect is different in the two systems. In the case of increased sensory fields, the number of neurons in the spinal or cranial ganglia, or in the sensory centers of the brain, enlarges through increased mitotic activity. In the case of a greater motor load, the motor centers are not changed but the axons branch peripherally, so that the same motor cells supply a larger number of peripheral units. The impulses which in all these reactions link the "periphery" with the cell center are obviously quite different from functional nerve conductivity. Hamburger speaks of "trophic relations," but the concrete nature of this particular type of induction remains quite obscure.

Well-being and degeneration are not the only characteristics for which neurons are dependent on the periphery. Their physiologic differentiation is partly directed by the type of terminal connections. If under experimental conditions some branches of the brachial nerve complex become attached to a wrong type of muscle of the limb, the center gradually becomes reconditioned and adapted for harmonious function. This ability, however, is limited, and limbs implanted

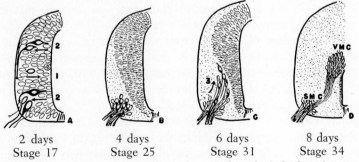

| 2 days | 4 days | 6 days | 8 days |
| Stage 17 | Stage 25 | Stage 31 | Stage 34 |

Figure 240.   Migration of cells in the spinal cord of chick embryos, as indicated by arrows 1, 2, 3; *SMC*, somatic motor column; *VMC*, visceral motor center (Hamburger and Levi-Montalcini 1950).

outside the reach of their corresponding plexuses do not become synchronized with the limbs in normal position.

Comparing equivalent experiments performed at identical stages of amphibians and birds, one finds again a higher *degree of determination* and more rigid fixation in the latter, greater *adaptability* and *regenerative capacity* in the former. For instance, if higher and lower sectors of recently closed neural tube are exchanged, in salamanders they differentiate in conformity with the new location (Detwiler), while in birds they retain their original character (Shieh). The *determination of the regional type*—cervical, brachial and so on—develops independent of the neighboring mesodermal tissues. It seems to be induced from centers at higher levels of the cord or the rhombencephalon.

On the other hand, *neuromery,* at least in the amphibians, does not develop as an intrinsic quality, but is induced by the metamery of the mesoderm. Implantation of additional somites, or their removal, is followed by corresponding increases or decreases in neural segmentation.

One of the most discussed subjects in neuroembryology is the problem of the *polarity of the neuron* and the *directional growth of the neurites.* Three hypotheses have been proposed, of which the *electrical* by Kappers and Child, and the *chemical* by Cajal and Forssman must now be considered as obsolete. The *mechanical hypothesis* of His and Harrison, especially in its recent development by Weiss, is the only one that conforms with the experimental facts. According to this, the outgrowing nerve fibers are guided by the structural pattern of the ground substance of the embryonic body.

b. **Brain.**   The fetal development of the brain is characterized by disproportionate growth of the *cerebral hemispheres* and the *cerebellum.* At the end of metamorphosis the roof of the latter is still a moderately thickened, evenly curved dome (Fig. 238c). At eight days, two shallow transverse folds initiate its separation into three major lobes. Later many secondary folds become added which, together with the first ones, give the rapidly growing body its leafed appearance (St. 35, Fig. 238d). The *cerebral hemispheres* get an earlier start and are already prominent bodies at the beginning of the fetal period (Fig. 238c). The *olfactory bulbs* at the entrance of the olfactory nerves attain considerable size, lending emphasis to the contention that the cerebrum develops primarily as a *rhinencephalon* or nose brain. The connections between cerebral and diencephalic ventricles become relatively narrow *interventricular passages* (St. 35, Fig. 238d).

c. **Spinal Cord.**   In contrast to the situation in mammals, the spinal cord extends permanently into the caudal region, and often even into the pygostyle (Fig. 241). In the chick the last two spinal ganglia form during the fifth day, but soon disappear again. Of the permanently persisting 39 pairs of spinal nerves, the first two have only ventral roots (Table 9). In the course of the ninth day the dorsal part of the primitive *neural canal* of the spinal cord becomes compressed and obliterates; its ventral, persisting part becomes the *central canal*. In the lower cervical and in the lumbosacral region, a number of segmental nerves combine in the formation of brachial and lumbar plexuses. Their composition conforms to the position held by the limb buds at stage 25. These nerves follow the later migrations of the limbs, especially the extensive descent of the wings, without changing their roots. The difference in this regard between systems of innervation and of vascularization is quite remarkable.

d. Glycogenic Body.   In advanced fetuses the left and right marginal and mantle layers of the spinal cord separate at the level of the sciatic plexus, while the roof transforms into a bulging mass of spongy tissue, the *glycogenic body* (Figs. 241, 242). The functional importance of this lumbar plug is not fully understood. The fact that its occurrence is restricted to the birds indicates that it is a relatively recent acquisition. In agreement with this conclusion is its late ontogenetic appearance. At eight days, the lumbospinal cord shows no trace of this structure. In songbirds it differentiates at stage 34, about the ninth day. It grows immediately into a large body, reaching full proportions about the eleventh day. In the chick its development begins nearly one day later and proceeds slowly up to the eleventh or twelfth day. From the

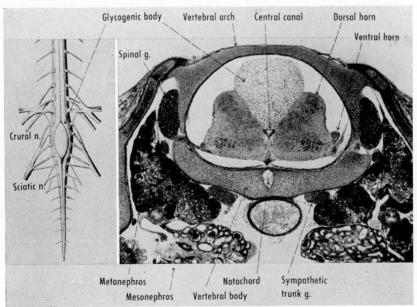

Fig. 241   Fig. 242

Figure 241.   Lower spinal cord of the flamingo. The glycogenic body lies between the roots of the sciatic nerves (Imhof 1905).

Figure 242.   Sparrow fetus, 10 days. Cross section through lumbar region with glycogenic body; × 33.

thirteenth on it gains rapidly until about the eighteenth day. During the growth period, the spongioblast cells become vesicular and filled with glycogen. It may be significant that in the sparrow, as well as in the chick and in hawks, the beginning of this period coincides with the opening of the chorio-amniotic duct and the start of albumen ingestion by the fetus. Since glycogen formation and storage are its outstanding characteristics, the name of *glycogenic body* seems more adequate for this peculiar structure than any of several other designations that were proposed, before its nature was sufficiently known.

e. **The Autonomic Nervous System** (cf. p. 285 f.) assumes an essentially adult topography early in the fetal period. The chain of sympathetic trunk ganglia follows the ventrolateral surface of the vertebral column (Figs. 239, 242) and henceforth they are designated as the *prevertebral trunk ganglia*. The more peripheral sympathetic and all parasympathetic ganglia of the head and the visceral organs are less regularly arranged. Some form plexuses of considerable size and involved composition (Fig. 239, St. 34).

The *pheochromatic or medullary cells of the adrenals,* derived from sympathoblasts of the 4th to the 7th thoracic segments, are interspersed in clusters between the cortical cords of this gland (Fig. 237).

Chapter 20

Metabolism of Avian

Development

1. NUTRITIONAL REQUIREMENTS AND CHEMICAL CONSTITUTION OF THE EMBRYO

The nutritional needs of the developing bird are closely reflected in the original composition of the egg (Table 1; p. 8). Its stores provide for growth and maintenance even beyond hatching. Usually a considerable amount of food is still contained in the withdrawn yolk sac when the young bird emerges from the shell. In the chick, it is sufficient to sustain life for about another four or five days. The developing embryo presents a number of very interesting physiologic problems. Located on top of the yolk mass and under the mantle of egg white, the embryo has to meet the exigencies of *changing needs* as well as of *procurement*. In regard to the latter, four periods may be distinguished.

(1) All cleavage cells contain large numbers of small yolk granules, and up to the early streak stage these *intracellular reserve materials* cover probably at least the major needs of the germ. Later only the cells of the peripheral zone of junction still contain yolk.

(2) With the exhaustion of intracellular resources begins a period of procurement by *diffusion*. The contents of the subgerminal cavity have been characterized as "liquid yolk" because of the high concentration of dissolved yolk constituents. This fluid penetrates between the loosely arranged cells of the hypoblast, but as some tissues grow thicker

363

and firmer, materials are also passed on from cell to cell in order to supply the remote layers.

(3) The establishment of *blood circulation* after the fortieth hour of incubation (St. 17) is also the beginning of the development of a *digestive yolk-sac epithelium* with septums and secondary folds. Nourishment follows now closely the adult type except that intake is restricted to an embryonic organ, the yolk sac, and the food is not of foreign origin and composition.

(4) Procurement by *digestive activity of the permanent intestinal tract* begins at an early fetal stage (St. 34b), following ingestion of the albumen.

We are much less informed about the stage by stage changes in the *needs* of the embryo for essential materials. It is easily seen that local demands for particular elements must arise with the beginning of special differentiations such as bone or feather formation.

The requirements of the early blastodermic stages are particularly important to the students of embryos in vitro. Spratt found that blastoderms of the primitive streak stage survive for only a short time if transferred into mere salt solutions (e.g., Ringer solution). But after addition of glucose they can survive, develop, and differentiate for another 24 to 28 hours. It was further shown that d-mannose, d-fructose, d-galactose, d-maltose, pyruvate, and lactate can replace glucose, with decreasing effectiveness in this order. A number of other carbohydrates cannot be utilized by the embryo, among them sucrose, lactose, and d-ribose. Some of Spratt's experiments seem to indicate qualitative as well as quantitative differences in the nutritional requirements for heart and brain formation.

The *origin* and the *synthesis* of specific *proteins* during development ranks among the most fundamental of biologic problems. A large number of types are simply inherited at the time of fertilization. Included among them are characteristic *proteinogens*—possibly sometimes single molecules—from which by autocatalytic synthesis may derive the normal proteins, enzymes, and antibodies characteristic of each species. Recent work with chick blastoderms has shown a greater manifoldness at early stages than expected. At least eight enzymes have been identified in embryos of not more than 36 hours. Immunologic methods have successfully been applied to identify the presence and possible first appearance of tissue-specific proteins. Suggestive are the *enzyme-distribution-patterns* brought to light by recent investigators. The further development of this particular phase of chemical embryology is linked to the progress in protein chemistry and immunology.

2. RESPIRATORY QUOTIENTS AND SUCCESSION OF METABOLIC SUBSTRATES

Probably the most comprehensive measurements of the various external manifestations of the energy metabolism in the intact hen's egg are those by Barott. An elaborate set-up of apparatus made it possible to control very closely the environment for temperature, humidity, and stability of atmospheric composition, while continuous measurements were made of oxygen use, and elimination of water, carbon dioxide, and heat. From the data thus gained were calculated the respiratory and thermal quotients (Figs. 243, 244).

The total gaseous exchange before the middle of the second day is very small. Fortunately the conclusion that even at this earliest period the respiratory quotient is close to 1.0 receives confirmation from studies on the metabolism of isolated blastoderms by Needham and Philips. In the light of considerations presented above in the discussion of amphibian metabolism, the respiratory quotients in Figure 243 suggest

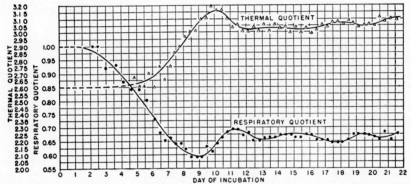

Figure 243. Domestic chicken. Thermal and respiratory quotients during incubation (Barott 1937).

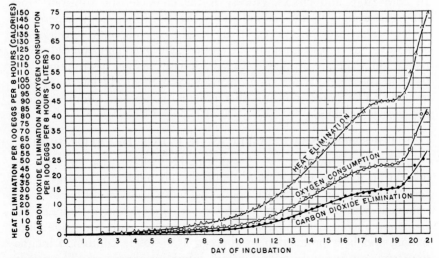

Figure 244. Domestic chicken. Energy metabolism during incubation at 37.8°C., relative humidity 60 per cent, oxygen 21 per cent and carbon dioxide below 0.5 per cent (Barott 1937)

that during the first and second days of incubation, the chick embryo burns only *carbohydrates,* but later it changes to *protein* and *fat.* These conclusions, based on the shape of the curve of respiratory quotients, are sustained by direct chemical analysis. Total free *glucose* falls from 200 mg. at the beginning of incubation to about 40 mg. during the first week (St. 8–32); after the tenth day it slowly rises again to reach a value of about 140 mg. at the end of incubation. Moreover, the protein metabolite *uric acid* first becomes detectable by the fourth day, and its production reaches a maximal rate on the ninth. Obviously these facts indicate again that, starting about the third day (St. 21), *carbohydrate* gradually becomes replaced by *protein* as fuel material. The later decline of uric acid production, following the tenth day, occurs at the time when a third substrate, namely fat, enters into the process. It appears that the embryo cannot make use of fat before the tenth day of incubation (St. 34).

Although glucose is the most easily metabolized material, fat gives the highest energy yield. The contribution of protein appears larger on the basis of the uric acid determinations by Fisk and Boyden, than of those by Needham. The summary of the major data shows a striking parallelism between the succession of metabolic periods in birds and in amphibians (cf. Fig. 123). In rounded figures metabolic oxidations during incubation follow this course:

METABOLIZED SUBSTRATE	WEIGHT mg.	WEIGHT per cent	CALORIFIC VALUE per cent	DEVELOPMENTAL PHASE
Glucose	160	5	2.5	St. 8–25
Proteins	250	8	4	St. 21–33
Fats	2750	87	93.5	St. 34–36

In both frogs and chicks, glucose is the characteristic substrate from early gastrulation to late tailbud stages (St. 8–21). In both, a period of protein catabolism intervenes at the height of embryonic development and serves as a transition to the period of fat combustion. Unfortunately no data are available for the phase before gastrulation (St. 0–7) in the chick, when amphibians have a relatively low respiratory quotient. The latter indicates that protein metabolism prevails during the cleavage stages.

3. THERMODYNAMIC ASPECTS OF CHICK DEVELOPMENT

a. Thermal Quotient. A study of heat elimination provides another way to gain information about the chemical and energy transformations within the intact egg. The most exact measurements are obtained with the *respiration calorimeter,* an apparatus designed for the simultaneous determination of oxygen intake, carbon dioxide elimination, and heat production by the egg at a closely controlled incubation temperature, and under constant humidity conditions. The results obtained at the optimal temperature (37.8° C.) are represented in the three curves of Figure 244. Heat is measured in Calories. The amount of fat which by oxidation gives 1 gm. of CO_2 produces 3.35 Calories of heat, whereas in the combustion of carbohydrates the ratio is 2.57 Calories per gram of CO_2. Thus from the data obtained with the respiration calorimeter a *thermal quotient* is calculated:

$$ThQ = \frac{Calories}{CO_2 \ (grams)}$$

Like the respiratory quotient (RQ), the thermal quotient (ThQ) assists in the appraisal of the possible chemical nature of the metabolites which are used at any particular stage of development. A glance at Figure 244 shows that *both indicate a prevalence of carbohydrate combustion during embryogenesis (St. 8–25), and a change to fat after the tenth day (fetal period).*

b. Metabolism and the Problem of "Organization Energy."   It is evident that a thermodynamic interpretation of metabolism must rely on the validity of the principle of conservation of energy. Consequently, from the amounts of metabolic substrates which disappear during incubation and from their calorific values, one can calculate the amount of energy released through their combustion. This energy either is completely released from the egg and can be measured by the calorimeter, or it is in part retained in the embryo, in which case the calorific value of hatching chick would have to be correspondingly higher than that of unincubated egg substance.

Tangl was the first to see this problem clearly. When he found that step by step the calculated and the observed curves for heat release progress in almost identical form, the result seemed somewhat of a surprise. Evidently a considerable amount of work goes into the elaboration of a highly organized chick from mere nutritive stores, such as represented by the albumen and yolk of the egg. Hence the question, whether morphologically organized substance should not have a higher energy potential than its homogenate. Or with Needham one may ask whether there exists a specific *organization energy*. Admittedly all biologic measurements are afflicted with a degree of error, deriving from incompletely controllable factors. A critical evaluation of Tangl's methods and data apparently does not exclude the possibility of hidden organization energy, if this were less than 4 per cent of the observed combustion energy.

Murray, Needham and other investigators have contributed toward the resolution of this problem. The question is whether or not the prevailing *exergonic reactions* are in part coupled with *endergonic reactions*. The latter would result in an over-all increase of calorific value in parallel with progressing embryonic differentiation. Murray has shown that from the fifth to the twenty-first day of incubation the combustion value of the isolated embryo rises from 5.1 Cal to 6.2 Cal per gram dry weight. But this change accompanies the later development of the nervous and muscular system and simply reflects the transfer of fats from the yolk sac to the embryo. At the end of its development the chick only approaches but never reaches the average fuel value of combined egg albumen and yolk, which is about 7 Calories per gram. During ovogenesis some high grade metabolic substances accumulate in the ovocyte. The over-all calorific value for the catabolized fraction of the egg has been determined as 10 Cal/gm. No single constituent of the chick is known to reach such high values. According to Tangl's measurements the average total energy value of the egg before incubation is 90 Calories. During incubation 23 Calories are lost, which is 26 per cent. On the other hand, the initial dry weight of 13 gm. decreases by only 18 per cent. This shows again that metabolism draws mainly on the substances with the highest calorific value. Recent discoveries in the field of substances with high energy bonds may eventually shed more light on the remaining unsolved problems.

Although in the complex of chemical processes in the egg some endergonic reactions certainly do occur, they are not particularly characteristic for differentiation processes and do not serve to separate an organization energy from the general energy production of the developing egg. Theoretically it would seem justifiable to distinguish between a *basic maintenance metabolism* and a *developmental work metabolism*. The former sustains the life processes of tissues formed at preceding stages, whereas the latter fuels the activities involved in the addition of new tissues and organs. But no practical way of measuring the two separately has been found yet.

4. GLYCOGEN METABOLISM

At nine days the respiratory quotient falls to 0.6. Throughout the fetal period it remains below the level of pure fat oxidations. Most likely this low value is the result of disappearance of some oxygen, used in the *synthesis of glycogen from oxygen-poor fats or proteins*. In the unincubated egg the total glycogen content as reported by Needham is only about 2 mg. In first-week stages, small deposits were found in the vascular area of the yolk sac. Within the embryo it seems to appear first in the muscles of the heart at the end of the first week. At seven days, when the respiratory quotient goes below 0.7 the liver begins to form glycogen. The rapid increase of glycogen deposits in the glycogenic body of the lumbospinal cord during and after the ingestion of the egg albumen was mentioned before. Needham's value for total glycogen at hatching is 33 mg.

5. PERIODS OF RESPIRATORY CRISES AND HIGH MORTALITY

The volume of the gaseous exchange increases with the growth of the fetus, but the respiratory surface of the allantois cannot be increased beyond that of the shell to which it is applied. Likewise the rise in blood pressure and speed of circulation are definitely limited. In the chicken, the seventeenth day obviously marks the end of increases in allantoic respiratory efficacy. Although the fetus still gains weight (Table 15), the volumes of oxygen intake and carbon dioxide elimination remain nearly stationary until the establishment of pulmonary respiration at nineteen days (Fig. 244). Heat elimination is not depressed to the same degree, and the thermal quotient, which quite constantly was at 3.02 from the twelfth to the sixteenth day, rises to 3.05 on the seventeenth and 3.07 on the eighteenth day. This points to the availability of some source of energy which does not contribute to carbon dioxide production. According to the rules of the *Pasteur effect*, it is to be expected that the energy is delivered by *glycogenolysis*. This assumption is supported by the observation of a precipitous depletion of the glycogen stores of the liver during this critical pre-hatching period. Even though chemical evidence for the transformation of liver glycogen into lactic acid is not complete, the role of glycogen as an energy storage system in the fetus seems assured. It becomes charged (glycogenesis) by drawing on combustion energy when the oxygen supply is ample, and it discharges (glycogenolysis) when combustion energy runs low. In spite of such provisions, the pre-hatching period shows a marked increase in fetal mortality. The anaerobic fermentation by which glycogen is transformed into lactic acid is not a desirable substitute for normal full oxidation to water and carbon dioxide. It also yields only about one-fifteenth as much free energy.

Reference should be made here to the fact that a respiratory crisis combined with high mortality develops also during the first week of incubation. Increasingly, diffuse gaseous exchange becomes insufficient to suppress lactic acid fermentation. Though early embryos can develop for some time under anaerobic conditions, this type of metabolism is clearly unfavorable. Lactic acid is produced in increasing amounts up to the fifth day. It disappears by the end of the first week, when circulation and respiratory movements of the amnion have reached a considerable degree of development. Obviously correlated with these respiratory crises is the distribution of high mortality in incubating chicks, which reaches high peaks from the third to the fifth and from the eighteenth to the twentieth days.

6. EVOLUTION OF THE CLEIDOIC EGG

The energy metabolism of the bird egg shows a striking similarity to that of the frog in regard to the succession of RQ values between stages 8 and 33. This is indeed the more remarkable as the two types of eggs develop in extremely different environments, and the tadpoles get their sustenance from ingested food, beginning at stage 25. The succession of metabolic substrates seems deeply anchored not only in inheritance but probably also in the fundamental type of vertebrate development. The embryo apparently cannot make use of fat before it has attained a fairly advanced stage in development. In birds the phase of *protein metabolism* appears secondarily shortened, judging from the relatively very small amount that disappears during the entire incubation period. This probably is a first adaptation to development within an egg shell. More important are the changes in the *course of protein catabolism*. In amphibians it leads to ammonia and urea as major nitrogenous waste materials, but in birds to the nearly insoluble *uric acid*.

Adaptation to the terrestrial environment has made a nearly closed and self-contained system of the egg of the bird. The porous shell permits only a free exchange of respiratory gases and the evaporation of some water. It prevents entirely the intake of food as well as the elimination of solid or liquid wastes. The early change from protein to fat combustion immediately creates two advantages. The oxidation of fat results in *metabolic water* which partly replaces the loss by transpiration; the other end product, *carbon dioxide,* is an easily eliminated waste material. Even more important is the substantial decrease in nitrogenous waste products, an advantage that becomes greatly enhanced by the shift to *uric acid* catabolism.

It is an interesting fact that the formation of uric acid, obviously acquired as an adaptation to specific conditions of embryonic and fetal life, persists after hatching and throughout the adult life of the birds.

Mammals

Chapter 21

Nurture. I

Linnaeus' adoption, in 1758, of the name *mammalia* for the "vivi-parous quadrupeds" in his *system of nature,* was a stroke of good luck as much as an act of sound judgment. The chosen characteristic proved to apply to all subsequently discovered species belonging to this class, whereas viviparity lost diagnostic value when, over a century later, it became known that the monotremes are egg-laying mammals. Ray and Oken, at about the same time, had proposed to name the class the *hairy animals* after another, similarly consistent, character. But this and a good number of other distinctive traits seem quite inconsequential if viewed in the light of the immense significance that nursing gained in the molding of the highly diversified class. Nurture manifestly was the leading motive of the most important adaptive lines of evolution in the mammals. It dominates instincts and behavior of parents and offspring as well as their structural and functional differentiation. Sur-vival and well-being of the young become more and more integrated with the maternal life. Nurture has a prenatal or *uterine phase* and a postnatal or *lactation phase.*

1. EVOLUTION OF GESTATION

Retention of offspring on or within the body of the mother, as a means of providing protection and nutrition, is widespread among plants and animals, many variants having arisen independently in widely separated taxonomic groups. The mammalian type is quite dis-

372

tinctive and has evolved largely within the amniote branch of the vertebrates.

a. Internal Fertilization and Viviparity.   Gestation with implantation of the fetus in the wall of a maternal uterus was, of course, preceded by internal insemination and retention of the fertilized eggs in the oviducts. Since such methods are well established in sharks and many teleosts, it seems not unlikely that they were in use also among the amphibian and reptilian ancestors of the mammals that started reproducing on land.

In most salamanders and some reptiles, only fertilization and the beginning of cleavage occur within the uteri. The eggs of birds are laid at early gastrula stages, but those of lizards from desert and mountain regions, and of many snakes, may be retained much longer. Prolongation of residence in the uterus necessarily leads to the exchange of respiratory and eventually of nutritional and excretory materials.

b. Secretions of the Oviducts.   The walls of the oviducts prepare a variety of substances which in different ways become associated with the eggs. Protective *shells, membranes,* and *jelly envelopes* are provided for aquatic eggs of fishes and amphibians. In the terrestrian egg-laying or oviparous species a supply of water is added in the form of solutions of albumen. Much of the water is later absorbed by the yolk during its rapid enlargement before and after laying. It is not known to what extent the nutritional value of the residual albuminous concentrate becomes utilized in egg-laying reptiles, and whether it is swallowed by fetuses, as in the birds. Delivery of food materials from the uterus to the fetus occurs in some viviparous reptiles and in all but the most primitive mammals. The food or *embryotroph* may be prepared by the glands and the cellular surface layers of the uterine wall. It then consists of secretions and cell debris, and is called *histotroph.* On the other hand, where uterine and fetal tissues intimately fuse, supplies are carried by the maternal blood stream to the fetal membranes in much the same way as to the mother's own tissues. The food which the fetus thus receives is therefore called *hemotroph.* Though the histotrophic is the more primitive process, it nevertheless may involve more chemical transformations than hemotrophy.

c. Fetal Membranes and Food Absorption.   The evolutionary history of *chorion, amnion,* and *allantois* can be reconstructed only hypothetically. Probably its early documents disappeared with the cotylosaurs. However, one may safely conclude that the envelopes arose in conjunction with terrestrial egg laying. The increasing need for large stores of water in the egg caused a secondary enlargement of the *yolk sac,* which tended to engulf the embryo between rising folds of the somatopleure. If not compensated for, the shrinkage of the yolk sac during later stages of fetal growth would create a respiratory deficiency, since its epithelium is not only a nutritional but also a respiratory organ. Therefore, in the stem reptiles, evolution may have passed through a phase similar to the condition above described for poeciliid fishes, where the space left by the receding yolk sac becomes occupied by amno-pericardial sacs with *chorio-amniotic folds* (Fig. 147). Continuation of such an evolutionary trend, resulting in caudal prolongation of the extra-embryonic celomic cavities, eventually must have led to herniation of the small intestine and outgrowth of the urinary bladder. The basic condition thus became established for the evolution of the last fetal membrane, the *allantois*. Institution of allantoic respiration obviously was the decisive step in the evolution of the *amniotes*.

Avian ontogenesis displays a sequence of stages in membrane formation which parallels the suggested evolutionary history (cf. Figs. 180, 188, 200, 220–222). In view of the plasticity of peripheral vascular systems it is not surprising that amno-chorionic circulation now is deficient, while the allantois becomes highly vascularized.

Ovoviviparous and viviparous *lizards* and *snakes* present various types of *uterine feeding*. In the most primitive cases, the eggs are large and enclosed in shell membranes; retention provides mainly protection. In other species, the eggs are conspicuously smaller than those of the nearest egg-laying relatives; they have no shells, and only thin albumen layers. Nutritious secretions from uterine glands and disintegrating uterine cells form a pasty or liquid histotroph, which is absorbed by the yolk sac and by the chorio-allantois. In species with very small eggs, the maternal and fetal capillaries closely approach each other, spreading through the apposed or fused surface layers. Originally, this peculiar feature of the reptile placenta seems to have facilitated only the gaseous exchange. However, it may also enter into the service of food transfer, nutrient materials finding their way from the maternal blood through the thin tissue barriers into the fetal circulation. The considerable increase in weight of the fetus over that of the egg proves unequivocally the importance of intra-uterine feeding. Nevertheless, even in these species, the reserves carried by the egg as it leaves the ovary suffice to sustain development beyond the embryonic and metamorphic periods. The uterine supplies become essential only at advanced fetal stages. Viviparity and placentation in lizards and snakes present an evolutionary line which parallels the more elaborate and varied developments in mammals, without being their direct prototype.

d. Reduction of Egg Size and Formation of Chorionic Vesicles.

The monotreme duckbills (*Ornithorhynchus*) and anteaters (*Echidna*) are the only mammals that have not progressed beyond ovoviviparity. Their newly ovulated eggs are within the size range of small lizard eggs (Table 3) and weigh about 30 mg. Uterine secretions add an albumen layer and provide a parchment-like shell. The eggs are retained in the uteri until embryos corresponding to bird stages of the second day of

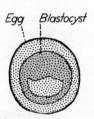

Figure 245.   Golden hamster (*Cricetus auratus*). Loss of egg substance during four days preceding implantation, illustrated by superposing outline drawings of the newly ovulated egg and the blastocyst of four days; × 300.

incubation have developed. Toward the end of this period their size has increased to about 15 mm., through absorption of nearly 2 gm. of water. At laying, they are placed into a nest (*Ornithorhynchus*) or the mother's brood pouch (*Echidna*). During the following incubation period the young pass through all but the last few stages of metamorphosis. At *hatching*, their legs—especially the lower pair—are still in a primitive developmental condition. Thus the nutritious stores of these eggs support development up to a fairly advanced stage, though not to one of self-sufficiency.

In all other mammals, the size of the egg is more radically reduced (Table 2, p. 38) and the young are retained much longer in the uteri. This combination depends on efficient methods of uterine feeding, at very early embryonic stages. The diameter of mammalian eggs usually is near 0.1 mm. Though small in comparison with eggs of other vertebrates, within its species the ovocyte still is one of the largest cells of the entire body and carries considerable stores of food materials. The cleaving eggs of many species become coated with albumen secretions of the oviducts (Figs. 38*a*, 251); but it is unlikely that the morulae and blastocysts, which float free in the lumen of the oviducts and uteri,

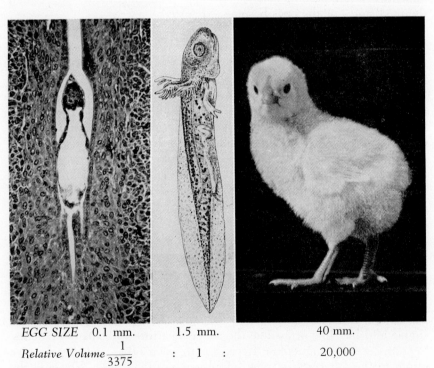

EGG SIZE	0.1 mm.	1.5 mm.	40 mm.
Relative Volume	$\frac{1}{3375}$:	1 :	20,000

Figure 246. Relationship between egg size and stage of development attained when feeding begins. Rat: Blastocyst (St. 9); Salamander: larva (St. 27) (Detwiler); Chick: juvenile bird (St. 36).

absorb and assimilate any food materials. Rather, it appears that the nutritional requirements before implantation of the blastocysts are satisfied entirely from the stores contained in the egg at the time of ovulation. During this period, which usually lasts four to ten days, the cytoplasmic substance shrinks considerably. The yolk-like (deutoplasmic) inclusions disappear. In the hamster, two-thirds of the original substance has been used up by the middle of the fourth day (Fig. 245).

The size of the extra-embryonic membranes of sauropsids and monotremes is limited by that of the eggs and egg shells. In the viviparous mammals, where their physiologic importance is increased, their growth is only restrained by the size of the expandable uterus. In fact they often attain enormous dimensions. The blastocyst cavity of the pre-implantation stages serves as the topographic center of membrane development. The entire fluid-filled system of fetal membranes and cavities is designated as the *chorionic vesicle*.

The direct *relationship between egg size and the developmental stage attained before feeding from the outside starts,* is illustrated in Figure 246. The mammal is at the blastula or beginning gastrula stage (St. 8), the salamander a free swimming larva (St. 27), and the chick an immature adult past metamorphosis and fetal stages (St. 36), when the food stores of the eggs become exhausted.

2. MAMMALIAN PLACENTAL TYPES

In the strict sense, the term *placenta* is applied to fetal and maternal structures which are morphologically specialized organs of material transfer between mother and offspring, during pregnancy. In some species the chorionic vesicle becomes only superficially attached to the uterine wall (superficial implantation); in others it grows deep into the endometrium, imbedding itself in the maternal tissue (interstitial implantation). Gross and microscopic morphology of the *fetal placentae* exhibit a wide diversity. The *maternal placentae* attain definite shape and histologic differentiation only in the rodents. In the other orders, gestational uteri show general reactions rather than a placental organization. If the fetal and maternal tissues grow into each other, the superficial layer of the uterine mucosa becomes a *decidua,* so-called because at parturition it is shed and forms a part of the *afterbirth.* However, there exists no clear line between deciduate and non-deciduate placental types (Table 19).

The absorbing and excreting surface of chorionic vesicles becomes increased by the outgrowth of *villi,* or of *septums.* A villus may be simple and hair-like or assume the shape of a tuft with many branches. Septums usually anastomose freely among each other and thereby give origin to the *labyrinthine types* of placentae (Fig. 249). Not only the superficial chorion, but also the yolk sac, the allantois, and even the

Table 19

Fetal Fluid, Placental Type, and Endometrial Differentiation of Some Eutherian Mammals

Species (Gestation Period) days	Adult Weight kg.	Birth Weight kg.	Total Fetal Fluids		Placental Types		Uterine Mucosa
			Maximal kg.	At Birth kg.	Morphologic	Histologic	
Horse (335)	600	50	20	10	diffuse (villous)	epichorial	nondeciduate
Pig (112)	100	2.500	0.250	0.080	diffuse (villous)	epichorial	nondeciduate
Cattle (285)	500	36	15	5	cotyledonary (villous)	mesochorial	transitional
Sheep (150)	60	5	2.500	2.500	cotyledonary (villous)	mesochorial	transitional
	50	3.500	1.200	1.000	cotyledonary (villous)	mesochorial	
Goat (151)	40	1.800	0.600	0.300	cotyledonary (villous)	mesochorial	transitional
Dog (62)	15	0.300	0.200	0.100	zonary (labyrinthine)	endochorial	deciduate
Cat (63)	2	0.100	0.030	0.030	zonary (labyrinthine)	endochorial	deciduate
Rabbit (32)	3	0.060	0.01	0.002	discoid (labyrinthine)	hemochorial	deciduate
Rat (22)	0.180	0.0045	0.0008	0.0008	discoid (labyrinthine)	hemochorial	deciduate
Guinea pig (68)	0.675	0.100	0.014	0.014	discoid (labyrinthine)	hemochorial	deciduate
Man (266)	70	3.400	2	1.500	discoid (villous)	hemochorial	deciduate

amnion, may become engaged in the exchange of materials and in the construction of specialized placentae.

Figures 247–249 exhibit the wide variety of placental types (compare with Table 19). All eutherians, starting as eggs weighing in the neighborhood of one microgram, increase during intra-uterine life from one million to several billion times. This is eloquent proof that respiratory, nutritional and excretory needs become satisfied by the most primitive, as well as by the highest differentiated, placental types. Nevertheless, definite evolutionary lines are recognizable which tend toward *substitution of hemotrophic for histotrophic nutritional methods* (Table 19). The physiologic changes are accompanied by structural modifications.

In comparison with the embryonic body, the placental apparatus differentiates earlier in the higher than in the lower and primitive types. In the opossum, as in the chick, the *chorio-amniotic folds* appear at the 12-somite stage and close at about 40 somites. In the pig they arise shortly before the first somite is formed, and the amniotic pore closes at the 12-somite stage. Finally, in the human embryo, a closed amniotic cavity is established in 7 to 9-day blastocysts.

The multichambered chorionic vesicles gradually become simplified, and in older human fetuses have only a single cavity. This is accomplished through reduction of yolk sac and allantois, and expansion of the amnion (Fig. 249). *With the yolk sac disappear also the vitelline*

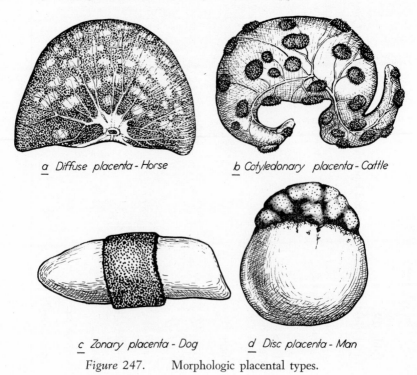

a Diffuse placenta - Horse   *b* Cotyledonary placenta - Cattle

c Zonary placenta - Dog   *d* Disc placenta - Man

Figure 247.   Morphologic placental types.

arteries and veins. Quite to the contrary, the allantoic vessels persist in all types, even in those with complete reduction of the allantoic sac and increasingly assume the role of a general supply system (Table 20).

As the chorionic vesicles penetrate deeper into the endometrium, they move closer to the very source of all supplies, the maternal blood stream. Layer after layer of the uterine wall becomes eroded until the villi come into direct contact with the maternal blood (Fig. 248, Table 19). Apparently the rate of exchange by diffusion is quite obviously improved by exploitation of the principle of counterflows. It is seen at work in the arrangement of the maternal and fetal networks of placental capillaries that forces the blood to flow in opposite directions (Fig. 248c). As the placentae become specialized and highly vascularized organs of exchange, they contract and cover only restricted regions of the otherwise smooth chorionic surface. One distinguishes *diffuse, cotyledonous, zonary,* and *discoid placentae* (Fig. 247, Table 19), in accordance with their gross shapes.

The primates most nearly represent the goal toward which all these lines converge. The following *characterization of major types* refers to the fully developed fetal conditions (cf. Fig. 249a–i). At younger stages, taxonomic differences are less pronounced.

a. Monotremes.   The monotremes are the only strictly non-placental mammals. Enclosed within an egg shell, the fetus subsists and grows at the expense of the yolk, contained in the large yolk sac. It is not known whether any use is made of the "egg white" except that certainly much of its water is absorbed by the growing fetus. The allantois attains a size about equal to that of the yolk sac. The conditions in nearly mature fetuses, ready to hatch, resemble those of the chick at about the seventh day of incubation.

b. Marsupials.   The opossum has an extremely short fetal period. In fact, the young are born immediately after completion of the meta-

Table 20

Reduction or Persistence of Yolk Sac and Allantois in the Mammals

	YOLK SAC		ALLANTOIS	
	Epithelia	Blood Vessels	Epithelia	Blood Vessel
Monotremes	+	+	(+)	(+)
Marsupials	+	+	+	+
Insectivores	+	+	+	+
Rodents	+	+	Vestigial or absent	+
Carnivores	(+)	(+)	+	+
Ungulates	Rudiment	Rudiment	+	+
Anthropoids	Rudiment	Rudiment	Rudiment	+

+ Fully or fairly well developed until end of gestation.
(+) Relatively small, but maintained until birth.

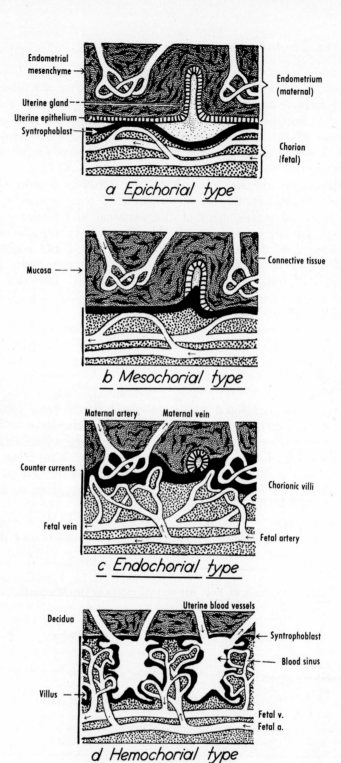

Figure 248.   Histologic placental types.

morphic changes (age 12 to 13 days). At that stage the vascular mesoderm covers barely half the surface of the yolk sac, and the allantois
is not in contact with the chorion. Thus the opossum acquires only
a primitive *yolk-sac placenta*. Circulation becomes established about
the tenth day, only three days before birth. The newborn is from 10
to 12 mm. long. It weighs about 150 mg., which represents a 100,000-
fold increase over that of the newly ovulated egg, not even including
in this calculation the weight of the placental membranes. Some Aus-
tralian marsupials have a more extended fetal period; their yolk-sac
placenta is histologically better differentiated but never seems to cover
the entire yolk sac. In at least two species, *Parameles* and *Phascolarctus*,
the allantois reaches the chorion and fuses with its inner surface, so
that during the late fetal stages vitelline and allantoic placentae function side by side.

   c. Horses.   The yolk sac, which is relatively large during the
early fetal stages, becomes permanently attached to the chorion. A small
yolk-sac placenta forms and persists until the end of the second month.
During the third month the yolk sac shrinks, causing formation of a
cleft-like recess in the surface of the chorion (Fig. 247a). Small yolk
sac vessels persist. The *allantois* spreads along the entire inner surface
of the chorion, disrupting the original chorio-amniotic connection. The
mature *chorionic sac* has a length of about 1.20 m. and a greatest diameter of 0.50 m. Short, branching *villi* cover most of the surface, except
for spots directly under the *endometrial cups* (see below). Up to the
twentieth week, a rich histotroph is formed through glandular activity
and copious breakdown of the surface layers of the uterine mucosa. It
is believed that during the second half of pregnancy nutrition is mainly
of hemotrophic nature, though maternal and fetal capillaries remain
separated by intact layers of endometrial tissues (Fig. 248a).

   Already during the first months of pregnancy, *endometrial cups* appear in the
uterine walls. They are 1 to 3 mm. in diameter and secrete a gelatinous substance rich in gonadotrophic hormone. These secretions, and later also the cups
themselves, project into the allantoic cavity in the shape of little chorio-allantoic
sacs.

   d. Artiodactyls.   In pigs and ruminants the yolk sac regresses
early; a yolk-sac placenta is not formed. The amnion never loses its
connection with the chorion and secondarily enlarges its adhesion. In
the center of the crescent-shaped chorionic sac the allantois is pressed
to the right wall. It also fills a large part of each of the two horns (Fig.
247b). In the pig the amnion finally almost completely displaces the
allantois; at term it contains about eight times as much fluid as the
allantois. In sheep the final ratio is about 1:1; in cattle the amnion
shrinks, particularly during the last phase of gestation, and at parturition
contains only about one-fourth of the total fetal fluids (Table 19). When-
ever the allantois recedes, its arteries and veins spread into the chorio-

amniotic membrane, and it is for this reason that one considers the
entire *placenta* as of *allantoic type*. Short and simple villi cover nearly
the entire surface of the chorion. The pig and the horse are the outstanding representatives of the *diffuse placenta* type. Nutrition is
probably hemotrophic as well as histotrophic.

In the *ruminants* large villi are arranged in patches called *cotyledons*
(Figs. 247b, 249d) which number about 100 in sheep and cattle, but
in the deer often are fewer than 10. The villi of the cotyledons pene-

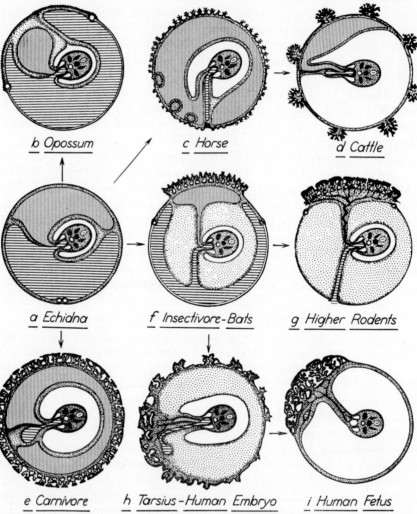

Figure 249.   Chorionic vesicles of various mammalian types in cross sections.
Some probable evolutionary relationships are indicated by arrows. White: Amniotic
cavity. Heavy horizontal lines: Gut and yolk sac. Light vertical lines: Allantois.
Light stipple: Extra-embryonic celom. (Compare with Figures 247, 248, and
Tables 19, 20.)

trate deep into the mucosal tissue, eroding away the uterine epithelia and partly also the uterine glands (Fig. 248b). Histotroph is formed in large quantities.

e. Carnivores.   The arrangement of the fetal membranes resembles that of the horse. Though the *yolk sac* is not attached to the chorion and no yolk-sac placenta is formed, a vestigial sac, as well as vitelline blood vessels, persists throughout the entire gestation period. At an early stage the surface of the chorion becomes covered with villi that partly fuse with each other. Later this labyrinthine placenta becomes restricted to a zone around the middle of the oblong chorionic sac (zonary placenta; Fig. 247c). It is well anchored in the uterine mucosa (Fig. 248c), and with the afterbirth, parts of the attached maternal tissues are shed. The carnivores therefore belong to the group of *deciduate* mammals (Table 19).

f. Insectivores and Bats.   Hedgehogs, shrews, and moles are a primitive group, retaining both yolk sac and allantois. The yolk sac varies in size but a primitive, non-villous *vitelline placenta* differentiates in most species of this group. Usually the proximal half of the sac invaginates into the distal half. The inside of this bell becomes well vascularized; its outside is only partly covered with mesoderm and mostly remains without blood vessels. Presumably, respiratory gases and some nutritious materials pass from the uterine cavity through the diplotrophoblast (two-layered trophoblast) into the yolk-sac lumen, become absorbed by the proximal yolk-sac epithelium, and are carried away by the vitelline veins. The disc-shaped *allanto-placenta* is of a highly differentiated labyrinthic type. The fetal membranes of the *bats* follow the same line of development, specific variants appearing only at late stages.

g. Rodents.   Rabbits and other primitive rodents start development with a complete set of extra-embryonic appendages, showing a close similarity to the insectivore type. However, the fully developed condition is characterized by drastic reduction or loss of the allantoic sac, and resorption of the distal half of the yolk sac, the so-called *omphalopleure* or bilaminar yolk sac. Thus the endoderm of the proximal half of the yolk sac becomes exposed, gaining direct contact with the histotroph in the uterine lumen, and even with the uterine wall. Some trophectoderm cells persist for a long time at the surface of the decidua and grow into *giant cells*. Some investigators contend that these giant cells are not of embryonic but of maternal origin. Their functional importance is unknown. The *allantoplacenta* consists of chorionic lamellae, partly fused and labyrinthine like that of the insectivores. The antimesometrial part of the decidua bordering on the yolk sac early begins to accumulate lipoids, while the mesometrial part, which is connected with the allantoplacenta, contains rich stores of glycogen (cf. Fig. 259). This distribution pattern suggests that the vitelline circulatory system may provide the fetus especially with fats, the allantoic system with carbohydrates. The latter probably is also the main avenue for proteins and serves for the exchange of respiratory gases. In the higher rodents—murids and cavies—the development even of rudiments of allantoic vesicles is completely abolished.

h. Primitive Primates.   Lemurs and *Tarsius* present conditions which seem to link the placental type of the insectivores with that of the higher primates, including man. Both yolk sac and allantois shrink. In lemurs, a transitory yolk-sac placenta exists during early stages; in *Tarsius,* the *yolk sac is vestigial* from the start. During the late fetal phase the amnion sac grows rapidly and becomes attached to the inner surface of the chorion. The *allantoplacenta* is *diffuse or discoid* and has a villous or a lamellar structure. The sloth (*Bradypus*), though a specialized type of its own, shows some similarity to this group.

i. Monkeys and Anthropoids.   The relatively simple conditions that prevail during the late phase of gestation in the higher primates, and especially in man, are the result of complex evolutionary and embryologic developments. The non-placental chorion has a smooth surface without villi (chorion leve) and is sparsely vascularized. The placenta is a single disc (man) or a double disc (monkeys). It contains a large cavity, filled with maternal blood, between two trophoblastic layers. The *surface layer* is firmly fused with the uterine decidua. From the *basal layer* rise the richly branching villi; crossing the blood-filled space, their main stems anchor in the surface layer. In man the blood-filled space (pot, potplacenta) is partially subdivided by septums which

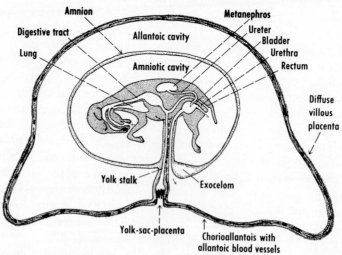

Figure 250.   Fetus of the horse within its membranes. Arrows indicate water intake by mouth from amniotic cavity and urine excretion into allantoic as well as amniotic cavities.

appear at the surface as deep furrows and divide the placenta into 15 to 20 round lobes, sometimes called cotyledons (Figs. 247*d* and 249*i*).

3. FETAL FLUIDS

During the embryonic and early fetal stages the chorionic vesicles of all species are relatively large and contain fluids which surpass the embryos several times in weight and volume. Suspension of the extremely soft embryos and fetuses in a fluid-filled cavity probably serves several purposes, but mainly, it prevents mechanical deformation. Later in gestation, the amount of the fluids remains at a constant level or decreases (Table 19). In all cases it diminishes in proportion to the weight of the fetus. Together with great and unexplained individual fluctuations, this seems to indicate a decline in functional importance of the fluids during the later part of gestation.

Like the cavity of pre-implantation blastocysts, the celomic, amniotic, allantoic and yolk-sac cavities also become filled by *transudation* through the enclosing tissues. During early embryonic stages, such fluids are almost directly derived from the mother. Later they are partly of fetal origin; for, when the kidneys begin to function, urine becomes voided into the allantoic sac through the allantoic stalk (urachus), or into the amnion by way of the urethra (Fig. 250). Near the end of gestation the fetal fluids resemble very dilute urine (Table 21). It is significant that the protein and urea contents are not higher in pigs and cattle than in man, even though the kidneys of the former give evidence of more excretory activity than those of human fetuses. Also, the amounts of their total fetal fluids are not relatively higher than that contained in the amnion of human fetuses (Table 19). The combined data prove that in eutherian mammals the nitrogenous wastes are not accumulated and stored in the fetal vesicles, but continuously eliminated through the placentae and released into the blood stream of the mother. The mechanisms of placental excretion are incompletely known; probably they differ according to placental types (cf. Chapter 29 on excretory organs).

Table 21

Nitrogenous Materials in Urine, and in Amniotic Fluids near Term. Contents in mg./100 ml.; approximated values, references in Needham, Windle, etc.

	MAN Urine of Adults	MAN Amniotic Fluid	PIG Amniotic Fluid	CATTLE Amniotic Fluid
Total N	1700	75	50	70
Urea	2000	40	30	38

Chapter 22

Nurture. II

4. MODIFICATIONS IN THE DEVELOPMENT OF FETAL MEMBRANES

The *blastocysts* of eutherian mammals (Fig. 251) resemble in principle the discogastrulae of birds (Figs. 35, 152). Relatively unimportant differences, such as their small size and the expansion of the subgerminal cavity into a spherical *blastocyst cavity,* are related to the absence of a non-cleaving yolk mass. *Trophoblast* differentiation occurs at earlier stages than in birds (Fig. 256*a, b, c*); but the separation of prospective embryonic and extra-embryonic ectoderm is far from complete in pre-implantation blastocysts. The so-called *embryoblast,* i.e., the solid accumulation of blastemic cells in the animal pole region (Fig. 251), still contains the entire prospective endoderm and mesoderm. Beginning outgrowth of the endoderm usually is coincident with the start of implantation (Fig. 252, St. 8). Experimentation and direct observation at early developmental stages of mammals being technically difficult, relatively little direct information is available concerning the localization of prospective areas of differentiation. However, the general similarity of the development of the *embryonic disc* of mammals to that of reptilian and avian blastoderms assists in the interpretation of the known facts. The diagrams of Figure 255 represent the three major types of fetal membrane formation in mammals. The left hand drawings are fate maps of pre-implantation blastocysts (St. 7). Those on the right side illustrate the state of differentiation attained at the primitive streak stage (St. 12).

386

a. Amnion Formation by Folding.

The simplest and most primitive type is clearly represented by the rabbit (Figs. 251, 254) and the pig (Fig. 253). At the blastocyst stage the presumptive chorio-amniotic folds (ectodermal parts) are contained in the ectotrophoblast, and the presumptive embryonic ectoderm lies at the surface of the embryoblast (Fig. 255a). The presumptive mesoderm forms a crescent-shaped rim of the embryoblast, remaining open ventrally. Therefore in the sagittal

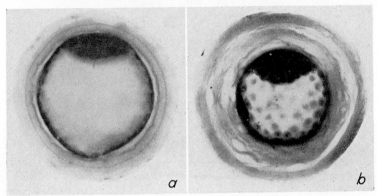

Figure 251.   Free blastocysts of the rabbit, 3½ days old (St. 7), surrounded by vitelline membrane and albumen layers; a, center focus: trophoblastic vesicle, embryoblast, and blastocyst cavity (gastrocele); b, high focus: nuclei of trophoblast wall; × 150.

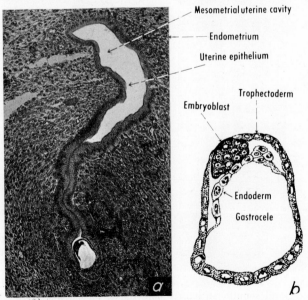

Figure 252.   Golden hamster; implanting blastocyst (St. 8). a, Blastocyst between epithelia of the antimesometrial uterine cavity; × 80. b, More enlarged drawing of blastocyst; × 450. Endodermal epithelium, following inner surface of trophectoderm, advances toward vegetal pole.

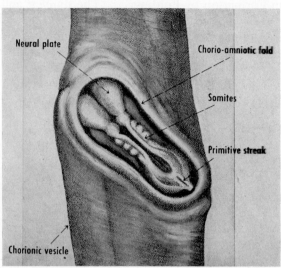

Figure 253.   Pig embryo, 13½ days, 3 somites (St. 15). Central part of chorionic vesicle (about 1 meter total length). Embryo surrounded by rising amniotic folds; × 20.

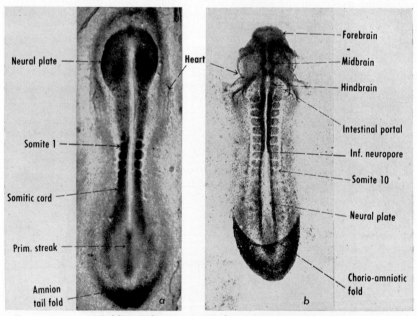

Figure 254.   Rabbit embryos. *a,* 7½ days, 5 somites (St. 15). Dark border around neural and somitic structures consists of prospective lateral and ventral body wall. Tubular heart primordia; × 20 (large breed). *b,* 8 days, 11 somites (St. 16), bag-shaped, caudal amniotic fold; small pericardial sacs; × 20 (small breed).

plane it is sectioned only at the dorsal side (black area), and during
subsequent stages of outgrowth a considerable delay in the formation
of the extra-embryonic mesoderm layer occurs in the region ventral to
the forehead ("above" the primitive streak) (Fig. 255b).

During gastrulation (Fig. 255b), a *yolk sac* is formed by the endoderm
cells issuing from the deepest layer of the embryoblast. At stage 12 the
endodermal outgrowth is followed also by that of a sheet of mesoderm.
Splitting into two layers it gives origin to the extra-embryonic celomic
sacs. While the *germ disc* gradually sinks into the blastocyst cavity
(now a gastrocele and yolk-sac-cavity), the somatopleure gives origin
to chorio-amniotic folds (Figs. 253, 255b). In the pig of the early primitive streak stage they start as a single, circular elevation and the amniotic
pore closes in embryos of 10 somites.

The chorio-amniotic stalk maintains a position in the head or upper neck region
until in pigs and cattle the adhesion spreads over large areas of the inner
surface of the chorion (Fig. 249d). In the rabbit, amnion formation begins at
the stage of eight somites with a crescent-shaped tail fold (Fig. 254). At 14
somites it covers the lower half of the embryo while the head folds just make
their appearance. As in the pig, closure eventually occurs in the upper neck or
head region. The cervical or occipital position of the chorio-amniotic stalk is
characteristic for most mammals. Development of the amnion by the folding
process is maintained by all ungulates and carnivores, most insectivores, some
rodents and the primitive primates.

b. Amnion Formation by Cavitation.   The start of amnion formation in the pig was seen related to the sinking of the germ disc into
the blastocyst cavity. In some species this translocation occurs earlier,
even during late cleavage stages. As a consequence, at the blastocyst
stage the embryoblast has a covering of ectotrophoblast, mainly prospective chorion and amnion cells (Fig. 255c). The closed amniotic
cavity appears before the primitive streak stage, as a space separating
amnion and germ disc. Related to the precocity of amniogenesis is a
widespread tendency for primary reduction of the size of the yolk sac
(Fig. 255d). Amnion formation through cavitation occurs in a few
insectivores, especially the hedgehog, in bats, and in many primates.
Among primitive primates and insectivores one finds types that are
intermediate between folding and cavitating.

**c. Formation of a Transient Ectochorionic Cyst in Combination
with the Amnion.**   The tendency toward early translocation of the
prospective embryo from the surface of the blastocyst into the depth
of its cavity culminates in the order of the rodents. While rabbits,
ground squirrels, and beavers still show the primitive type of folding
at the surface of the blastocyst, in the pocket gopher (*Geomys*) and
in the kangaroo rat (*Dipodomys*) the chorio-amniotic folds arise in the
depth of a crater-shaped depression of the chorion. This brings the
embryonic shield deep into the cavity of the blastocyst, and, as a
further consequence, it leads to the formation of a small chorionic pouch

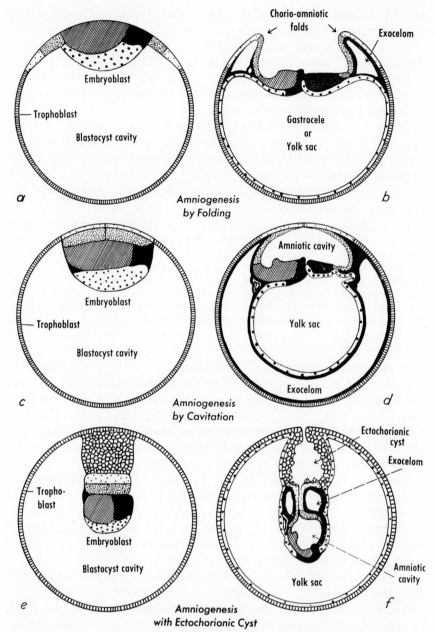

Figure 255.   Interpretation of fetal membrane development. Diagrams at left: Areas of prospective differentiation at the blastocyst stage (St. 7). Diagrams at right: State of differentiation at primitive streak stage (St. 12). Ectochorion: cuboid cells, or loosely stippled (the latter indicating parts that participate in formation of chorio-amniotic folds). Ectamnion: densely stippled. Embryonic ectoderm: shaded by oblique lines. Mesoderm: black. Endoderm: dotted.

above the chorio-amniotic folds. Investigations of Hisaw and Mossman indicate that this is an intermediary condition in the evolution of the *ectochorionic cyst.* This much discussed cavity is a characteristic occurrence in many rodents. However, in the large family of the murids it develops by an abbreviated process that starts with an early ingrowth of a solid plug of ectoblastema cells (Fig. 255*e, f*).

The *blastocysts of all murids,* but especially those of the rats, are actually not spherical like the diagrams (Fig. 255*e, f*), but have a cylindrical shape (Fig. 256). At an early stage the ectotrophoblast forms a pointed placental cone and then proliferates to the inside (Fig. 256*d*), pushing the inner cell mass deep into the blastocyst cavity (Fig. 255*e*). The entire embryoblast now has the shape of a *pendant* with a spreading surface layer of prospective endoderm and a core of mostly ectodermal blastema. The lowest segment also includes the prospective mesoderm (Figs. 255*e*, 257*a*). For a short period the innermost part almost separates while it acquires a primary amniotic cavity *by cavitation* (Fig. 257*b*). But presently this vesicle opens at the top, and its cavity expands into the stalk of the pendant. Evidently the larger hollow thus formed (Fig. 257*c*) is the equivalent of the chorio-amniotic tube of *Dipodomys.* It becomes subdivided into an *ectochorionic cyst* and the true *amniotic cavity* by the rise and fusion of the *chorio-amni-*

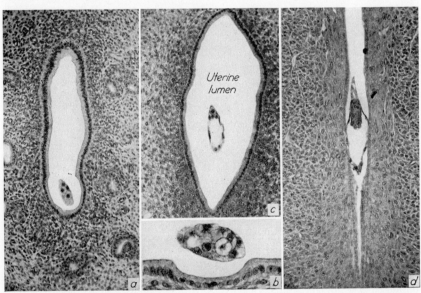

Figure 256.   Rat, blastocysts. *a, b,* Early blastocysts of 4 days (St. 6), with blastocyst cavity appearing near lower pole; × 100 and × 250. *c,* Fully differentiated blastocyst of 5 days (St. 7), free in uterine lumen; × 100. *d,* Implanting and already growing blastocyst of 6 days (St. 8) with trophoblastic cone; placental reaction in the uterine endometrium; uterine glands disappear after fourth day; erosion of uterine epithelium begins on sixth day; × 100.

otic folds (Fig. 258*a, b*). These folds contain mesoderm-lined cavities which, united, form a third cyst-like cavity in the center of the pendant, the *extra-embryonic celom* or *exocelom*. For a few hours the amnion remains connected across the exocelomic cavity with the ectochorionic cyst; but this *chorio-amniotic stalk* is very ephemeral (Fig. 258*b*). Meanwhile endoderm cells, spreading from the embryoblast (Figs. 252, 256*c*, 257), have provided a continuous lining of the blastocyst cavity, which thereby becomes transformed into a bell-shaped *yolk sac* (Figs. 258, 259).

In the further development, the ectochorionic cyst becomes flattened against the *ectoplacenta* with which it eventually fuses (Figs. 258*b*, 259*a*, 260). The purely *mesodermal allantoic stalk*, growing out from the lower end of the embryo into the exocelom (Figs. 258*b*, 259), reaches this fortified ectoplacenta in 6-somite embryos, less than 10

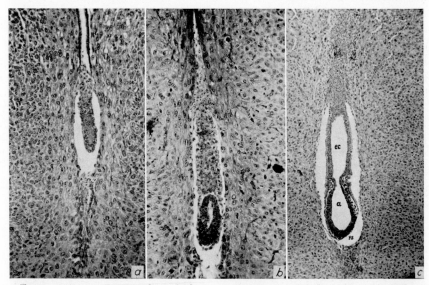

Figure 257.   Rat, implanted blastocysts. *a*, Germ of 7 days (St. 10). Where the diplotrophoblast (ectotrophoblast plus endoderm) is in contact with the uterine wall, the uterine epithelium has disappeared. Embryoblast, now a long *pendant*, consists of ectoplacental cone, chorio-amniotic blastema, and embryonic ectoderm plus mesoderm. The surface of the entire pendant is covered with an endodermal cell layer; × 100. *b*, Completely implanted blastocyst of 7¾ days (St. 11). Uterine lumen has disappeared; the embryonic part of the pendant consists of an endodermal epithelium covering an ecto-mesodermal vesicle. The central lumen may be considered as a primary amniotic cavity; × 100. *c*, *Primitive streak stage* (St. 12) 8½ days; amniotic (*a*) and ectochorionic (*ec*) cavities, connecting between rudiments of amniotic folds. The primitive node is at the lowest point of the amniotic cavity; the primitive streak extends from here to the right, the neuroderm to the left; blastemas of primordial heart and pericardium (under the left amniotic fold). Two notches in endoderm (under right amniotic fold) indicate primordia of allantois and hindgut; *ys*, yolk sac; × 50.

days old. *Allantoic circulation* starts a few hours later (Fig. 260). Thus forms the *chorio-allantoic placenta*. By this time the ectochorionic cyst has disappeared.

d. Blastocyst Cavity, Gastrocele, and Yolk Sac. The formation of a large blastocyst cavity in place of the uncleaved yolk mass of birds and monotremes is an outstanding trait of early mammalian development. Through the outgrowth of an endodermal epithelium from the deepest layer of the embryoblast (Figs. 252, 255), it becomes a *primitive yolk-sac cavity.* The subsequent supply of the trophoblast with mesoderm, and its separation into splanchnic and somatic layers, completes the formation of a double layer *yolk-sac epithelium,* surrounded by a chorion. Temporarily the roof contains a strip of axial mesoderm (Fig. 258*b*), and the cavity is an equivalent of the gastrocele of an amphibian gastrula. Finally, by umbilical constriction, the gastrocele is divided into separate *gut* and *yolk-sac* cavities (Fig. 260).

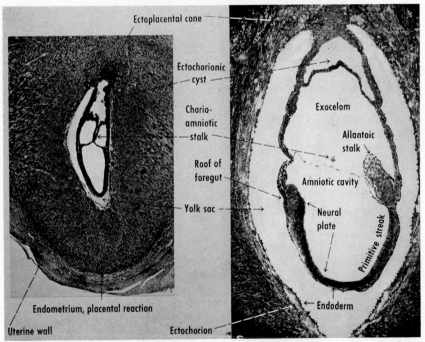

Figure 258. Rat. *a,* Presomite neurula (St. 13), 9 days, cross section, showing fusion of chorio-amniotic folds (chorio-amniotic stalk) and consequent separation of the amniotic cavity from the ectochorionic cyst. From primitive node rise neural plates; × 28. *b,* Open neurula stage (St. 14) at inception of somite formation. Ectochorionic cyst partially compressed toward ectoplacental cone. Extra-embryonic celom with small remnant of chorio-amniotic stalk and ingrowing allantoic stalk; blood islands in lateral (splanchnic) walls of the celomic sac and in cone of the allantoic stalk initiate formation of vitelline and allantoic circulatory systems; segmentation of cephalic neural plate (left side) indicated; rudiment of the notochord in roof of archenteron; primitive streak in right wall of amniotic cavity; × 56.

When, in the last week of gestation, the bilaminar distal part of the yolk sac (omphalopleure) disappears, the endoderm of the proximal half comes to lie at the surface of the larger part of the embryonic vesicle (Fig. 249g).

The original *dorsal concavity of the embryo* lessens as the longitudinal diameter of the chorionic vesicle gains and eventually surpasses the length of the polar axis (Fig. 260). At 11 days, i.e., toward the end of the embryonic period, the usual ventral concavity is attained (Fig.

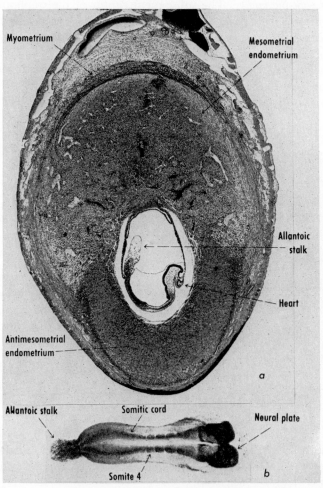

Figure 259.   *a,* Cross section through gravid uterus of the rat, with parasagittal section through embryo of four somites, 9½ days (neurula, St. 14). Ectochorionic cyst reduced to narrow cleft. Allantoic stalk approaching roof of exocelomic cavity. Section through lateral mesoderm and primitive streak. Foregut and hindgut are visible; in front of the latter (right side) lies the tubular heart; × 16. Note difference of endometrial reaction in the mesometrial and the antimesometrial regions. *b,* Whole mount (dorsal aspect) of a 4-somite embryo of the hamster (*Cricetus auratus*), very similar to that of the rat; × 24.

261). The embryo within its amnion now lies crosswise to the former polar axis, its left side resting in the concavity of the yolk sac and its right turned toward the allantoplacenta.

Also in some insectivores the *yolk sac* maintains a considerable size and functional importance throughout the fetal period. But in the other orders it regresses during or immediately following metamorphosis (Fig. 249c, d, e). In the sloth (*Bradypus*), *Tarsius* and the anthropoid primates the reduction is a primary feature; the endoderm vesicle never fills the entire blastocyst cavity (Fig. 249h, i).

The persistent early formation of yolk sacs of considerable size, though empty, is understandable in view of their role in the development of the circulatory system. From the selachians to the birds, blood islands, blood vessels, and blood cells differentiate first on the surface of the yolk-sac endoderm, that is, in the immediate neighborhood of the big nutritional stores. It is not surprising that this topographic relationship is maintained in mammals even if the original functional significance is changed or lost. In human embryos numerous blood islands still differentiate on the surface of the relatively small yolk sacs. However, vascular plexuses, giving rise to chorionic blood vessels, appear independently also in the mesoderm of the body stalk and of the chorionic vesicle. Similarly, vascular plexuses develop in the allantoic stalks of rats, far from endodermal tissues (Figs. 258–260). It is probable that at the embryonic level the vitelline circulatory systems of all mammals retain some respiratory and even trophic functions. In murids they are very important throughout fetal life (Fig. 249g).

e. Precocious Development and Reduction of the Allantoic Sac.
The allantois, originally a urinary and later also a respiratory organ, assumes additional functions with the evolution of gestation. Abundantly

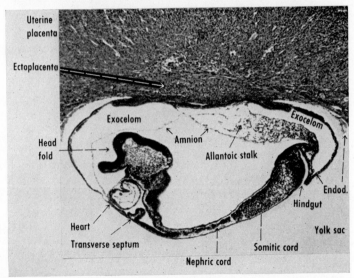

Figure 260. Parasagittal section through 8-somite rat embryo of 10 days (neurula, St. 15). Allantoic stalk with vascular plexus attaches broadly to ecto-placenta (fused ectochorionic cyst and placental cone); × 40.

vascularized and extending to the inner surface of the chorion, it is well suited to participate in the new task of carrying food materials and waste products in the exchange between uterine wall and embryo. The series opossum-echidna-horse (Fig. 249) exemplifies the gradual ascendancy gained by the allantoic over the vitelline system. In insectivores the allantois, though smaller than the yolk sac, becomes more important through higher specialization (Fig. 249). Allantoic circulation persists and expands even if, in connection with evolutionary changes in the excretory system, the allantoic sac itself becomes reduced (Fig. 249*d*, *h, i*) or disappears (Fig. 249*g*). In human embryology it has become customary to designate the allantoic vessels as *umbilical* arteries and

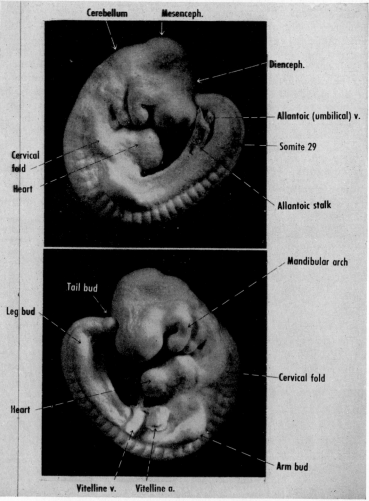

Figure 261.   Rat embryo of 27 somites, 12 days old (tailbud St. 19). The series of somites continues into the tailbud as the somitic blastema cord. Note emerging maxillary and mandibular processes of first visceral arch; × 16.

veins, since they are the only ones to be found in the fetal umbilicus after the second month. The same terminology is often extended to those mammals (e.g., the rat) which retain vitelline vessels throughout the fetal period, and to the fetuses of birds (Chapter 17).

The predominance attained by the allantoic system finds expression also in its precocious development. In the chick and the opossum it begins to push out from the floor of the hindgut at about the 30-somite stage; in the rabbit at 14, and in the pig at six somites. In human embryos, with very rudimentary yolk sac formation, the tubular bladder or *urachus* reaches a considerable length during presomite stages (Figs. 303, 305). In the rat, also, the allantoic stalk begins to grow out before the differentiation of the first somites (Fig. 258b).

5. PLACENTAL PERMEABILITY AND BARRIER

In describing the different placental types it was pointed out that two closely linked trends may be recognized, one toward *contraction and specialization of the absorptive area* of the chorion, the other effecting an *approach of chorion and maternal blood* through erosion of endometrial tissue barriers. The mere fact that horse and man, both with long gestation periods, represent types from opposite ends of these evolutionary lines suffices to dispel the idea that evolution is necessarily linked with improvement in the sense of increased chances for survival. At every level of embryonic and fetal development the primitive equines compare favorably with the primates in regard to speed of differentiation and growth rate. Similar conclusions may be derived from a study of small species with short gestation periods, such as the mouse, the opossum, and the golden hamster.

In regard to the possible *physiologic importance of placental types,* it must not be forgotten that their characteristic morphologic and histologic differences develop relatively late, mostly during the metamorphic period (stages 26 to 33, Fig. 262). Consequently, functional particularities of the placental types may be expected to become manifest mainly during the fetal period (stages 34 to 36; Fig. 262). Moreover, there is little indication that the placental types are particularly related to methods of food procurement. However, striking parallelisms exist between (1) the reduction of excretory functions of the fetal kidneys, (2) the regression of the allantoic vesicles, (3) the condensation of placental areas, and (4) the thinning of endometrial tissue barriers. *It appears therefore that the placental types are related to changing methods of fetal excretion rather than of nutrition.*

Extensive changes occur in the trophoblast cells of the blastocyst at the time of implantation, when they acquire the faculty of absorbing food from the environment. The *mechanisms of absorption* at the early embryonic stages are practically unknown except for directly observable *phagocytic incorporation* of some solid particles of the histotroph. Many dissolved materials, especially inorganic substances, chlorides and phosphates, may pass by *diffusion,* like water and oxygen. The latter two, of course, are already entering free blastocysts at preimplantation stages. The absorption of carbohydrates, fats, and proteins obviously is more complicated, requiring *enzymatic transformations and considerable expenditure of energy.*

An entirely *new outlook on placental permeability* was gained through the research of Flexner and associates. Using isotopes such as heavy

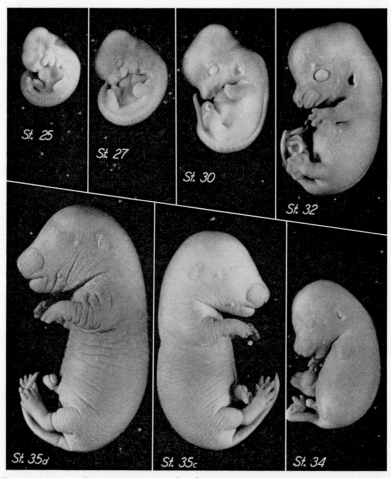

Figure 262.   Rat; intra-uterine development during second half of pregnancy. St. 25, Embryo 42 somites, 6.5 mm., 12½ days, at inception of metamorphosis. The next three figures illustrate progressive stages of metamorphosis; note transformations of visceral arches and limbs. St. 27, Metamorphic embryo, 48 somites, 7.7 mm., 13½ days. St. 30, Metamorphic embryo, 60 somites, 10 mm., 14¾ days. St. 32, Embryo near end of metamorphosis, 14.5 mm., 15½ days. St. 34, End of metamorphosis, fetus of first phase with open eyes (16.5 mm., 17 days). St. 35c, Fetus of second phase, with closed eyelids (24 mm., 19½ days). St. 35d, Fetus of second phase, near birth (28 mm., 21 days). Upper row × 3.3; lower row × 2.3.

water and radioactive sodium for tracer substances, they found that fetuses do not merely absorb the amounts necessary for growth, but maintain an exchange with the maternal blood plasma at an astonishingly high rate. The human fetus of 14 weeks admits 700 times as much *water* as becomes incorporated in its growing tissues. The proportion increases to 3800 times by the thirty-first week. At 35 weeks 3.6 liters per hour cross the placenta toward the fetus. Since the volume of fetal fluids at this stage amounts only to about one-half this amount, one may conclude that on the average it is exchanged twice per hour. The rate declines again toward the end of gestation, and it was calculated that, on the average, complete renewal of the human amnotic fluid occurs once every 2.9 hours. The distribution channels of this irrigation system are not known. Obviously the entire volume of water cannot pass the fetal kidneys; but it is certain that at least part of it flows through the fetal body. *Sodium* passes the placenta with about one-fifth the speed of water. As in the case of water, the larger part is returned to the blood of the mother.

Since a high rate of water exchange was found also in the guinea pig, it can be assumed that it is a general feature of placental physiology and probably plays an important role in the transport of all other materials across the barrier.

Very little is known about the factors that normally maintain the volume of fetal fluids at fairly precise levels. Wolff observed an enormous increase in size of rabbit fetuses—a condition called *polyhydramnios*—after surgical removal of the kidneys of the mother. This suggests that the concentration of waste materials, probably urea, may determine the volume of the retained water. In man, polyhydramnios is often associated with abnormalities of the head and particularly with fetal erythroblastosis, primarily an abnormality of the blood.

Many dyes and chemicals pass unaltered through the placenta, and it is generally found that the speed of penetration depends largely on *molecular size.* In the case of the above mentioned erythroblastosis, the Rh negative mother produces two antibodies. One has a molecular weight of about 900,000 and rarely enters the fetal system in harmful amounts. The other, called albumin antibody, with the molecular size of 150,000 passes much more easily and is the usual cause of fetal erythroblastosis and accompanying abnormalities. Some evidence has been obtained indicating that vitamin A, gamma globulin, and various antibodies pass from the maternal into the fetal circulation in man, but only rarely, if at all, in the ungulates. This lends support to the view that the hemochorial placenta admits passage of larger molecules than the epichorial and mesochorial types.

In conclusion, the placentae primarily provide for the passage of nutrients and waste products; but they serve also as barriers, protecting mother and fetus against the influx of high-molecular, potentially incompatible substances, particularly proteins.

6. INTRA-UTERINE GROWTH

Whether expressed in weight or in linear measurements, growth usually follows a sigmoid curve. The absolute increases, small at the beginning, become almost linear during the middle phase and then taper off as the curve bends toward a plateau. The *growth rate* on the other hand reaches the maximum shortly after implantation and generally falls first rapidly, then more gently with advancing age. At the beginning, the extra-embryonic parts grow faster than the embryo itself, and in sheep their weight surpasses that of the fetus up to the middle of the gestation period (Fig. 263). Embryonic weights are hard to get before a distinct umbilicus has formed at late tailbud stages (about St. 22).

The following series of weights and growth rates of purebred rabbits is based on data by Hammond. Starting at early somite stages (St. 15–17), it indicates that the growth rate of embryos and fetuses has its maximum about the time of metamorphosis (St. 25–33). It is noteworthy that growth is more intensive during embryogenesis, i.e., during the period of differentiations, than in the fetal period.

Age, days	8	12	16	20	24	28	32
Stage	16	25	33	35a	35c	35e	35g
Average weight (gm.)	.01	.07	.60	3.30	13.72	38.00	64.03
Four-day growth rate		7	8.5	5.5	4.2	2.8	1.7

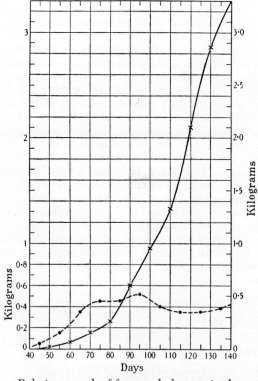

Figure 263.   Relative growth of fetus and placenta in sheep (Barcroft 1947). x——x——x——, Average growth-weight curve of fetuses, and ---. , ---. , of their placental cotyledons.

General laws and mathematical interpretations can scarcely be derived from summary growth curves, since embryos and fetuses are composed of organs and tissues that increase at unequal speeds and reach maximums at different embryologic stages. Data collected by Wallace show that in sheep fetuses the liver is over four times the weight of the gut at 78 days, twice its weight at 120 days, and lighter than the gut at 140 days. Nevertheless, over the same span of time, crown-rump length and total body weight increase in almost *straight line fashion* (Fig. 263).

It has already been mentioned that the morphologic differentiation of the placentas is completed early in the fetal period. Soon afterwards they attain their maximal size. The constancy of placental size over most of the fetal period may be one of the factors that determine the regularity of food supply as expressed in the almost linear weight increase of the fetus (Fig. 263). Conditions in man are no exception to the rule. The human placenta attains its greatest diameter about the middle of the pregnancy period (fifth month). Earlier, during the third and fourth months, its functional capacity keeps improving through increased density of vascularization, and continued thinning of the tissue barriers between fetal blood vessels and the maternal blood. At the beginning of the fetal period (eighth week) the mesenchymal core of the villi of human placentas is covered by continuous layers of cytotrophoblast and syntrophoblast. But at four months the former regresses, while the plasmotrophoblast thins out and in many places fuses with the endothelium of superficial capillaries, forming tiny specks of *placental membranes* about 2 μ thick—the extreme reduction of the placental barrier (Fig. 248d).

One is usually inclined to think of embryos and fetuses as efficient parasites that extract from the mother whatever materials they need for growth according to their own hereditary constitution. Indeed, the *genic pattern* includes the fundamental factors of growth control and expresses itself clearly at early stages. Figure 254 presents an example of different growth rates in large and small breeds of rabbits. But soon also the *placental and uterine environment* gains far-reaching influence. Furthermore, it is now clearly established that *nutritional conditions of the mother,* especially starvation and specific deficiencies, can greatly modify the progress of fetal growth. Differences in reciprocal mule breeding demonstrate the importance of the maternal environment for the growth of the fetus. The antigen production of Rh negative mothers, which thwarts the development and life of genetically normal embryos, demonstrates even more drastically the fact that the maternal organism is not merely a passively yielding depot of food.

The work of Barcroft and his collaborators in the physiology of prenatal life directs attention to the physicochemical differences between mother and fetus. Relative water contents of tissues, osmotic and hydrostatic pressures of the bloods, quantitative and qualitative variations in the mineral, fat, sugar, and protein composition, changes in the oxygen-dissociation curves of the hemoglobins, all have an obvious although not yet fully comprehended bearing on the mechanisms that govern fetal nutrition and growth.

7. BIRTH AND POSTNATAL DEVELOPMENT

a. Body Weight, Litter Size, and Length of Gestation Period. Although the eggs of all eutherian mammals are of nearly the same size, measuring around 0.1 mm. in diameter and weighing about one micro-

Table 22

Selected Data about Newborn Mammals and Their Development

	Wt. Mother kg.	Wt. Newborn Single kg.	Twins kg.	Mult. kg.	Eye Opens	Ear Opens	Hair (Coat)	Feeding Begins (days)	Weaning (days)	Puberty (days)	Gestation Time (days)	Number in Litter*
Horse												
Shetland	200	19			o	o	+	60	200	700	335	1
Shire	800	70			o	o	+	60	200	700	335	1
Cow	600	35			o	o	+	60	200	300	285	1
Sheep	62	6	4.7	3.6	o	o	+	25	50	250	150	1–3
Pig	100			2.5	o	o	+	20	60	200	112	7–12–23
Fin whale	54000	1000			o		+		200	700	330	1
Man	65	3.4			o		+			5000	267	1
Chimpanzee	35	1.9			o	o	+	200	700	2500	236	1
Rhesus monkey	6	0.45			o	o	+	140	200	1000	164	1
Armadillo	4.5			0.15	o	o	+			450	250 (–120)	4
Chinchilla	0.7			0.044	o	o	+	i	60	150	110	1–4
Guinea pig	0.65	0.11	0.093	0.065	o	o	+	i	20	24(♀)60(♂)	68	1–3–7
Hare	6				o	o	+	i			42	3
Rat	0.2	0.0016		0.0045	16d	13d	5d	20	25	72	22	1–7–18
Mouse	0.030	0.0015		0.0011	15d	12d	4d	18	21	28	19	1–7–13
Hamster	0.090			0.0022	14d	4d		8	21	29(♀)60(♂)	16	3–6–14
Bat	0.037	0.005			5d			50	50	450	50	1
Opossum	1.3			0.00013	55d	40d	14d	80	90	200	13	4–7–11

o open at birth.   i immediately following birth.   + present at birth.   * middle number is most frequent.   d age in days.

gram, the dimensions of the newborn range widely (Table 22). The baby fin whale, at birth 6 meters long and weighing over a ton, is more than a million times heavier than the newborn mouse. As may be seen from the data assembled in Table 22, the weight of the newborn most often is between 2.5 and 10 per cent of that of the mother. Relatively the largest young are borne by the guinea pig. In single births their weight may be over 15 per cent of the mother's. Passage through the pelvis becomes possible through loosening of the iliosacral joints and extreme relaxation of the ligaments of the pubic symphysis (for comparable conditions in birds, cf. p. 39). The pubic bones may separate as far as 1.5 cm. Similar though not as extensive *relaxation* at the inception of parturition is observed in many other species, including man. It is elicited and controlled by a combination of hormones— *estrogens, progesterone,* and *relaxin*—the last one produced by the uterus of the mother (Hisaw).

The weights of the newborn vary with *litter size.* The distinction between monotocous and polytocous species (animals reproducing by single or by multiple births, respectively) lacks deeper significance, since the number of young is inconstant in both groups. In the domestic pig and the African multimammate mouse up to 20 are counted in single pregnancies, and up to 30 in the insectivore tenrec of Madagascar. In statistically investigated species, it has been shown that the individual weights fall as the size of the litters increases. Thus, in a given stock of sheep in which the ewes average about 60 kg., Wallace finds that single lambs weigh 6 kg., twins 4.7 kg., and triplets 3.6 kg. Similar inverse relationships between litter size and birth weight appear also in the following three groups of observations.

RABBIT (after Hammond)

Number in Litter	1	2	6	7	10	13
Average weight in gm. (of individual young)	100	80	57	54	50	44

MOUSE (after Crozier and Enzman)

Number in Litter	1	2	6	7	13
Average weight in gm. (of individual young)	1.63	1.53	1.33	1.31	1.14

GUINEA PIG (after Ibsen)

Number in Litter	1	2	3	6	7
Average weight in gm. (of individual young)	110	93	90	73	65

Obviously the reduction of individual size compensates only incompletely for numerical increases. The entire mouse litter of 13 weighs about nine times as much as a single-born offspring. The number of placentae and the total volume of fetal fluids increase with the number of fetuses. In mice and guinea pigs, mothers pregnant with large litters may increase from 60 to 80 per cent in weight.

The *smaller birth weights in large litters* are partly explained by the shortening of the gestation periods. In the rabbit large litters are often born on the thirty-first day; small ones and especially a single offspring may be retained until the thirty-fifth. It is well known that in human births the weight of infants increases with the duration of pregnancy. Pre-term babies of 26 weeks average only 1.2 kg., compared with about 3 kg. of term deliveries at 38 weeks and 4 kg. and more of post-term infants of 42 weeks. The *onset of parturition is partly hormonally controlled*. Delays with corresponding increase of birth weight have been induced experimentally in pregnant rabbits by the injection of crude hypophyseal preparations. It seems possible that the usual precociousness of deliveries of large litters in rodents, and of twins in horses and in man, is related to an increased hormone production by the multiple placentae. The fact that most species with long gestation periods produce only one young at a time would agree well with this assumption.

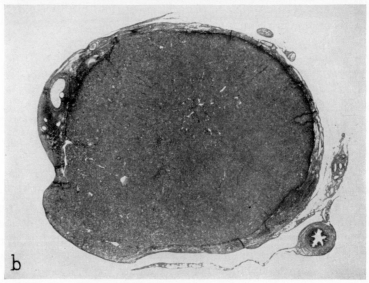

Figure 264.   Armadillo, *Dasipus novemcinctus. a,* Mother with newborn quadruplets; runners (St. 36). *b,* Single corpus luteum of female with a pre-implantation blastocyst in uterine cavity; × 11.5.

Table 23
Relative Speed of Development in Avian and Mammalian Species and General Condition of the Young at Hatching or Birth

STAGE		HAWK	CHICK	SPARROW	OPOSSUM	RABBIT	HAMSTER	RAT	PIG	SHEEP	RHESUS MONKEY	MAN
2	2 cells		3h		40h	8h	16h	24h	30h	30h	24h	38h
3	4 cells		3¼h		56h	11h	40h	50h	34h	34h	36h	48h
—	Implantation begins	—	—		6d	7d	4½d	6d	7d	10d	9d	6½d
12	Primitive streak	1½-2d	1½-2d	7-7½d	6½-7d	6½-7d	6½-7d	8½-9d	11-12d	13d	18-20d	17-21d
16	13–20 somite embryo	4½d	2½d	2½d	9d	9d	8d	10½d	16d	17d	25d	27d
17	Tailbud forms		3¼d	3¼d	9½d	9½d	8½d	11½d	17d	18d	26d	29d
25	End of embryonic period	9d	5d	5d	10d	10d	9d	13d	20d	21d	28d	36d
33/34	End of metamorphosis	13d	8d	7½d	12d	14d	13½d	16d	24d	32d	40d	60d
—	Sex differentiation	12d	6½d	6½d	15d	13½d	13d	13½d	21d	28d	36d	45d
35	Eyelids closed	23d	13d	11d	12¼d	19d		17d	32d	42d	48d	70d
36	Eyelids open		20d	19(6)d				38(16)d		84d		180d
	Hatching or Birth											
	Age	35d	21d	13d	12½d	32d		22d	112d	150d	164d	267d
	Stage	35/36	36	35	35	35+	35	35	36	36	36	36
	Weight, absolute	12 gm.	34 gm.	1.7 gm.	0.13 gm.	57 gm.	2.2 gm.	4.5 gm.	2.5 kg.	5 kg.	450 kg.	3.2kg.
	relative to mother		3%	6%	0.01%	3%	2.3%	2.25%	2.5%	8%	7.5%	5.5%

Hours (h) and days (d) are counted from the time of fertilization. In birds one day was added to observed incubation times. In mammals observed mating ages were reduced by the estimated number of hours necessary for the establishment of contact between egg and sperm (opossum 8, rabbit 14, hamster 8, rat 9, pig 8, sheep 6). In the monkey the ovulation age (Lewis-Hartman) was reduced by 2 hours.

Litter size does not always reflect exactly the number of ovulated eggs. In man, as well as in animals, a considerable loss of progeny through death at pre-placentation and fetal stages is a common occurrence. The extreme in this regard seems to be the African insectivore *Elephantulus myurus,* in which regularly only two out of some 120 ovulated and fertilized eggs develop into fetuses. The regularity of such wastage suggests that the correspondingly high *number of extra corpora lutea* may become of importance as supplementary hormone producers. The armadillo is of interest because its litter size exceeds the number of ovulated eggs (Fig. 264).

The importance of *hereditary factors* for the control of *embryonic growth rates* was previously referred to. Yet they are a highly heterogeneous group, and bear on most diverse processes which contribute to the complex effect measured as body size or body weight. The proportion of birth to adult weight may change in closely related genetic breeds. Thus the calves of Jersey cattle average only 6.5 per cent of the weight of their mothers (25 kg. and 400 kg.), but those of Holsteins about 8 per cent (40 kg. and 500 kg.). The inherited birth weight depends not only on the genetic constitution of the offspring, but also on that of the mother. In cross-breeding, by artificial insemination, the heavy Shire horse and the Shetland pony (cf. Table 22), Hammond found that the birth weights of hybrid foals are nearly the same as those of purebreds of the maternal races (Fig. 265). During the postnatal growth period, both types of hybrids tend toward intermediate values though they remain always closer to the maternal proportions. This interesting situation indicates that the racial character of the mothers includes a capacity of controlling growth and birth weight of the fetus, probably by means of endocrine or nutritional factors. Possibly also the plasmatic constitution of the egg plays some role—a question that might be elucidated through exchange of fertilized eggs between small and large breeds.

b. Developmental Condition of the Newborn.   At the time of birth the young have attained different stages of development which

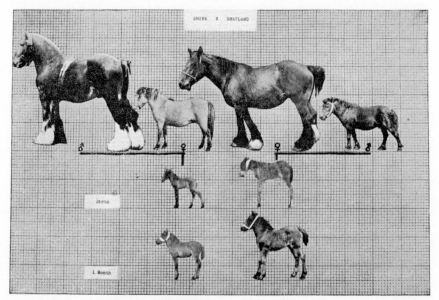

Figure 265.   Parents and offspring from reciprocal Shire-Shetland crosses (Walton and Hammond 1938).

generally correspond to the length of gestation. However, this rule has many exceptions, owing to specific differences in developmental speed. The data compiled in Table 23 show that *embryogenesis* (stages 1–25) proceeds more slowly in mammals than in birds. The *metamorphic period* (stages 25–34) lasts from two to four days in rodents, but up to two weeks in ruminants, primates, and other large eutherians. As one might expect, extensive variations occur in the phylogenetically most recent *fetal period*. It occupies less than one day in the opossum and extends to over one year in the elephant. *Birth occurs at different ages not only in the chronological but also in the developmental sense.* The duckbill, according to available information, hatches during the metamorphic period, and the opossum is born immediately after its completion (stage 34). More primitive than any bird at hatching, the opossum is barely one-tenth the weight of a newborn mouse (see Tables 22, 23).

Although birth in mammals and hatching in birds in some ways are similar events, their evolutionary trends move in opposite directions. In the primitive megapods, the young hatch late, as near adults, from large eggs and get no maternal care, while in the most highly differentiated finches and hummingbirds they hatch early, blind and naked, from small eggs with the most demanding need for parental nurture. It is evident that birth dates in mammalian evolution move in the opposite direction, and that the two series of adaptational changes are fundamentally different, in spite of striking analogies at certain levels.

In analogy with conditions earlier described for birds, one may distinguish between early-born nest sitters (stage 35) and late-born nest quitters (stage 36). But only a few species, mainly mice and burrowing rodents, construct nests that approach in artfulness those of birds. Gorillas and chimpanzees build crude litters of branches for the night, but like the monkeys they carry their young with them all the time. Some primitive human races, such as certain wandering tribes of the South African bushman, live without any kind of housing.

Taking into consideration both the condition of the young at birth and its postnatal way of life, one may distinguish the following five types:

(1) POUCH YOUNG (Fig. 266). Newborn marsupials have precociously developed arms and hands. With their help they cling to the fur of the mother. Guided by an instinctive negative geotropism, they climb up along the abdomen until they reach a teat, on which they may attach themselves more solidly. Usually these teats are located inside a furry pouch, the *marsupium;* yet the most primitive and smallest representatives of the order, such as the arboreal mouse opossums of Central America, lack this accommodation and the young adhere to the mother only by their hold on nipples and fur.

(2) NESTLINGS (Fig. 267). Typical nest young are born blind and naked (St. 35). Their external appearance is fetal. However, with the

initiation of lung respiration following birth, the circulatory system early changes from the fetal to the adult eutherian type. Nests are usually well hidden at the end of tunnels, in caves, or under dense vegetal matter. The mother also may cover the young with plucked hair and nesting material, when leaving on foraging tours. Thus the young are kept in near complete darkness. In accordance with the rule that pigments develop upon exposure to light, or in immediate preparation to life in the open, typical nest young are born unpigmented, appearing fleshy pink in their thin and transparent skins. *Melanin granules* appear first, and even before birth, in the pigment layer of the retina. Otherwise their manufacture normally seems limited to the *melanophores* which are widely spread in the epidermis and enter also the matrix layer of the hair germs (Fig. 268). They furnish the coloring matter for skin and hair, injecting it into the young, not yet cornified, cells. They do not otherwise contribute to the growth of either epidermis or hair. In contrast to conditions in amphibians, melanin production in the skin of

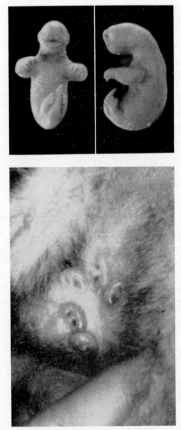

Figure 266.   Opossum, *Didelphys virginiana.* below: Newborn litter in pouch, ⅘ natural size (Reynolds 1952); above: newborn pouch young (St. 35); × 2.8.

mammals starts only after the melanophores have arrived at their final locations. This makes it difficult to trace their origin back to the neurula stage. However, Rawles was able to furnish experimental proof of neural crest origin and migration of the embryonic, colorless *melanoblasts*. Before the young are ready to leave their nest, they acquire pelage as well as protective coloration.

The newborn nestlings are unable to maintain *body temperature* at a constant level. During the first week rats and mice closely follow changes in the outside temperature, much as do poikilothermic amphibians. At very low temperatures (5° C. and lower) they go into a state of cold anesthesia, in which they can survive for a considerable length of time without damage. Since blood circulation becomes very slow, this form of anesthesia is most helpful in surgery of the newborn. During the second week the hypothalamic heat regulation center gradually assumes control, and when the young leave their nests at the time of weaning the adult homoiothermism has become fully established.

Eyes and *ears* of typical nest young are solidly sealed by growth of the epidermal surface layer called *periderm*. In the rat the eyelids close on the eighteenth day of pregnancy, i.e., four days before birth, and remain closed during the first two weeks after birth. The ear follows a similar cycle. The outer ear duct, in addition to being plugged with periderm, becomes covered also by the distal, folded-over part of the pinna. This attachment lasts only till about the fifth postnatal day, while the peridermal plug persists up to the fifteenth (Fig. 269).

The closure of eyes and ears during the early postnatal weeks in pouch and nest young, having the effect of dulling their senses, prob-

Figure 267.   Hamster, *Cricetus auratus,* female with newborn nestlings.
¾ natural size.

ably must be considered as an adaptation to living conditions which require the young to remain quiet and not to disperse. Indeed, as soon as eyes and ears have opened, they make excursions out of pouch or nest, and start to eat food, supplementing and gradually replacing the mother's milk. The time of weaning is subject to great variations; the data given in Table 22 are mere approximations.

In large rodents the gestation period becomes extended, and the young spend an accordingly shorter time in the nest. *Rabbits* are born blind and naked, but the pinnas of their ears become free and flattened against occiput and neck before birth. Also, the newborn are pigmented and their pelage begins to grow immediately. The closely related *hares* have an even longer intra-uterine period and are born with fur and open eyes and ears. A shallow depression between tall grasses serves as a shelter rather than nest, and even on the first day the young run off if they are frightened. They nibble green food from the first day on. Pregnancy extends over even longer periods in the guinea pig (68 days) and the chinchilla (110 days), whose young are born accomplished runners, and with temperature controlling mechanisms fully established.

Similar lines of development are observed among insectivores and carnivores. Of related forms, the smaller species usually have shorter periods of gestation and give birth to young of immature type. Newborn cats are blind while lion cubs have open eyes from the start.

(3) Runners (Fig. 270). All species belonging to the ungulates

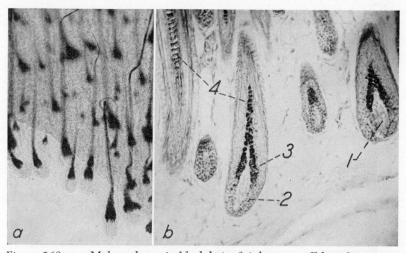

Figure 268.   Melanophores in black hair of 4-day rat. *a,* Edge of cut piece of skin with some club-shaped roots protruding; × 85. *b,* Sections through roots and shafts; 1, corium papilla; 2, proliferating epidermis with melanophores; 3, granular layer, cells supplied with melanin granules; 4, cornified layer with lightly pigmented cortex, and medulla of heavily pigmented discs (pulp caps); × 136.

have greatly extended periods of intra-uterine development. Under natural conditions the characteristic representatives of the group, e.g., cattle and horses, live in slowly migrating groups. Newborn animals would be exposed to grave dangers if they could not immediately get on their legs and, with their mothers, follow the herd. Surprisingly, as the intra-uterine phase lengthens and eventually absorbs not only the entire stage of blindness (St. 35) but also a later phase of development (St.

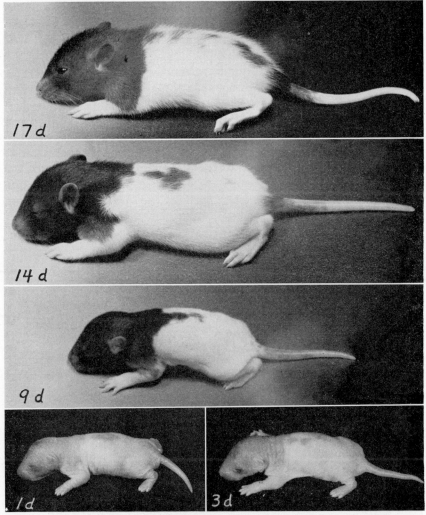

Figure 269.   Postnatal development of the rat. *1 day old* (St. 35e), 7 gm., eyelids closed, pinna of ear folded over external meatus; pigmentation very light, in hair follicles. *3 days*, 9 gm., pinna lifting. *9 days* (St. 35f), 19 gm., eyelids closed, pinna extended but external meatus of ear closed by periderm plug. *14 days*, 29 gm., ear plug has dissolved. *17 days* (St. 36), 32 gm., ears and eyes are open; all ¾ natural size.

36), the feature of temporary closure of the two major sensory organs is maintained almost unchanged. The lids and the ears open again long before birth. Closure is maintained as an ancestral character though having lost its original functional value. In the pig the eyes open about one month before birth, but in most *runners* the intra-uterine open-eyed period is even considerably longer. Numerically stage 35, comprising the part of the fetal period with closed eyes, and stage 36 are distinguished, the latter extending from the resorption of the peri-dermal seal of the lids until birth. In contrast to nest young, the runners are born with fully colored juvenal pelages and with homeostatic heat regulation. The armadillo, hiding its young in burrows, links this type with that of the nestlings (Fig. 264).

(4) SWIMMERS. Many aquatic mammals return to the shores to give birth to their young, but in whales the very large calf is expelled directly into the open sea. It is as advanced in development as the best of runners. According to reliable reports the mother brings the newborn immediately to the surface, where it may fill its lungs with air. The two teats of the mother lie in pockets along the genital opening. As far as is known, the calf does not actively suckle; but the mother, with the help of a special arrangement of muscles, presses a stream of milk into its mouth. Sometimes the mother floats at the surface and, lying on

Figure 270.   Hereford dam with new calf. An umbilical protrusion and the remnant of the umbilical cord still present. (Courtesy of the College of Agriculture, University of Missouri.)

the side, tugs her calf along while it remains attached to a nipple. Since the larynx projects into the nasal cavity, the young should then be able to drink milk and to breathe air at the same time.

(5) BREAST YOUNG (Fig. 271). Primates and sloths are born, like the *runners,* with open eyes and ears, and with protective pelages. They immediately attach themselves securely to the bodies of their tree-climbing mothers, anchoring with hands and feet in the fur and holding on to a nipple most of the time, even when not actively suckling. During the first postnatal weeks young monkeys and sloths scarcely ever detach themselves, and up to weaning time they keep close to the mother, regaining their hold at the least sign of danger. Mother apes

Figure 271.   Rhesus monkeys in mangroves of Isla de Santiago, Puerto Rico. Mothers with breast young.

take a human-like interest in their babies, often holding them in their
arms and helping them to their breasts. The litter size in this group is
always small and usually reduced to a single offspring.

Newborn *bats* occupy an interesting position between the primitive types of
insectivore *nest young,* and the just described *breast young.* They are relatively
among the largest young born to any mammal, with about one-eighth to one-sixth
the weight of the mother in single births. Nevertheless, they are blind, nearly hair-
less, and only the wings and feet are slightly pigmented. They are quite agile and
immediately fasten themselves to the fur of the mother. The first dentition occurs
before birth; the teeth are promptly used to grab and hold one of the two axillary
nipples. Until the fifth day, when their eyes open, the young remain attached,
even if the mother should leave the nursery for a flight. Later, the rapidly growing
young bat leaves the parent and remains in the hide-out during the mother's hunting excursions, though only to regain its hold upon her return. Weaned about seven
weeks after birth, the young bat is nearly full-grown and practically indistinguishable from adults.

The *human infant,* born after one of the longest of gestation times
(average fertilization age of 38 weeks), with eyes and ears reopened
about the middle of this period, and covered with first generation
lanugo or even with second generation hair, distinctly belongs to the
type of *breast young,* together with all the other primates. However,
sensory and motor faculties are so little developed that it is as helpless
and dependent on maternal care, as the *nest young* of small rodents and
carnivores. This apparently is not a primitive condition but a secondary
regression, which may have developed when primitive ancestral man
became a cave dweller. Symmetric grasping and clasping reflexes show
some degree of improvement up to about the twenty-fourth week. Other
rudiments of prehensory behavior may be seen in thumb-sucking with
simultaneous grasping of another object by somewhat older children.

Chapter 23

Nurture. III

7. LACTATION

a. Evolution.   Theories about the evolution of lactation are largely speculative. All mammals have mammary glands whereas none of the other vertebrates do. Many birds carry food to their young and select it, to serve the special needs of successive developmental stages. Frequently they predigest the fare, adding saliva and enzymes, and in some instances profoundly change its composition. The albatross and the petrel prepare an oily, almost fluid, food from fish and squids by partial digestion and sifting. The nestling birds are gorged to such a degree that fishermen have dried and used them as candles. But outside of the mammalian class *doves* and *pigeons* are probably the only vertebrates that produce exclusively by secretion a complete diet, the *crop milk* for hatched offspring.

The *origin of lactation in mammals* is conjectural. Evidently it has not developed from a primitive feeding mechanism. The mammary glands are a differentiation of the epidermal skin, closely related to hair follicles and sweat glands. Both glands and pelage are essential implements of heat control and certainly arose in pre-mammalian ancestry, in conjunction with the establishment of homoiothermism. From here evolution almost necessarily would lead to habits of incubation. Like brood patches of birds, some regions along the ventral sides of these hairy ancestors must have acquired an increased vascularization, facilitating heat transfer to the eggs. Through the presence of sweat glands

415

a humid and warm contact with the eggs was thus established, favorable for conveyance, not only of warmth, but also of water, then mineral salts, and finally of food materials from the parent's body to the young. Water may have been transmitted even across the egg shell.

The *duck-billed platypus,* lowest of the mammals, is an amazing living record and exhibit of primitive evolutionary conditions. The female deposits two soft-shelled eggs in a nest of twigs and leaves, located in a chamber of a subterranean tunnel. Their elastic shells measure about 17 × 14 mm. The incubating parent, curling up in the nest, holds them with the paddle-shaped tail against its abdomen. The incubation temperature seems to be about 32° C. and the hatching time is estimated at 2 to 3 weeks. The tiny, naked, and blind fetal young are further held in the same protected place. They seem to be quite active and furnish the necessary external stimulus for the initiation of lactation. At the time of hatching the *mammary glands* of the parent have not yet reached the functional condition. Anatomically and histologically they resemble sweat glands. Though of considerable size, they are externally recognizable only as two *longitudinal welts* under the abdominal fur. Like sweat glands they open through a large number of pores that are scattered in the covering skin. No teats are formed. The young simply lick the milk from the wet hairs. It must soon flow quite freely, for available reports indicate that without other food sources the young grow on milk alone from the hatching length of 1.5 cm. to the size of 30 cm., i.e., the stage when they leave their burrows.

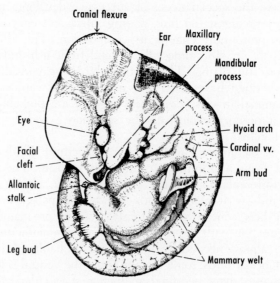

Figure 272.   Rat embryo, 13 days (St. 27); mammary welt with primordia of mammary glands; × 8.

Even the most primitive of the *marsupials* have progressed considerably beyond the platypus. Their eggs are much smaller and the blastocysts become dependent on uterine alimentation. Interestingly enough, the beginnings of prenatal and postnatal food preparation show many similarities. The uterine walls, like the mammary glands, originally secrete mainly water and then gradually change to the production of *"milk,"* mixtures of water, salts, and food materials.

At birth the opossum will approximate the size of a hatching platypus. It depends likewise on lactation. The maternal mammary apparatus, while of similar productivity, is morphologically of higher differentiated type than that of the monotremes. All marsupials and eutherians have fewer, but more complex, mammary glands which open on projecting *teats* or *nipples*. In the marsupials they are usually arranged within a pouch.

b. Development.   In eutherians a pair of *mammary welts* appear on the lateral body walls of the embryos about the middle of the metamorphic period (Fig. 272, St. 27). They extend on either side from the thoracic region to the groins, with the ends passing along the inside of arms and legs. These broad elevations consist of abundantly vascularized mesenchymal tissue. Immediately following their first appearance, the epidermis along the crests begins to proliferate *mammary ridges*. One may assume that originally they extended the full length of the welts, as they still do in the pig. In the rat they form only in the pectoral and the lower abdominal regions while the middle parts remain smooth. In primates only pectoral, and in ruminants only inguinal ridges are formed. Through concentration of the epidermal proliferations, the definite *primordia of individual mammary glands* take shape. Their number shows specific as well as individual varia-

Figure 273.   Adult rat; primary type of mammary gland distribution in eutherian mammals (after Henneberg, from Meisenheimer).

tions. In man, manatees, elephants, and bats usually a single pair of *pectoral glands* are formed, while ruminants and horses have one or two pairs of *inguinal mammaries*. Rats and mice most often have three pairs of thoracic and three of abdominal glands (Fig. 273). Pigs and dogs, with similarly high numbers, show them arranged in continuous series from the chest to the groin.

The development of the *gland* begins by proliferation of the distinctly separate basal and superficial layers of the epidermis. The latter, usually a film-like *periderm*, produces a protruding pile of round cells. The former transforms into a *placoid thickening* that presently assumes

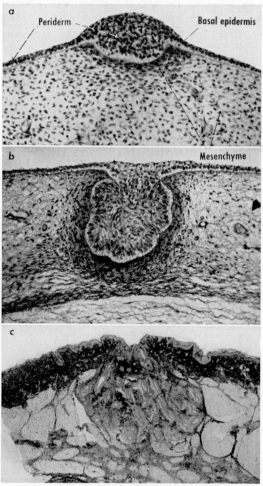

Figure 274.   Three stages in the development of the human mammary gland. *a*, Embryo, 14 mm. (St. 29), cup-shaped primordium filled with periderm; × 115. *b*, Embryo, 23 mm. (St. 33), flask-shaped primordium, beginning duct formation; × 115. *c*, Stillborn female child, 320 mm. (St. 36), well developed but only slightly branched ducts; × 10.

the shape of a *cup* or a *flask* (Fig. 274a, b), enclosing the peridermal cell plug in its cavity. In rats the similarity to the simultaneous development of whisker hairs is striking, though the latter soon acquire a mesodermal papilla and become supplied by strong nerve branches.

In man, during its further development, the bottom of the cup becomes verrucose and then sinks solid sprouts into the corium of the skin (Fig. 274c). These are the primordia of the *mammary ducts, tubules,* and *alveoli.* Their number is in general agreement with that of the primary ducts in adult glands and therefore, in man, ranges between 15 and 25. The periderm takes no part in these developments. On the contrary, its cells disintegrate during the later fetal stages (Fig. 274c). They disappear completely when, toward parturition, the cup everts and forms the epidermal surface of the *nipples* and the surrounding *areolae.* At birth and during early childhood the duct system shows only a moderate degree of secondary branching and the glands are about equally developed in both sexes.

In young women an extensive secondary development becomes stimulated by ovarial hormones at the time of puberty. The *primary tubules* grow, multiply through branching, and finally their distal ends differentiate into *vesicular alveoli,* lined with *secretory epithelia.* The very numerous alveoli become grouped in racemous lobules and drain through the system of tubules into the mammary ducts. Each of the latter develops an ampullary swelling where it enters the nipple. Typical ducts open in a crater-like depression at the apex of the nipple (Fig. 291).

Actual secretion is controlled by the hypophyseal *prolactin.* Significantly, this is the same hormone which in birds causes broodiness, parental behavior, and, together with estrogenic hormones, the formation and swelling of the brood patches. In pigeons it induces also growth and secretion of the crop glands.

The *mammary glands of some animals* differ in constructional details from the described human or primate type. A distinctive variant is the *udder* of the cow. In metamorphosing embryos two pairs of glands become established on the abdominal mammary welts. From the bottom of each primordial cup sprouts only one single *mammary duct* which later develops into the *milk cistern.* Secondary and tertiary sprouts issuing from the primitive cistern differentiate into a system of *mammary tubules* and *alveoli,* similar to those in man. The cistern enters also the teat where it attaches to the *streak canal,* which is a relatively narrow invagination of the skin epidermis (Fig. 275a). In the lactating cow this outlet is usually kept closed by a smooth muscle sphincter. While the glandular development at the fetal stage is similar in both sexes, an udder forms only in the female. In the bull the mammary glands come to lie on the scrotal swellings and remain inconspicuous. In the female there is a considerable development of mesenchymal and fatty tissue around each of the four glands, resulting in the formation of the large, pendulous body called the *udder.* Within, the glands remain separated through fibrous septums (Fig. 275b). The udders of the mare and the goat are similarly constructed but develop from only one pair of glands and have only two teats instead of the four of the cow.

c. Abnormalities.   *Supernumerary mammary glands* (polymastia) occur occasionally in animals as well as in man. They form most often along the embryonic mammary welts, but in consideration of their developmental relationship to hair follicles, it is not too surprising that in rare cases they are found in almost any place on the surface of body and thighs.

The embryonic and early fetal phase of mammary development is identical in both sexes. At least some rudiments of the mammary apparatus are still present in adult males. It is said that the male of a Madagascan bat nurses as actively as the female. Reports on exceptional milk-producing males abound not only in mythology, but also in the scientific literature. However, on scrutiny the cases with *gynecomastia* usually are found to be intersexuals rather than males. Probably the potentialities of the embryonic primordia are the same in both sexes. But after the differentiation of the gonads, hormonal factors induce divergent courses of development. In cattle this begins to show about the seventh month of gestation and in mice after the fifteenth day. After puberty the rudiments in bulls, steers, male rodents, and, as

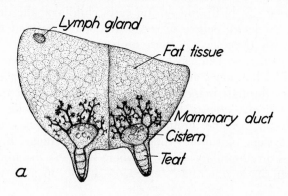

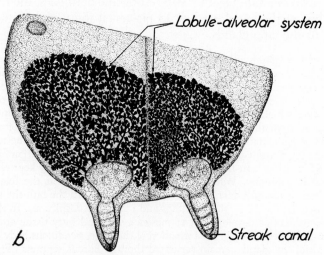

Figure 275.   Development of the udder of the cow. *a*, Heifer before maturity;
     b, heifer about middle of pregnancy (C. W. Turner 1934).

Table 24
Composition of Milk in Some Mammals Representing Various Ecologic Types

| SPECIES | Water | PERCENTAGE COMPOSITION | | | Minerals (*) | TYPE OF YOUNG | % ADULT WT. AT BIRTH | AGE (Days) OF DOUBLE WT. |
		Sugar	Fat	Protein				
Man.	88.0	7.0	3.4	1.4	0.2 (.05)	Breast	5.5	180
(Colostrum).	(90.3)	(4.6)	(2.6)	(2.1)	(0.35)			
Chimpanzee.	89.7	7.2	2.3	0.6	0.2	"	5.5	110
Horse.	90.7	5.7	1.2	2.0	0.4 (.13)	Runner	9	60
Elephant.	67.9	8.8	19.6	3.1	0.7	"		
Cow.	87.0	4.8	4.0	3.5	0.7 (.20)	"	6	47
(Colostrum). . . .	(73.0)	(3.6)	(8.5)	(14.0)	(0.9) (.47)			
Sheep.	80.3	4.8	8.6	5.5	0.8 (.29)	"	8	15
Pig.	83.6	3.3	6.1	6.2	0.8 (.31)	"	2.5	14
Cavy.	85.0	2.3	7.3	5.1	0.5	"	15	
Dog.	75.5	3.2	11.9	7.3	1.3 (.51)	Nestling		9
Rabbit.	68.4	2.0	16.7	10.4	2.5 (.99)	"	3	6
Rat.	63.4	3.0	20.0	11.8	1.6	"	2¼	6
Porpoise.	44.8	2.0	40.0	12.0	1.2	Swimmer	2	60
(Whales)								

* Phosphoric acid.

clinical experience shows, also in human males can still be stimulated by administration of female hormonal substances, though the response is restricted, and shows wide individual and taxonomic variations. As Hammond suggests, bulls might be made to produce milk on an economic basis, if a method were found to support the early growth of the glandular system in male calves.

d. Composition of Milk in Relation to Growth.

Milk being the sole food of most newborn mammals during a period of weeks of rapid growth, its composition reflects the nutritional needs of this phase of life. In referring to Table 24 it should be pointed out that some of the data are based on thousands of chemical analyses, as in the case of cow's milk, while others, e.g., those of the chimpanzee, were obtained from few or single casual samples. The table gives characteristic averages but disregards the existing wide variability. Certain breeds of cattle yield relatively more fat than others, and the composition of all milks changes in the course of the lactation period, in keeping with the needs of the young. Also, milk consumption per unit body weight should be taken into consideration in appraising the rate of supply of various constituents. In spite of all these reservations, certain relationships are obvious enough to deserve attention.

Evidently *porpoises and whales* represent a special group. All observers agree on the astoundingly rich fat content and low value of sugar. The former is needed to build up the tremendous subcutaneous fat layer of the fast-growing young. The low water content may be an adaptation to the life in salt water which demands a rigorous economy in the water metabolism of this group of mammals.

The other cases fit a fairly uniform pattern. The nutritional value of the milk is highest in the species that give birth to nestling young of a relatively low birth weight. Runners and breast young, born at more advanced stages, hence having been carried through a much longer stretch of development by uterine nutrition, get a more diluted milk with a relatively low phosphorus fraction. The high sugar percentage of herd and family-forming species serves to make the milk attractive and thereby to attach the young more closely to their mothers.

The more extensive the intra-uterine phase, the less important becomes lactation. The young of the cavy (guinea pig) begin to eat soon after being born, and survive even if no milk is available. Considering that lactation is already fully established in the oviparous monotremes, whereas placentation originated more recently and evolved to high expediency as a nursing device only within the mammalian class, one is led to conclude that the latter substitutes functionally for the former and that there exists an evolutionary trend toward reduction of lactation.

Exceptional but highly *adaptational conditions* exist in the bats. Like fledging birds, the young bats attain the faculty of flight only when practically full grown; and since bats catch their food in flight, lactation is protracted to the very extreme. While the other mammals are weaned when they reach about 20 per cent of the adult weight, the young bat lives on milk alone, until it approaches adult size.

e. Physiology of Milk Production.   The blood that flows through the mammary glands is the source of all the constituents of the milk. The mammary arteries and veins are branches of those that supply the arms and legs.

Of interest is the persistence, in the cow, of a pair of subcutaneous abdominal veins. Also called *milk veins,* they run full length along the site of the embryonic mammary welts, up to the sixth rib, where they penetrate the body wall ("milk well"). They then join the internal thoracic or mammary veins, and through them the subclavian veins. Thus, a considerable part of the inguinal mammary organ of the cow is drained through channels which in other species (e.g., man) are closely associated with pectoral glands. This peculiarity of an adult circulatory system becomes comprehensible if viewed on the background of the primary unity of the entire thoraco-abdominal mammary system.

In the formation of milk the nutritious substances contained in the blood go through processes of selection as well as of chemical transformation. The left column of Table 25 lists some of the possible precursors and elementary substances of the blood. Comparison with the right column shows that the monosaccharide glucose is transformed into the disaccharide lactose. The milk fat differs from the neutral fat of the blood by the prominence of short-chain fatty acid components (e.g., butyric and caproic acids), which are completely absent in the blood. It has been suggested that some of the neutral fats of the blood may directly enter the alveolar cells, but more generally it is assumed that most if not all fats are first broken down and then resynthesized

Table 25

Percentage Distribution of Some Nutritional Substances in the Blood and in the Milk of the Cow (Adapted from C. W. Turner)

	BLOOD PLASMA %	MILK %
Sugar		
Glucose	0.05	—
Lactose	—	4.8
Fat		
Neutral blood fats	0.2	
Milk fats		4.0
Protein		
Casein	—	2.7
Albumin	0.5	0.6
Globulin	0.22	0.2
Minerals		
Sodium	0.335	0.061
Potassium	0.019	0.193
Calcium	0.010	0.184
Phosphorus	0.013	0.234
Water	91.0	87.0

within the glandular cells. The proteins pass through similar processes and become largely transformed into casein, a compound that is not represented in the blood.

It is noteworthy that in spite of the complexity of these chemical and physical processes, no differentiation of alveolar cells has occurred. All are of the same glandular type and evidently engaged in the simultaneous preparation of all the constituent compounds of "milk."

Early in the present century it became increasingly evident that milk also contains traces of very important *accessory food factors* in the absence of which development could not proceed normally. These observations led to the discovery and chemical definition of a class of substances now known as the *vitamins*. The *colostrum,* i.e., first milk, of ruminants is especially rich in the fat-soluble vitamin A. The view has been expressed that in species with placentae of the epichorial and mesochorial type, this vitamin is not transmitted to the fetus in adequate amounts. Hence, the rich store in the colostrum should balance the deficiency. In support of this view is the observation that calves grow better if they are started with colostrum, than with regular milk.

It is well known that the newborn young of one species generally do not thrive on the milk of another, but often die of *gastrointestinal disturbances.* The quantitative differences in main constituents (Table 24) usually do not seem to offer a rational explanation; besides, reciprocal substitutions do not always produce the same effects. Goat and cow milk seem almost identical, but while kids usually tolerate the exchange, calves do not. Foals thrive on goat milk but not on cow milk; pigs react in just the opposite way. To interpret these conditions it is assumed that the gastrointestinal walls of the young animals are partly permeable to unhydrolyzed proteins, letting them pass directly into the blood. If of foreign origin, they may become the cause of allergic reactions and thereby of the fatal intestinal disease.

The endocrine factors of lactation are dealt with in Chapter 25.

8. PLAY, TRAINING, AND EDUCATION

Play among parents and offspring is a mammalian characteristic. Only rudiments of it have been observed in birds of the nest-sitter type, particularly hawks, at fledging time. But in mammals from the duckbill to the primates, play of the mother with her young as well as among the young themselves is a universal behavior trait. In family-forming species the father also may partake. The close association of at least the more primitive manifestations with lactation reveals itself at the time of weaning, when suddenly the affection of the mother turns into disinterest and sometimes animosity. In social and herd-forming species the association may endure, though playfulness usually disappears. Equal in importance with lactation is the high development of the mammalian brain and particularly the faculty of memory. The ability to remember agreeable and disagreeable experiences is the prerequisite for the development of conditioned reflexes and of learning.

In all animals, behavior develops mainly on a hereditary basis. In insects and birds complicated habits of nest construction, courtship, and caretaking of offspring develop automatically, without any previous individual experience. However, slowly there evolves another method of transmitting the results of experience from one generation to the next, namely *tradition*, which short-cuts the route by the germ plasm. Teaching and learning at the animal level mainly helps to develop faster and more completely the inherited, instinctive behavior. Foxes and lions certainly inherit some basic hunting instincts; but in both species it has been established that the young are systematically trained by parents in the finer arts of their profession. The question as to which of the faculties of higher animals could not automatically develop in the absence of teaching has often been posed but never satisfactorily answered. Interesting is the observation related by Yerkes, that female chimpanzees, raised in captivity, often do not know how to take care of their first baby and may even be frightened by the sight of it. Apparently the instincts of nursing are waning in the ape societies, where teaching by experienced older females has assumed an important role. This may indicate the road which was traveled also by man, whose children are born with relatively rudimentary instincts, but with the highest capacity for learning.

Chapter 24

Physiology and

Endocrinology of

Reproduction. I

1. FERTILIZATION

Although the cytology of the fertilization process shows that the nucleus of one single sperm unites with the egg pronucleus (Fig. 25), studies in human and animal fertility lead to the conclusion that millions of sperms are needed to bring about the successful insemination. MacLeod reports that the average ejaculate of fertile men measures close to 3.5 ml. and contains 350 million sperms, of which about 80 per cent are morphologically normal but only 60 per cent are motile, five hours after emission. In domestic animals the number of sperms may be even higher. The boar, according to McKenzie, produces ejaculates of 125 to 500 ml. with the total number of sperms ranging from 3 to over 300 billion. Nevertheless, it is found that in artificial insemination only from two to five sows may successfully be bred with one emission. Conditions for artificial insemination are more favorable in cattle and sheep, where the much smaller ejaculate may be used to fertilize 40 to 100 females. In artificial insemination of rabbits, Cheng and Casida obtained good fertility with 20,000 sperms per 0.2 ml.

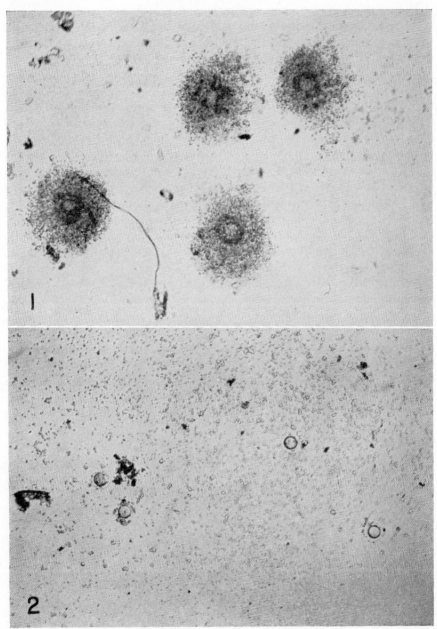

Figure 276.   Ovulated rat eggs. 1, Corona unchanged, 2, dispersal of corona
cells by hyaluronidase (Leonard and Kurzrok 1945).

By ablation of various parts of the urogenital organs of the boar, McKenzie showed that normally the seminal fluid is made up of contributions from various secreting glands along the male genital tract (Table 26). In view of the qualitative differences among the components, it is surprising that removal of the seminal vesicles and the bulbo-urethral glands does not lower the capacity of the boar to impregnate sows successfully. However, this result agrees well with observations on human and animal fertility and sterility. The quality of the semen is a function of such factors as total number of normal sperms, sperm motility, and essential chemical constituents carried by the testicular fraction of the semen. Among the last named, *hyaluronidase* has been studied to some extent. It is an enzyme with mucolytic properties which has been extracted from testes and other organs, and of which appreciable amounts are released with the spermatic fluid. It dissolves some of the cementing materials between cells, and, notably, it disperses the corona cell clusters around newly ovulated tubal eggs (Fig. 276). Since hyaluronidase and sperm both issue from the testes, it is not surprising that in seminal fluids a rather close correlation is found between the number of sperms per milliliter and enzyme concentration.

2. SEASONAL BREEDING

Many wild mammals are seasonal breeders, having annual successions of a breeding and an eclipse season, like nearly all birds and lower vertebrates. A few species produce only one litter per year; in others, the non-pregnant females are receptive throughout the summer season and may bear several litters in succession. It has been shown by Bissonnette and Lyman that an artificial increase of day length brings wild rabbits into breeding condition even in midwinter. On the other hand, permanent short-day lighting does not entirely prevent development of the breeding condition in spring. Apparently, seasonal breeding follows an inherent physiologic cycle, but is also partly controlled by environmental factors. Changes in day length or similar

Table 26

Contribution of Various Parts of the Genital Organs to the Composition of the Semen in the Boar (data from McKenzie)

Sex Organs, Secreting Part	Volume Contribution Per cent	Specific Contributions
Testis and epididymis............	2– 5	Sperms
Seminal vesicles.................	15–20	Most of K, P, N; entire glucose
Prostatic and urethral glands.......	55–70	Most chlorides
Bulbo-urethral glands............	10–25	Most of Na, Ca, Mg; considerable N

conditions are responsible for the maintenance of the agreement between breeding cycles and the seasons of the year. The domestic and the wild rabbits are representative of this type.

a. The Male. In males of the wild cottontail the seasonal changes of the sex organs are more pronounced than in the domestic rabbits. In fall the testes return to a completely immature condition. They decrease in size, and their germ cells are all of the spermatogonial type (Fig. 277). In late November the testes begin to grow, and in early spring they reach 50 to 100 times the weight of the inactive phase. Spermatogenesis progresses rapidly and the epididymides contain billions of mature sperms. Changes in size and functional condition of the secondary sex organs, especially seminal vesicles, prostate, and bulbo-urethral glands, follow those of the testes.

All these changes are under the direct or indirect control of the hypophysis, particularly its anterior lobe, which has periods of high and low activity. In spring the hypophysis of the male rabbit releases relatively large quantities of a gonad-stimulating hormone (gonadotrophic hormone). The responding testis reacts with the production of sperms, and the release of a testicular or male hormone. The latter stimulates growth and function of the above mentioned secondary sex characters, and awakens the male mating instincts. The chemistry of the gonad-

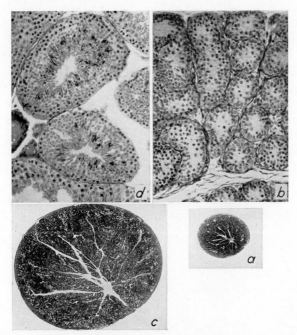

Figure 277. Cottontail rabbit, *Sylvilagus floridanus. a, b,* Testis in November, 0.5 gm.; seminal tubules with spermatogonia. *c, d,* Testis in April, 18 gm.; seminal tubules with all stages of spermatogenesis; *a* and *c* × 4; *b* and *d* × 120.

stimulating hormone of the hypophysis, a glycoprotein, is incompletely known, but the constitution of the testicular hormone, a steroid, was established by Butenandt and Rudzika in 1935, and it was given the name *testosterone*. It is rapidly metabolized by the body tissues, especially the liver, and is either destroyed or excreted in the less active form of androsterone and other ketosteroids and their salts.

Testosterone
$C_{19}H_{28}O_2$

Androsterone
$C_{19}H_{30}O_2$

b. The Female.   The ovaries of wild rabbits are inactive in winter and contain only small follicles with primary ovocytes. The behavior of the female is asexual; she usually fights off the approach of any other rabbit, male or female. This is the *eclipse season* and the rabbit is in the *anestrus* condition.

The enlargement of the ovaries in spring is less spectacular than that of the testes. Since all ovocytes are formed before and shortly after birth, the spring changes consist mostly of the growth of a restricted number of follicles. Only about a dozen at a time reach full size (Fig. 278). The follicular growth is a reaction to hypophysis activation of the same kind as that described for the male. It is so characteristic that the released hypophyseal hormone is designated as the *follicle stimulating hormone* (FSH). The growing ovarian follicles produce a steroid hormone, *estradiol,* which induces enlargement and histologic differentiation of the secondary sex organs, especially uterus and vagina. It also changes the mating instincts of the doe, making her receptive to the male. The sequence of these reactions is represented in the first diagram of Figure 278.

Estradiol was isolated by Doisy from ovaries of the sow. Its constitutional formula shows it to be an unsaturated steroid.

Estradiol ($C_{18}H_{24}O_2$)

The doe remains "in heat," or *estrus,* if not mated, throughout the summer; domestic rabbits reproduce during the entire year. Individual full grown follicles probably do not last longer than a month. They then become hemorrhagic and degenerate, without ever releasing the egg. But the losses by such follicular atresia are constantly replaced by other enlarging follicles.

Mating elicits a double chain of events (Fig. 278, second diagram). The seminal fluid deposited in the vagina passes through the cervical canals into the uteri. A relatively small fraction of the total number of sperms then enters the oviduct tubes. About 12 hours after copulation the sperms meet the ovulated eggs in the upper segments of the convoluted tubes.

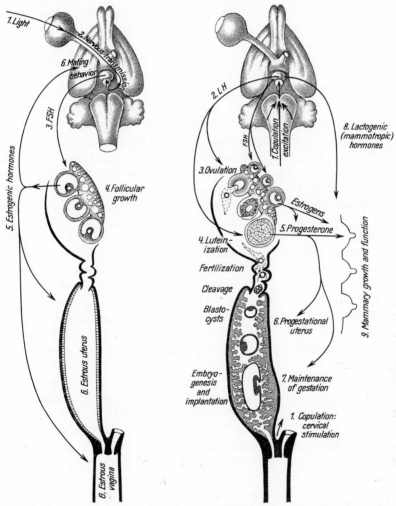

Figure 278.   Reproduction in the rabbit. Left: Reaction sequences leading to the estrus condition. Right: Reaction sequences following mating.

The other series of reactions starts with the mechanical stimulation of the uterine cervix and the nervous excitement during copulation (1). Visceral afferent nerves transmit an impulse by way of spinal ganglia and spinal cord to the brain stem. Here the excitation apparently becomes reinforced by other stimuli resulting from the mating act. By way of the infundibular stalk, the excitation is transmitted to the hypophysis which releases a second gonadotrophic hormone (2). This so-called luteinizing hormone (LH), added to the FSH, causes the final growth and maturation of the large ovarian follicles, leading to ovulation (3), about 10 hours after copulation. Furthermore, it induces the transformation of the emptied ovarian follicles into luteal bodies (corpora lutea, 4). The latter produce and release *progesterone* ($C_{21}H_{30}O_2$), another steroid hormone, which has a structural formula (p. 445) more closely related to that of testosterone than to that of estradiol. Progesterone elicits several reactions (5), of which the most important and best investigated is that of *progestational growth and differentiation of the uterine endometrium* (6).

Since the cleaving eggs and early blastocysts are extremely small, the linkage of the mating act with the preparation of the uteri for implantation certainly seems biologically advantageous. In cases of *sterile mating*, experimental *mechanical stimulation* of the cervix, or *electric stimulation* of the brain stem, a progestational condition called *pseudopregnancy* is induced which usually lasts 16 to 17 days. It represents a waiting period, during which the uteri remain in readiness for implantation of blastocysts. In normal pregnancies, implantation occurs on the eighth day. Between the eighth and the sixteenth day another factor for the maintenance of pregnancy up to parturition (thirty-second day) must develop. It is now generally assumed that the fetal placenta secretes some substance which exerts this control by way of hypophysis and corpora lutea. Corner has shown that after the third day of free development in the lumen of the oviducts, the eggs of the rabbit become dependent on progesterone stimulation of the oviducts. If the corpora lutea are removed 14 to 18 hours after copulation, the blastocysts regress and die, instead of expanding into large vesicles.

In pseudopregnancy and in pregnancy, progesterone exerts a depressing effect on the output of FSH. However, in the rabbit it does not as completely prevent stimulation of follicular growth as, for instance, in the ferret. Follicles of considerable size are found intermingling with the luteal bodies in ovaries at all stages of pregnancy. Even though they degenerate before reaching ovulation size, they produce enough estradiol to keep the pregnant female more or less in receptive condition. Matings occur, but they are infertile.

Other seasonal breeders with ovulation induced by copulation are the spermophile (*Citellus*), the squirrels, the American shrew, the weasel, the ferret, and the cat.

3. ESTRUS CYCLE

The reproductive cycles of the majority of mammalian females are quite independent of the seasons. Although actual breeding has a tendency to remain restricted to the most favorable months, the animals of this second group develop short heat periods, with recurrences that are not externally determined. The decisive event in bringing about the cyclic character is the *spontaneous ovulation* which occurs at the peak of each follicular growth period. As in the rabbit, ovulation is directly precipitated through an output of LH by the hypophysis. But the hypophyseal reaction is no longer provoked by nervous stimulation, originating from the mating act; it develops in response to the increased output of estradiol by the ovarian follicles. In other words, *the female hypophysis releases LH, when the concentration of estradiol in the blood reaches a level that indicates the presence of full-grown follicles.*

In the following description the rat, which has been used more than any other species for studies of the reproductive processes, is chosen as the representative of this simplest type of true sexual cycles.

a. **Cycles of Unmated Female Rats.**   Female rats that are separated from males run estrus cycles in four-day periods. Actual heat lasts from 9 to 15 hours. It begins most often about 6 P.M., reaches its height from 7 P. M. to 10 P.M., and then gradually subsides. During this period the animals exhibit behavioristic peculiarities such as general unrest, quivering of the ears, arching of the back (lordosis) in response to stroking or grasping, and willingness to receive the male, if tested. Outside of this period, i.e., for about three days and 14 hours, the females are unresponsive if tested with males.

The behavioristic cycle is paralleled by a series of characteristic *developments in the sex organs* (Figs. 279, 280). If the day on which heat begins is arbitrarily counted as the third day of the cycle, then the first three days may be described as the *follicular or proliferating period*. In response to FSH stimulation about one dozen or more ovarian follicles grow to full size (cf. Figs. 20, 21). Releasing more and more estradiol, they cause a progressive enlargement of the uteri. The last phase of this process consists of a distention of the uterine lumen by fluid. The estradiol also evokes a massive proliferation of the vaginal epithelium (Fig. 279). As many cell layers pile up, the surface cells become squamous and cornify. The presence of scaled-off cornified cells in the vaginal lumen coincides with the heat period. The characteristic changes in the *vaginal smears* (Fig. 279) provide the basis of a test reaction for estradiol and other estrogenic substances (Allen-Doisy test). In the normal estrus cycle of the rat, the presence of numerous polynuclear leukocytes in the diestrus smears and their disappearance during heat is likewise of great diagnostic value.

Ovulation occurs spontaneously about 8 to 11 hours after the start of estrus (or close to six hours following copulation, if the female was mated). Thus, ovulation as a rule takes place during early morning hours of the fourth day. The eggs, wrapped in corona cells and mucus, pass into the ovarian capsules and enter the tubes of the oviducts (Figs. 22, 24). Unfertilized, they begin to shed their corona cells late on the same day. On the fifth they fragment and disappear.

The *importance of LH in the evocation of receptivity and ovulation* was demonstrated in the following set of experiments. The male rat, having no cyclic changes, maintains a constant, relatively high level of FSH. In ovaries transplanted into males that were castrated after puberty, some follicles enlarge to mature size, but never ovulate. On the other hand, if the castration was done immediately after birth, ovulation and luteal body formation occur as in females. This suggests

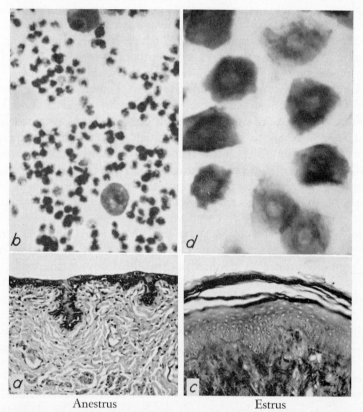

Anestrus   Estrus

Figure 279.   Anestrus and estrus in the rat. *a,* Thin anestrus vaginal epithelium; cuboid cells, infiltrated with leukocytes; × 150. *b,* Vaginal smear; few nucleated epithelial cells and numerous polynuclear leukocytes, × 450. *c,* Thick estrus vaginal epithelium; cornification of top layers, × 150. *d,* Vaginal smear; only cornified cells with ghost nuclei; × 450.

that the non-cyclic male hypophysis develops through exposure to testicular hormones. It was shown also that females can be induced to produce FSH at a constant level by the implantation of a testis shortly after birth, or by daily testosterone injections throughout the juvenile period. When they reach maturity, such females have ovaries with numbers of mature or nearly mature follicles but without corpora lutea. The vagina is always cornified. Histologically this is a condition of *constant estrus,* but the females remain unresponsive; i.e., behavioristically they are not in heat. A single injection of LH changes this picture. The females immediately go into full heat and ovulate a normal number of eggs. If placed with males, they mate and the eggs become fertilized. Such experiments prove that quantitative fluctuations in FSH alone are not sufficient to control the entire cycle. *At the peak of the proliferating phase the development of mating behavior and of ovulation depends on the accession of some luteinizing hormone.*

In the course of the fourth day, a short period of regression and rest, called *diestrus,* returns the sex organs to the conditions from which a new cycle may start. The cornified layers of the vaginal epithelium are shed, and in the vaginal smear leukocytes and a few large nucleated epithelial cells appear between the cornified platelets. About four to

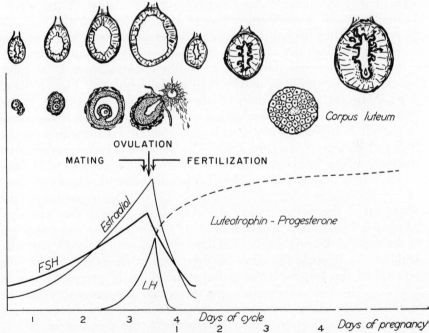

Figure 280.   Hormonal relationships in the estrus cycle and in pregnancy of the female rat. The curves in general express quantitative changes of hormone levels as estimated on the basis of biologic reactions; a single curve is given for luteotrophin and progesterone (broken line) since the production of the latter depends directly on the presence of the former. The second level of the diagram correlates follicular development, ovulation, and corpus luteum formation with the hormonal conditions; the top level indicates parallel changes in the uterus.

six hours after ovulation the pores of the empty ovarian follicles are closed and healed over. Follicular fluid accumulates again in the central cavity. The granulosa becomes invaded by theca cells and the follicle begins to luteinize. By the end of the second postovulatory day (first day of the new estrus cycle), the formation of *corpora lutea* is completed. They persist for a considerable time and the ovaries of adult female rats always contain several sets of them in various stages of disintegration. But judging from the appearance of the uteri, only small amounts of progesterone are produced during the fourth day of the cycle. Maximal distention is attained a few hours after ovulation. Later in the day, the endometrium exhibits some transitory signs of progestational transformation, but presently the entire uteri become reduced to the slender and fairly thin-walled tubes that are characteristic for the interval (first and second day of cycle). *The corpora lutea of the sterile four-day estrus cycles are practically non-functional, at least in regard to progesterone production.*

b. Mating and Pregnancy.   The progestational differentiation of the uterus becomes initiated, much as in the rabbit, by mating. Likewise, it may be induced experimentally by stimulation of the cervix. In the latter case, a *pseudopregnancy* of 12 to 14 days' duration becomes established. After normal fertilization, the *implantation* of the blastocyst occurs on the sixth day and pregnancy lasts until the twenty-second.

The *progestational development of the endometrium* is morphologically less extensive in murids than in the rabbit (cf. Figs. 280 and 278). However, the sensitivity of the uteri to the presence of blastocysts and to non-specific mechanical and electrical stimuli is the same; in the rat it appears on the fourth day, reaches the maximum on the fifth and disappears after the sixth. The infractions induce endometrial reactions, which in pseudopregnant uteri are almost identical with those which follow normal implantations. After the eleventh day *deciduomas* of pseudopregnancy regress. *Parturition* occurs most often during the afternoon of the twenty-second day. Up to the twelfth day hypophysectomy is immediately followed by developmental arrest and resorption of the embryo. During the last ten days, development proceeds normally without the hypophysis, while at any stage ovariectomy, or the sole removal of the corpora lutea, causes termination of pregnancy within two days. In view of the fact that in either case pregnancy can be maintained by daily injections of progesterone, it may be concluded that the *corpora lutea* maintain pregnancy by the secretion of progesterone. During the first phase the stimulating *luteotrophic agent* is a hypophyseal hormone. Quite to the contrary the luteotrophic substance of the second phase, as shown by Astwood and Greep, is secreted by the fetal placenta and *directly* maintains the ovarial corpora lutea. Although evoking similar effects, the luteotrophic substances produced by hypophysis and placenta are not identical. Of the more closely

Table 27

Time Table of Events Related to Reproduction in Three Murid Rodents

SPECIES	ESTROUS CYCLE DURATION	HEAT PERIOD DURATION	PSEUDO-PREGNANCY	IMPLANTATION AGE P.C.*	GESTATION PERIOD DURATION	VAGINA OPENS AGE—DAYS	SEXUAL MATURITY AGE
Rat.......	4 days	9–15 hours	12–14 days	6 days	22 days	42	42 days
Mouse.....	4 days	9–15 days	10–12 days	5 days	19 days	34	34 days
Hamster...	4 days	20–30 hours	7–12 days	5 days	16 days	9	28 days

* P.C. after copulation.

studied hypophyseal hormones, prolactin shows definite luteotrophic properties, and is believed normally to act in this capacity. On the other hand, the nature of the placental hormone is entirely unknown.

The described relationships and reactions are diagrammatically represented in Figure 280, which includes a four-day cycle followed by pregnancy.

The timing of the events shows a certain amplitude of variation. In large rat colonies, one may find that about 60 per cent of females follow the four-day schedule. But not infrequently estrus appears delayed by a full day or a fraction of a day. The calculated average length is therefore somewhere between four and five days. Similar short estrus cycles are found also in other murid rodents (Table 27).

4. PROGESTATIONAL CYCLE

In the *guinea pig* and in *ungulates,* the progestational phase is not induced by mating but is an automatic event, like ovulation. The entire cycle is now longer, lasting as a rule from 15 to 24 days. In contrast to the menstrual cycle (see below), the transition from the progestational phase to the start of the proliferative phase of the next cycle is not very marked. As a rule the follicles grow slower than in the rat. The heat period belongs essentially to the late proliferating phase. Asdell has pointed out the parallelism that exists in the ungulates between the duration of heat and the relative preponderance of FSH hormone in the hypophysis (Table 28). Ovulation takes place near the end of the heat period. All indications favor the concept that heat is contingent upon a high estradiol level. Cows and mares sometimes develop cystic ovaries, with numbers of large but non-ovulating follicles. They then remain in estrus for abnormally extended periods of time (nymphomania).

The *horse* is peculiar within this group, not only because of the high content of hypophyseal follicle stimulating hormone and the very long heat period (Table 28), but also for its production of excessive quantities of pregnancy hormones. About

Table 28

Duration of Heat (Receptivity) in Relation to Gonadotrophic Quotient of Dried Whole Hypophysis (Witschi 1940)

SPECIES	DURATION OF SEX CYCLE	DURATION OF HEAT	Qgt
	Days	Days	
Cow.	20	$\frac{3}{4}$	1000
Ewe.	16	$1\frac{1}{8}$	340
Sow.	21	$2\frac{1}{2}$	60
Mare.	20–25	5–10	8
Woman.	28	28	1

Qgt = 20 FSH/LH. In this formula FSH and LH represent dry weights of powdered hypophysis that contain one unit of follicle stimulating or of luteinizing hormone respectively.

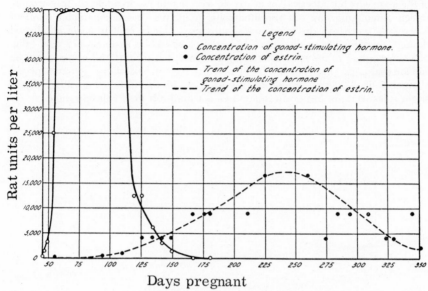

Figure 281.   Concentration of gonadotrophin in blood serum, and of estrogen in urine of a mare, throughout pregnancy (Cole and Hart 1942).

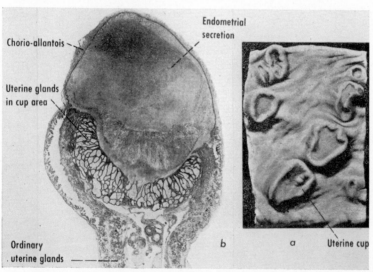

Figure 282.   Endometrial cups from pregnant mares. *a*, Inner aspect of uterine wall after removal of the fetal membranes (Schauder, 1912). *b*, Single cup from mare on 105th day of pregnancy (Cole and Goss 1943); × 5.

the forty-second day of pregnancy a gonadotrophic hormone appears in the blood of the mare which is identical, or nearly so, with that of the hypophysis. It is strongly follicle stimulating, but has also luteinizing properties. Its gonadotrophic quotient is the same as that of the hypophyseal substance (Table 28). It is not eliminated through the kidneys but disappears from the blood stream at about 175 days (Fig. 281). According to the most convincing evidence it is formed and excreted by the endometrial cups (Fig. 282). Throughout the second half of the gestation period a number of estrogenic substances are excreted in the urine (Fig. 281). Their origin is less certain, but ovariectomy does not diminish their concentration.

Chapter 25

Physiology and

Endocrinology of

Reproduction. II

5. MENSTRUAL CYCLE

Menstrual cycles are exclusively characteristic of *primates*. They are more extended than the progestational cycles. The average duration varies from about 27 days in the rhesus monkey to 35 in the chimpanzee. The human cycle is highly variable, though 28 days is generally considered as its typical length. Menstruation itself, i.e., the shedding of the superficial layers of the endometrium with accompanying bleeding, has sometimes been likened to the stage of embryotroph formation, which follows implantation in the course of normal pregnancy. But in many ways it also resembles the postpartum shedding of the entire decidua. At any rate, the menstrual cycle is more inclusive than the progestational, and represents the most highly diversified of all reproductive cycles (Table 29). Mating in no way modifies its course, if not followed by fertilization.

Ovulation divides the cycle into a preovulatory *follicular phase* and a postovulatory *luteal phase* (Fig. 287). These are of nearly equal length.

441

The first one is characterized by the presence, in the ovary, of rapidly growing follicles (Fig. 283), the second by at least one corpus luteum (Fig. 284). For practical reasons the day on which menstrual bleeding starts is counted as the first of the cycle (Fig. 285). It presents an easily recognizable indication that a luteal phase has ended and that a new follicular phase has become established.

Ovulation time is not linked with obvious events like mating or estrus. In man, coincident changes in electropotential differences and in body temperature have been discovered, but they are too small to be of much practical or diagnostic value. The best available data place ovulation in man on about the fourteenth day of the menstrual cycle, in the rhesus monkey on the thirteenth, and in the chimpanzee, the eighteenth day.

a. Endocrinology.   *Estrus* is a relatively long and not always definitely limited period. In monkeys and apes it finds visible expression in the bright color and tumescence of sexual skins and external genitalia. These changes and also the sexual receptivity of the female are related to the levels of the estrogenic hormones circulating in the blood. Heat culminates about the time of ovulation.

In the human, receptiveness spreads over the entire cycle, which is in agreement with the previously mentioned rule of direct relationship between FSH content of the hypophysis and duration of heat (Table 28). The human hypophysis has the lowest gonadotrophic quotient of all species so far studied. Related to the *high FSH content* of the hypophysis is the *prevalence of follicular over luteal elements* in the ovary (Fig. 283) and the *high estrogen production* throughout the entire cycle (Fig. 285). According to Markee, the endometrial growth as well as its regression is controlled by the fluctuations of blood estrogens. At its peak, the estrogen content per liter of blood has been determined to be about 60 IU (international units) or the equivalent of 6 μg. of estrone; it falls to about one half this concentration at the inception of menstruation. The estrogen curve in Figure 285 probably reflects quite closely the quantitative variations of FSH.

Table 29

Breeding Cycles of Female Mammals

TYPE OF CYCLE	SPONTANEOUS REACTIONS		
	OVULATION	PROGESTATION	DECIDUATION
Seasonal (rabbit)..................	—	—	—
Estrus (rat).......................	+	—	—
Progestational (cow)..............	+	+	—
Menstrual (primates)..............	+	+	+

+ Autonomous elements of cycle.

— Only by mating or by implantation induced events.

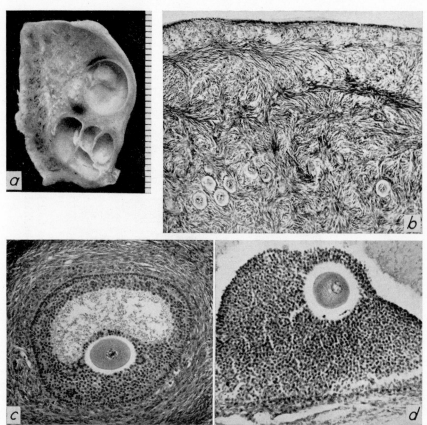

Figure 283.   Ovary of 19-year-old woman; *a,* transected six days after onset of menstruation; several enlarged follicles, some with degenerative changes (atretic follicles; total view from cut surface, × 1.5; *b,* section; primary follicles, imbedded in fibrous tissues, × 110; *c,* small secondary follicle, ovocyte nearly full grown, × 110; *d,* ovocyte in cumulus of medium size follicle, × 110.

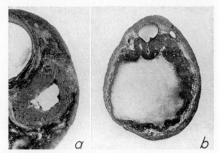

Figure 284.   Human corpora lutea. *a,* From ovary of 19-year-old woman, sixth day of menstrual cycle; *b,* from ovary of 2-year-old girl with premature menstrual cycles since birth; both × 2.5.

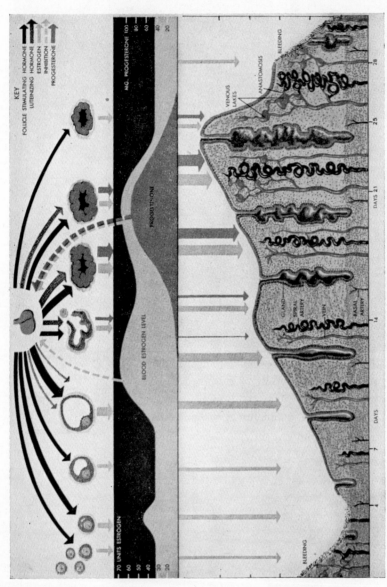

Figure 285. Hormonal relationships and morphologic changes in ovarian follicles and uterine endometrium during the menstrual cycle of the woman. (Reproduced from full color illustration in: Functional Uterine Bleeding, Ciba Clinical Symposia, *1*:140, 1949.)

Experiments with ovariectomized monkeys prove that the endometrium can be built up to premenstrual size with estrogen alone, and that menstruation will follow if estrogen is suddenly withdrawn. This indicates that progesterone is not necessary for the maintenance of a progestational uterus. Nevertheless, the reaction chains LH⟶ luteal body, and prolactin⟶ progesterone secretion, have a definite importance for the initiation and maintenance of a luteal phase and thereby of the natural cycle. It is quite certain that ovulation and the formation of the corpus luteum are induced by the appearance of *traces of hypophyseal LH* in the blood stream. Later, under the *luteotrophic stimulation by hypophyseal prolactin,* the corpus luteum produces *progesterone.* This seems to bring about the increase of secretory activity which is characteristic for the uterus of the postovulatory phase. Also, in case of fertilization, progesterone is necessary for the maintenance of a healthy blastocyst, and probably for the control of implantation.

The *human corpus luteum* (Fig. 284) retains a central cavity that becomes invaded by loose fibrous cells. It seems to produce both estradiol and progesterone; this double function may possibly be related to its origin in both the granulosa and the theca of the ovarian follicle.

Progesterone, like all other steroid hormones, becomes partly destroyed within the body and partly transformed into physiologically less potent derivatives which are eliminated through the kidneys. Probably somewhat over 10 per cent of the progesterone formed during the menstrual period of normal women passes into the urine in the form of water-soluble, but physiologically inert, *sodium pregnanediol glucuron-*

Progesterone
$C_{21}H_{30}O_2$

Pregnanediol
$C_{21}H_{36}O_2$

ide. This product of hormone metabolism appears in the urine 24 to 48 hours after ovulation and disappears one to three days before the onset of menstruation. Although it corresponds to only a fraction of the total progesterone, its absence before ovulation suggests that progesterone is not formed during the follicular phase (Fig. 285).

The presence of progesterone seems to have a stimulating effect on general metabolism. During the luteal phase the average body temperature of women is about 0.2° C. higher than before ovulation. Figure 285 presents a comprehensive summary of the changing endocrine conditions during the menstrual cycle.

b. Endometrial Morphology.   The primate uterus consists of three main layers, known as *perimetrium* (peritoneal surface), *myometrium* (muscle layer), and *endometrium* (Figs. 286, 289). The last is made up of a thin *uterine epithelium* bordering the *uterine lumen* and the highly vascular *mucosa*. Into the abundant stroma of the mucosa are sunk numerous *uterine glands* which, developmentally, are tubular invaginations of the uterine epithelium. The height of the endometrium varies between about 0.5 mm. at the end of menstrual bleeding and 5 to 7 mm. on the twenty-fourth day of the normal cycle (Fig. 285). One distinguishes a foundation layer or *basalis* that remains of almost constant thickness, serving as the source of regeneration following menstruation, and a so-called functional layer or *functionalis,* which in case of pregnancy becomes the *decidua,* but is shed at the end of each menstrual cycle. In the menstrual breakdown, the uterine epithelium is lost together with the larger parts of the uterine glands. Both regenerate from the bottom parts of the latter, which persist because of their location in the basalis (Fig. 286).

The uterus is supplied by arteries that enter by way of the broad ligament and circle the myometrium (Fig. 286). From these *arcuate arteries* issue the *radial arteries* that supply the myometrium and basalis before ending in *spiral arterioles* within the functional layer. Branches from these spirals approach and supply the uterine glands while their ends spread into dense capillary plexuses under the epithelial surface. The *venous drainage system* in general parallels the arterial distribution, though without the coiling which is the exclusive feature of the terminal arterioles.

In the *endometrial cycle* one may distinguish four distinct periods (Fig. 285).

1. The *proliferative phase* extends from the end of menstrual bleed-

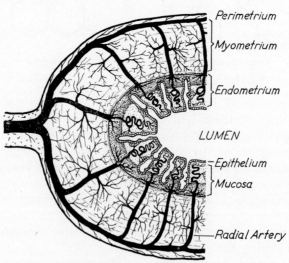

Figure 286.   Cross section through half of human uterus; uterine artery entering by way of mesometrium (broad ligament).

ing (4th day) until ovulation (14th day). Under the influence of the increasing FSH and estrogen concentrations, the regenerating endometrium grows to a height of 3 mm. while the glandular and vascular pattern of the functional layer becomes restored.

2. The *secretory phase* gets its name from the increased glandular activity which follows upon the appearance of progesterone in the blood stream. It consists of two parts, the *progestational,* which lasts from ovulation to about the 21st day (i.e., the six to seven days needed by a fertilized egg to develop into a blastocyst ready for implantation); and the *pseudodecidual,* which corresponds to the four days following implantation in a fertile cycle. During the first part the endometrium remains stationary; during the second it gains rapidly in height, growing to 5 or more millimeters in thickness. Of particular interest is the decidual transformation of many of the mesenchymal cells of the superficial compact layer of the functionalis. The spindle cells assume a cuboid and epithelioid character with a dense eosinophile cytoplasm. This last growth phase and histologic differentiation constitute the characteristic and particular progressive feature of the menstrual cycle. They can be valued as an automatic early phase of maternal placenta formation. They also prepare the stage for the following two dramatic regressive changes.

3. The *dehydration phase* is notable for the rapid shrinkage of the functional endometrium, which loses half its height, and the concomitant increased coiling of the spiral arteries. The latter feature may become a mechanical hindrance to normal blood flow. However, the developing difficulties seem more directly the result of the beginning necrosis leading to the formation of toxins in the stroma that act as vasoconstrictors. The formation of extensive venous lakes and of arteriovenous anastomoses during this three-day period initiates the final breakdown of the functionalis.

4. The *menstrual bleeding phase,* although actually representing the last chapter of the endometrial cycle, overlaps with the first four days of a new follicular development. For this reason, and also because of being the most easily recognizable stage, it is placed at the beginning of the entire cycle.

Regression is followed by histologic restoration. The open ends of arteries and veins again become connected by capillary plexuses. The regeneration of the uterine epithelium starts from the openings of the many remnant tubular glands. Depending on the length of the individual cycle a short rest period may follow, or the healed endometrium may immediately enter a new proliferative phase.

c. **Hormonal Conditions of Pregnancy.** In the primate group, man holds a similarly peculiar place to that of the horse among the ungulates, inasmuch as the LH content of the hypophysis is very low (gonadotrophic quotient = 1), the period of sexual receptiveness is greatly extended, and pregnancy hormones are produced in large quantities. Nevertheless, the particular features of the two cases show many differences. The understanding of the hormonal conditions in human pregnancy has been greatly aided by extensive normal and experimental studies on the rhesus monkey. This species exhibits the same series of endocrinologic events, but without the quantitative excess in the production of placental hormones that make human pregnancy a singular and highly specialized type. The following presentation is mainly based on the work of Corner, Delfs, Hartman, Hisaw, Newton, Streeter, Simpson, van Wagenen, and Wislocki.

In the monkey, after fertile mating, the luteal phase of the menstrual cycle becomes modified through events that follow the implantation of the blastocyst on the ninth day after ovulation (Fig. 287). During the critical days, while the hypophyseal luteotrophin loses its effect on the corpus luteum, the embryonic trophoblast begins to release into the blood stream a new luteotrophic principle. Its concentration rises rapidly and by the twenty-seventh day of the cycle is identifiable by bioassay methods. This *chorionic luteotrophin,* by prolonging the life of the corpus luteum, prevents the menstruation which otherwise would be expected. Its concentration increases for another week but falls off rapidly toward the end of the first month of pregnancy (Fig. 287). If it is still produced during the remaining six months until parturition, no proof of its presence in the blood has been obtained so far.

The chorionic luteotrophin differs from that of the hypophysis, i.e., from prolactin, by being able to prolong the active progesterone-producing life of the corpus luteum by about two weeks. Prolactin, even if injected in large amounts, is not able to do this; at the end of the normal menstrual cycle the luteal bodies become insensitive to prolactin. It appears that the chorionic principle stimulates the ovary to secrete estrogen as well as progesterone. Therefore, it is usually given the designation of *chorionic gonadotrophin.* In the monkey its secretion coincides in time with the villous stage of the chorionic vesicle.

Beginning with the second month the now differentiated fetal discoidal placentas take over the complete hormonal control of pregnancy. From here on neither corpora lutea nor ovaries are necessary for its maintenance. That the placenta alone are in control was experimentally proved by removal of the fetus. Even when both ovaries were removed together with the fetus on the seventy-third day, the placentas were retained in the uterus for 90 days, to be "born at term" on the one hundred

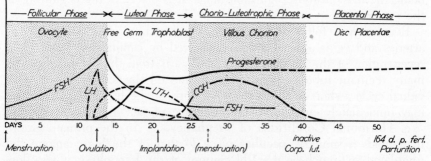

Figure 287.   Hormonal sequences in the gestation of the rhesus monkey (based on the work of Hartmann, and of Hisaw).

and sixty-third day. It is assumed that the placentas produce progesterone as well as estrogen, though only the latter has been definitely identified.

The *hormonal picture in human pregnancy* differs mostly by the relatively enormous quantities of hormones that are produced in the chorionic placentas, particularly *chorionic gonadotrophin, estrogen,* and *progesterone.* Under the influence of the high levels of blood hormones, the maternal hypophysis stops production and release of its own gonadotrophic hormones. However, it resumes this activity very quickly (within six days) after termination of pregnancy by either abortion or parturition.

The *chorionic gonadotrophin* appears in the blood and in the urine (Fig. 288) of the mother immediately following the attachment of the blastocyst. Two weeks after fertilization of the egg, i.e., even before the time of the first missed menstrual period, its concentration is high enough to give positive pregnancy tests. The output rises rapidly, and from about the seventh to the tenth weeks more than 50,000 R.U. (rat units) daily are excreted with the urine. The production then falls off and after the third month until term the daily urinary elimination remains around 2000 R.U. The content is always higher in the blood

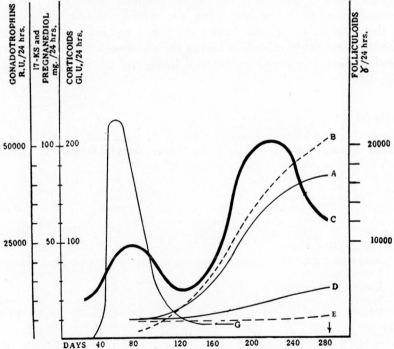

Figure 288.   Excretion rates of urinary hormones in human pregnancy. *A,* Pregnanediol, *B,* estrogens, *C,* corticoids, *D,* 17-ketosteroids (DNB method), *E,* 17-ketosteroids (SbCl₃ method), *G,* gonadotrophins (after Venning from Selye 1947).

serum than in the urine (6 to 10 times). At seven weeks 500,000 R.U. per liter are not unusual; during the second half of the period a level of about 6000 R.U. per liter is maintained. The chorionic gonadotrophin is a glycoprotein and the rat unit weighs about one-fourth of a microgram.

The *estrogen* content of the blood is comparatively low during the first half of pregnancy, fluctuating between 30 and 60 I.U. (international units), i.e., within the maximums and minimums of the non-fertile menstrual cycle. During the second half, the concentration rises steadily and reaches values ranging from 1200 I.U. to 2000 I.U. per liter. However, the urine contains much larger quantities. The estrogens are usually excreted as biologically inert sulfates and glucuronides. They are easily set free by acids, and one finds that they rise from about 5000 I.U./day in midpregnancy to 200,000 I.U./day at term (equivalent of 20 mg. of estrone).

Together with that of the estrogens, the output of progesterone increases, as indicated by the rising curve of the urinary pregnanediol (Fig. 288).

Clinical experience shows that ovariectomy after the second month—possibly even during the second month—will not interfere either with the normal progress of a pregnancy, or with the normal production and excretion of hormones. The site of hormone production is not the endometrium, as in the horse, but the syntrophoblastic surface layer of the chorion. By far the largest quantities are immediately released into the maternal blood which bathes the chorionic villi. Only relatively small amounts are found in the fetal fluids and tissues (Table 30 and Fig. 289).

Table 30

Distribution of Chorionic Gonadotrophic in Maternal and Fetal Tissues and Fluids; Human Pregnancies of 11 to 12 Weeks (Data by Bruner). Contents in R.U. (rat units) per gm. of fresh tissue per ml. of fluids

MATERIAL	R.U./GM. tissue	R.U./ML. fluid
Maternal		
Hypophysis..........................	7	
Muscle of thigh........................	8	
Uterine muscle.........................	20	
Uterine endometrium....................	100	
Blood................................		100–33
Urine................................		10–5
Fetal		
Placental chorion......................	500–100	
Chorionic fluid........................		20
Amniotic fluid........................		10
Body tissue..........................	1.25–1.0	

The shedding of the afterbirth, including the chorion, removes the source of all placental hormones. However, the entire bodies of mother and child are still permeated with large quantities of hormones which are slowly lost during three or four days following birth.

A comparison of placental gonadotrophin production in the horse and in the human reveals some very interesting differences. *In the mare* the biologic qualities of the hormone are identical with those of hypophyseal extracts. Since it originates in the endometrium, it is a *maternal hormone. In man*, quite to the contrary, it is a *fetal hormone*—the only one, so far known, that is formed exclusively by embryos and fetuses. Though it belongs to the same chemical class of glycoproteins as the hypophyseal gonadotrophins, biologically it is quite different from them. It has no follicle-stimulating effect on the ovaries of primates. On the contrary, it causes the disintegration of the larger follicles, if administered during the follicular phase of the menstrual cycle. Its gonadotrophic effects in rodents are produced indirectly by activation of their hypophyses. The ovaries of hypophysectomized rats show little or no response. The role of this hormone in human pregnancy awaits further

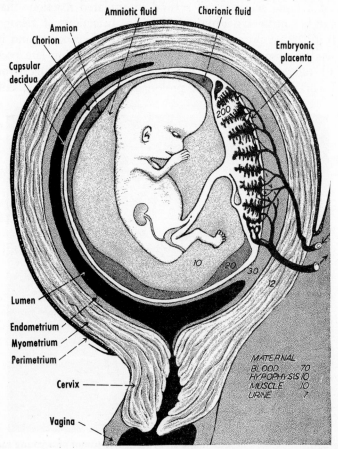

Figure 289.   Human fetus of 11 to 12 weeks (St. 34); distribution and concentration of chorionic gonadotrophin in maternal and fetal tissues and fluids; rat units per gram of fresh tissue or per milliliter of fluid (data from Bruner 1951).

investigation. Its main function, as shown by Bradbury, is that of a *luteotrophin;* it stimulates, during a critical period, the uninterrupted progesterone production by existing corpora lutea.

In the ovaries and testes of young women and men, occasionally one or several germ cells begin to develop by some kind of abortive parthenogenesis. The resulting embryos are highly abnormal (Figs. 28, 290) and often consist merely of irregular, infiltrating ectodermal cells and syncytial masses. Such *embryomas* may become highly malignant, and spread metastases especially in the lungs and the brain. Now generally recognized as chorionepitheliomas, they produce the same chorionic gonadotrophin as the placentas of normal pregnancies. The hormone may be excreted in quantities that far surpass those of seven-week pregnancies.

6. PARTURITION

The duration of gestation is a hereditarily fixed character. It is the product of a long evolutionary development and probably in most species still has a tendency to increase. It terminates with parturition, which consists of a rapid sequence of several interrelated reactions that starts from some yet unknown physiologic cause. Injections of *estrogens* following fertilization prevent implantation of the blastocysts and in some species lead to absorption of early embryos. But during late pregnancy nearly all tolerate even very high administrations. *Progesterone* distinctly favors maintenance and prolongation of pregnancy; clinically,

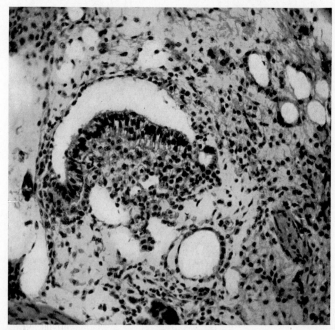

Figure 290.   Chorionepithelioma from testicular tumor of a young man; typical tube and vesicle formation showing structural resemblance to normal germs of the end of the second week (cf. Figs. 299, 300) (original preparation of A. Peyron); × 170.

it is successfully used to prevent threatened abortions, and its deficiency is probably one of the major causes of abortions and premature births. Nevertheless normal parturition seems not to be brought on by a decline of progesterone production, for the high rate of pregnanediol excretion continues right up to birth. A certain involvement of the adrenals is indicated by the steady decline of the *corticoids* after the two hundredth day. The oxytocic principle of *pituitrin,* an extract of the posterior (neural) lobe of the hypophysis, especially if injected together with an estrogen, has a stimulating effect on the muscular activity of the uterus. It is clinically used to expedite the expulsion of dead fetuses. Though it is possibly of some assistance also in normal parturition, the fact that completely hypophysectomized rats usually deliver their young spontaneously at the regular time proves that it does not act as a primary cause.

It now seems quite certain that the *true control of parturition* rests with the *placenta.* Older concepts about the possible importance of the fetus, its growth, and the consequent expansion of the uterus with pressure on sensory nerve endings in the cervix, had to be abandoned when van Wagenen showed that after removal of the fetus, the placenta alone still induces parturition at term. Evidently the fetal placenta develops to an age that is characteristic for its species and, when thus matured, initiates parturition. Most probably it then releases some substance that engages the endocrine as well as the nervous control systems of the birth mechanism. Necrotic changes and a partial separation of the placenta from the uterine wall have been considered to expedite the process.

In this connection it is of interest that in marsupials the chorion and eventual placental formations usually remain in the uterus, where they are resorbed. In the horse the entire chorion detaches itself quite early, and the foaling must progress speedily, or the young might suffocate. In cattle, as in man, the placenta remains solidly anchored until the young has been born; the persistence of placental respiration and circulation during the often much prolonged birth act enables the young to survive. Precocious detachment of the placenta is sometimes the cause of still-birth of perfectly developed children.

One may distinguish three main components of the process of parturition. *First,* the approach of birth is recognized by several phenomena of *relaxation.* The cervical canal and the entire birth passage begin to widen. The pubic symphysis of the pelvis loosens and the ossified connection transforms into an elastic ligament. Hisaw's work on the guinea pig resulted in the identification of a special relaxation hormone. The *second phase* is mainly characterized by *muscular contractions,* first of the uterus and later also of the abdomen, which eventually result in the expulsion of the fetus. In some instances movements of the fetus collaborate in bringing about this result. The *third phase,* which in some instances, especially in horses, may be delayed by an interval of days, consists in the removal of the fetal membranes, the placenta and the decidua. In the rat the placenta often is born together with the individual young. In many animals the mother eats most or all of this *"afterbirth."*

7. ENDOCRINOLOGY OF LACTATION

The major hormonal relationships in lactation are diagrammatically expressed in Figure 291. However, they are not identical in the various orders and species; the diagram expresses mainly the conditions as now known for man. With respect to controlling factors one may distinguish at least five successive phases.

a. Embryonic Differentiation.   The first differentiation of mammary welts and primitive glands obviously is induced by local morphogenetic factors, not hormones. The observation of Raynaud that experimental treatment with high dosages of estrogens suppresses the differentiation of the glands, but at the same time stimulates the formation of nipples, shows that even the preprimordial cells are hormone responsive. Nevertheless, it is not indicated that hormones normally influence the course of development before the stage of mammary cups has been attained (Fig. 274).

b. Prepubertal Growth.   Except in the marsupials, this phase begins at the fetal stages. Experiments by Jost and Raynaud show that in rodents the secondary female sex characters, including mammary glands, continue differentiation and growth in the absence of gonads in both genetic sexes. On the other hand, the presence of testes inhibits the development of the female characters and thus becomes responsible for the early lag of mammary development in the male fetuses. The observed lack of responsiveness of the secondary sex characters toward female sex hormones may possibly be an adaptation, protecting the fetus against interference by extraneous maternal hormones. It is probable that in all other eutherians also the early lag of mammary development in male fetuses is the result of inhibition through testicular hormones. In the human, chorionic and maternal hormones passing through the placental barrier have a definite stimulating effect on the late fetal development of the mammaries in both sexes. This is borne out by the presence of colostrum in the glandular ducts of the newborn and by the histologic and quantitative reductions that follow parturition.

Toward the approach of puberty, when some ovarian follicles begin to enlarge and increasing amounts of estrogens enter circulation, the glandular sprouts which lay dormant during the juvenile period (Fig. 291) become reactivated. They grow and form new branches, developing the basic pattern of the mammary lobules.

c. Alveolar Differentiation in the Nonpregnant Adult.   After the establishment of maturity and consequent to the formation of corpora lutea in the ovaries, small alveoli begin to differentiate from the terminal branches of the glandular tubules. This effect is usually attributed to the progesterone secreted by the yellow bodies.

d. Development of Secretory Epithelia during Pregnancy. Under the influence of the continually high level of both estrogen and progesterone, the cells of the inner lining of the alveoli gain considerably in size and assume the character of secretory cells. The initial growth is probably a combined result of FSH, LH, and prolactin release by the hypophysis gland. Later, after implantation of the embryos, the chorion begins to substitute for hypophyseal activity, maintaining

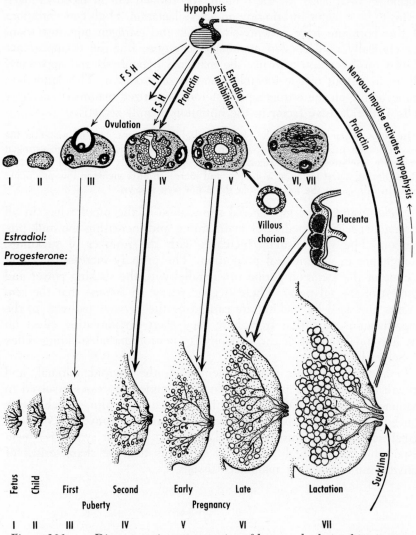

Figure 291. Diagrammatic representation of hormonal relationships in mammary development and lactation. The villous chorion, by the production of *chorionic gonadotrophin,* prolongs progesterone secretion of the corpus luteum (stage V).

the ovarian corpora lutea and their progesterone production. Finally, the placenta takes over the entire hormonal functions. During the last seven months of pregnancy, while the production of chorionic gonadotrophin becomes reduced, the placenta releases large quantities of estrogen and progesterone. Thus, with progress of gestation the control of both maintenance of pregnancy and development of the mammary apparatus passes gradually from maternal to fetal endocrine systems.

e. Initiation and Maintenance of Milk Secretion. With the shedding of the afterbirth, following parturition, the source of placental hormones disappears. In the human, the sudden fall in blood estrogen seems to be a factor in bringing on active lactation. High concentrations of this hormone have a depressive effect and estrogen administrations are clinically used to stop mammary secretion. But the disappearance of this inhibitor also activates the maternal hypophysis and apparently elicits an output of considerable amounts of *prolactin*. This latter hormone, acting on the estrogen-progesterone sensitized mammary secretory cells, is the decisive factor in the initiation of milk secretion.

In *cattle, sheep,* and *goats* the picture is slightly different. During gestation the blood estrogen titer is much lower than in man. With this goes a high estrogen sensitivity. Relatively small amounts of estrogens (usually implanted stilbestrol tablets) bring about lactation in heifers and increased milk yields in low producing cows. In this group the role of prolactin is not well known.

Sucking and other mechanical stimulation of the nipples has, in all observed species, the effect of maintaining and increasing the milk production. The yield usually increases with the number of sucklings, though not in arithmetical proportion. The primary increase and later decline of the lactation period run parallel with the sucking power and interest of the offspring. There is good reason to assume that the sensations produced by sucking are carried by the nervous pathway to the hypothalamus, and that from here they exert a stimulating effect on the hormonal output of the hypophysis (neurohumoral suckling reflex of Selye; Fig. 291).

In addition to those already mentioned, the thyroid, adrenal, and growth hormones also play a role in the complex processes involved in mammary function. Of particular importance is insulin, which seems concerned with the carbohydrate metabolism and the conversion of blood acetate and glucose into fat. The latter processes (fat synthesis) seem responsible for the high respiratory quotients that are characteristic of actively milk-producing mammary tissues.

Chapter 26

Human Development. I

In the course of time the old Teutonic term *egg* and its Latin equivalent *ovum* have acquired various meanings and definitions. It is probable that both were first used as designations for bird eggs, without regard to the developmental stage of embryos and fetuses within the shells. Later they were given an even broader meaning, extending not only to shelled eggs of insects but also to other immotile stages, particularly pupae (e.g., "ant eggs"). Harvey (1651) applied the term ovum also to the mammalian conceptus in utero, particularly the implanted chorionic vesicle. On the other hand, von Baer (1827), discoverer of the true mammalian ovarian egg, sometimes considered the entire Graafian follicle as an equivalent of the bird's egg. With the establishment of the cell theory and following the elucidation of germ cell development, fertilization, and cleavage, it became necessary to restrict the scientific use of both terms to the unicellular ovocyte stages (pp. 19–41). However, in the case of birds and insects, where the early developmental stages are hidden under hard, opaque shells, the old traditional usage serves a definite practical need. Double connotations in this instance seem preferable to the introduction of new names, the more so as misunderstandings are not likely to occur.

No similar good argument could be raised in favor of the still continued designation of uterine stages of mammals as ova. It is, of course, unfortunate that the word *germ* which originally referred to a developing rudiment of a new organism, and later metaphorically was used to

457

allude to the cause of a disease, has now become a synonym for mi-
crobe. *Conception* or *conceptus* is often applied as a summary designation of the early products of internal fertilization. The similar use of
embryo leads to ambiguity, since more strictly the embryo of a mammal
is only a part of the germ. *Germ* and *conceptus* are the most acceptable
terms for general reference to early stages of human development.

1. CLEAVAGE (ST. 1–4)

Exactly one hundred years after von Baer's discovery of the mammalian egg within the ovarian follicles, Edgar Allen, with a group of

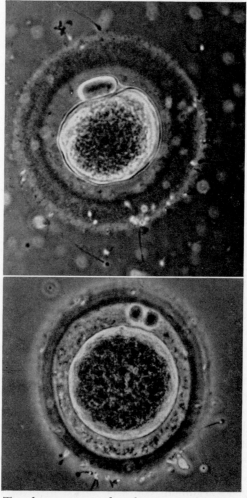

Figure 292.   Two human eggs taken from mature ovarian follicles and inseminated in vitro. A polar body was given off which in the egg of the lower figure
has divided. Extra sperms surrounding and penetrating the corona. The pellucid
membrane appears black in these phase contrast photographs; it surrounds the
perivitelline space, the egg and the polar bodies; × 200 (courtesy of Dr. Shettles).

clinical collaborators, succeeded in collecting a number of normally ovulated, unfertilized human eggs which had been flushed from the oviducal tubes of women who happened to undergo laparotomy shortly after ovulation. More recently Menkin and Rock transferred several hundred eggs from large and nearly mature ovarian follicles of human ovaries to culture dishes. Of 138 which later were exposed to sperms, 4 apparently became fertilized and passed through early cleavage stages. Preserved from 40 to 46 hours after insemination, they had progressed to the 2-cell and the 3-cell stages (Fig. 293). Polar body formation in similarly treated eggs was observed by Shettles (Fig. 292).

The progress of cleavage of normally fertilized eggs is illustrated by a number of well spaced stages that were recovered by Hertig and Rock in the course of surgical interventions (Fig. 294). The 2-cell stage, obtained 60 hours after the last coitus, is estimated to be 36 hours old, counted from the time of sperm entrance. It is essentially identical with the corresponding stages that were obtained by artificial fertilization. Two days later the germ has only reached the 8-cell stage. It has acquired a small central cavity and is just entering the lumen of the uterus. The specimen shown in Figure 294b is not judged to be entirely normal.

2. THE BLASTULA OR BLASTOCYST STAGE (ST. 5-7)

A conceptus of about four days, that was found floating free in the uterine lumen, is changing to the blastocyst stage (Fig. 294c). Of its 58 cells, five form a nodular *embryoblast*. The other 53 are arranged in a trophoblastic shell. A second free blastocyst, about half a day older and with 107 cells, consists of a single-layered *trophoblastic vesicle* which at its animal pole carries an *inner cell mass*, the *embryoblast* (Fig. 294d). Older free stages have not, so far, been found; but there is

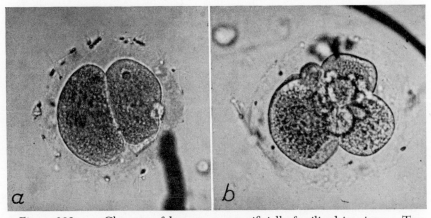

Figure 293.   Cleavage of human eggs, artificially fertilized in vitro. *a,* Two cells; *b,* three cells, starting abnormality; × 300. Accessory sperms have penetrated the pellucid membrane or attached themselves to it (Menkin and Rock 1948).

good reason to assume that up to the sixth day the blastocyst cavity becomes further extended and that the prospective germ layers become arranged in a pattern approximating that of Figure 255c. As previously explained, the free blastocyst of mammals is the equivalent of the blastula of lower vertebrates (Fig. 39a), but more particularly of the disc blastula of birds (Fig. 35).

3. THE BILAMINAR OR GASTRULA STAGES (ST. 8–11)

In the course of the sixth day the blastocyst attaches itself to the uterine epithelium. With its animal pole leading, it penetrates the progestational endometrium in which it becomes entirely buried, within the following two days (Fig. 295).

The youngest known implanted human germ is approximately seven days old (Figs. 296, 297). With the blastocyst cavity collapsed, it has the over-all shape of an irregular disc, measuring $0.125 \times 0.300 \times 0.450$ mm. It is superficially embedded in the spongy mesenchyme of the mucosa. Only the edges of the disc are covered by overgrowing endometrium (white ring in Fig. 296). In the surface view one recognizes the remnant blastocyst cavity (dark ring) and the central em-

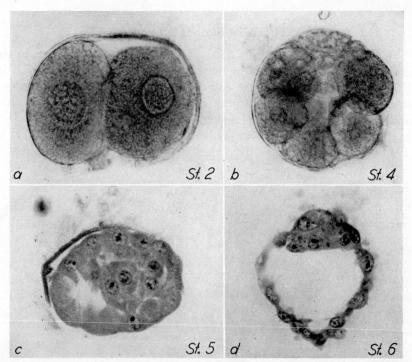

Figure 294. Very early stages of human development. Stage 2, two cells; stage 4, eight cells; stage 5, 58 cell blastocyst; stage 6, early blastocyst, with trophoblast and embryoblast; all × 400. Note steady loss of substance. (Hertig, Rock, Adams, and Mulligan 1954, Carnegie Contrib. 240.)

bryonic mass (white), both still exposed to the lumen of the uterus (compare Fig. 296 with 297). The vegetal half of the *trophoblast* is of the thin membranous type that is characteristic for the free blastocysts. On the other hand the animal half has tremendously gained in thickness. Obviously its cell number is increased, but more striking is the tendency toward giant cell formation. The rapid growth of the animal trophoblast constitutes proof of a tremendous capacity of trophoblast cells to break down maternal tissues, rendering them into *embryotroph*. The difference between the two sides illustrates the inability of the trophoderm to absorb food from the liquids of the uterine cavity.

The *inner cell mass* has become differentiated into *epiblastic and hypoblastic layers* (St. 8). They are incompletely separated by a *basilar membrane* (at left side in Fig. 297). The *epiblast* is a bulky, lentoid body. The fissure, visible at the upper right, is the *primitive amniotic cavity*. A few rather loose cells at the rim of the lentoid are early differentiating *extra-embryonic mesenchyme* cells (diagram, Fig. 301a).

The 9-day specimen of Figure 298 (St. 9) has about doubled in thickness, but the gain in equatorial dimensions is not equally great (0.256 × 0.404 × 0.422 mm.). The specimen is nearly completely invested by endometrial tissue. The trophoblast has encroached upon the sinusoids of the arteriovenous anastomoses. Through erosion of the endothelia it causes the flow of maternal blood into a system of *lacunae* within the trophoblast (diagrams, Fig. 301a, b). This constitutes the first step toward the development of primary (ectoblastic) villi and results in a manifold increase of the absorbing surface of the trophoblast.

The derivatives of the *embryoblast* have barely increased in size. Epiblast and hypoblast still adhere closely to each other. The *amniotic cavity* is considerably enlarged. A hypoblastic vesicle, usually called the *primary yolk sac*, has made its appearance; its cavity is a *gastrocele*. The bilaminar plate between amniotic cavity and gastrocele represents essentially the prospective embryo; this is the *embryonic disc*. While

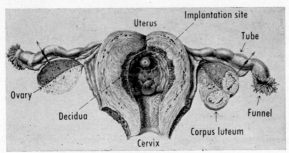

Figure 295.   Implantation of 12-day germ in the thickened endometrium of the uterus. Ventral aspect of the opened uterus, tubes, and funnels. Sliced ovaries with corpus luteum on left side (after Eden and Lockyer from Ramsey, 1937, Carnegie Contrib. 156).

Fig. 296

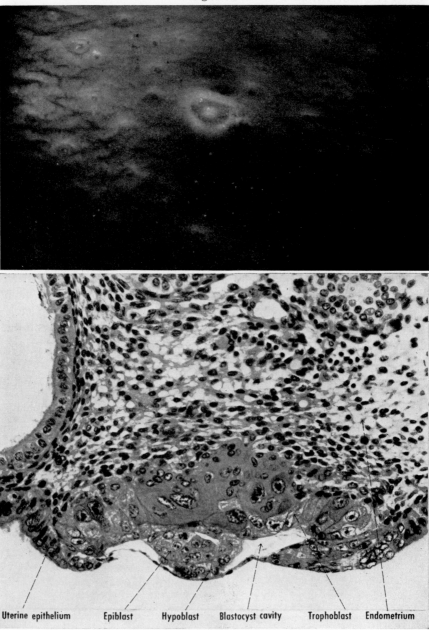

Uterine epithelium   Epiblast   Hypoblast   Blastocyst cavity   Trophoblast   Endometrium

Fig. 297

Figure 296. Implantation site of 7-day human germ in uterine wall, surrounded by openings of uterine glands; × 35 (Hertig and Rock 1945, Carnegie Contrib. 200).

Figure 297. Section through implantation site shown above. Blastocyst embedded superficially in mucosa and only partly overgrown by uterine tissue. *Trophoblast* consists of thick giant cells on endometrial side, but thin epithelium toward uterine lumen. Embryoblast bilaminar (St. 8), *hypoblast* oriented toward uterine lumen; fissure in *epiblast* is probably the primitive amniotic cavity; at the left, part of uterine gland; × 300 (Hertig and Rock 1945, Carnegie Contrib. 200).

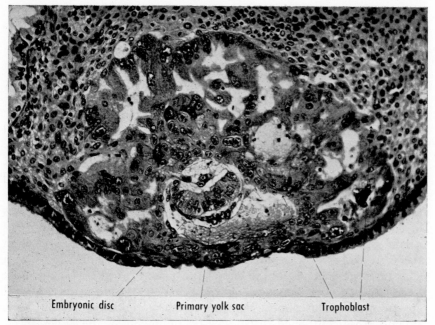

Embryonic disc   Primary yolk sac   Trophoblast

Figure 298.   Human germ, 9 days (St. 9), fully embedded in uterine mucosa. Much thickened trophoblast with numerous lacunae. Hypoblast with slit-like primary yolk-sac cavity (archenteron). Amnion formation by cavitation. Loose mesoderm cells around rim of embryonic disc; × 200 (Hertig and Rock 1945, Carnegie Contrib. 200).

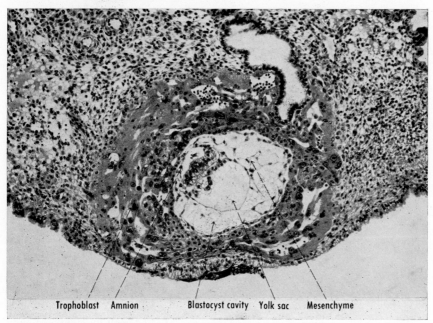

Trophoblast Amnion   Blastocyst cavity Yolk sac   Mesenchyme

Figure 299.   Human germ, 11 days (St. 10), embedded in endometrium (with uterine gland). Archenteron vesicle (yolk sac) much enlarged; mesenchyme spreading from embryonic disc fills blastocyst cavity; at right beginning organization of chorion (mesodermal and ectodermal layers loosely attached); maternal blood enters trophoblastic lacunae; × 100 (Hertig and Rock 1941, Carnegie Contrib. 184).

it is still two-layered, the extra-embryonic mesenchyme ring has considerably increased and now spreads through the remnant blastocyst cavity (Fig. 301*b*). A particularly dense accumulation of mesenchyme between amnion and inner wall of the trophoblast represents the rudiment of the *body stalk*.

The bilaminar condition of the slowly growing germ disc lasts until the end of the second week (St. 8, 9). Then, gradually, the third embryonic germ layer begins to appear (St. 10, 11; Figs. 299, 300). Its formation is only partly connected with the processes of concrescence and primitive streak formation and will be discused following the description of more advanced stages. Figure 301 (*a–d*) shows dorsal aspects of embryonic shields of the gastrula period. The *primary yolk sac* has a late start and never fills the entire trophoblast cavity, as it does in the early embryos of most other mammals (compare Fig. 255*d* with 255*b, f*). Nevertheless, at the end of this period it becomes temporarily larger than the amniotic sac (Figs. 300, 301*c–f*). Often it has a ventral appendix that may connect with an accessory endoderm vesicle. Such structures are considered to be atavistic rudiments of the larger ancestral yolk sac.

During the gastrulation period the trophoblast differentiates into a

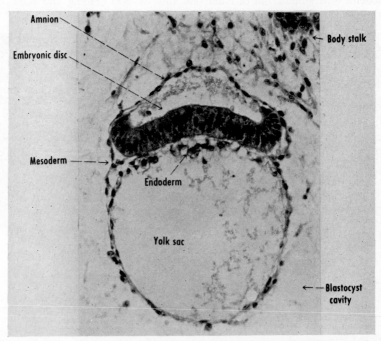

Figure 300.   Human embryo, 13½ days (St. 11); well differentiated amniotic and primary vitelline sacs. Embryonic disc invaded by mesoderm from the rim. Mesoderm also forms investing epithelia over outside of entire embryo; × 120 (Heuser, Rock, and Hertig 1945, Carnegie Contrib. 201).

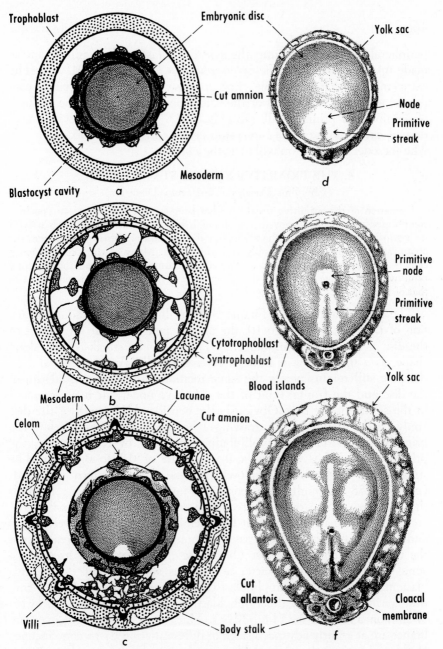

Figure 301. Stages of early development. Embryonic discs viewed from above; amnion removed; in *d, e, f* chorion removed. *a, b, c,* Development of villous chorion, extra-embryonic mesoderm, celom, and body stalk. *a,* Stage 8, solid ecto-trophoblast; ring of loose mesoderm cells around rim of embryonic disc. *b,* Stage 9, lacunae in syntrophoblast; separation of syn- and cytotrophoblast; mesenchyme spreading from embryoblast through the blastocyst cavity. *c,* Stage 10, formation of true villi and of extra-embryonic celomic cavity; diameter of yolk sac exceeds disc. *d, e, f,* Development of embryonic shield and blood islands. *d,* Stage 11, short primitive streak. *e,* Stage 12, full primitive streak. *f,* Stage 13, presomite neurula with primitive streak and invagination pore; short notochord and prechordal plate visible through transparent neural floor plate. Areas of prosencephalon, mes-encephalon, rhombencephalon, and spinal cord recognizable; semidiagrammatic.

peripheral spongy syncytium, the *syntrophoblast,* and an inner capsule made up of cuboid cells, the *cytotrophoblast* (Figs. 299, 301*b*, *c*). The extra-embryonic mesenchyme, first a loose meshwork, becomes condensed along the inner wall of the ectotrophoblast and over the surfaces of amnion and primary yolk sac (Fig. 300). The resulting wide mesodermal cavity is the *extra-embryonic celom* (Figs. 255, 300, 301*b*, *c*). The mesoderm-lined trophoblast is the *chorion.*

4. THE PRIMITIVE STREAK STAGE (ST. 12)
(Chorionic Vesicles of 7–10 mm. Diameter)

Formation of the primitive streak signifies concrescence and hence an epoch of complicated morphogenic movements. Though histologic differentiation is only at its beginning and the cells of the embryonic disc are still of blastemic character, the organization attained is now visibly of higher order. Many of the loose blastemic cells of the previous stages have assembled into firm epithelia, and the resulting primitive streak stage of human development presents an obvious resemblance to that of the other vertebrates.

The three blastodiscs of Figures 301*c–e* illustrate the gradual formation of the streak. At stage 10, the animal pole lies near the center of the disc of about 0.2 mm. diameter. The tip of the streak is just taking shape, as a thickening or node of blastemic cells. At stages 11 and 12 the pole still retains nearly the same relationship to the ventral rim of the disc and the frontal limit of the primitive node; but it no longer is in the center of the disc. Obviously the considerable growth of the disc (only partly shown in the drawings) has occurred mainly below the primitive node. Through proliferation, and also by concrescence, the primitive streak has attained a total length of 0.3 to 0.4 mm. The streaming of blastemic cells follows the same general pattern as in birds (cf. Fig. 158), though there exists one important difference: In birds the blastema of the extra-embryonic mesoderm takes part in the concrescence, while in mammals it becomes independent at an early stage and develops directly, without passing through the primitive streak. From the rim of the embryonic disc (blastodisc), where some of its cells assume a mesenchymal character as early as stage 8 (Fig. 301*a*), this blastema grows into the trophoblast cavity. Presently it furnishes a continuous inner lining to the trophoblast, and covering mesoderm layers to amnion and yolk sac (Fig. 301*b*). Thus the exocelom and its membranes are at a fairly advanced stage of differentiation when concrescence of the remaining mesodermal blastema is only beginning (Fig. 301*c*). Their relative precocity involves not only a shift in the sequence of events (heterochrony) but also a radical change of the course and the mechanics of mesodermal development.

A section through a germ of the primitive streak stage embedded in the uterine endometrium offers an impressive picture of the enormous size and the advanced histologic differentiation of the *chorion* as compared with the embryo (St. 12, Fig. 302). The *chorionic villi* are up to 1 mm. high. They consist of a mesenchymal core, covered with both cellular and syncytial trophectoderm, and merge peripherally with the syncytial *trophoblast shell*. Though the histolytic breakdown of mucosa is still in progress, the presence of blood in the intervillous spaces indicates that a maternal blood flow through the placenta already has become established. The embryo, with *yolk sac* and *amnion*, remains attached to the chorion by means of the *body stalk*. In the mesoderm covering the yolk, but also in the mesenchyme of the body stalk and the chorionic villi, many *blood islands* and segments of endothelium-lined vascular plexuses have made their appearance (Fig. 303). It is noteworthy that the last named differentiate at a considerable distance from any endodermal structure. This supports the now most widely accepted notion of the *mesodermal origin of the blood cells and the endothelial system*. It also indicates that during the preceding stages the angioblastema was migrating and spreading from the edge of the embryonic disc, together with the mesenchyme.

Peripheral mesoderm penetrates also between the two original layers of the embryonic disc except in the region of the primitive streak

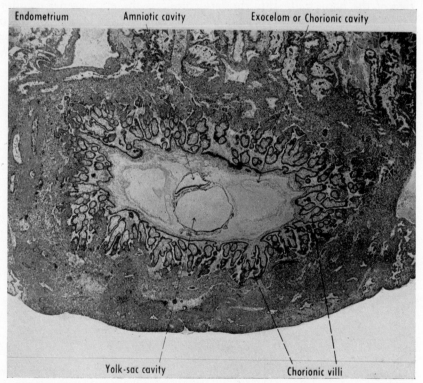

Figure 302. Primitive streak stage (St. 12); human germ with villous chorion, wide chorionic (exocelomic) cavity containing coagulated proteins. Mesodermal layer in embryonic disc; section cuts across the primitive streak; × 15 (Jones and Brewer 1941, Carnegie Contrib. 185).

(Fig. 303). Virtually the entire disc is supplied with a middle layer, at a stage when the primitive streak has barely started contributing toward mesoderm formation (Fig. 302).

After removal of the amnion, the surface of the *epiblast* appears round or slightly pear-shaped (St. 12, Fig. 301*e*). An easily recognizable *primitive groove* marks the sagittal plane of the tapering lower part of the disc. Above this, the center gently rises into the *primitive node* which, however, is continuous with the neural area and so poorly defined that its approximate borders may be determined only with the help of serial sections. Similarly ill defined is the *neural plate*, which has barely started histologic differentiation.

A sagittal section reveals that epiblast and hypoblast are intimately fused only in the node region (Fig. 303). Beneath the primitive groove the endoderm is only loosely attached to the streak. Probably this condition is a consequence of the early splitting of the rim, following formation of the amniotic and vitelline sacs.

Below the streak the amniotic cavity dips deeply toward the endodermal epithelium. This is the *area of the cloacal membrane*, at the *root of the body stalk*. Into the latter projects the endodermal *allantoic diverticulum*. It has developed by evagination from a thickening of the endodermal epithelium that first becomes noticeable at stage 11. Now it lies embedded in a mesenchymal condensation, which also contains some of the best differentiated vascular plexuses and blood islands.

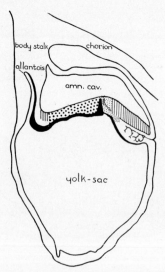

Figure 303. Reconstructed sagittal section through embryo of primitive streak stage (Fig. 302), with rudimentary invagination canal. Interpretation of embryonic disc: ectoderm (vertical lines), endoderm (black), node mesoderm (fine stipple), streak mesoderm (coarse stipple). Frontal ingrowth of mesoderm and angioblastema (modified, after Jones and Brewer 1941).

5. THE NEURULA STAGES: 0 TO 24 SOMITES (ST. 13–17)
(Chorionic Vesicles 8–22 mm.)

Embryo formation progresses through two easily distinguished periods. The first one or neurula period is characterized by *neural tube differentiation* through folding of the neural plate, and *mesodermal growth* by streak-invagination. Closure of the neural tube and disappearance of the primitive streak mark the transition to the second or tailbud period.

The development of the external body form is illustrated in the Figures 301*f* and 305–312. The embryo, first spread out flat in the embryonic disc, gradually folds off; though even at stage 17 its body is still quite broadly attached to the yolk sac. The upper *neuropore* closes at about 20 somites, the lower at 24 somites. The main body axes develop several *flexures,* which may be more or less characteristic for special stages, but are of temporary existence only. There is a remarkable tendency to form a concavity somewhat below the middle of the back (Figs. 310, 312). Moreover, the lowest part of the body of late neurulae is curved ventrally, which brings the cloacal membrane toward its final location and out of the course of tailbud formation. The *flexure of the midbrain* is most constant and for a long period assists in the recognition of the major segments of the upper head region. In the second half of this period the first *two visceral arches and grooves* make their appearance. The neurula period starts late in the third week and extends throughout the fourth week of development.

a. **Neural Plate and Neural Tube.**   The most obvious indication that a germ has developed beyond the primitive streak stage is the appearance of a slight swelling in the midline of the neural plate above the primitive node (Fig. 301*f*). It is caused by underlying axial mesoderm. In transparent preparations prechordal plate and notochord become plainly visible (St. 13, Fig. 304). At this stage the *neural plate,*

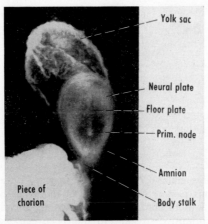

Figure 304.   Human presomite neurula (St. 13), 19 days; body stalk, embryonic shield and yolk sac; × 16 (Heuser 1932, Carnegie Contrib. 138).

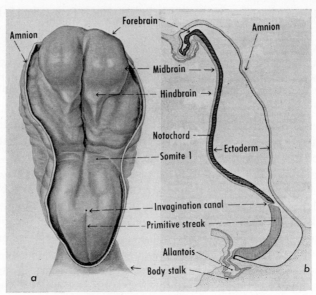

Figure 305.   Human neurula, 1 somite (St. 14). *a,* Dorsal aspect, chorion and amnion removed, open neural plate, formation of floor plate, 1st somite; *b,* reconstructed sagittal section; × 32 (Ludwig 1928).

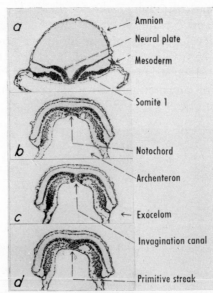

Figure 306.   Same embryo; four cross sections. *a,* Level of 1st somite, thin notochordal plate forms part of archenteric roof; *b,* between 1st somite and invagination canal; thick notochordal plate inserted in endoderm; *c,* through invagination canal; *d,* primitive streak. No limit between mesoderm from streak invagination and mesoderm immigrated from edge of the disc is recognizable; × 30.

having gained considerably in thickness, is a horseshoe-shaped primordium, with a broad, crescentic part in front of the primitive node
and tapering ends along the upper half of the primitive streak. The
embryonic epidermis forms the relatively narrow margin of the disc and
is best recognizable in cross sections (Fig. 306*a*–*d*).

By the end of the third week, the *head fold* rises above the plane of
the embryonic disc (St. 14, Fig. 305). Through the upper two-thirds
of the neural plate now runs a deep groove which broadens below into
the deltoid *floor plate* issuing from the *axial rudiment of the primitive
node*. The prosencephalic and mesencephalic parts of the neural plate
form common lateral lobes, one on each side, which bulge into the
amniotic cavity. The knee of this bend is the *cranial flexure,* landmark
of the midbrain. A minor lobe below the flexure belongs to the rhombencephalic plate, which in the general region of the later pontine
flexure bends deeply into the archenteric cavity (Fig. 305*b*). The
resulting dorsal concavity is found in the majority of embryos of all
neurula stages. Returning again to the general plane of the embryonic
disc, the neural plate bifurcates, and encloses between its limbs the
upper half of the primitive streak.

In slightly older embryos of four somites, the entire neural plate is
still open, but left and right rhombencephalic folds are approaching
each other.

Closure of the folds and formation of the *neural tube* starts in five-
or six-somite embryos at the border of brain and spinal cord. In the
seven- to eight-somite embryo described by Payne (Fig. 307) the tube
extends from the third to the seventh somites, remaining open through
an *upper* and a *lower neuropore*. From here on closure progresses

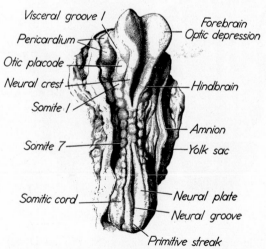

Figure 307.   Human neurula, 7 somites (St. 15a); dorsal aspect, with upper
    and lower neuropores; × 28 (Payne 1925, Carnegie Contrib. 81).

rapidly up and downward over brain and spinal tube. At 10 somites it has outdistanced somite formation, extending from the otic to the thoracic level (Fig. 308). In the 14-somite embryo shown in Figure 309 the upper neuropore lies at the mesencephalic flexure and the lower opens in the lumbar region. The prosencephalic folds still are far apart, leaving a gaping opening through which may be seen the inner grooves of the primordial *optic evaginations* and the inner walls of fore- and midbrain. In 16- to 18-somite embryos fusion nears the *crosswise frontal fold,* so that merely a small round opening is left (Fig. 312). Its closure at stages 17 (Fig. 310) marks the upper ends of the neural tube and of the embryo. Later the frontonasal process takes its origin from this region (cf. Fig. 330).

The neurula period comes to an end in embryos of about 24 somites and at the same time the *lower neuropore* closes. The neural tube is best differentiated in the rhombencephalic and cervical regions. At the upper and lower ends it is still incomplete, and large sections, the telen-

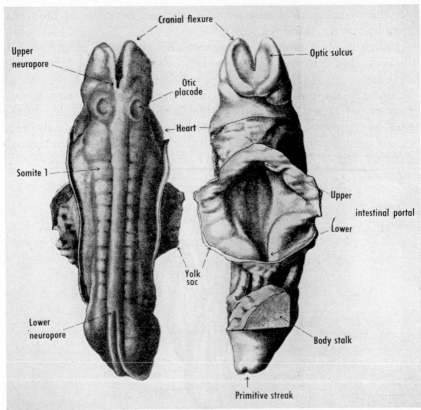

Figure 308.   Human neurula, 10 somites (St. 15b). *a,* Dorsal, *b,* ventral views;
× 18 (Ludwig 1929).

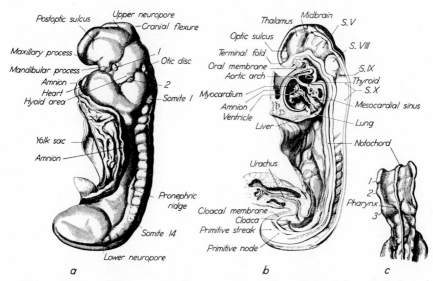

Figure 309.   Human neurula, 14 somites (St. 16); model. *a*, Left lateral aspect; *b*, right half from sagittal plane. *c*, Dorsal view of foregut, with notochord; × 29 (Heuser 1930, Carnegie Contrib. 131).

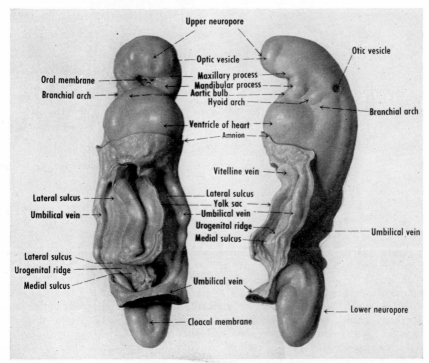

Figgure 310.   Human late neurula of 20 somites (St. 17); model, *a*, ventral view, *b*, left lateral view; × 22 (Davis 1923, Carnegie Contrib. 72).

cephalon and the lower half of the spinal cord, remain to be added
through formative growth from remaining blastemic centers.

b. **Primitive Streak, Notochord and Paraxial Mesoderm.**
Throughout the period of primitive streak formation (St. 10–12) the
primitive node is a solid mass of mesodermal blastema. Consequently
the roof of the archenteric vesicle becomes partly mesodermal. In the
course of the neurula stages 13 and 14 the node completes mesoderm
invagination and then shifts caudally, away from the animal pole. In

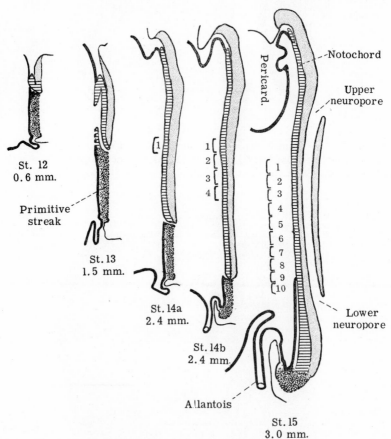

Figure 311.   Five stages in human development. Growth of embryo and
primitive streak. Sagittal sections. Midbrain curvature kept at constant level. Absolute length of primitive streak remains nearly the same, during this period. Longitudinal dimensions × 33, others not to scale. Neural ectoderm (fine stipple),
primitive streak mesoderm (coarse stipple), notochord and prechordal plate
(hatched), endoderm (heavy black); somite levels (1–10). St. 12: primitive streak
stage. St. 13–15: neurulae. *Invagination canal* open in 13 and 14a, early rudiment
in 12, disappearing in 14b. Notochord in roof of archenteron 12–14b; partly in
middle layer position in 15.

so doing, it leaves a double trail: the ectodermal *floor plate* in the neural groove and a *mesodermal cord,* which becomes inserted in the otherwise endodermal wall of the archenteron (Figs. 303, 305, 306*a, b,* 311). As its later history proves, the short tip of this cord is the *prechordal plate* (head mesenchyme) while its main body is the upper part of the *primitive notochord.* Growth is sustained by proliferation of the node blastema.

The occurrence of an *invagination canal* (chorda canal of some authors) is evidence of gastrulation, and gastrulation movements (St. 12–14; Figs. 301, 304, 305, 306*c,* 311). The canal has but a transitory existence, and in some embryos may never actually open. However, inasmuch as node blastema becomes a part of the hypoblast, the formation of the upper notochord presents a process of true gastrulation.

Usually the invagination canal closes in embryos of six to seven somites (St. 15). Future notochord production no longer becomes inserted into the archenteron but is laid down as an independent rod in the space between the roof of the endoderm and the neural plate (Fig. 311). Presently, the upper part of the chord also becomes free, and with its exclusion the archenteron transforms into a purely endodermal vesicle (Fig. 309*b, c*).

The *paraxial mesoderm* issues from the *primitive folds* by invagination and proliferation in much the same way as the notochord arises from the node. However, it never becomes a part of the hypoblast. Growing into the space between hypoblast and epiblast, it presently joins the mesoderm sheets from the rim of the embryonic disc (Fig. 306*d*) to form continuous layers on either side of primitive streak and notochord. It is not fused with the latter but loose contacts are maintained through mesenchymal cell bridges. The exact border between *rim-mesoderm* and *streak-mesoderm* in terms of later derivatives has not been ascertained. It seems beyond doubt that the celomic epithelia are produced by the former, the somites by the latter. Possibly the entire segmented mesoderm may develop from the streak. The fate maps shown in Figure 313 review the course of the morphogenic movements and their relation to differentiation in the mammalian embryonic discs.

c. **Endoderm.**   Even before the end of the neurula stages the *endodermal vesicle* differentiates into three distinct parts: *foregut, yolk sac, and hindgut* (Fig. 312). The first meets the ectoderm in the *oral membrane* which ruptures at stage 17 (Fig. 310). Three pairs of pharyngeal pouches also approach the ectodermal surface. Ventral pharyngeal pockets are the primordia of the *thyroid* and the *laryngo-tracheal-pulmonary complex* (Fig. 309). The dorsal longitudinal ridge over the wide opening of the yolk sac begins to differentiate into a roof of the *midgut.* Diverticula growing from the upper root of the yolk sac into the transverse septum below the heart form the *liver primor-*

dium (Fig. 312). The hindgut approaches the ectoderm in the *cloacal membrane*. From its ventral wall the *allantoic diverticulum* projects into the mesenchyme of the body stalk (Figs. 303, 311, 312).

d. Comparative Consideration of Primordial Differentiation in Vertebrates.   Before continuing the description of stages of human development it seems timely to pause and evaluate some of the presented facts on human embryo formation in the light of our knowledge gained from the study of lower forms.

Germ-layer formation follows the same general principles in the mammals as in the other chordates. However, progress toward direct development was achieved through relaxation of the ancestral routine of morphogenic movements. Beginning with teleosts and sharks, an evolutionary change occurred from rigid tactical maneuvering of interlocked blastemic areas, to more individualized migrations of cells and cell groups, with short cuts toward their places of differentiation. In *teleosts* the entire mesoderm including the angioblastema participates in concrescence and moves with the other prospective mesoderm areas into the primitive streak (blastopore). The circulatory system of the yolk sac consequently forms by outgrowth from the embryo. However, in *selachians, birds,* and *mammals* much of the angioblastema separates from the rim of the embryonic disc (blastodisc). Omitting the entire round trip through the primitive streak, these cells begin *in loco* their

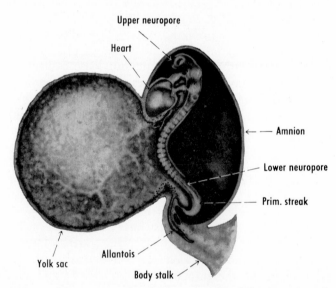

Figure 312.   Human neurula of 16 somites (St. 16), about 4 weeks; without chorion; reconstruction; × 14 (Witschi 1948, Carnegie Contrib. 209). Two visceral arches; the first aortic arch contains blood, indicating that circulation was established. Left umbilical vein, transected below allantoic stalk, again shown where it joins left vitelline vein before entering the venous sinus. Black dots in hindgut and yolk sac indicate location of primordial germ cells.

differentiation into the vascular plexuses that later produce the extra-embryonic system of blood vessels and the first generation of blood cells (Figs. 134, 160, 169c). Finally, in the *mammals* large parts of lateral mesoderm likewise emancipate themselves and develop *directly* into extra-embryonic and embryonic celomic epithelia (Figs. 301, 313). In sheep and most other species with large primary yolk sacs the outgrowing mesoderm carries the angioblastema only to the vitelline membranes. The supply of the chorionic villi occurs at a relatively late stage by branching allantoic vessels. In primates and particularly in man the diffusely spreading mesoderm disperses the vascular blastema throughout the blastocyst cavity (St. 9, Figs. 298, 301b). Consequently, blood islands organize independently in the chorionic villi and the body stalk, as well as over the surface of the small yolk sac (Fig. 301c). The common trait of these evolutionary changes is the tendency toward simplification through *direct development*.

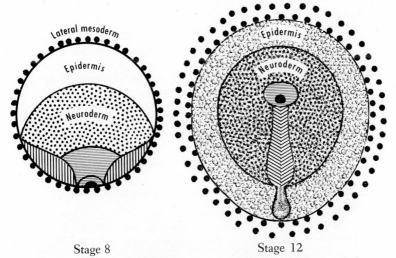

Stage 8   Stage 12

Figure 313.   Fate maps of human embryonic discs. Epidermis (white, transparent), neuroderm (heavy stipple), notochord and prechordal mesoderm (hatched horizontally), somitic mesoderm (hatched vertically or slanting), lateral mesoderm (black dots around the edge of the disc, or bubble structure, if seen through ectodermal surface layer); surface endoderm (black).

Stage 8, early gastrula: *Prospective endoderm* reaches up into the dorsal rim of the epiblast (compare Figs. 130, 159). *Loose mesoderm cells* around edge of the disc represent lateral plate mesoderm and angioblastema.

Stage 12, primitive streak stage (compare with sagittal sections, Figs. 303, 311): The *epiblastic endoderm* lies now in the primitive node, probably below the surface (participating in formation of invagination canal). The *primitive streak*, below the somitic area (stippled), is relatively inconspicuous in mammals (cf. Fig. 304). The *lateral mesoderm* does not invaginate, but spreads peripherally, giving rise to the exocelom; it also penetrates between epiblastic and hypoblastic layers of the embryonic shield (bubbles in figure), where it differentiates into embryonic lateral plates and vascular system.

The *primitive streak is a derivative of the blastopore*. While in *ascidians* and *Amphioxus* gastrulation starts with invagination movements from the vegetal pole, in *amphibians* it begins at some point nearer the equator on the dorsal side of the blastula, progressing only slowly to the lateral and ventral sides. As a consequence there develops a *time gradient of differentiation*. At stage 10 blastema cells, accumulating in the dorsal lip, initiate primitive node formation; that is, at a time when ventrally, gastrulation is barely starting (Fig. 39). After withdrawal of the yolk plug, when the lateral blastopore lips move together, the time gradient persists in the primitive streak, the upper levels preceding the lower ones in further development and differentiation.

As eggs get larger and concrescence of the lower blastopore lips becomes relatively more delayed, the differences in the developmental status of upper and lower body regions assume greater proportions. Special controls develop which retard or suspend embryonic determination and differentiation in the open blastoporal lips.

A comparison with certain abnormal occurrences in frog development proves that this deferment is a very necessary adaptation. Under a number of experimental conditions, frog gastrulae form an unusually large yolk plug; consequently, closure of the blastopore is retarded (Fig. 314a). In external appearance the abnormal neurula at stage 16 resembles the corresponding stages in normal shark and trout development (cf. Figs. 134 and 140). Yet the specific time gradients of the frog permit differentiation to proceed independently in the separated blastopore lips. *Caudal duplications* or more localized *bifid spine* defects result (Fig. 314b, c), de-

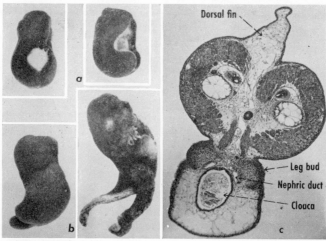

Figure 314.   Delayed closure of blastopore in the frog and axial duplications. *a,* Neurulae of stage 16, from overripe eggs. *Closure of blastopore* is outrun by differentiation processes of the neurula stages. *b, Caudal duplications* at stages 18 and 22 that develop from such embryos (Witschi 1952). *c, Bifid spine,* duplication extending only over a limited part of the back; develops from moderately inhibited concrescence.

pending on the size of the yolk plug. As in teleosts, each blastoporal lip is competent to produce more than a mere half-embryo by a process of supplementation, called *post-generation*. As in amphibians, likewise in mammals and man spina bifida and axial duplications in the lower body region result from abnormal delay of concrescence at the primitive streak and early neurula stages.

The *mammalian egg* was secondarily reduced to the size of that of *Amphioxus* and of ascidians; but far from returning to a primitive type of gastrulation, it has evolved the *most direct mode of streak development*. With the precocious development of the extra-embryonic membranes, blastopore formation has become abolished. The primitive streak arises by the accumulation of blastemic cells at the dorsal rim of the germ disc. Only in a very generalized sense can this disc still be likened to the blastodisc of the chick. The morphogenic movements during streak development of mammals show a resemblance to those in other vertebrates only in the axial and paraxial parts. *Concrescence is reduced to a minimum.*

The changing aspect and importance of morphogenic movements, and their reduction in the mammals, suggest that originally the translocations serve in the rearrangement of diversified materials including inductor substances and enzymes. But the movements in themselves do not assume the role of inductive agents. The highly variable character of the morphogenic movements, concrescence, invagination, and ingression, assigns them a rather subordinate role in embryonic differentiation.

It may be expected that future experimental work on mammalian embryos will reveal even greater independence of blastemic cells from ancestral patterns than now known. This must significantly bear upon some aspects of the *concepts of specificity* and of *structural organization* of eggs and germs. However, in spite of the great variability in the mechanics of their production, *the tailbud embryos* that emerge at the end of the neurula stages *are of a surprisingly uniform pattern in all vertebrate classes.* Evidently even quite radical evolutionary changes in early ontogenesis do not necessarily modify all later stages or even the final character of the species.

Chapter 27

Human Development. II

6. THE TAILBUD STAGES: 25 TO 38 SOMITES (ST. 18–29)
(Chorionic Vesicles 20–30 mm.)

a. Tailbud. Transition from the neurula to the tailbud stages is marked by an important change in the method of segmental proliferation. The remnant *primitive streak* becomes included in a *tailbud*. Composition and morphogenic capacities of this bud can best be understood by a close examination of the process of its formation. At stage 17 (Figs. 310, 311) the lower end of the embryo is usually curved so that the short primitive streak lies nearly crosswise to the embryonic axis, extending from the closing neuropore to the cloacal field. The primitive folds have become continuous with the neural folds. Ventrally they fuse just before reaching the cloacal field. At the transition to stage 18 the closure of the neuropore is immediately followed by the union also of the left and right primitive folds. The epidermis, rushing in from all sides, covers the thus formed cone of neural and mesodermal blastema. At the place of closure, the blastema remains attached to the epidermis. Sections through tailbuds (Fig. 315) show that its core contains the roots of the three axial organs: tailgut, notochord, and neural tube. They are closely attached to each other where they emerge as histologically differentiated structures from the blastema. The

480

paraxial and the lateral mesoderm differentiate relatively late, and thus for some distance their blastema forms a mantle around the lateral and ventral sides of the axial organs. Although morphologically uniform, the blastema cells of the tailbud certainly are not all of the same developmental potentiality. However, no experimental analysis has yet been made that would shed light on the dynamics of differentiation in mammalian tailbuds.

b. Mesoderm Formation. So far four types of mesoderm formation have been described and a fifth one will now have to be added. To characterize them briefly we distinguish:

TYPE 1. *Direct mesoderm differentiation* from the embryoblast at the rim of the germ disc, starting as early as stage 8. *Derivatives:* extraembryonic mesenchyme, mesothelia, and angioblastema; embryonic lateral plates.

TYPE 2. *Mesoderm formation by gastrulation-invagination and secondary separation from the hypoblast,* during stages 12 to 14. *Derivatives:* prechordal plate and upper part of notochord.

TYPE 3. *Mesoderm formation by invagination through the primitive streak into the blastocelic cleft,* during stages 12 to 17. *Derivatives:* middle part of notochord, largest part of the paraxial and intermediate mesoderm.

TYPE 4. *Mesoderm formation from the tailbud,* during stages 18 to 25. *Derivatives:* lowest part of notochord, caudal paraxial and lateral mesoderm.

TYPE 5. *Ectomesenchyme proliferation from the neural crest.* The

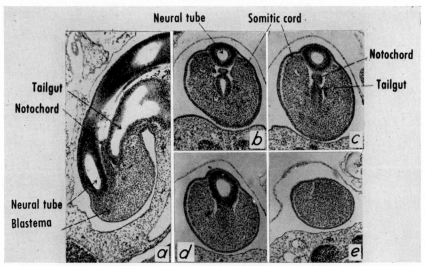

Figure 315. Armadillo, tailbud embryo (St. 18). *a,* Sagittal section through actively proliferating tailbud; *b* to *e,* cross sections through tailbud of an identical twin embryo; fusion of lower tip of notochord with floor plate of neural tube is seen in *a* and in *d;* × 40.

formation of mesoderm from this source in mammals is more or less accepted by inference from observations on lower forms, mainly amphibians. The formation and proliferation of neural crests in human embryos were described by Bartelmez and Evans, and the role of crest

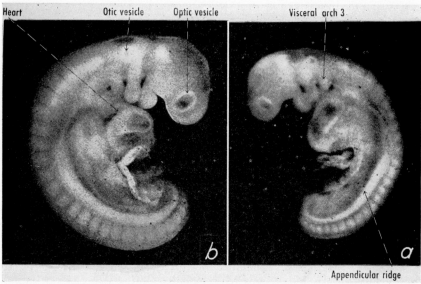

Figure 316.   Human early tailbud embryos; a, 25 somites (St. 18); b, 28 somites (St. 19). Well separated visceral arches I, II, III, visceral clefts 1, 2, 3; (Streeter 1942, Carnegie Contrib. 197); both × 15.

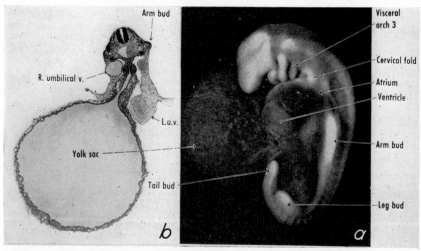

Figure 317.   Human tailbud embryo, 30 somites (St. 20a). a, Left lateral view; narrowing yolk stalk; four visceral arches, cervical fold (Streeter 1945, Carnegie Contrib. 199); × 12. b, Cross section, level of yolk stalk, open connection of yolk sac with midgut (courtesy Carnegie Inst.); × 15.

cells in the development of the cranial and spinal ganglia is well known. But actual descriptive or experimental evidence for participation in the formation of the cartilaginous skeleton of the head or the meninges of brain and spinal cord is scanty. Nevertheless the probability that the neural crests of mammalian embryos contribute to mesoderm formation much as in the lower vertebrates is generally admitted.

c. **General Development.**   In human embryos tailbud prolifera-

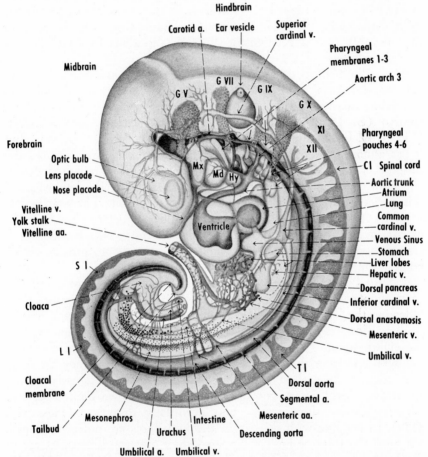

Figure 318.   Reconstruction, human tailbud embryo of 32 somites (St. 20b); 4½ weeks; × 25. GV–GX, Ganglia of corresponding cranial nerves; XI, XII, roots of accessory and hypoglossal nerves. C1, Ganglion of first cervical nerve; T1 of first thoracic nerve; L1 of first lumbar nerve; S1 of first sacral nerve. Mx, Md: Maxillary and mandibular processes of first visceral arch; Hy, Hyoid arch. (Pointers to pharyngeal membranes 2 and 3 are not completely carried through.) Black dots on lower gut, mesentery, and mesonephros represent loci of primordial germ cells.

The basilar and vertebral arteries are not yet organized, but along the base of the brain some small arterial branches are present which will contribute to their formation. Compare with Frontispiece, color reproduction.

tion is in progress throughout the fifth week, increasing the number of somites to 38. During this time the back curves in the shape of a letter C, and usually it assumes also a slight lateral twist that results in a flat spiral, with the tail deviating to the right side (Figs. 316, 319). This spiral develops after the connection of the embryo with the yolk sac has narrowed to a slender stalk (Fig. 317a, b) that permits the embryo to rotate on its side. Most mammalian embryos—like the chick—turn their left side toward the yolk sac and the right toward the allantois or the body stalk (Fig. 319). However, there are numerous exceptions to this rule (e.g., Fig. 317). It would be interesting to know whether they possibly bear a relationship to such variations in asymmetry as left-handedness.

The tailbud stages carry on with differentiations started during neurulation, but also bring a number of new developments. The *oral membrane* disappears at the outset of this period. The younger tailbud embryos (St. 18, 19) have only three distinct *visceral arches and clefts* (Fig. 316). In older ones a fourth arch is added (St. 20, Fig. 317), but it lies almost hidden in the depth of the depression that becomes the *cervical sinus*. The *optic bulb* partly constricts the brain and gradually transforms into an *optic cup* (Fig. 318); during the late stages of this period the *lens placode* begins its invagination. The *otic vesicle* separates from the epidermis (Fig. 318) and the *olfactory placode* makes its appearance. The *ganglia* of the fifth, seventh, ninth, and tenth cranial nerves grow into large bodies that become externally visible bulges (Fig. 318).

d. Paired Appendages are, next to the tailbud, the most distinctive acquisition of this period. They begin their development immediately following the last neurula stage. Embryos of 25 somites show a definite swelling along each side of the body, beginning at the ventral edge of the eighth somite (Fig. 316). These lateral ridges consist of blastemic proliferations from the parietal lateral mesoderm. Since they are early primordia of the paired appendages, they may be designated as *appendicular ridges*. Very soon they grow higher in two limited regions, while otherwise they flatten, and eventually disappear (Figs. 317, 319c). In keeping with this origin the limb buds are not cone-shaped, but have the form of fin-like flippers. Their greatest dimensions are at the base, where they rise from the primordial ridges (Figs. 316, 317, 319c). At stage 20 (Fig. 317) the armbuds extend along somites 8 to 13, the legbuds along 24 to 30. Both shift later in the caudal direction, but their innervation (Fig. 318) always reflects the original position.

7. THE FULLY FORMED EMBRYO: 6–7 MM., 38 SOMITES (ST. 25)
(Chorionic Vesicle 28–35 mm.)

By the end of the fifth week the developmental history of the human embryo reaches a veritable turning point. Construction of the body has

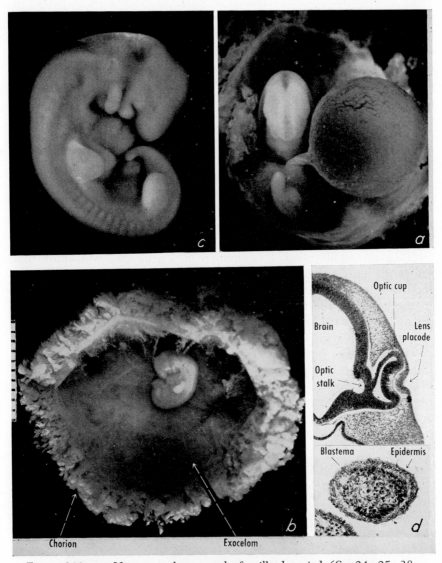

Figure 319.   Human embryos, end of tailbud period (St. 24, 25; 38 somites). *a,* Within part of chorionic vesicle; ventral view; yolk stalk and yolk sac turned to the left, allantoic stalk to the right (Streeter 1945, Carnegie Contrib. 199); × 7½. *b,* Attached by umbilical cord, within chorionic vesicle; villi cover entire surface; × 2.6. *c,* Same embryo, viewed from right side. Regressing tailbud; four aortic arches; cervical fold; otic and optic cups; large armbuds and legbuds; × 9. *d,* Same embryo; above, section through optic cup and invaginating lens placode; × 37.5; below, cross section through tip of tail, showing regression of blastema; × 128.

come to an end, and the embryo prepares to embark on a period of extensive rebuilding of already laid-out parts, designated as *metamorphosis*. At the present stage, it has the generalized structure of fishes and amphibian larvae, though most of their particular adaptations to the aquatic environment do not attain functional state. Also, reptiles, birds, and mammals are more like each other at this stage than at any other. Even such exceptionally constructed animals as the snakes are, at this stage of their life, still remarkably close to the fundamental structural type. Proliferation of the tailbud often continues beyond stage 25. In human embryos, the bud-like swelling characteristically shrinks at this time and the short tail acquires a slender, filamentous end. Sections show a general regression or absence of blastema within the epidermal sheath (Fig. 319*d*). In the otherwise strikingly similar embryo of the monkey, the terminal knob persists (Fig. 320) and continues production of tail segments for about another week. At stage 28, depletion of the tailbud sets in and later growth is by diffuse and not by terminal proliferation. Examination of Figure 262 will show that tail formation continues in the rat even to fetal stage 34, when finally the characteristic shrinkage of the tip occurs (St. 35e, Fig. 262). Since in the adult rat the tail is physiologically important as a temperature regulator, it seems probable that this is an example of a secondarily extended formative period.

The first and second occipital somites are externally not visible. Otherwise the complete somitic series may be recognizable, especially in preserved specimens. The *armbuds* have shifted downward, the upper attachment now lying at the root of the ninth somite. They still are flipper-shaped as are also the *buds of the legs* (Fig. 319*c*). The prominent *heart bulge* contains the coiled, but still single, tubular heart.

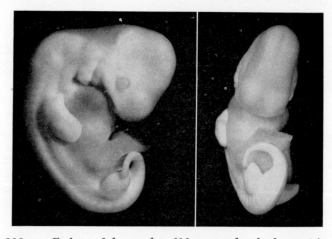

Figure 320.   Embryo of the monkey (*Macaca mulatta*) of stage 26, with continuing tailbud proliferation (Heuser and Streeter 1941, Carnegie Contrib. 181);
× 6.

The photographs show clearly the furrows between venous sinus, atrium, and ventricles. Below the heart, partly hidden beneath the arm-buds, one recognizes the *liver*. The *abdominal bulge* rises to the *umbilicus*. This latter may bifurcate within the tail spiral, the yolk stalk turning to the left, the allantoic stalk to the right (Fig. 319*a*).

The *venous sinus* is formed by the confluence of three major veins, the upper and lower cardinals and the lower caval. The last one collects within the liver the returns from the vitelline, mesenteric, and umbilical venous systems (Fig. 318). The swelling of the *cervical fold* containing the upper cardinal vein is considerably enlarged by an accompanying massive cord of epibranchial ganglia. The last visceral arches get almost buried under this broad welt. The first or *mandibular arch* is V-shaped, the shorter limb representing the upper jaw or maxillary process. The longer one, the mandibular process, is the primordium of the lower jaw and the chin. The very distinct swelling above the angle of this arch is caused by the development of the trigeminal ganglion (compare Figs. 319*c*, 318, and frontispiece). The second or *hyoid arch* with its distinct dorsal and ventral segments is accompanied by the ganglial complex of the facial nerve, composed of a dorsal root and an epibranchial component. The third and the fourth, which are the first two *branchial arches,* are similarly related to the ganglia of the glossopharyngeal and vagal nerves. The combined nerve cell and fiber track of the vagus and accessory nerves is distinctly visible in the photograph of the right side (Fig. 319*c*).

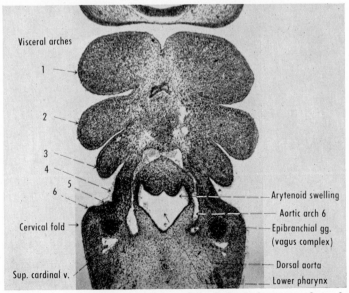

Figure 321.   Same embryo as Fig. 319*b–d;* frontal section through ventral parts of the six visceral arches and the cervical folds. The ventral aortas are cut at the roots of the fourth aortic arches; × 40.

The *fifth and sixth visceral arches* develop only slight external ridges. They are bent laterally, by the development of the above mentioned *cervical fold* rising from the cardiac bulge. They are best seen in a frontal section cutting through the ventral part of the visceral arch region (Fig. 321). The epibranchial ganglia cord passes along these two rudimentary arches and continues, as a tissue condensation, toward the primitive trachea and its pulmonary diverticula.

The condition of the *vascular system* will be considered separately (Chapter 28). The arrangement of the aortic arches resembles most closely that of the larval frog.

In discussions on the *evolutionary implications* of the piscine structural type of the human and other amniote embryos, the importance of the visceral arches has often been questioned. In human development

Fig. 322

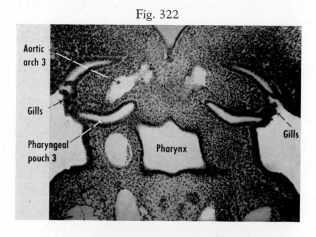

Fig. 323

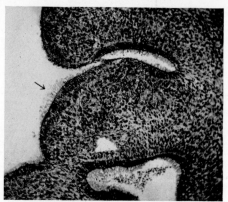

Figure 322.   Vestigial filamentous gills on the third visceral arches of a rabbit embryo of 12 days (St. 25); × 60.

Figure 323.   Third visceral arch of same embryo as Fig. 319c (St. 25). Ciliated and presumably endodermal epithelium (arrow) covering outside surface; × 100.

they function as primordia of structurally diversified adult parts and organs. Therefore their presence could be considered as necessary on dynamic grounds. However, it is of considerable interest that some of the most striking atavisms have no apparent functional importance in individual development. It was mentioned earlier that Boyden discovered the transitory formation of gill rudiments on the visceral arches of birds. Similar ephemeral gills are sometimes seen also in mammalian embryos, particularly in rabbits (Fig. 322). These stubby vestiges are partly or entirely formed through proliferation of the thickened endodermal lining of the third and fourth pharyngeal pouches. It was pointed out that in frogs, and probably in all gill-carrying animals, the surface epithelia of the filaments consist partly, or entirely, of endoderm. Judging from the thickness and the high mitotic index of large parts of the epithelia covering the branchial arches and much of the cervical sinus, they also seem to be of endodermal origin. In human embryos the endodermal epithelium of the pharyngeal pouches is very thick and strongly ciliated. The same type of epithelium also covers large parts of the outer surfaces of the branchial arches (Fig. 323) but never those of the maxillary or the hyoid. Another piscine feature that could hardly be of importance for future organogenesis is the temporary opening of some of the gill clefts through breakdown of the thin closure membranes (Fig. 321). All these spurious and short-lived developments are hard to interpret on other than evolutionary principles.

One may, however, admit that the embryo at best is a very imperfect fish. Its sense organs and the central nervous system have not attained a functional level. Olfactory pits, lens sac, eye bulb, and otic vesicles are only dimly visible, either directly or through the transparent, unpigmented skin. These shortcomings are understandable as adaptations to existent conditions. The embryo floats, fully protected and cared for, in the hollow of its own nutritional, respiratory, and excretory organ, the *villous chorion,* which now has an outside diameter of about 32 mm. (Fig. 319*b*). Through the production of chorionic hormones it even controls essential functions of the maternal body. Most of all this embryo is to furnish evidence of its true higher organization through its further development.

8. METAMORPHOSIS FROM EMBRYO TO FETUS: 7–24 MM.
(ST. 26–33)
(Chorionic Vesicle 30–60 mm., 6th to 8th Weeks)

The changes subsequent to the attainment of the final embryonic stage follow the pattern set by the amphibians in their metamorphosis from the aquatic to the terrestrial phase. However, there occur some important deviations which can be referred to two major sources. The first is common to all amniotes and concerns the necessary *adaptations to the conditions of fetal life.* With few exceptions such as presented by the opossum, metamorphosis does not lead to actual terrestrial life but to a more or less extended fetal period during which free locomotion, pulmonary respiration, oral food intake, and urinary excretion are partly or completely suspended.

The second group of deviations derives from a widespread tendency of pre-dating, and projecting into the metamorphic period, the first appearance of characters which in the evolutionary sense belong to later stages. An example of such *heterochrony* was presented in the developmental history of the mammary glands (Chapter 23). Their primordia appear during the early metamorphic stages (St. 26), even though in the evolutionary history of the mammals they must have originated at the late reptilian or at the mammalian level. Heterochronies of this type are so numerous, that the result of metamorphosis is not an amphibian type of fetus, but a multitude of reptilian, avian, and mammalian fetuses, all exhibiting many particular specific traits. Comparison of the stages 33 or 34 of sparrows (Fig. 206), of rats (Fig. 262), and of human fetuses (Figs. 327, 328) will bear out this point in regard to external appearance. Closer anatomic study would likewise fail to produce a common amphibian-like type. In view of the large number of pre-datings into this developmental period, it is significant that few, if any, specifically mammalian or avian characteristics make their appearance at premetamorphic stages.

The series of embryos shown in Figures 324 to 328 illustrates the profound changes that occur in the short period of 2½ or 3 weeks.

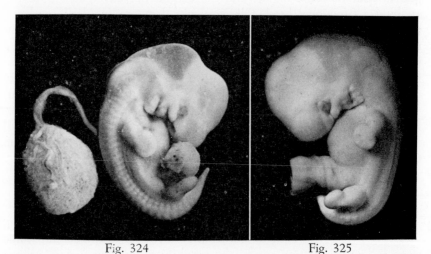

Fig. 324   Fig. 325

Figure 324.   Human embryo in early metamorphosis (St. 27) (Carnegie, no. 792); × 6.

Figure 325.   Human embryo in mid-metamorphosis (St. 28) (Streeter 1948, Carnegie Contrib. 211); × 4.4

a. Locomotor Organs.   Right at the start of metamorphosis, each appendicular bud differentiates into a cylindric stem, and a flat hand or foot plate (St. 27, Fig. 324). By stage 28 (Fig. 325) the development of the cartilaginous skeleton has progressed so far that the pentadactyl organization of these plates become externally recognizable. As fingers and toes grow, the rim of the plates becomes notched. At the approach of the fetal stage the feet retain their original orientation, the plantar surfaces usually apposed to each other. The forearms and hands rotate, turning their volar sides toward the chest (Figs. 327, 328).

At the end of the metamorphic period, the limbs are relatively short, histologically immature, and still below the functional level. This obvious retardation must be causally related to their non-use. Not only the legs of amphibians, but also the arms of the opossum, are much larger and fully functional at corresponding stages of development (Fig. 266).

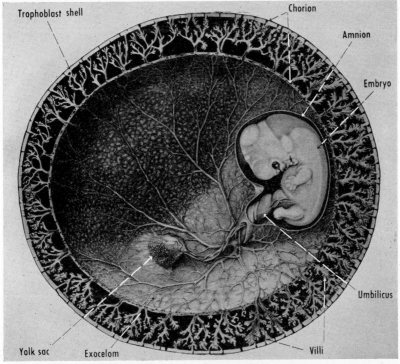

Figure 326.   Human embryo in mid-metamorphosis (St. 29). Chorionic villi on the side opposite to the attachment of the embryo begin to shrink; spaces between the villi shown in black are filled with maternal blood; peripheral *shell of syntrophoblast* with pores for entrance and exit of maternal blood. Yolk sac still supplied by vitelline vessels. The much larger umbilical vessels supply the villi; × 2.5.

b. Visceral Arches and Formation of the Face.   In amphibians
the change from branchial to pulmonary respiration involves an extensive reconstruction of the visceral part of the head. Metamorphosis
in mammals, even though the functional aspects have been lost, still
follows the same course and, at the end, the fetus emerges with a *new
face*. A comparison of stages 20 (Fig. 317), 25 (Fig. 319c), and 26
(Fig. 324) shows that the opercular fold of the second or hyoid arch
encroaches more and more upon the cervical sinus. Growing toward
the cervical fold, it fills the shallow depressions and buries the third
and all following arches.

The frontal transformations are represented in the series of drawings
of Figure 330. In the construction of the face the first two visceral
arches are joined by a proliferation from the very frontal end of the
head, the *frontal ridge*. The latter originates in the region where, at
stage 17, the upper neuropore closed (Fig. 330a); its area extends
laterally between the nasal placodes and the telencephalic bulges (Fig.
330b). This location suggests that the blastemic substance of the ridge
may be derived from the neural crest. As the nasal placodes transform
into deep pits and move toward the midplane, they become walled in
by *lateral* and *median nasal processes* of the frontal ridge. The septum

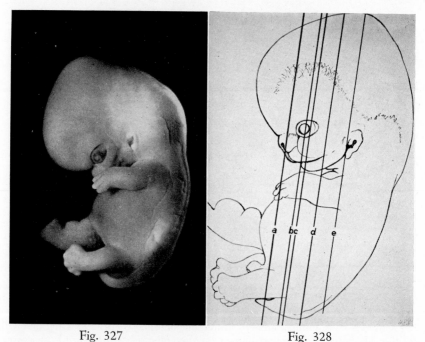

Fig. 327   Fig. 328

Figure 327.   Human embryo, 17 mm., near end of metamorphosis (St. 32)
                  (Carnegie, no. 6150); × 3.8.
Figure 328.   Human embryo, 23 mm., at end of metamorphosis (St. 33)
                  (Carnegie, no. 966); × 3.6.

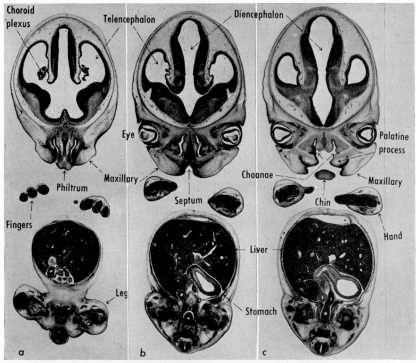

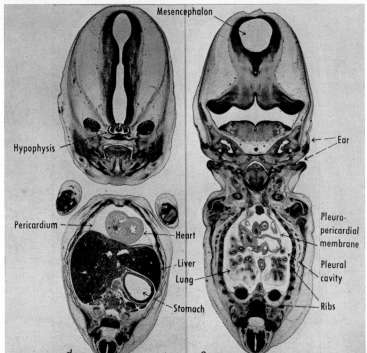

Figure 329.   Same embryo (St. 33), five frontal sections, planes indicated in Fig. 328; × 6.

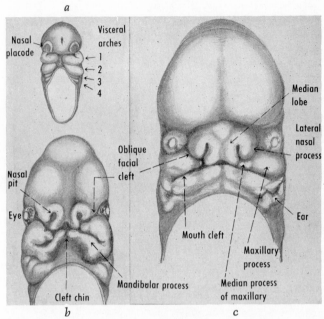

Figure 330.   Formation of human face during metamorphosis; *a*, stage 25; *b*, stage 29; *c*, stage 31.

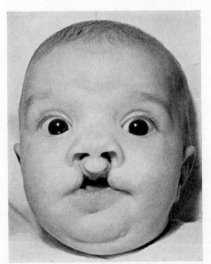

Figure 331.   Bilateral harelip and cleft palate in a child (courtesy State University of Iowa, University Hospitals).

between them forms the *nasal septum* and, near its root, the tip of the nose (Fig. 330*b*, *c*).

The mandibular arches contribute extensively to the formation of the ears as well as all parts surrounding the mouth—except the upper central region. From each upper segment a *maxillary process* grows in, with a broad base below the eyes and a much more slender terminal piece that fits under the lateral nasal process and projects toward the median process (Fig. 330*b*). The former contributes the bulk of the upper half of the *cheek*, the latter, the lateral part of the *upper lip*. The lower segments of the mandibular arches similarly grow a pair of *mandibular processes*, which meet directly in the midplane and thus produce the entire lower jaw and the chin. The angular middle section of the mandibular arch takes an independent course, contributing *helix* and *tragus* to the formation of the external ear or *auricle*. The larger part of the auricle, however, develops on the basis of adjoining sectors of the *hyoid arch*. Between the two is located the *external ear duct* (external auditory meatus), a derivative of the first visceral groove.

In the last steps of the formation of the upper lip, a downgrowth from the median nasal processes and the septum forms a wedge between the maxillary processes. The remaining *naso-stomodeal clefts* (Fig. 330*b*, *c*) close superficially at about the seventh week; but under these tissue bridges, each nasal cavity remains in communication with the oral cavity by inner nasal openings, the *choanae*. These openings are shifted deeper toward the throat through the development of the *palatine processes* from the maxillae (Fig. 329*c*). If they fail to join with the nasal septum from both sides, a gaping hole, a so-called *palatine cleft*, results as in the child shown in Figure 331. The outer openings, *nostrils* or *nares*, become temporarily closed by *periderm plugs* at the start of the fetal period (Fig. 333).

The lines of fusion between the maxillary and the frontonasal components of the upper lip usually rise as ridges that become very distinct at later fetal stages. The center piece thereby becomes a shallow groove, called *philtrum*. If fusion fails to be completed during metamorphosis, the cleft remains permanently open, a relatively frequent malformation known as *harelip*. This and other facial malformations resulting from developmental failure during this important period are illustrated in Figure 330.

9. THE HUMAN FETUS: 26–320 MM. (ST. 34–36)
(Chorionic Vesicle 50–350 mm., 9th to 38th Weeks)

The long fetal period of human development (30 weeks) is embryologically not very eventful, particularly if compared with the first eight weeks. The proposed distinction of three stages is based on the external appearance of the fetuses. At termination of metamorphosis the human shape and organization is well established (Fig. 328). But now follows a remarkable process of *closing and plugging of the external orifices,* especially those of the sense organs. It has been referred to above in the description of fetal development in the rat. In the species with nest young, the peridermal seals obviously serve the purpose of protecting the helpless offspring from sensory upset, mechanical injury and infection. No corresponding functional importance can be attributed to them in the human, and other species with extended

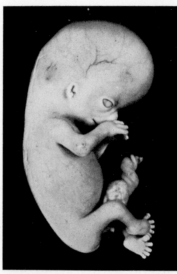

Figure 332.   Human fetus shortly after metamorphosis; crown-rump 32 mm. (St. 34). Growing eyelids, but eyes still open (Carnegie, no. 5154).

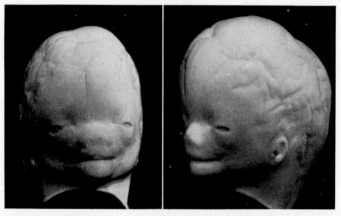

Figure 333.   Human fetus, 37 mm., closing eyelids (late St. 34); periderm plugs in nostrils and ears; note composition of upper lip by philtrum and median maxillary processes; × 2.8.

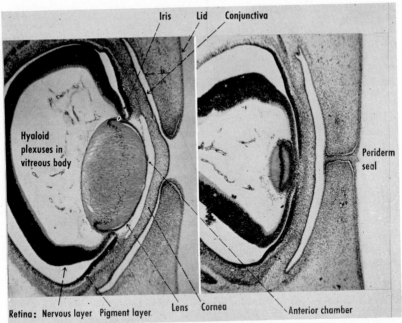

Figure 334.   Same fetus as in preceding figure, parasagittal sections through the head. *a,* More lateral section through eye with lids still open; *b,* more median section through part with closed lids and periderm seal; both × 36.

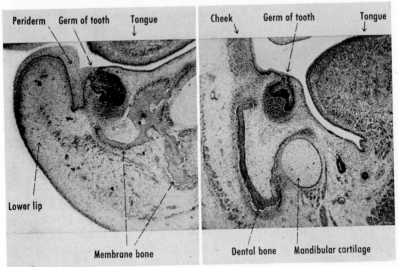

Figure 335.   Same fetus as in Fig. 333. *a,* Parasagittal section; *periderm* formation covering lower lip and part of the jaw, filling also the enamel sac of the primordial tooth (incisor). *b,* Frontal section (here almost cross section) through tongue, lower jaw and cheek; Meckel's cartilage cross sectioned, *membranous bone formation* (dental), and primordium of premolar tooth (first dentition); × 36.

Table 31

Stages of Human Development

Stage	Size mm.*	Weight	Age in Days	Text Fig.	Characterization	Reference	Streeter *Horizons*
					Cleavage and Blastula (free stages)		
1	0.125	1 μg.	1	292	1st division	Menkin, Rock '48 Shettles '53	I
2	0.115		2	293 294	2 cells	Menkin, Rock '48 Hertig et al. '54	II
3					4 cells		II
4	0.100		3	294	8–12 cells, morula	Hertig et al. '54	II
5	0.101		4	294	Early blastocyst (58 cells)	Hertig et al. '54	III
6	0.095		4½	294	Free blastocyst (107 cells)	Hertig et al. '54	III
7					Attachment		III
					Gastrula (implantation)		
8	0.05 (0.30)		7–8	297	Bilaminar disc	Hertig, Rock '45	IV
9	0.1 (0.5)		9	298	Ex. embr. mesoderm	Hertig, Rock '45	V
10	0.15 (1.0)		11–13	299	Beginning streak	Hertig, Rock '41	VI
11	0.3 (2.5)		14–17	300	Half length streak	Heuser, Rock, Hertig '45	VII
					Primitive Streak		
12	0.7 (8)		19	302	Complete streak	Jones-Brewer '41	VIII
					Neurula		
13	1.5 (12)		20	304	Presomite N.	Heuser '32	IX
14	2.0 (13)		22	305	Occip. somites 1–4	Ludwig '28 Sternberg '27	X
15	2.8 (16)	1 mg.	24	307 308	Cervical somites 5–12	Payne '25, Ludwig '29 Corner '29	X
16	3.3 (22)		27	309 312	Thoracic somites 13–20	Heuser '30, Witschi '48	XI
17	3.5		28	310	Thoracic somites 21–24	Davis '23, Johnson '17	XII
					Tailbud		
18	3.8 (24)		29	316a	Lumbar somites 25–27	Carnegie 5056, 7852	XII
19	4.0 (25)		30	316b	Lumbar somites 28–29	Carnegie 5923, 6473	XII

* Greatest lengths of embryos, crown-rump of fetuses; (in parentheses approximate chorionic size). *Age:* Estimates based on available information and comparison.

Table 31 (*continued*)

Stage	Size mm.*	Weight	Age in Days	Text Fig.	Characterization	Reference	Streeter *Horizons*
20	4.3 (26)		31	317 318	Sacral somites 30–32	Carnegie 8066, 7889	XIII
21	4.6 (27)		32		Sacral somites 33–34	Carnegie 6473	XIII
22	4.8 (28)		33		Caudal somites 35–36	Hertwig-Ingalls '07	XIII
23	5.0 (29)		34		Caudal somites 37	Carnegie 8119	XIII
24	5.4 (30)		35	319a	Caudal somites 38	Carnegie 1380, 7433, 7618	XIII

Embryo

Stage	Size mm.*	Weight	Age in Days	Text Fig.	Characterization	Reference	Streeter *Horizons*
25	6.0 (28–35)	0.02 gm.	35–37	319	End of somite formation	Iowa E6	XIV

Metamorphosis

Stage	Size mm.*	Weight	Age in Days	Text Fig.	Characterization	Reference	Streeter *Horizons*
26	8	0.05 gm.	38		Hand plate appears. Begin. of umbilical hernia	Carnegie 7394, 3441	XV
27	8–10 (35)		40	324	3rd and 4th Visc. arches covered by operculum	Carnegie 792, 6510, 6511	XVI
28	12		42	325	Pentadactyle rudiment. Cervical sinus closes	Carnegie 6521	XVII
29	12.5–14 (40)		44	326 330b	Median processes of maxillaries	Iowa E12.5	XVII
30	14.6		46		Premaxillary processes. Begin sex differentiation	Carnegie 1909	XVIII
31	15.6		48	330c	Facial clefts closing	Carnegie 6529	XVIII
32	17	1 gm.	50	327	Phalanges. First links	Carnegie 6150	XIX
33	22–25	1.5 gm.	56	328	Facial clefts closed. Auricle. Large umbil. hernia	Carnegie 3527, 966	XX–XXII

Fetus I

Stage	Size mm.*	Weight	Age in Days	Text Fig.	Characterization	Reference	Streeter *Horizons*
34	26–45	2–15 gm.	56–70	332 333	Growth of eyelids. Gut withdrawn from hernia	Carnegie 4570, 5154 Iowa TA11	XXIII

Fetus II

Stage	Size mm.*	Weight	Age in Days	Text Fig.	Characterization	Reference	Streeter *Horizons*
35	45–180	15–400 gm.	70–140	336	Sealed eyelids Periderm	Iowa TA8, HF5, TA9, TA7	

Fetus III

Stage	Size mm.*	Weight	Age in Days	Text Fig.	Characterization	Reference	Streeter *Horizons*
36	180–340	400–3400 gm.	140–266		Periderm resorbed. Eyelids cornified, separate	Iowa TA3, HF3	

gestation periods. The eyelids which become prominent folds at the closing days of metamorphosis (Figs. 327, 329*b*) rapidly grow over the surface of the eyeballs (Fig. 332) and fuse solidly, progressing laterally from the inner corners (Figs. 333, 334, 336). Periderm plugs also close the nostrils and the outer ear ducts; the upper and lower lips develop high layers of periderm which partly fuse and thus reduce the size of the oral opening. This periderm extends to the upper and lower jaws where it plays a role in the development of the teeth. Its accumulation in the cavities of the cup-shaped primordial mammary glands was previously described (Fig. 274).

The primitive open-eyed condition, or stage 34, lasts not more than two weeks. During stage 35 the fetus, sealed up with periderm, has somewhat the appearance of a mummy (Fig. 336). It lasts until about the twentieth week of pregnancy, when most periderm structures degenerate. The epidermis acquires a cornified surface layer. The various plugs disappear (Fig. 274c) and the eyelids become separated; though usually not actually opened, they can now be easily lifted. This initiates the third fetal stage (St. 36), which lasts until parturition. Having reached this stage, premature births have a chance of survival, if properly incubated and fed.

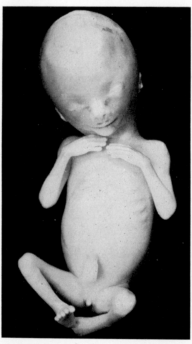

Figure 336.   Second fetal period (St. 35), *periderm-sealed eyelids.* Female fetus, 80 mm. crown-rump length, weight 31 gm.; × 1.

10. STAGES OF HUMAN DEVELOPMENT, AGE, AND GROWTH

A summary of the stages of human development, grouped into larger periods, and with short characterizations is presented in Table 31. Most embryos and fetuses with the reference "Carnegie" are listed and described in Streeter's *Developmental Horizons* (1942–1951), and those from the Iowa collection are listed in Bruner's study of chorionic gonadotrophins (1951). For fuller information about individual stages the type specimens under "reference" should be consulted. Since collecting of human embryonic stages depends on largely uncontrollable circumstances, data on age and growth have only the value of approximations. Streeter has adopted a method of pairing human embryos with those of monkeys of exactly known age. But as the monkey obviously develops faster, the method lacks practical value (cf. Table 23). Age estimates are made by widely differing methods that are not always specifically designated. In our table available data are converted into a "fertilization age," according to principles explained under Table 23. Weight studies have been badly neglected and few data can properly be correlated with definite stages. In general both growth and weight curves have sigmoid shapes. The slow gain in absolute weight at the start is, however, deceiving, for the relative growth rate is actually highest at the youngest stages. Table 32 furnishes a practical characterization of the ebbing growth rate and surprisingly close approximations to actual embryonic and fetal sizes. With doubling time the growth rate falls off exponentially. This easily remembered rule may assist better in determining the age range of fetuses than any of the complicated formulas that have been proposed.

Table 32

Growth of Human Embryos and Fetuses between 5 and 40 Weeks

AGE IN WEEKS	SMALL SIZES	LARGE SIZES	MULTIPLICATION FACTOR	STAGE
5	5 mm.	6 mm.		25/
			× 8	/34
10	40 mm.	50 mm.		
			× 4	35
20	160 mm.	200 mm.		
			× 2	36
40*	320 mm.	400 mm.		

* The average time of parturition is 38 weeks.

Chapter 28

Organogenesis. I

1. CARTILAGINOUS SKELETON AND OSSIFICATION

Skeletal development is retarded in comparison with the conditions in other vertebrates. This is particularly true for the skeleton of the appendages. Ossifications occur in the two typical forms, either as *cartilage bones* or as *membrane bones*. The former differentiate within the primitive cartilages which they gradually replace (endochondral formation). The cartilage is completely eroded and never transforms into bone. However, the *perichondral connective tissue* becomes the *periosteum,* and some of its cells develop into *osteoblasts* (Fig. 337a). The *membrane bones* develop as separate ossifications or as sheaths and plates applied to the surface of cartilages (Fig. 335); in either case they arise within membranous condensations of connective tissue (intramembranous bone formation) and through the activity of osteoblasts of mesenchymal origin. Most characteristic membrane bones are the large plates that form the cranial roof (Fig. 3c).

The development of the *vertebral column and the ribs* progresses through a sequence of three levels of histologic differentiation, characterized by membrane, cartilage, and bone formation. Materially involved are the *notochord* and the proliferations of the *sclerotomes*. The latter arise from the medioventral parts of the somites, which loosen up where they contact the neural tube. They also send processes toward the notochord (Fig. 351, St. 15). Soon proliferation becomes very active. While some cells disperse and form connective tissue, the ma-

502

jority accumulate around spinal cord and notochord, giving rise to the primitive *membranous vertebral column*. The transformation of a closed primary somite into an actively proliferating one is illustrated by Figures 182 and 185. With more detail it may be studied in serial sections through a two-day chick embryo (Fig. 181), which shows a progression of stages between the 27th and the 5th somites. For a short time the membranous vertebral column is an almost continuous cylinder, though the somitic or sclerotomic segmentation is never completely lost. However, as early as tailbud embryos each sclerotome becomes divided into an upper and a lower half through the development of the *sclerotomic fissures*. Since the primordia of vertebral bodies, neural arches, and ribs arise from the *fusion of each lower sclerotome half*

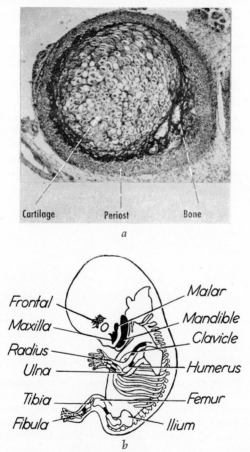

Figure 337.   Bone formation. *a*, Human fetus 37 mm. (late St. 34). Cross section through collar bone; *cartilage-bone formation*; × 55. *b*, Human embryo 23.5 mm. (St. 33) stained with alizarin, showing early ossification centers (black); × 2. (By permission from Human Embryology by B. M. Patten. Copyright 1946. Blakiston Div., McGraw-Hill Book Co.)

with the upper half of the next segment (Fig. 338), the formation of fissures actually initiates the final segmentation of the vertebral column. As a consequence, the vertebrae alternate with the somites and muscle segments, while the ribs grow out through the intersegmental ligaments. These general arrangements are the same in all vertebrates (compare Table 9). Cartilage formation or *chondrification* of the vertebral bodies begins in six-week-old embryos (St. 28). *Cartilage* is a hyaline secretion of the cells of the membranous primordia. It is laid down in the intercellular spaces and thus separates and isolates the cells from each other. In man, as in birds (Fig. 242), a purely *cartilagenous axial skeleton* persists throughout the first fetal stage. Its *ossification* starts only in fetuses with closed eyes (St. 35, 45 to 180 mm.). Separate ossification centers appear within the vertebral bodies, the neural arches and the ribs. *Endochondral bone formation* prevails though the perichondral membranes also contribute. Specialized mesenchyme cells, the *osteoblasts,* invade the cartilage where it is being eroded by a spreading capillary network. Arranging themselves in chains they first secrete

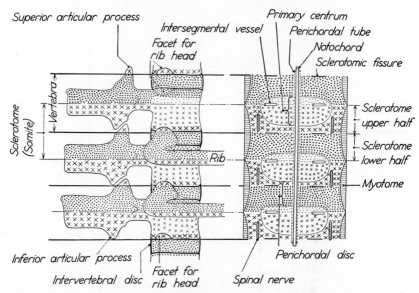

Figure 338.   Participation of the sclerotomes (sclerotome halves) in the formation of vertebrae and ribs (diagrams by Sensenig 1949, Carnegie Contrib. 214). Left figure: Three thoracic vertebrae and two attached ribs, seen from the right side. Right figure: Frontal section through the center of three vertebral bodies, notochord and perichordal tube. Contributions by a lower sclerotome half are *stippled,* those by an upper half are marked by *crosses.* Heavy stipple and crosses indicate high cellular density.

In general each vertebra is formed by fusing halves of sclerotomes, which themselves derive from two adjacent somites. However, as the left diagram shows, *three* successive sclerotome halves actually contribute to the formation of the articular processes of the vertebral arches, and of the ribs.

strings of collagenous fibers, the *ossein*. Later, by the deposition of calcium salts, this spongy framework is transformed into loose *cancellous bone*. By continued activity of the osteoblasts, this may further develop into *compact bone*.

The *notochord* may be of value as a supporting element in premetamorphic embryos. During the early stages of sclerotomic proliferation it becomes enclosed in a *perichordal tube* and serves as the central axis in the formation of the vertebral bodies (Fig. 338). With the progress of chondrification it becomes segmentally compressed by the growing cartilages; later also the parts in the *intervertebral discs* regress and disappear.

The equivalence of all types of bone formation is emphasized by the simultaneous appearance of a perichondral and a membranous ossification center at the very start of bone formation, late in the period of metamorphosis (stage 32)—one in the clavicle, the other in the mandible. At the end of metamorphosis (St. 33, Fig. 337*b*) a few more centers have become added, again representing both major types. Characteristic for mammalian skeletal development is the formation of separate diaphyseal and epiphyseal ossification centers in the long appendicular bones. The *diaphysis* usually ossifies during the first half

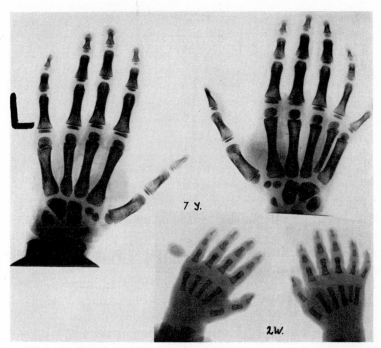

Figure 339. X-ray pictures of the hands of one of identical triplet boys, taken at the ages of 2 weeks and 7 years, the latter showing epiphyseal discs. All three boys were polydactyl (courtesy of State University of Iowa University Hospitals).

of fetal development while the *epiphysis* becomes noticeable only during the development of the child (Fig. 339). Fusion of the two elements occurs after puberty and is delayed in eunuchoids and castrates. Even under normal conditions ossification of the human skeleton spreads over a span of twenty years.

The development of the structural detail of bones under normal and abnormal conditions of growth presents some of the most challenging problems. Particularly the *trabecular pattern of the human femur* in its response to changes in mechanical stress has been made the subject of mathematical analysis as well as of philosophical speculations on the intrinsic "fitness" of organic structure.

2. DEVELOPMENT OF MUSCULAR MOVEMENTS

In birds and mammals, the beginnings of muscular activity occur in the heart. In the chick, irregular fibrillations of a few muscle cells of the ventricle appear early during the second day of incubation (9-somite stage). Rhythmic beats of the ventricle result from coordination of the contractions at or before the 15-somite stage. By this time, the atrium also has joined in pulsating, and shortly afterward the activity spreads into the sinus region. However, the blood is not yet driven in any definite direction but simply agitated. Circulation becomes established at the 22-somite stage, late in the second day, when with the formation of the vitelline arteries a peripheral vascular circuit becomes completed.

In mammalian embryos, ventricular pulsations start even earlier. In the rat, rhythmic contractions were observed by Goss at the 3-somite stage, that is, even before fusion of the primitive paired tubes (cf. Figs. 254, 259). This precocity is an adaptation to the early need of the embryo for supplies from the outside, which have to be secured by way of a circulating blood stream.

In comparison with birds and mammals, heart development lags considerably in the amphibians, where every body cell is well supplied with stored foodstuffs. In fact, contractions of somitic muscles of the neck and trunk occur before the first fibrillations of the cardiac ventricle, at early tailbud stages. (Table 33).

There can be no doubt that in regard to *general motility* the amphibians represent the more primitive, and in the evolutionary sense, an ancestral type. The stored food reserves are of modest amount; consequently, early motility of the body in preparation for obtaining outside supplies is an obvious necessity. Swimming, feeding, and respiratory movements develop during the embryonic stages. Embryos with all the trunk somites indicated, but with a rounded tailbud composed of undifferentiated cells (St. 18), respond to localized mechanical stimulation of the neck region by rather slow bending of this part of the body. These contractions of the yet incompletely differentiated muscles are therefore *myogenic,* that is, they originate in the muscle without nerve stimulation. Soon afterward, the reactions become more extensive, enabling the embryo to bend its body into a complete coil. Shortly before hatching, swimming movements are established by coordination of waves of contraction that run from the head to the tail, alternatingly on the left and right sides (compare Fig. 61).

Since, in birds and mammals, extra-embryonic sources of food are made available through the development of vitelline and allantoic circuits, the necessity for early motility of the body no longer exists. As in amphibians, muscular activity is established in three steps closely following one another. The muscles first contract on direct stimulation (*myogenic reaction*); later they may be stimulated from connected nerve roots in the central nervous system (*neuromotor reaction*); finally true reflex arcs become established, when the embryo begins to move after peripheral stimulation of the proper sensory nerve endings (*sensory-motor reaction*). However, the earliest contractions can be elicited only in fully developed embryos (St. 25) of birds, or in early fetuses of mammals (St. 33–34). Since these stages correspond to the range of amphibian metamorphosis, the delay in development of motility in birds and mammals is indeed remarkable (Table 32). Moreover, in normal pregnancy, spontaneous movements start even much later. In the human fetus, they have not been observed before the fourteenth week, and the mother usually does not feel any before the seventeenth to the twentieth week of pregnancy.

The adaptive character of these time relationships comes dramatically into evidence in the case of the opossum. The tiny newborn, only 13 days after fertilization, have well developed arms which they use immediately to climb up through the fur of the mother to get into the brood

Table 33

Earliest Contractions in Cardiac (C) and Skeletal Muscles (S)

	STAGE	AMPHIBIA		BIRDS		MAMMALS	
14	1–4 somites	—	—	—	—	C⁴	—
15	5–12 somites	—	—	C¹	—	C⁵	—
18	Tailbud (early, 20 somites)	—	S	C	—	C	—
20	Tailbud	C	S	C	—	C	—
25	Embryo	C	S	C	S²	C	—
34	Fetus	C	S	C	S	C	S³

¹ Irregular fibrillations at 9 somites.

² In the pigeon, myogenic movements appear toward the end of the 4th day of incubation.

³ Cat, 11–14 mm.
 Rat, 16th day, 11–12 mm.
 Sheep, 20 mm.
 Man, 22–25 mm.

⁴ Goss, rat, hanging drop observations.

⁵ Long, 8-somite rat; Heuser, pig, before 10 somites.

pouch (Fig. 266); but their legs, not yet functionally needed, are in the undeveloped condition which is more characteristic of early fetuses.

The differences in the time of appearance of contractility (Table 33) are fully reflected in the *histogenesis* and the *chemical development* of the muscles. Whether arising from somitic myotomes (skeletal muscles) or from the lateral mesoderm plates (visceral and heart muscles), muscle fibers are formed by round or slightly elongated *myoblasts*. Preceding the differentiation of functional muscle, *a wave of high mitotic activity leads to a rapid increase in the number of myoblasts*. In the somitic myotomes it starts in the neck region at stage 29 or 30 and progresses, slowly, in the caudal direction. During this time the relative content in *nucleic acids* reaches a maximum. It decreases during the closing stages of metamorphosis, when mitotic activity subsides and the nuclei are pushed against the cell walls by the development of numerous *myofibrils* (St. 32, 33). These fibrils are the contractile elements of the muscle fibers. They form in the cytoplasm through rearrangement of granular particles, but mainly by biosynthesis of proteins such as *myosin*. Muscle fibers may attain considerable length and become multinuclear by fusion of numbers of myoblasts. The myofibrils of visceral *smooth muscles* are of even structure along their full length, but those of cardiac and skeletal muscles are *cross striated* because they are made up of alternating zones of isotropic and anisotropic substances. Nicholas finds that cross striation and birefringence appear immediately before stage 34. Moreover, he reports a rapid increase in myosin content during the first fetal stages.

While the development of mammalian skeletal muscle is characterized by a protracted myoblastic phase, that of *cardiac muscle is remarkable for the precocity of differentiation*. When fibrillations begin, at stage 14, the myofibrils are structurally still very primitive. Altogether the muscle fibers of embryos and fetuses are relatively coarse and only slowly acquire the more delicate morphology of adult muscles.

If prospective heart or skeletal muscle blastemas are isolated and cultured in vitro, they develop into sheets or pads of cytologically incompletely differentiated muscle cells which relatively early begin to show twitching or pulsating movements. The frequency of such contractions varies from less than one to over 100 per minute. These "in vitro" cultures furnish proof of the independence of the development of contractility from innervation.

3. CIRCULATORY AND RESPIRATORY ORGANS

a. Hemopoiesis.   As described before, centers of differentiation of vessels and blood cells appear at presomite stages in the mesenchyme of the body stalk as well as in the blood islands scattered over the surface of the yolk sac. This furnishes compelling evidence of the independence of angiogenesis from the endoderm. On the other hand, a close relationship between angioblastema and mesenchyme is emphasized. Indeed it is now widely believed that mesenchyme cells even of the adult body may become angioblasts, i.e., mother cells of endothelium and blood cells. One should not, however, exclude the alternative possibility that residual angioblasts as a strictly specific cell type might be scattered widely among the true connective tissue mesenchyme.

With the growth of the embryo the angioblastema gives rise to more and more highly differentiated cells and tissues. Assuming that all lines of differentiation issue from a single cell type, the *angioblast*, the first step involves a differentiation into either *endothelioblasts* or *hemocytoblasts*. The former are the source material for the endothelial lining of the heart, the blood vessels, and the lymphatic ducts. Possibly even the reticular tissue, which connects endothelia with mesenchyme, is of the same origin. This would justify in the embryologic sense the union of the two under the common term of reticulo-endothelial tissue.

The *hemocytoblasts* differentiate along a large number of divergent lines, beginning as *erythroblasts, lymphoblasts,* or *granuloblasts,* to mention only three prevailing types.

Differentiation does not progress very far within the original blood islands for, as the network of blood vessels spreads, the immature angioblasts and hemocytoblasts get into the blood stream and migrate into various organs of the embryo. Settling especially into fine-meshed plexuses, they establish a *succession of blood-forming centers* particularly in the mesonephric bodies, the liver, the spleen, and finally the *bone marrow* and the *lymph glands*. Thus with progress of age and migration, more highly differentiated erythrocytes and white blood cells appear in the blood.

Immunologic studies have shown that in twins of cattle and sheep with communicating chorionic blood vessels, the hemocytoblasts of each member are carried also into its twin. Settling down in the usual sites of hemopoiesis they may produce mosaic patterns of blood types which are maintained also after birth. These observations clearly demonstrate the migratory and colonizing habits of the hemocytoblasts. However, they do not definitely rule out the possibility of blood formation by transformation of mesenchyme cells.

b. Morphogenesis of the Fetal Circulatory System.   The precocity of the development of a functional system of blood vessels corresponds to the early need for external supplies. In neurulae of one to four somites two pairs of tubes make their appearance; the dorsal pair are the *rudiments of dorsal aortas*, the ventral are *primitive hearts*. Both are located above the first somite and their upper ends merge in a common plexus of blood islands, forerunners of the first pair of *aortic arches*. Gradually the other arches are added (Table 34). At stage 19 the first three are present and in functional condition, the second one being the largest. After this, regression of the upper arches accompanies the further development in the lower visceral arches. At stage 20 the first aortic arch has become discontinuous and the third one is more capacious than the second (Fig. 318, Frontispiece). The fourth is added at stage 21 when the second also has disappeared. The third and the fourth pairs still convey almost the entire volume of blood flow to the dorsal aortas at the end of embryo formation (stages 24 and 25); but paired fifth, sixth, and seventh arches are recognizable in the plexus of small vessels that web around the lower pharynx, the pulmonary primordium and the upper pharynx (Fig. 340).

The general arrangement of this system of aortic arches resembles that of amphibian larvae (cf. Fig. 63*b*), except that in human embryos the three lowest pairs pass only very little blood. However, the *metamorphic changes* which now follow in both classes differ considerably. The mammalian variant is primarily adapted to the necessity of deflecting the pulmonary blood stream of the fetus and returning it to the body circulation. This is accomplished by the rapid widening of the sixth pair of aortic arches, at the very inception of metamorphosis. Figure 321, showing both arches in a section through an embryo just preceding metamorphosis, illustrates the very beginning of this process. At stage 27, with metamorphosis well under way, the sixth arches are about equally as wide as the third and the fourth. Meanwhile the vestigial fifth arches have disappeared and the primitive dorsal roots of the pul-

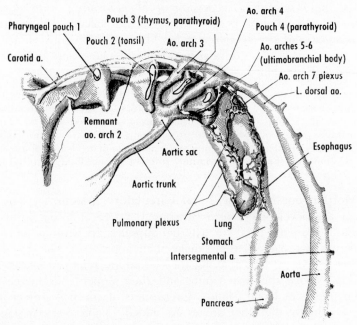

Figure 340.   Human embryo of 38 somites (St. 24); pharynx and blood vessels; (modified, after Congdon 1922, Carnegie Contrib. 68).

monary plexuses are also regressing. Instead, connections are established with the ventral roots of the sixth arches, by anastomoses that rapidly develop into the definitive *pulmonary arteries* (Fig. 340).

It is interesting to correlate these and the following developments with the conditions in frogs (Figs. 73–76), a form which has neither fetal stages nor extra-embryonic organs.

Next follows an *interruption* of the dorsal aortas between the third and fourth arches. For the understanding of the other changes in the aortic system it is necessary to consider first the metamorphic development of the heart.

At the start of metamorphosis, *the heart* is still a single tube; but presently a number of changes are initiated which eventually result in the creation of the *four-chambered heart*. The *septum* between the two atria remains incomplete throughout the fetal periods and its *oval foramen* closes only after birth. On the other hand, the *interventricular septum* effects a complete division of the ventricle into left and right chambers at about stage 30, i.e., before the end of metamorphosis (Fig. 341).

The separation of passages for pulmonary and body (systemic) circulation within the heart is immediately followed by a sequence of *asymmetric developments in the aortic system*. The *interventricular septum* formation is continued in the arterial trunk, splitting it into *an aortic and a pulmonary part*. Beginning with stage 29 or 30 this leads to rapid regression of the right distal segments of the fourth and the sixth aortic arches. The left fourth arch, now receiving the entire volume of blood from the left ventricle, becomes the *systemic arch*. From it branch not only the former third aortic arches, now called *carotid arteries,* but also directly or indirectly two newer large vessels, the *subclavian arteries* (Fig. 341). The right fourth disappears or is absorbed in the formation of the common root of the right carotid and subclavian arteries. At the same time also the distal part of the sixth arch regresses and disappears; that is, the segment between the root of the pulmonary artery and the vanishing right dorsal aorta. The persisting distal part on the left side becomes a fairly wide vessel known as the *arterial duct*. It conveys the excess of blood entering the pulmonary (sixth) arch into the persisting *left dorsal aorta*. The latter now may be considered as the uppermost section of the *descending aorta*. A study of fetal circulation as illustrated in Figure 341 shows that its most specific structures, the *arterial duct* and the *oval foramen,* at least partly cancel the effectiveness of the separation of *pulmonary circuit* and *systemic circuit*.

Though the fetal lungs are well vascularized, the volume of the blood flow is smaller than after birth. The *pulmonary veins* return an amount to the left atrium which would be insufficient to serve the systemic circuit, if it were not augmented at the oval foramen by a substantial contribution from the *inferior caval vein*. After absorption of the *primitive venous sinus* into the wall of the right atrium, the caval vein enters the heart directly from below, continuing into a bifurcating *caval channel* that runs between the two atria to the free edge of the atrial septum (Fig. 341). The main flow is directed toward the left chamber. The edge of the septum serves as a *dividing ridge*. The free ends of the vein project into the cavities of the two chambers; the smaller one at the right is the eustachian valve, the larger at the left is the *valve of the oval foramen*.

The tree of *pulmonary veins* is progressively absorbed into the wall of the left atrium so that finally the fetal heart receives four separate veins, two from the left and two from the right lung.

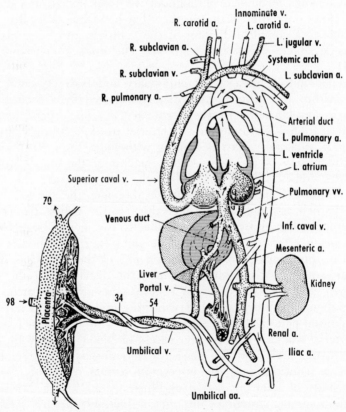

Figure 341.   Diagram of fetal circulation, ventral aspect. The ventricle of the heart is completely divided into left and right chambers by the *interventricular septum*. The *atrial septum* is incomplete, leaving a wide communication, the *oval foramen*, between the two chambers. Percentage oxygen concentration is indicated for maternal and fetal placental arteries and veins.

One of the most important consequences of these arrangements is the well balanced distribution of working load between left and right chambers, preventing functional atrophy or overdevelopment of any part of the fetal heart.

The *placental system of blood vessels* develops on the basis of arteries and veins that are already present in the aplacental amphibians. The arteries, usually called *umbilical arteries,* are early developing branches of the *iliac plexus,* which supplies the bladder and the legs. Though in human development the allantoic vesicle remains rudimentary (urachus, see Figs. 312, 346–350), the vascular system still retains a pair of large umbilical arteries, supplying the placenta and its villi. The fetal placental collection is returned by a single *umbilical vein* which by way of the left abdominal vein reaches the falciform ligament and the liver. In the liver it gives off branches into the various lobes, eventually mixing a large part of its blood with that which is returned by the mesenteric veins through the hepatic portal. A strong branch, however, passes the liver transversely as a nearly straight *venous duct,* opening directly into the inferior caval vein (Figs. 341, 350). The entrance into the venous duct is provided with a muscular sphincter which regulates the relative amounts of blood that pass either directly or by way of the liver sinusoids. Since the latter way is slower, constriction of the sphincter also increases the expansion of the liver with blood.

The three umbilical blood vessels are embedded in a loose mesenchymal tissue known as *Wharton's jelly.* It is continuous with the adventitia or outer coat of the vessels. The walls of the vessels contain bundles of muscle fibers which by their state of contraction control to some degree the rate of umbilical circulation.

c. **Functional Aspects of Fetal Circulation.** Evidently growth and energy metabolism of the fetus depend almost entirely on the placental circulation for bringing in of supplies and removal of waste materials. It is therefore surprising that this circulation is fed only by tertiary branches of the circulatory system. The general picture of fetal circulation makes it quite clear that only a relatively small fraction of the total blood volume passes through the placenta. Correspondingly the exchange between the maternal and the fetal blood is relatively slow; in many instances this results in considerable differences in the concentrations of dissolved materials. The conditions of placental transmission were discussed before. In regard to oxygen intake and distribution reference is made to the data entered in Figure 341. They show that the oxygen content of the fetal blood even at its highest value (in the umbilical vein) is still relatively low—below that of the maternal venous blood as it drains from the placenta.

As a result of the described pattern of mixing of bloods returned from the placenta and from the various parts of the body, it appears that a large portion of the liver, the heart, and the head are supplied with blood of higher oxygen concentration than the remainder of the body, particularly its lower parts.

The study of oxygen dissociation values of fetal and maternal bloods has shown that the hemoglobin of young animals—frog larvae, embryos of birds and mammals —characteristically differs from that of the adult. Possibly this is related to the difference in blood-forming beds, e.g., liver and bone marrow. Under equal conditions of hydrogen ion concentration and oxygen tension, fetal blood becomes more highly oxygenated than maternal blood. The transfer of oxygen is probably even more effectively supported by the usually high hemoglobin level of fetal blood. In the human it reaches its peak at the time of birth, when it equals that of adults living at high altitudes. This may be taken as another expression of the fact that the fetus lives under a condition of oxygen scarcity.

d. Changes at Birth.   With the attainment of stage 36 at or shortly after midterm the fetus is ready to be born, at least in the sense that the birth changes are ready to take effect. The most obvious and important ones are related to the change from placental to pulmonary respiration. The child at delivery is still connected with the placenta by its *umbilical cord,* and the placenta is still attached to the uterine wall. The longer the cutting of the cord is delayed, the more complete is the withdrawal of the blood from the villous placenta into the child. It has been questioned whether such collection is desirable. Since the hemoglobin level of the newborn is too high in any case and is lowered immediately following birth, possibly an early severance could be of some advantage. The extensive destruction of erythrocytes immediately following birth is almost certainly the cause of the "physiologic jaundice" which is so frequently observed in first-month babies. The bilirubin content of the blood, still low at birth, rises rapidly during three to four days and may remain fairly high for a month or longer.

After severance of the cord the muscle sheaths of the umbilical vessels immediately contract, so that little if any blood is lost. Similar contractions occur in the muscular wall of the arterial duct and the sphincter of the venous duct. This active stoppage of blood flow is soon followed by a fibrous degeneration of the empty vessels. The umbilical arteries become reduced to an *umbilical ligament;* the umbilical vein, between umbilicus and liver, to the *ligamentum teres.* The venous and arterial ducts (Fig. 341) are similarly reduced to *venous and arterial ligaments* respectively.

The *oval foramen* closes in response to the changes in blood volumes returned to the atrial chambers. With the constriction of the arterial duct and following the inflation of the lungs, a larger amount of blood is returned to the left atrium by the pulmonary veins. Moreover, the flow of their blood, especially that of the caudal right vein, is directed toward the surface of the valve of the foramen (Fig. 341). Since at the same time pressure from the right side lessens because of severance of the umbilical circulation, this valve is pressed against the edge of the septum. This temporary mechanical closure of the foramen later becomes permanent by fusion of the valve with the septum. However, a pinhole-size opening remains in as many as 25 per cent of adult humans, and much larger persisting foramina are observed as a rather frequent abnormality at anatomic dissections.

Actually very little is known about the factors that initiate *lung respiration*. As in the adult, high carbon dioxide levels may stimulate the respiratory centers of the nervous system. The first breathing movements usually do not fill the entire lung and all its alveoli. In prematurely born babies respiration at first may not be alveolar at all; in some instances survival over several weeks has been observed with respiration restricted to bronchial ducts only. Prenatal irregular respiratory movements with intake of some amniotic fluid have often been suspected to be an essential factor in pulmonary development. On the other hand, they may be explained as automatic reactions in response to oxygen deficiency and without importance for the developmental process.

e. The Embryonic Lungs, arising as a seventh pair of pharyngeal pouches, are essentially an endodermal organ. At late tailbud stages they consist of a single tube, the *trachea,* and a *pair of lungbuds* (St. 24, Fig. 318). The pharyngeal entrance to the trachea is the *larynx;* its narrow opening is laterally bordered by the *arytenoid swellings* (Fig. 321) and in front by the rudiment of the *epiglottis.* As the embryo enters the metamorphic period, the primary lungbuds start growing

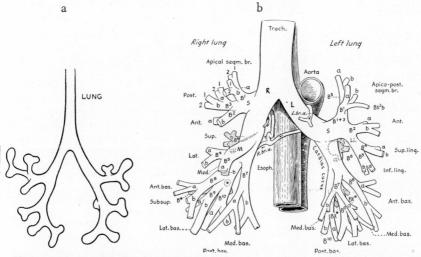

Figure 342.   Development of the human lung. *a,* Bronchial tree at stage 30 with about 20 lobules; *b,* ventral view of bronchial tree of the adult, with segmental bronchi (Streeter 1948, Boyden 1953).

and dividing. At stage 30 to 31 a *bronchial tree* with about 20 lobules is present which already exhibits the basic structure of the adult lung (Fig. 342*a*, *b*). Each lobule is the rudiment of a *bronchopulmonary segment.* Through continued division arise, first, the branching *bronchi* and *bronchioli* and finally the terminal *alveoli.* At birth, as many as 18 generations have been counted and multiplication still continues neonatally.

The growing *endodermal lungs* pushing into the pleural diverticula of the celomic cavity remain covered with celomic epithelium. This *mesodermal component,* by abundant proliferation, forms a solid surface epithelium and the *lung parenchyma* that fills the spaces between the branches of the bronchial tree. Through the latter spreads the dense network of *pulmonary blood vessels.*

Loosli and Potter distinguish three steps of histologic development. (1) The *glandular period* lasts to the end of the third month (fetuses with closed eyes); the peripheral branches are lined with a high columnar, endodermal epithelium. (2) The *canalicular period,* from the fourth to the sixth month, is characterized by a rapid increase of the interstitial mesoderm, while the tubular branches of the tree become more compressed. (3) The *alveolar period* begins with the seventh month. The endodermal lining of the bronchi becomes discontinuous and gradually disappears. The blood capillaries protrude into the denuded channels and take an active part in the formation of the final alveoli. From this time on, the prematurely born fetus is able to use its lungs without great difficulties.

As a result of these transformations the lung, which started as an endodermal primordium, becomes an essentially mesodermal organ.

Chapter 29

Organogenesis. II

4. NERVOUS SYSTEM AND SENSE ORGANS

The nervous system of human embryos develops in accordance with the general vertebrate pattern. However, a comparison of embryos of various classes (Figs. 119, 141, 197, 343) reveals some peculiarities of the human type that seem related to the extremely retarded morphologic and functional development of its sense organs.

a. Brain and Major Sense Organs. In fully developed human embryos (38 somites, St. 25) the differentiation of the nasal placodes, the eyes, and the ears is barely at the level that in amphibians and birds is attained in early tailbud embryos (compare Figs. 116, 181, and 319*d*). Consequently the nerves and the central nuclei of these organs differentiate late and slowly. A comparison of Figures 343 (St. 27) and 238*b* (St. 26) indicates the relatively much larger size of the cerebral hemispheres in birds. Even at the end of metamorphosis, only the basic plan of the human telencephalon has been laid down (St. 33, Fig. 329).

After its slow start, the human *telencephalon* grows very rapidly during the fetal stages. At about three months (St. 35) its size equals that of all other parts of the brain taken together. Later it covers them almost completely. The disproportionate growth involves not the entire cerebrum, but particularly an area in each dorsolateral wall of the primitive rhinencephalon. These areas first bulge out as thin vesicles but later become thick-walled hemispheres. Beginning in the fourth month, rapid surface development leads to the formation of folds, con-

517

volutions and fissures. Through this excessive development of the
neopallium, or non-olfactory hemisphere, the human telencephalon
becomes relatively larger than that of any other vertebrate.

The differentiation of the *optic vesicle,* the separation of a *nervous*
and a *pigment layer* of the *retina,* and the formation of a hyaloid canal
with a vascular plexus are reviewed in Fig. 344. Though much delayed,
these developments do not essentially deviate from the course taken in
lower vertebrates. Considerable differences appear only in the construction of the central nervous pathways and nuclei. Possibly the tardy histologic differentiation of the retina into *visual cells, bipolar neurons,* and
ganglion cells, with correspondingly late outgrowth of nerve fibers,
is linked with the changes. Nerve fibers from the ganglion layer,

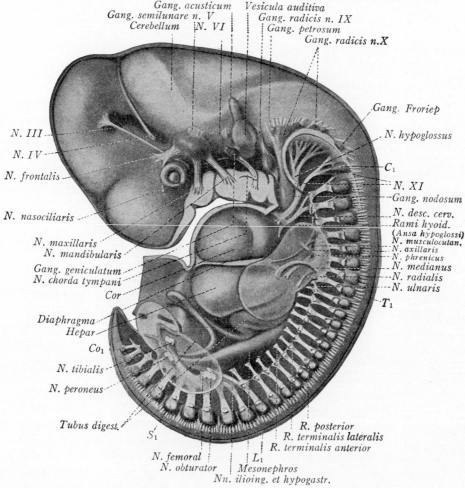

Figure 343.   Reconstruction of the nervous system of a human embryo of 10
mm. (St. 28) (after Streeter from Arey 1954); × 12.

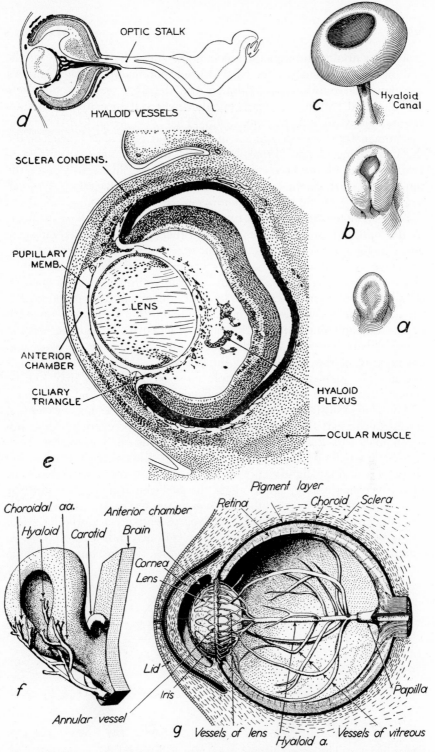

Figure 344.   Eye development in man. *a–c,* Development of the optic cup, stages 25, 27, and 31; *d,* stage 31, section through eye and optic stalk; *e,* late stage 33; *a–d,* × 25; *e,* × 60 (Streeter 1951, Carnegie Contrib. 230). *f, g,* Vascularization of the eye (after Mann from Walls 1942).

growing centrally through the *optic stalk,* enter the brain only at the end of metamorphosis (St. 30). In all non-mammals the bulk of the optic nerve fibers pass through the thalamic walls of the dien-cephalon and end in the mesencephalon, where their central *nuclei* are accommodated in bulging *optic lobes* (Figs. 117, 238). Conversely, in the human fetus they terminate in the lateral *geniculate nuclei* of the thalamic diencephalon. From here optic impulses are transmitted to visual centers of the cerebral cortex. Only a few fibers still enter the upper roof plate of the mesencephalon, ending in the relatively small *upper colliculi* of the corpora quadrigemina.

Equally noteworthy is the *incompleteness of decussation* of fibers in the *optic chiasma.* Whereas in all other classes of vertebrates the entire optic nerves cross over to the opposite side, in mammals this exchange is restricted to the fibers originating in the median halves of the retinas (Fig. 345). In man and other primates about one-half of all fibers remain uncrossed. In other mammals the proportion is smaller, namely one-third in the cat, one-fourth in the dog, one-fifth in the rat, and one-sixth in the horse. Evidently the number of un-crossed fibers increases with the degree of frontality of the eyes and overlapping of the visual fields. But the rule is restricted to mammals and another supplementary principle must be involved; it may well be concerned with the particular embryologic conditions of the mammals.

The *stato-acoustic organ* changes little, from frog to man, except in regard to the part that specifically serves acoustic perception. This end-organ makes its first appearance, in amphibians, as a primitive endo-lymphatic papilla on the sacculus (Fig. 114). Enlarging, it assumes the shape of a plump, slightly curved protuberance in reptiles and birds. In man it becomes a long, spiral organ, the *cochlear duct.* In the adult ear it is enclosed in a loop of the *perilymphatic space.* Starting from the spacious cistern or vestibulum, this loop ascends as a *vestibular canal* (scala vestibuli) along the cochlear duct, and descends as the *tympanic canal* (scala tympani) to the round window. In the human embryo

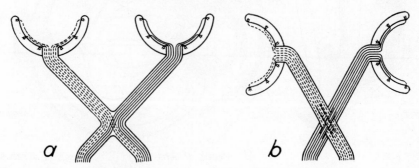

Figure 345.   The optic chiasma; *a,* of man with partial decussation of nerve fibers, *b,* of bird, with total decussation (Walls 1942).

the cochlear duct grows out and completes about two and one-half spiral turns during the metamorphic phase (Fig. 329c). The perilymphatic system is added only during the second fetal stage.

The middle ear derives from the dorsal part of the first pharyngeal pouch and differentiates into *inner ear tube* and *tympanic cavity*. Through the development of an *outer ear canal* from the first visceral groove, the *tympanic membrane* becomes sunk deep into the tissues and bones of the head. Its vibrations are transmitted to the oval window by a *columella* of three *auditory ossicles*. Of these, *malleus* and *incus* occur only in mammals and are derived from the joint of the primitive mandibular arch. The third ossicle or *stapes* is obtained from the second visceral arch. It occurs in the ears of frogs, reptiles, and birds. The *external ear* or *auricle* is a composite product of surface developments from the first and second visceral arches (Fig. 330).

The functional improvements arising from the evolution of the ear probably are related less to threshold sensitivity than to the capacity for simultaneous perception of sounds of various wave lengths. The cochlear sensory receptor, the *spiral organ* (of Corti), represents an extended scale of maxima and minima for different frequencies of vibrations.

A late start is also a characteristic feature in the development of the *metencephalon* or *cerebellum*. This center of control mechanisms for the maintenance of balance is only indirectly connected with the vestibular nerve and the semicircular canals of the stato-acoustic organ. This may explain why its differentiation begins only after completion of metamorphosis. Still a mere thickening in the dorsal wall of the upper rhombencephalon throughout the first fetal stage (St. 34), the *cerebellar plate* acquires a first crosswise fold or *primary sulcus* in fetuses of about 70 mm., at the age of three months. During the following two months it becomes heavily pleated.

b. Cranial Nerves.   The composition of the twelve cranial nerves (I–XII) shows considerable variety, which permits the distinguishing of three groups of more closely related type.

NERVES OF THE MAJOR SENSE ORGANS.   Three nerves, namely the *olfactory* (*I*), the *optic* (*II*), and the *stato-acoustic* (*VIII*), are made up of sensory fibers. They originate from neuroblasts in the peripheral organs and grow relatively late into the walls of the brain. Here they synapse with central neurons, which are arranged in definite groups, called *nuclei*.

NERVES OF THE EXTRINSIC EYE MUSCLES.   The seven muscles of the orbit develop from presomitic head mesenchyme. They are supplied by three nerves, the *oculomotor* (*III*), the *trochlear* (*IV*), and the *abducent* (*VI*). These nerves grow out from neurons of the basal plates of the mesencephalon and the myelencephalon. They contain mostly somatic motor fibers.

NERVES OF THE VISCERAL ARCH REGION. The segmented part of the head contains more or less distinctly recognizable somatic and visceral components. Though regular somites are restricted to the occipital region, at the neurula stage a pair of strands of somitic head mesenchyme connect the first somites with the blastema condensations of the eye muscles and the prechordal plate. The visceral element is of course best represented at the level of the four uppermost visceral arches; but indications of the presence of further vestiges are found even at the level of the first and second cervical segments. The *somatic sensory neurons* arise from dorsal neural crest cells and form superior root ganglia. The *visceral sensory neurons* develop from the epibranchial placodes and aggregate in inferior root ganglia. The *motor neurons* of both types are located in the basal plate of the myelencephalon. Their fibers grow out through ventral motor roots. Characteristically the *visceral motor fibers* innervate muscles derived from the primitive branchial arches, while the *somatic motor fibers* connect with muscles of somitic origin. The basic plan becomes greatly modified through uneven development of the peripheral somitic and splanchnic areas, and through fusion of parts of segmental units. As a consequence, development and composition of the six nerves of this group show considerable individual differences.

The *trigeminal nerve* (*V*) develops in the area of the mandibular arch and innervates its muscles, particularly the strong masticator (masseter). It collects a wide range of sensory fibers which outnumber several times the motor fibers. Hence, its semi-lunar ganglion is the largest of all the cranial ganglia. It comprises in one body elements of crest as well as of epibranchial origin. An entire complex of its ganglia cells even is located within the brain, namely in the wall of the midbrain. The sensory fibers leading to this *mesencephalic nucleus of the fifth nerve* collect from a large part of the head, with numerous sensitive terminals, *proprioreceptors,* located in ligaments and between muscle bundles. The *facial nerve* (*VII*) is mostly composed of motor fibers. It innervates the mimetic facial musculature derived from the second or hyoid arch. In the course of early embryonic development its superior root ganglion becomes completely reduced (compare Figs. 318 and 343). From the inferior or geniculate ganglion issue afferent fibers that terminate in taste buds of the tongue and in other sensory organs of the facial area. The *glossopharyngeal nerve* (*IX*) retains separate superior and inferior root ganglia; the latter is also called the petrosal ganglion. This is the nerve of the third visceral arch; it supplies various organs in the upper throat region and in the root of the tongue.

The last three cranial nerves (X–XII) are closely interrelated. The *vagus* (*X*) is a composite of elements from the fourth to the sixth visceral arches. It retains separate superior (jugular) and inferior (nodose) ganglia. As in birds (cf. Table 9) this visceral region coincides segmentally with that of the occipital somites. At early stages, the dorsal crest ganglia of the vagus, the occipital and the spinal regions form one continuous bar (Fig. 318 and Frontispiece). Below the jugular condensation either this bar does not establish connections with the occipital motor roots at all, or eventual contacts are of only transient nature. The unattached ganglia crest is called the accessory ganglion. Along its ventral border appear visceral motor fibers, some starting even from the level of the first and the second cervical segments. First they ascend to the edge of the jugular ganglion, curve ventrally, and then form the separate *accessory nerve* (XI). Gradually it becomes an almost pure motor nerve that supplies the long muscles of neck and shoulder, derivatives of the branchial arches (Figs. 318, 343). Lastly, the ventral roots of about four occipital somites unite and form the *hypoglossal nerve* (XII). It contains exclusively somatic motor fibers and supplies muscles of the tongue and ventral neck which all arise from occipital myotomes.

c. **Spinal Cord and Nerves.**   The lateral walls of the embryonic spinal tube are incompletely separated into dorsal and ventral parts, the *alar* and *basal plates*, by a deep longitudinal groove or *sulcus*. This division is still noticeable at the end of the metamorphic period, when the neural canal is already laterally compressed, and the separation of ependymal, mantle, and marginal layers is practically complete (Fig. 329e, St. 33). The *white marginal layer* consists of longitudinal and cross connecting fibers, the *gray mantle layer* mainly of the cell bodies of neurons. The basal plates, besides central association neurons, contain the *efferent neurons*, with fibers that emerge from the spinal cord in the ventral roots of the spinal nerves. The alar plates contain only *association neurons*. However, they receive, through the dorsal roots, afferent nerve fibers from the sensory neurons of the spinal ganglia. During fetal development the ependymal layer, which contained mainly *proliferating neuroblasts*, becomes exhausted and the left and right walls of the tube fuse, reducing the neural cavity to a small *central canal*. The mantle layer assumes the mature aspect of the gray matter of the spinal cord, with characteristic *dorsal and ventral horns*.

During the formation of the vertebral column the spinal cord becomes encircled by dorsal arches that combine into a *vertebral canal*. From the somatic mesenchyme arise also at least two membranous envelopes or *meninges* of the spinal cord, *dura* and *arachnoid*. The innermost *pia* seems to arise in part or entirely from neural crest cells. After the third month of pregnancy vertebral column and canal gain length more rapidly than the spinal cord. This results in the detachment of the dura with formation of a wide *dural sac*, and arrangement of the lumbar and sacral nerves in the shape of a horse tail within the empty vertebral canal.

The *spinal nerves* show a comparatively simple and uniform pattern of development. In embryos of 32 somites (Frontispiece, St. 20), the paired neural crests have become chains of ganglia. However, they still form continuous bars with smooth dorsal borderlines. No dorsal roots have formed yet and the ganglia are still incompletely separated. *Ventral roots* appear beneath the upper ganglia and in the region of the armbuds a tendency toward formation of a *brachial plexus* is noticeable. It is obvious that differentiation progresses in cranio-caudal direction. At metamorphic stages (Fig. 343, St. 28) all ganglia are well differentiated, with dorsal roots establishing connections with the spinal cord. The peripheral sensory fibers join the motor fibers of the ventral roots in the formation of mixed nerves. Spinal nerves and ganglia vary in size, in proportion to the fundamental importance of the areas which they supply. They grow largest in the segments of the brachial and lumbosacral plexuses which supply arms and legs respectively.

    d. Autonomic Nervous System.   The autonomic system consists of efferent neurons which are located either in the spinal cord and the brain, or in peripheral plexuses and ganglia other than the sensory ganglia of spinal and cranial nerves. The former originate in close association with motor nerves. They are called *preganglionic neurons* since their fibers synapse with peripheral *autonomic ganglia cells.* This second type of neurons derive from neural crest cells, most often by way of the primitive superior root ganglia of cranial nerves and of primordial spinal ganglia. The above mentioned depletion of the superior seventh root ganglion and the accessory ganglion may be related with the formation of autonomic ganglia cells. While of considerable size in 32-somite embryos (Frontispiece) they have nearly or completely disappeared at early metamorphic stages (Fig. 343). Development and differentiation of the system is considerably delayed in the lower body region, but is well under way by the end of metamorphosis.

    Anatomically one distinguishes *cranial, thoracolumbar,* and *sacral divisions* in accordance with the type of nerves that carry the supply of preganglionic fibers. However, the first and last are physiologically closely related, both ending in cholinergic synapses. Together they constitute the *parasympathetic system.* In contradistinction the thoracolumbar division, which has adrenergic terminal synapses, is designated as the *sympathetic system.* The two systems also show striking morphologic differences. The ganglia of the sympathetic system are regularly, almost segmentally arranged, in a prevertebral chain (trunk ganglia), while the parasympathetic neurons are widely scattered, singly or in groups, ganglia and plexuses, mainly in the viscera, the head, and the urogenital organs.

5. CELOM AND MESENTERIES

    The lateral plate, separating early into somatic and splanchnic sheets, gives origin to the *celomic cavities* and their lining *epithelia.* In human embryos the extra-embryonic celom appears first (Figs. 299–302, 306). Within the embryo celomic differentiation accompanies that of the primitive heart tubes and starts about the time of first somite formation. As the paired sacs widen, they meet in the sagittal plane, enclosing between their epithelia the splanchnic organs, particularly the primitive endodermal gut. The viscera thus gain a mesodermal sheath and become suspended in *dorsal and ventral mesenteries.* From the beginning this arrangement becomes more complicated because the ventral mesentery encloses also heart and liver; in many parts it disappears again by resorption. The dorsal mesentery serves as a route for the nervous and vascular supply of the viscera. It differentiates regionally and is designated by various names. Along the esophagus where it is broad and filled with much connective tissue, it is known as the *mediastinum.* The dorsal mesentery of the stomach expands into a large pouch that eventually drops like an apron over the intestinal loops of the abdomen; this is the *greater omentum,* and it forms the *omental bursa.* The mesenteries of the small and large intestine become arranged in a complicated pattern, owing to extensive loop formation of the gut. Large parts fuse with the celomic epithelium covering the body wall or organs like the kidneys; this leads to *fixation* of parts of the intestinal tube to the body wall (Figs. 346–350).

The celomic epithelia that apply themselves to the endothelial heart or *endocardium* furnish the entire muscular apparatus of the heart, the *myocardium.* The ventral *mesocardium* disappears and the dorsal *mesocardium* also regresses over most of its length. Thus the heart swings freely, being attached only near its venous inlets and arterial outlets.

Around the liver the two mesenterial epithelia form the *liver capsule* (of Glisson). The remaining mesenteries are the *hepatogastric ligament* (between liver and stomach), and the *falciform ligament,* attaching the liver to the ventral body wall.

In later development the general embryonic celom becomes divided into four chambers: *pericardium,* left and right *pleural cavities* and *abdominal* or *peritoneal cavity.* The celomic epithelia lining these cavities are distinguished as *pericardial epithelium, pleura,* and *peritoneum.*

The partitioning of the primary celom is brought about mainly by ingrowth of folds rising from the body walls. Even in amphibian larvae a pericardial sac is formed in connection with the bending of the primary heart tube, but pleural and abdominal cavities separate completely only in the mammals. The pericardium is essentially constructed from contributions of the transverse septum (Figs. 343, 350) and the paired *pleuropericardial folds* (Fig. 329e). The appearance of these folds is visibly connected with the relocation of the cardinal veins during the formation of the ventricular loop of the heart.

At the time when the transverse septum differentiates, it lies at the level of the uppermost cervical somites and ganglia (Fig. 312). Here it becomes supplied by branches of the corresponding upper cervical nerves. When later it moves down and becomes the major part of the diaphragm, these *phrenic nerves* simply grow in length but maintain their roots as well as their peripheral attachment (Fig. 343).

In mammals the *completion of a diaphragm* across the entire body cavity is brought about by downgrowth from the dorsolateral body wall of additional *pleuroperitoneal folds,* which are later met by secondary extensions from the septum, the hepatogastric ligament, the ligament of the caval vein and others. Wells distinguishes nine or, with respect to origin, possibly six subdivisions; however, the contributions of the septum and the pleuroperitoneal membranes are the most important. The diaphragm is permanently pierced by three openings (hiatuses), through which pass *esophagus, descending aorta,* and *inferior caval vein.* Temporarily, before completion of the ingrowth, the diaphragm contains a pair of passages from the pleural to the peritoneal cavities; these are the *pleuroperitoneal canals.* In Figure 348, with only the body wall over the diaphragm removed, one sees the left lung sac entering the abdominal cavity by way of this canal. At stage 30 (Fig. 349) the canal has become reduced to a mere pore. It is completely closed when the metamorphic period terminates (St. 33, Fig. 350). All normal fetuses have completely separated pericardial, pleural, and abdominal cavities.

6. DIGESTIVE SYSTEM

From the primitive endoderm arise in addition to *digestive tube, yolk sac,* and *lungs,* a number of annexal organs which often assume a glandular character.

The *derivatives of the embryonic pharynx* are summarized in Table 34, and their origin, as far as recognizable, is indicated in Figures 318

Table 34

Derivatives of the Embryonic Human Pharynx

No. of Pouch	Position	Derivatives
1	Lateral	Tympanic cavities and eustachian tubes
	Midventral	Thyroid gland
2	Lateral	Crypts of palatine tonsils
3	Dorsolateral	Lower parathyroids
	Ventrolateral	Thymus gland
4	Dorsolateral	Upper parathyroids
	Ventrolateral	Thymic rudiment
5, 6	Common lower end	Ultimobranchial body (Lateral thyroids)
7	Midventral	Trachea
	Ventrolateral	Lungbuds

and 340. Compared with those of the lower vertebrates, particularly amphibia, the endocrine glands develop very late. The *thyroid* is still an undifferentiated blastemic rudiment through the larger part of the metamorphic period. Primitive follicles develop about stage 31, but signs of true activity, as evidenced by iodine storage in its colloid, are found only in fetuses of 70 mm. (St. 35). The *palatine tonsils* and the *thymus gland*, when histologically differentiated, consist prevailingly of lymphoid tissue. The nature of the *ultimobranchial bodies* is still unclear. In the human they become incorporated into the thyroids, but their endocrine capacities have not been ascertained.

The *liver* is the first to appear of all the endodermal specializations. In the 16-somite neurulae (St. 16, Fig. 312) it is a flat rudiment composed of mesenchyme and endodermal epithelial trabeculae. As the attachment of the yolk sac narrows, it becomes a voluminous organ of sponge-like structure. The endodermal trabeculae form a meshwork of *parenchyma,* single-layered sheets of large cuboidal cells that enclose the branching *portal* and *umbilical veins* (St. 24, Fig. 347). In the fetal and adult liver these walls radiate toward the main branches of the veins and thus organize in larger units, the *liver lobules*. The lacunae are lined with mesodermal *reticulo-endothelium*. Their blood,

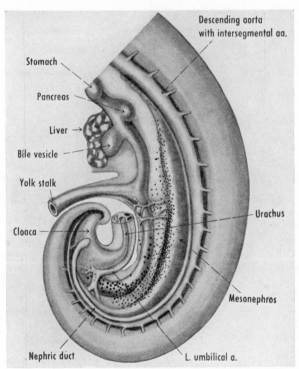

Figure 346.   Human tailbud embryo; 32 somites (St. 20). Viscera; migration of germ cells. Partial reconstruction (Witschi 1948, Carnegie Contrib. 209); × 30.

augmented by that of the *hepatic artery*, drains through two short *hepatic veins*, first into the venous sinus and later the inferior caval vein (Figs. 350, 341). Between the parenchymal cells spread the *bile canaliculi* which collect in a *hepatic duct*. In the meanwhile the gall bladder has elongated, and its narrow proximal part has become the *cystic duct*. Through its union with the hepatic duct arises the *common bile duct*, which also receives the outlet of the small *ventral pancreas* (St. 27, Fig. 348). In the course of displacements and fixation of the duodenal loop, the common bile duct with the ventral pancreas comes to lie under the duodenal ligament (St. 30, Fig. 349) and the ventral fuses with the dorsal pancreas. Subsequently the duct of the dorsal pancreas disappears, the entire pancreatic complex draining through the ventral duct into the bile duct. Certain groups of cells of the pancreas differentiate into an endocrine organ, the *islet cells* of Langerhans. They eventually will produce *insulin*. The embryonic and fetal liver differs from the normal adult by its hemopoietic function, evidenced by the presence of numerous blood islands.

During the tailbud stages, the *yolk sac* acquires a narrow stalk and

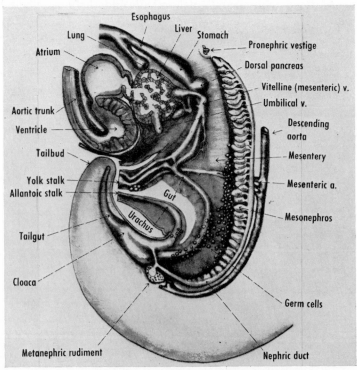

Figure 347.   Human embryo (Carnegie no. 1380) of 38 somites (St. 24). Viscera. Migration of germ cells. Partial reconstruction (Witschi 1948, Carnegie Contrib. 209); × 30.

rapidly moves away from the embryo (Figs. 319, 324). At about stage
27 (8 mm.) it breaks off from the intestine but survives, attached to
the chorion (Fig. 326). In the meanwhile it appears as if the intestine
with its triangular, dorsal mesentery were pulled by the yolk stalk into
the umbilicus. Figures 346 to 350 show how this leads to the formation
of the *umbilical hernia*. At stage 27 appears a sac-like extension in the
lower limb of the loop, the *caecum,* marking the limit between the small
intestine and colon. Before the retraction of the hernia at stage 34 the
vermiform appendix of the caecum also makes its appearance (Fig.
350).

Into the metamorphic period (sixth to eighth week) fall also the
separation of the *cloaca* into *rectum* and *urogenital sinus,* the *reduction
of the tailgut,* the *rupture of the cloacal membrane,* and the *formation of
the perineal body* (Figs. 346–350). The perineal body derives largely
from a wedge-like downgrowth of the peritoneum which at stage 24
(Fig. 347) lies as a fold between the urinary bladder and the colon,

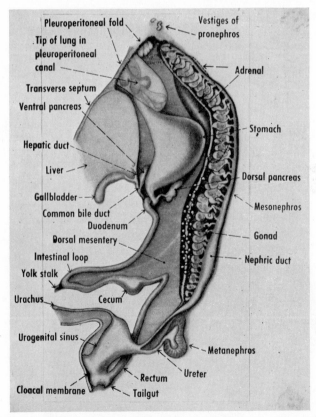

Figure 348.   Human embryo (Carnegie no. 792) 8 mm. (St. 27). Viscera.
Primordial sex gland with germ cells (relatively too large); partial reconstruction
(Witschi 1948, Carnegie Contrib. 209); × 30.

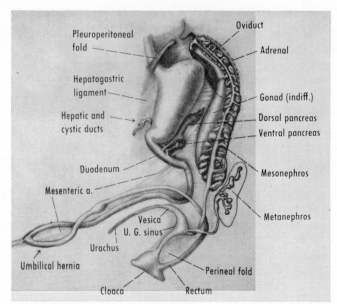

Figure 349. Human embryo in advanced metamorphosis; 14.6 mm. (Carnegie no. 1909). (St. 30). Viscera; early umbilical hernia; partial reconstruction; × 20.

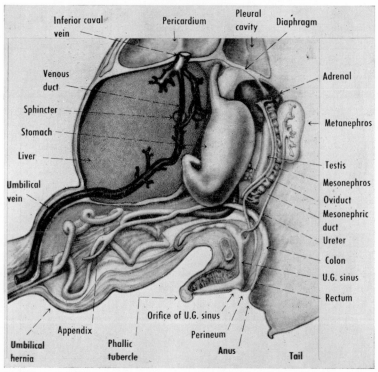

Figure 350. Human embryo at end of metamorphic period (Carnegie no. 966), 23 mm. (St. 33). Viscera; partial reconstruction; × 13.

where both enter the cloaca. From this *urorectal fold,* mesenchyme proliferates that may actively assist in the *separation of urogenital sinus and rectum.* Thus a crosswise partition forms which finally reaches the surface skin. In the perineal body there develop at least three layers of fascia and muscles, which attach themselves to the pelvic girdle. They provide an elastic bottom for the lower abdominal cavity, and sphincters, controlling the external orifices of the intestine and the urogenital organs.

7. EXCRETORY SYSTEM

The vertebrate urinary system develops from the intermediate meso-derm through differentiation of *nephrons* (Figs. 87, 88) and organiza-tion of more or less sharply defined nephric bodies or kidneys. Traditionally, the latter are distinguished as *pronephros, mesonephros,* and *metanephros,* though they do not always comprise homologous sections. The amphibian mesonephros includes also the metanephric levels, and that of the human some pronephric elements.

a. Pronephros.   At the time of early somite formation, segmented *nephrotomes* differentiate at the levels of the uppermost eight somites. In most of them a temporary central cavity, the *nephrocele,* establishes a connection with the celom by means of a funnel-shaped primitive *nephrostome.* Separate somatic and splanchnic layers are often recog-nizable, from the celom all the way to the somites (Fig. 351). Except for the formation of some fragmentary tubules and minute nephric chambers, no further differentiation occurs (Figs. 346, 347, 348). Most cells of the nephrotomes disperse or degenerate early.

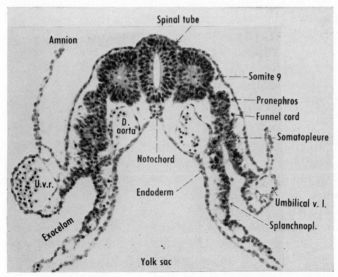

Figure 351.   Human embryo of 10 somites (St. 15); cross section at level of ninth somite; × 120 (Corner 1929; Carnegie Contrib. 112).

b. Mesonephros.   Below the eighth somite the segmental separation in the intermediate mesoderm remains incomplete. A knotty
blastema cord becomes established, the *nephrogenic cord,* in which the
differentiation of nephrons begins as early as stage 16. Progressing
rapidly following somite development, the caudal end of mesonephros
differentiation is reached at stage 24 (Fig. 347). The mesonephros
now extends from the fifth cervical to the third lumbar somitic levels
and contains over forty nephrons, the lower ones still in rudimentary
condition. The lower mesonephros reaches full size only at stage 30
(Fig. 349), when the upper half is already regressing. At stage 33 the
mesonephros has descended into the sacral region. Regression with
detachment of the nephrons from the nephric duct and eventual complete disappearance progresses now from both the upper and the lower
ends. Only the small middle region persists, which is connected with
the sex gland. As *epididymis* it becomes a part of the seminal duct
system in the male, but it is also retained as a non-functional vestige
in the female (sometimes designated as epoophoron; Fig. 364c).

In the development of the mesonephric body the *cervical segments*
(somite levels 9 to 12) play a distinctive role. Though continuous with
the lower mesonephros, they exhibit characteristically pronephric features. Most important is the faculty of producing a *nephric duct.* Its
primordium arises from a fusion of the distal ends of the four to six
cervical nephrons. This rudiment then grows independently downward along the blastema cord. It gains, not by assimilation of new
tissues, but by proliferation of the cells at its own free end. At lower
somitic levels, additional nephrons differentiate only after the tip of
the duct has passed alongside the blastema cord. It is probable that the
development of the true mesonephric elements depends somehow on
the presence of the duct (compare experimental evidence in the chick;
Fig. 202). Their tubules grow distally toward the duct, fuse with its
wall, and eventually open into its lumen. Somewhat later, a funnel-
shaped depression forms in the *thickened epithelium* at the upper end
of the nephric body. By terminal growth of its stem, it forms the *oviduct*
(Figs. 349, 350) which runs along the lateral side of the nephric duct.
In birds and particularly in amphibians a close relationship of the
oviducal primordium to the pronephros is even more clearly evident.

With regard to *histologic differentiation,* the human mesonephros
occupies an intermediate position between the distinctly functional type
of the ungulates and the non-functional type of the murids. In the
former the mesonephros gives every indication of active urinary excretion at the time before the metanephros is sufficiently developed to take
over this function. The passage from the kidneys into the bladder and
the allantois is open. But the allantois being a closed sac, it causes some
back-pressure and the mild degree of hydronephrosis which is so characteristic for embryos of the pig. On the other hand, not only do rats

and mice lack a reservoir into which to void urine, but the mesonephros remains rudimentary and non-functional. The nephrons are tubules without glomeruli. The longitudinal section through the human mesonephric body of Figure 352 shows an abundance of large renal corpuscles with blood-filled glomeruli. Obviously there exists some

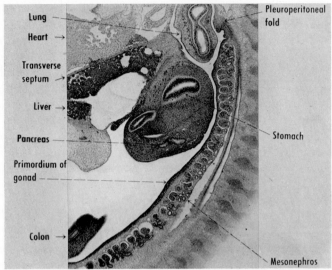

Figure 352.   Human embryo, 8 mm. (St. 26), longitudinal section through mesonephros; × 30 (courtesy Carnegie Institution).

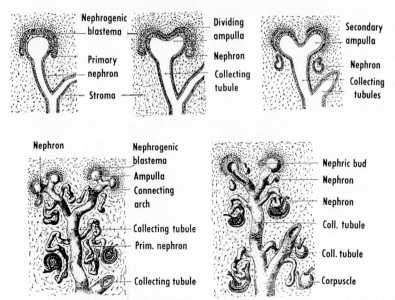

Figure 353.   Development of collecting tubules and nephrons of the metanephros; diagram (Corning 1925).

excretory activity and reabsorption, as indicated also by the histologic differentiation of proximal and distal segments of the tubules. But judging from the small size of the bladder, no urine is released before the rupture of the cloacal membrane.

c. Metanephros. When at stage 24 mesonephric expansion comes to a standstill, a bud pushes out from the lower nephric duct and lodges itself in the caudal remnant of the nephric blastema cord (Fig. 347). Thus the primordial metanephros is a composite of double origin. The diverticulum of the nephric duct by stretching and terminal branching first differentiates into *ureter* (metanephric duct) and *pelvis,* the central cavity of the kidney (Figs. 348, 349). From each major branch or calyx of the pelvis sprout bundles of smaller tubules; each continues branching, and thus forms a small tree of straight *collecting tubules.* The end of each forms a small ampulla. It becomes covered with a cap of dense nephrogenic blastema which in time produces a pair of *nephrons* (Fig. 353). Each nephron, as it matures, differentiates into a *renal corpuscle* with glomerulus and capsule, and a *convoluted tubule* with distinct proximal and distal segments, connected by Henle's loop. While the distal end of the convoluted tubule attaches itself to the adjoining branch of the collecting tubule, new ampullae rise from the stem of the latter. Thus generations upon *generations of tubules* are formed and the number of nephrons increases in geometric progression. Even though the first few generations later are resorbed, by the time of birth at least 12 generations are present and the kidney contains over a million renal corpuscles.

Secretory activity is established some time during the second fetal period (St. 34). Davies comes to the conclusion that the immature fetal glomeruli are quite permeable to proteins and sugar (physiologic proteinuria and glycosuria). Both substances are present in the amniotic fluid in higher concentrations at 10 weeks than at term. The data contained in Table 35 are significant, even though the amniotic fluid is by no means identical with the fetal urine. Davies also shows that some of the proteins that pass through the glomeruli are immediately reabsorbed by the proximal tubules.

Table 35

Concentration of Some Constituents of the Human Amniotic Fluid

Substance	At 10 Weeks	At Term
	Mg. per 100 cc.	Mg. per 100 cc.
Urea nitrogen	9	23
Uric acid	3.2	4
Total protein	450	230
Glucose	63	20
Fructose	3.5	2.0

In the late embryonic and early fetal stages the metanephroi ascend retroperitoneally until they become lodged permanently near the diaphragm. The ureters accordingly grow considerably in length. As a consequence partly of absorption of the lower nephric ducts into the urogenital sinus and partly of migratory displacement, the lower ends of the ureters shift from the mesonephric ducts to the neck of the urinary bladder (Figs. 349, 350).

Chapter 30

Organogenesis. III

8. ADRENALS AND SEX GLANDS

The intermediate mesoderm and its first derivative, the nephrogenic cords, are not entirely spent in the formation of the kidneys. During the early blastemic stages some cells seem to wander off into the surrounding mesenchyme; but more important is the participation in the formation of the adrenal and gonadal primordia. As a matter of convenience the entire blastema at the level of the mesonephros is designated as the *mesonephric blastema cord*. This seems justified because of its topographic location. Moreover, recent experiments with amphibians have revealed that at blastemic stages the cells of the intermediate mesoderm still are pluripotential; they may differentiate either into nephrons, adrenal cortex, or gonadal medulla, depending on environmental influences (Chapter 10).

a. **Adrenal.** The early stages of human adrenal development barely differ from those described for the chick (Figs. 185, 193, 194, 195). During the tailbud period the cortical elements become organized at the expense of the blastema remnants of the upper one-third of the mesonephric cords. The organ begins to protrude into the abdominal cavity at early metamorphic stages (St. 27, Fig. 348). The location of these bodies along the medial borders of the urinary mesonephroi suggests that they arise mainly from the inner nephrotome (Fig. 354). The medullary elements detach themselves from the large ganglionic plexuses of the sympathetic system, which have aggregated along the aorta

536

and particularly around the root of the mesenteric artery. In an embryo of 14 mm. crown-rump length (St. 30, Fig. 354), one finds these cells collecting at the medial border of the now quite large cortical body. To some degree they also infiltrate between the loosely interwoven cortical strands. However, the adult structure with clear separation of three cortical layers and one medullary layer is only established during childhood. The adrenal of the human fetus grows to a size out of proportion to that of other organs (Fig. 350). However, it shrinks immediately following birth, no matter whether delivery was early or late. The tendency of the adrenal cortical cells to form strands with cylindric arrangement of the cell nuclei is reminiscent of tubule formation in the urinary mesonephros and in the gonadal medulla.

   b. Primordial Sex Gland.   The sex glands originate as composites of elements from three distinct sources: *primordial germ cells, peritoneal cortex* and *mesonephric medulla* (Fig. 94).

   The *germ cells* are probably set apart from the body or soma cells in the course of early cleavage. In various invertebrates the entire *germ* track has been traced from the cleaving egg to the formation of the gonads. The *somatic cells* are split off from *stem cells* that carry the *germ plasm,* during the first four to eight cleavage steps. The stem cells then become *primordial gonia* which by further mitotic steps only enlarge their own number but never contribute further somatic elements (Fig. 2). On the other hand, somatic cells do not transform into germ cells. It was shown in the introductory chapter that in another type of invertebrates some totipotent stem cells persist as so-called residual blastema cells. They may be scattered throughout the entire body or localized in more restricted regions. In ascidians, annelids, turbelarians, and many others, the blastema cells can produce gonia as well as soma cells, particularly in regeneration and in asexual reproduction. The vertebrates quite definitely belong to the first type. Even though the earliest stages of the germ

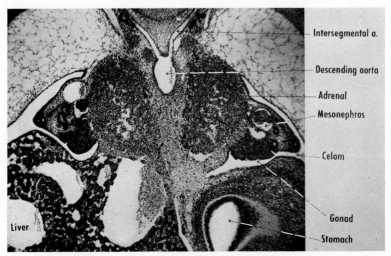

Figure 354.   Human embryo, 14 mm. (St. 30); cross section through mesonephros, sex gland, and adrenal bodies; × 40.

track are not completely known, it is well established that in the adult no toti-potent blastema cells remain.

In human development the germ cells first become easily identifiable in embryos of 12 to 13 somites (St. 15). They are located in a fairly circumscribed area of the endodermal yolk-sac epithelium just above the allantoic rudiment (Fig. 312). They are not very different from the en-doderm cells, with which they mingle. Their number seems to vary within the limits of 30 and 50. Immediately afterward their migratory history begins. In the course of about one week (the fifth week), they transfer into the mesoderm of the primordial gonadal folds, along the inner edges of the mesonephric bodies (Table 36). In neurulae of stage 16 (Fig. 312) the majority have already become lodged in the ventral wall of the gut. This may largely be a passive transfer, since parts of the yolk-sac epithelium contribute directly to the formation of the midgut. However, some already have left the endodermal epithe-lium, starting active migration of their own. A few days later, the gonia have increased their number by mitotic division to one thousand or more and swarm toward the dorsal root of the mesentery (Figs. 346, 347, 355a). They have the shape of large amebae (Fig. 355b) that work their way through the dense tissue. When actively moving, they stretch out pseudopodial processes; when at rest, they assume globular shape and become temporarily enclosed by somatic cells. At the end of the fifth week they turn around the celomic angle and reach their goal and destination, entering the mesonephric fold.

The primordial germ cells thus are of extragonadal origin. When they arrive at the site along the mesonephric bodies they combine with two somatic elements: *cortex* and *medulla*. The former is a thickened peritoneal epithelium, the latter consists of strands and condensations of mesonephric blastema. A fine clear line separates these rudiments;

Table 36

Migration of Germ Cells from the Yolk Sac to the Gonadal Primordia

(Actual number of germ cells are given for the youngest three embryos, general estimates for the older three)

STAGE (No. somites)	YOLK SAC	GUT	GUT MESEN-CHYME	MESENTERY, CELOM. ANGLE	GONAD PRIM.	TOTAL	FIG.
16 (16)	24	85	—	—	—	109	312
20 (32)	—	146	242	978	—	1366	346
24 (38)	7	110	19	315	—	451*	347
25	—	—	—	few	many	incr.	
26	—	—	—	very few	most	,,	
27	—	—	—	—	all	,,	348

* Probably incomplete count.

it is the *albuginea,* a thin layer of mesenchyme (Figs. 348, 356). Upon arrival, the germ cells lodge themselves preferably among the cells of the cortex, but some also enter the medullary cords. Within a few days both cortex and medulla gain rapidly in depth while the germ cells increase further in number (Fig. 357). The *primordial sex glands* are not yet separated from the mesonephric bodies but adhere broadly to their surface. *Mesorchia* and *mesovaria,* the suspensory ligaments of the sex glands, form gradually during the period of sexual differentiation.

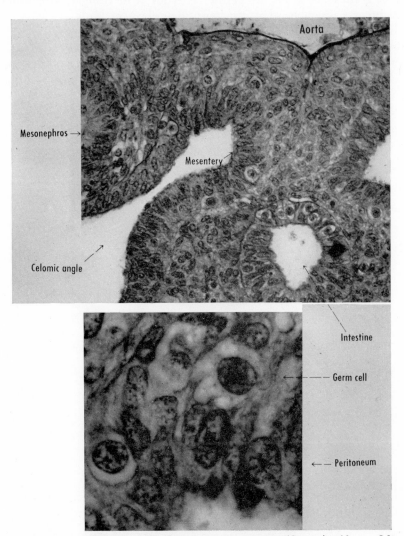

Figure 355.   Human tailbud embryo, 32 somites (St. 20). Above: Migration of primordial germ cells. Large germ cells are contained in the gut, the mesentery, and at the celomic angle; × 333. Below: Ameboid germ cell; × 1333 (Witschi 1948, Carnegie Contrib. 209).

c. Sex Differentiation.   The sexual differentiation of the gonads becomes recognizable during the last stages of metamorphosis. At stage 30 (Fig. 349) the tip of the indifferent sex gland overlaps with the lower pole of the adrenal. Cross sections through this region show a spurt in growth of the medulla with further accentuation of its medullary cords (Fig. 354). At stages 31 to 33 it can be seen that either the medulla or the cortex becomes dominant, taking the lead in further differentiation. The dominant system gains rapidly in size and in number of germ cells, while its partner is reduced to vestigial proportions. The process resembles that previously described for birds.

In *testicular differentiation* a definite basement membrane sets off a thin peritoneal epithelium from the deeper layer of the cortex (Fig. 359). The latter attaches itself to the medullary cords and becomes itself organized in short radial cords. The joined cortical and medullary

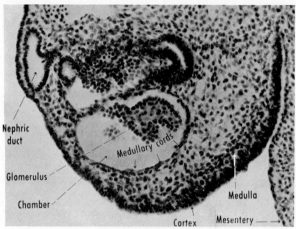

Figure 356.   Indifferent stage of primordial sex gland; cross section, human embryo, stage 27; × 200 (Witschi 1948, Carnegie Contrib. 209).

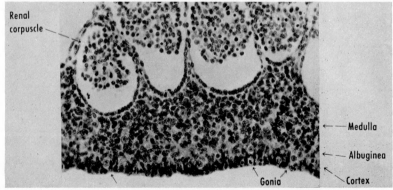

Figure 357.   Late indifferent stage of sex gland; longitudinal section, human embryo, stage 28; × 200 (Witschi 1948, Carnegie Contrib. 209).

Fig. 358

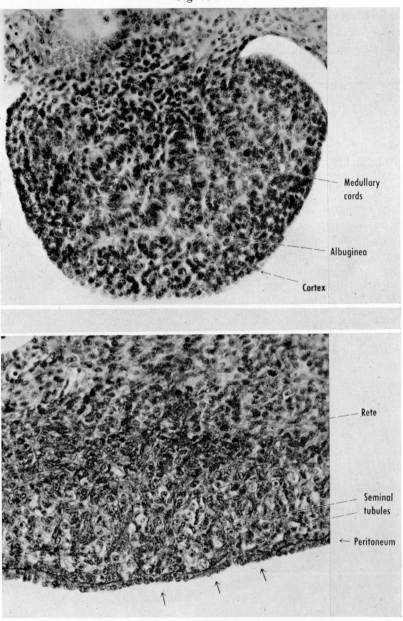

Fig. 359

Figure 358.   Earliest stage of ovarian differentiation; cross section, human embryo, stage 32; × 250 (courtesy Carnegie Institution).

Figure 359.   Earliest stage of testicular differentiation; longitudinal section, human embryo, stage 32. Arrows point to primitive seminal tubules; × 250 (courtesy Carnegie Institution).

cords become the *primitive seminal tubules* (Fig. 359). All germ cells, whether previously located in the cortex or in the medulla, become included and are now *spermatogonia*. In the separation of the cortical layer into cords, the mesenchyme of the albuginea plays an important role. It grows between the cylinders, investing them with fibrous walls, and then spreads peripherally under the peritoneum. Thus the albuginea displaces itself to the subsurface. It is accompanied by the major blood vessels which subsequently are arranged in a characteristic network that may easily be seen shining through the surface epithelium. Figure 360 (St. 35) shows a late phase of these changes. At the right periphery a patch of cortex still adheres to the peritoneum but is also in communication with medullary cords. The course of the blood vessels in the hilum between the seminal tubules and through the albuginea is easily recognized, though in the section the vessels are cut in short pieces. At this stage the mesonephros still maintains its structure of a kidney. In an older specimen, just entering the last fetal stage, the renal corpuscles have all but disappeared and the mesonephros is transforming into a purely tubular system of efferent and storage ductules, the *epididymis*.

The section shown in Figure 361 is particularly interesting because it contains also a well developed nephrostome (arrow in Fig. 361) that connects the peritoneal epithelium with the proximal part of the medullary complex, the primordial *rete of the testis*. The seminal tubules have become arranged into lobules. By fusion with each other, as well as by stretching, they develop into meandering long secondary

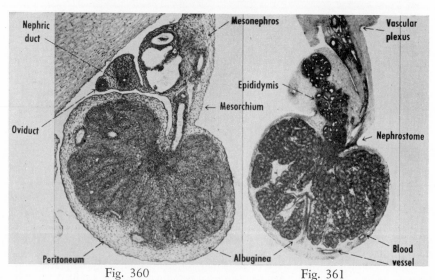

Fig. 360   Fig. 361

Figure 360.   Testis of 56-mm. human fetus (St. 25); × 56.
Figure 361.   Testis of 180-mm. human fetus (St. 35/36); × 15.

tubules. The intertubular space still contains only few *interstitial cells* (of Leydig). It is, however, one of the most distinctive features of human testicular development that in the last fetal phase the interstitial gland develops to such an extent that in bulk it about equals the tubular system.

Ovarial development is mainly a continuation of the developmental type of the indifferent stage. The cortex remains permanently connected with the surface epithelium. The albuginea maintains the position between cortex and medulla and, by widening into a distinct layer of fibrous connective tissue, provides the first indication of ovarian differentiation (St. 31, Fig. 358). Spreading blood vessels further emphasize the separation of the cortical and medullary rudiments. The medullary cords have not yet started to regress (Fig. 358) and contain a good number of germ cells. But they have reached the peak of their development. In a fetus of 60 mm. (St. 35, Fig. 362) the medulla remains nearly unchanged even in size. It still contains hundreds of germ cells which one may call spermatogonia. None of the medullary germ cells ever seem to join the cortex; ordinarily they degenerate during the last fetal stage. In the cortex the germ cells have greatly multiplied. They are arranged in cords which seem to grow toward the medulla. In fact, however, the movement is centrifugal. Even the albugineal zone moves out and the surface of the ovary is rapidly enlarging.

The germ cells of the ovaries enter maturation stages much earlier than those of the testes. In the section under discussion (Fig. 362) the inner halves of the cortical cords ("egg tubes" of Pflüger) contain ovocytes of the various synaptic stages. Mitoses are now confined to

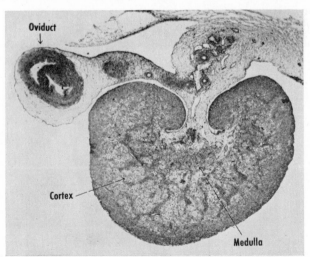

Figure 362.   Ovary of 60-mm. human fetus (St. 35); × 50; note central medullary remnant with gonia.

the more peripheral, ovogonial layer. Strands of darkly staining cells grow out from the medulla and between the cortical cords; later they establish contact with the individual auxocytes, furnishing them with *theca cells.* The origin of the follicle or *granulosa cells* is less clear. Probably they arise from the particular celomic epithelium which serves in the formation of the cortex. At four to six months there are very few ovogonia left; but the two ovaries contain about 5 million ovocytes. Since during the reproductive life of women rarely more than a total of 400 eggs leave the ovaries by ovulation, and since on the other hand the ovaries are found empty of germ cells at the climacteric, it is evident that the vast majority must disappear by degeneration. This process starts at the fetal level and reaches a high peak toward the time of birth, when many primary follicles enter the last maturation stages, but atrophy following birth.

> *True hermaphrodism,* meaning the simultaneous or successive presence of testicular and ovarian parts in the same individual, including both male and female germ cells, is very rare in mammals, and particularly in man. Complete maturation of eggs and sperm has never been reported, nor even fertility of one or the other of the sexes. In the pig, where rudimentary hermaphrodism has frequently been observed, the effect seems to result from underdevelopment of the medullary portion in males. The upper part of the gland, remaining without a medullary rudiment, is capable only of cortical, i.e., ovarial, differentiation (Fig. 363).

9. ACCESSORY SEX ORGANS

The *accessory sex organs* fall into two quite distinct groups according to their development from either *discrete primordia* or *neutral primordia.* To the first belong the gonaducts: *sperm ducts* and *oviducts.* They are early laid down as separate primordia, running parallel to each other in full length (Fig. 350). Sexual differentiation involves the maintenance and further development of one and suppression of the other. The *nephric duct,* which in the male sex becomes the *deferent duct,* reaches the wall of the cloaca at the earliest tailbud stages (Fig.

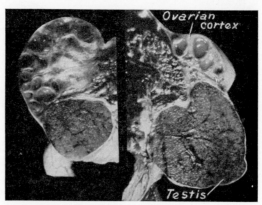

Figure 363.   Hermaphrodite sex glands of a pig (Krediet 1933).

346), but usually breaks into its lumen only at the end of the embryonic period (St. 24–25, Fig. 347). The oviducts are still incomplete in the 23 mm. embryo shown in Figure 350. But before stage 33 ends, the left and right ducts have grown down to the dorsal wall of the

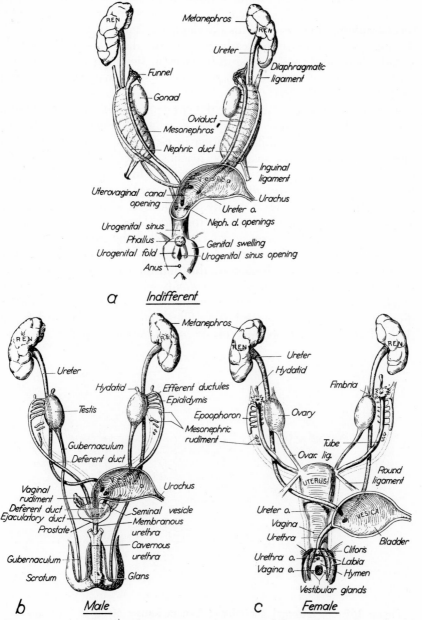

Figure 364.   Urogenital systems in man; *a*, indifferent stage, *b*, male differentiation, *c*, female differentiation. Diagrams (modified, after Corning 1925).

urogenital sinus. On their way they cross over the nephric ducts and fuse into a single, median *uterovaginal canal*. The upper, paired ducts are now called *tubes*. So far the development is identical in both sexes. Both have double sets of gonaducts as they enter the first fetal period (St. 34). But soon afterward a rapid regression of the heterologous system sets in, while the concordant one grows and acquires its higher specializations (Fig. 364). This development starts in fetuses of about 34 mm. At 55 to 60 mm. (early St. 35) the ducts at the level of the gonads show very considerable differences in size (Figs. 360 and 362). Small remnants of the heterologous duct system may persist even in the adult (see Fig. 364).

The second group arises from the *urogenital sinus* and its external opening. They constitute a complex of *neutral primordia* which have the capacity of further differentiation in either the male or the female direction. As a rule the male type reaches higher levels of differentiation than the female. The male urogenital sinus becomes subdivided into an upper, *prostatic urethra* and a lower, *membranous urethra*. The upper part becomes a highly complicated system, receiving the *vesical urethra* (neck of bladder), the *ejaculatory ducts*, and the vestigial remnant of the uterovaginal canal called the *utricle*. The ejaculatory ducts are the ends of the *deferent ducts* below the outpocketing *seminal vesicles*. This division of the urethra receives its name from the numerous endodermal *prostatic glands* which sprout from its wall.

The homologies in the development of the *external genitalia* are illustrated in Figures 364 and 365. The *urethral folds* to the left and right of the external opening of the sinus remain separate as *minor*

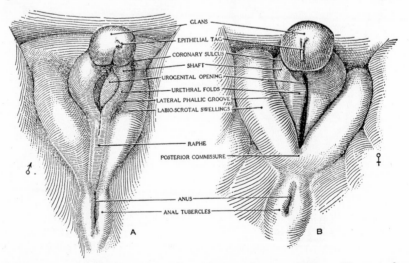

Figure 365. External genitalia of human fetuses of 45 to 50 mm., showing early male (A) and female (B) differentiation (Spaulding 1921, Carnegie Contrib. 61).

labia in the female fetus, while in the male they become united at the crest in the so-called *raphe*. This leads to the formation of a fourth or *cavernous section* of the male urethra. The *glans* of the penis and the female *clitoris* derive from the *phallic* tubercle, which appears early at the ventral circumference of the sinus.

In man, as in most other mammals, the testes leave the abdominal cavities and descend into the scrotal sacs. So-called *labio-scrotal swellings,* laterally accompanying the urethral folds, appear in fetuses of both sexes. Like all other parts of the external genitalia they are of identical shape and proportion throughout the indifferent phase. Externally recognizable sex differences appear only at the end of stage 34 (Fig. 365). The *descent of the testes* is preceded by the formation of two evaginations of the abdominal cavity. From the peritoneum issue a pair of *vaginal sacs* that pass through the muscular abdominal wall above the pubis and, about the seventh month, enter the scrotal swellings. The passages through the muscle layers become the *inguinal canals.* They remain incomplete in female fetuses. During the last two or three months of pregnancy the testes, together with epididymis and part of the deferent duct, descend retroperitoneally through the inguinal canal and into the scrotal sac (Fig. 364).

10. SEX DETERMINATION

The age-old search for the factors that dominate sex differentiation has, in our century, been rewarded with success in various fields of research, particularly genetics, developmental physiology, and chemistry.

The discovery of the *sex chromosomes* revealed a simple mechanism for the genetic perpetuation of a 1:1 sex ratio. Although in the human species the number of chromosomes in diploid cells is 48 in both sexes, in the male one pair consists of unequal mates, X and Y (Fig. 366, upper row, last pair). Corresponding female chromosome sets have only equal pairs, the *sex chromosomes* being designated by XX. Consequently through the meiotic process following chromosome conjugation, the male must produce sperms with either X or Y in equal numbers, while the female produces only one kind of eggs, all carrying the X chromosome. Figure 367 gives an interpretation of these facts on the assumption that *sex is genetically determined* on the basis of a *quantita-*

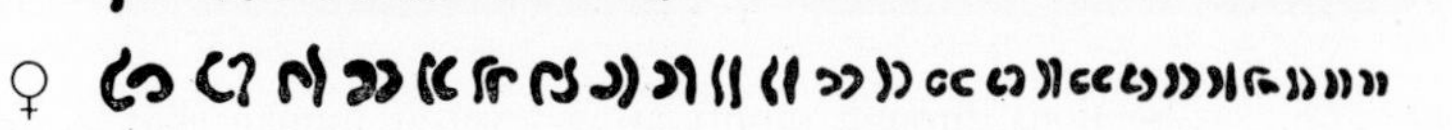

Figure 366.   Diploid sets of human chromosomes, arranged in pairs, according to size and shape. At the end of the male series an uneven pair (XY) (Evans and Swezy 1929).

tive balance between male-determining (M) *and female-determining
genes* (F and f); the latter are localized in the X and Y chromosomes.

Recently Barr discovered a sex difference in chromatin distribution
in the nuclei of resting cells (Fig. 368). The relationship of the single,
compact body of *"sex chromatin"* of female nuclei to the sex chromosomes is not clear; but the regularity of its occurrence makes sex
identification possible from skin biopsies or from smears of oral mucosa.

The method of Barr already has become a valuable aid in the investigation of
the many types of abnormal sex development in man. Evidently genetic and physiologic factors combine in the determination of the normal sexes and of sex intergrades
in human development, much as in the more fully analyzed amphibians (cf. Chapter 10). However, research in this field and in that of mammalian sex development
in the broader sense is complicated by the special conditions of pregnancy, under
which the embryo exists during the critical period of sexual differentiation (St.
30–33). The high concentrations of pregnancy hormones cannot be without influence on gonad development. So far experiments with mammals have borne
mainly on the development of secondary sex characters; but progress in regard
to primary sex differentiation seems imminent.

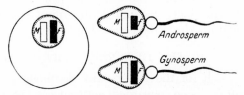

Figure 367.   Chromosomal and genic sex constitution of the three classes of
gametes in man (diagram). Only the two sex chromosomes are drawn in each diagram; their height represents the quantitative value of the male (M) or female
(F, f) determining sex genes. In man the y chromosomes may have lost all importance for sex determination; the value of f would then be zero.

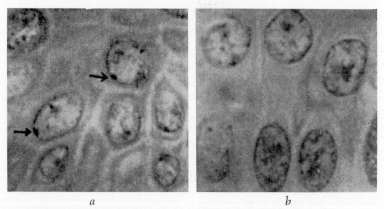

a   b

Figure 368.   Sections through proliferating layer of human skin. *a,* Female;
arrows pointing to sex chromatin; *b,* male, without sex chromatin; × 1600 (Moore,
Graham, Barr 1953).

11. ENDOCRINE ACTIVITIES IN THE FETUS

The *chorionic syntrophoblast* can be considered as the first endocrine organ of the human embryo. It starts production of the *chorionic gonadotrophin* immediately following implantation, i.e., at the gastrula stage. The organ is peculiar insofar as the hormone is liberated not into the embryonic, but the maternal system (Fig. 298). Its target is the corpus luteum of the mother's ovaries.

The *persisting endocrine organs* differentiate comparatively later and more slowly in mammalian embryos than in the amphibians with their free-living larvae.

The first evidence of "intrafetal" endocrine activity is possibly presented by the *adrenals,* which in man are of surprisingly large size throughout fetal life, and hypertrophy even as early as in embryos of stage 30 (Fig. 354). It has long been known that in acephalic monsters without hypophyses the adrenals are very small. Evidently the adrenocorticotrophic hormone (ACTH) of the mother enters only in negligible amounts through the placenta. Recent experiments with amphibians and with rodents suggest that the hyperactivity of the fetal hypophysis is a response to the high concentration of estrogenic hormones of pregnancy.

During the metamorphic stages the *thyroid* grows slowly from a blastemic primordium to the characteristic adult shape of a flat and broad shield. A tendency of follicular differentiation is recognizable at stage 31, but colloid does not appear before the first fetal period. If radioiodine (I^{131}) is injected into the circulation of mothers 13 weeks pregnant, it soon appears and collects in the peripheral layer of fetal follicles (St. 35; Fig. 369). Selective accumulation of iodine is usually regarded as evidence of hormonal activity in the thyroid follicles. The

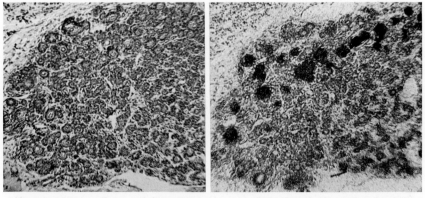

Figure 369.   Parts of consecutive sections through a lobe of the thyroid of a 13-week-old human fetus (St. 35). Left: Control, normally stained; right: radio-autograph, showing accumulation of I^{131} in the peripheral follicles; × 145 (courtesy of T. Evans).

late initiation indicates that thyroxin is not necessary for the stimulation of metabolic processes in embryos and early fetuses.

Significant observations on *testicular activity* have been made by Jost in experiments on the rabbit. If the *testes are removed* in utero at the fetal age of 19 days, i.e., at the time when the primary oviducts and nephric ducts still are sexually indifferent (cf. Fig. 350, St. 33), the former will persist while the nephric ducts disappear. In short, in the absence of gonads, genetic males and females both acquire the female type of gonaduct system. On the other hand, if the *hypophysis is removed* at 19 days, the testes still induce the reduction of the oviducts and the development of the nephric ducts into deferent ducts. However, at 28 days the external genitalia are underdeveloped, indicating the lack of androgenic hormones. These experiments may express a *double function of the testes:* as endocrine organs they produce androgenic hormones and depend on hypophyseal stimulation; as inductors of male differentiation of the duct system, they become active independently. Such a double function is also suggested by implantation experiments (Fig. 370). Whereas a *testis* implanted next to an ovary at the age of 19 days induces a partial masculinization of the ducts, spreading with a declining gradient of effectiveness, similarly placed crystalline hormones do not affect duct differentiation, but stimulate the growth of the external genitalia.

These experiments sustain a rule that endocrines stimulate already differentiated organs, but will not induce primordial differentiation. However, the borderline between hormones and inductor substances is not sharply defined. In fact, continued experimentation may greatly change present concepts.

In keeping with the animal experiments, one observes in human cases of complete *gonadal agenesis* (congenital absence of sex glands) that the entire gonaducts and the external genitalia are of the female type.

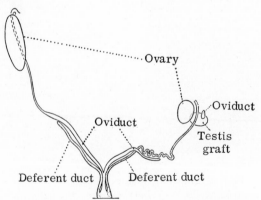

Figure 370.   Genital tract of a 28-day-old female rabbit fetus, with testis grafted on 20th day close to left ovary (Jost 1947).

Yet, the sex chromatin test reveals that such individuals often are genetically of male sex. As *born castrates* who even at embryologic stages never had more than very rudimentary gonads, they exhibit a distinctive constitutional type. It results from a pre- and postnatal development that remained unaffected by hormones and inductors of individual gonads. Possible influences of maternal and chorionic hormones are difficult to assess, but no obvious relationships have been recognized so far. Though agonadal individuals have a uterus, they never menstruate; nor do they show puberal breast development. The voice remains unbroken and they grow no beards. The pelvis does not assume the broad feminine type. With hormone therapy it is possible to induce a puberal development of the retarded female organs. However, neither sex glands nor fertility can be restored by such treatment.

Bibliography

A comprehensive *Bibliography of Vertebrate Embryology* was published by C. S. Minot in the Memoirs of the Boston Society of Natural History, 1893, Vol. IV (pp. 487–614). This and the lists contained in O. Hertwig's Handbuch of 1906 still serve as guides to the older literature. The vastly increasing number of reports and monographs of the present century are listed, classified, and partly also abstracted by various bibliographic services. Moreover, embryologic publication is largely concentrated in some professional journals and serials or monographs. Proficiency in finding the literature pertaining to a given subject is equally important for students, teachers, and research workers. The following lists are intended only as an introduction to the use of the embryologic literature and as a guide to collateral reading. The titles under Special References are followed by parenthetic references to appropriate chapters of this book. No exhaustive coverage or documentation is attempted.

BIBLIOGRAPHIC SERVICES

Biological Abstracts. Section B: Basic medical sciences. University of Pennsylvania, Philadelphia.
Excerpta Medica. Section I: Anatomy, Anthropology, Embryology, and Histology. Amsterdam.
Zoological Record. Zool. Soc., London.
Berichte über die wissenschaftliche Biologie. Springer, Berlin; Göttingen, Heidelberg.

JOURNALS AND SERIAL PUBLICATIONS

Contributions to Embryology. Carnegie Institution of Washington. Publications. Washington, D. C.
Annual Report of the Director of the Department of Embryology. Carnegie Institution of Washington. Year Book. Washington, D. C.
The American Journal of Anatomy. Wistar Institute, Philadelphia.
The Anatomical Record. Wistar Institute, Philadelphia.
Journal of Experimental Zoology. Wistar Institute, Philadelphia.
Journal of Embryology and Experimental Morphology. Clarendon Press, Oxford.
Journal of Morphology. Wistar Institute, Philadelphia.
Archives de Biologie. Valliant-Carmanne, Liège. Masson, Paris.

Archives d' Anatomie microscopique et de Morphologie expérimentale. Masson, Paris.

Wilhelm Roux' Archiv für Entwicklungsmechanik der Organismen. Springer, Berlin; Göttingen, Heidelberg. J. F. Bergmann, München.

Zeitschrift für Anatomie und Entwicklungsgeschichte. Springer, Berlin; Göttingen, Heidelberg.

Ergebnisse der Anatomie und Entwicklungsgeschichte. Springer, Berlin; Göttingen, Heidelberg.

GENERAL TEXTS

A. TERMINOLOGY

Emmel, V. E. 1927. The B N A arranged as an outline of regional and systematic anatomy. Wistar Institute, Philadelphia. 2nd Ed. xxxi & 256 pp. The Basel Nomenclature of Anatomy (abbr. B N A) of 1895 is still the authoritative list of accepted anatomic names. It is now being revised, and a tentative new list of Nomina Anatomica was presented at the Sixth International Congress of Anatomists in Paris, 1955.

Dorland, W. A. N. 1954. The American Illustrated Medical Dictionary. W. B. Saunders Co., Philadelphia, London. 22nd Ed. xxvi & 1736 pp.

Roux, W. 1912. Terminologie der Entwicklungsmechanik der Tiere und Pflanzen. Engelmann, Leipzig. xii & 465 pp.

Henderson, I. F., and W. D. Henderson. 1949. A Dictionary of Scientific Terms. Oliver and Boyd, Edinburgh, London. 4th Ed. xvi & 480 pp.

Jaeger, E. C. 1950. A Source Book of Biological Names and Terms. Charles C Thomas, Springfield, Baltimore. 2nd Ed. xxxv & 287 pp.

B. HISTORY

Meyer, A. W. 1939. The Rise of Embryology. Stanford University Press. xv & 367 pp.

Needham, J. 1934. A History of Embryology. Cambridge University Press, Cambridge. xiii & 274 pp.

Roux, Wilhelm 1905. Die Entwicklungsmechanik ein neuer Zweig der biologischen Wissenschaft. Engelmann, Leipzig. xiv & 283 pp. This is a report on the first twenty years of experimental embryology, with extensive historical and theoretical considerations by the founder of the "new branch of biologic science."

C. GENETICS AND EVOLUTION

De Beer, G. R. 1951. Embryos and Ancestors. Clarendon Press, Oxford. Rev. Ed. xii & 159 pp.

De Robertis, E. D. P., W. W. Novinski, and F. S. Saez. 1954. General Cytology. W. B. Saunders Co., Philadelphia. 2nd Ed. vii & 456 pp.

Gates, R. R. 1946. Human Genetics. The Macmillan Co., New York. 2 vols. 1518 pp.

Goldschmidt, R. B. 1955. Theoretical Genetics. University of California Press, Berkeley, Los Angeles. x & 563 pp.

D. EXPERIMENTAL AND CHEMICAL EMBRYOLOGY

Barth, L. G. 1949. Embryology. Dryden Press, New York. xiv & 330 pp.

Brachet, J. 1950. Chemical Embryology. Interscience Publishers, New York. xiii & 533 pp.

Hamburger, V. 1947. A Manual of Experimental Embryology. University of Chicago Press, Chicago. xvii & 213 pp.

Huxley, J. S., and G. R. De Beer. 1934. The Elements of Experimental Embryology. Cambridge University Press, Cambridge. xii & 514 pp.

Kühn, A. 1955. Vorlesungen über Entwicklungsphysiologie. Springer, Berlin; Göttingen, Heidelberg. ix & 506 pp.

Lehmann, F. E. 1945. Einführung in die physiologische Embryologie. Birkhäuser, Basel. 414 pp.

Needham, J. 1931. Chemical Embryology. The Macmillan Co., New York. 3 vols. xxii & 2021 pp.

Needham, J. 1942. Biochemistry and Morphogenesis. Cambridge University Press, Cambridge. xvi & 785 pp.

Raven, C. P. 1954. An Outline of Developmental Physiology. McGraw-Hill Book Co., New York. viii & 216 pp.

Spemann, H. 1938. Embryonic Development and Induction. Yale University Press, New Haven. xii & 401 pp.

Weiss, P. 1939. Principles of Development. A Text in Experimental Embryology. Henry Holt & Co., New York. xix & 601 pp.

Willier, B. H., P. A. Weiss, and V. Hamburger. 1955. Analysis of Development. W. B. Saunders Co., Philadelphia. xii & 735 pp.

E. PHYSIOLOGY AND ENDOCRINOLOGY

Asdell, S. A. 1946. Patterns of Mammalian Reproduction. Comstock Publishing Co., Ithaca. x & 437 pp.

Barcroft, J. 1947. Researches on Pre-Natal Life. Charles C Thomas, Springfield. Ill. xiii & 292 pp.

Corner, G. W. 1947. The Hormones in Human Reproduction. Princeton University Press. Rev. Ed. xix & 281 pp.

Gesell, A. 1945. The Embryology of Behavior. Harper & Bros., New York. 2nd Ed. xix & 289 pp.

Jones, I. C., and P. Eckstein. 1956. The Comparative Endocrinology of Vertebrates. I. The Comparative Physiology of Reproduction and the Effects of Sex Hormones in Vertebrates. Memoirs of the Society for Endocrinology., No. 4. Cambridge University Press, Cambridge. x & 253 pp.

Parkes, A. S. 1952. Marshall's Physiology of Reproduction. Longmans, Green & Co.; London, New York, Toronto. 3rd Ed. Vol. 2. xx & 880 pp.

Selye, H. 1947. Textbook of Endocrinology. Acta Endocrinologica, University of Montreal. xiv & 914 pp.

Williams, R. H. 1955. Textbook of Endocrinology. W. B. Saunders Co., Philadelphia. 2nd Ed. xii & 776 pp.

Windle, W. P. 1940. Physiology of the Fetus. W. B. Saunders Co., Philadelphia. xiii & 249 pp.

F. VERTEBRATE EMBRYOLOGY

Brachet, A. 1935. Traité d'Embryologie des Vertébrés. Masson & Cie, Paris. 2nd Ed. viii & 690 pp.

Dalcq, A. et J. Pasteels. 1954. Le Developpement des Vertébrés. In Grassé's Traité de Zoologie, Vol. 12, pp. 35–201. Masson & Cie, Paris.

Hertwig, O. 1906. Handbuch der vergleichenden und experimentellen Entwicklungslehre der Wirbeltiere. Gustav Fischer, Jena. 3 vols. (in 6).

Jordan, H. E., and J. E. Kindred. 1948. Textbook of Embryology. Appleton-Century, New York. 5th Ed. xiv & 613 pp.

Keibel, F. 1897–1938. Normentafeln zur Entwicklungsgeschichte der Wirbeltiere. Gustav Fischer, Jena. 16 vols.

McEwen, R. S. 1949. Vertebrate Embryology. Henry Holt & Co., New York. 3rd Ed. xv & 699 pp.

Nelson, O. E. 1953. Comparative Embryology of the Vertebrates. The Blakiston Co., New York. xxiii & 982 pp.

Waterman, A. J. 1948. A Laboratory Manual of Comparative Vertebrate Embryology. Henry Holt & Co., New York. viii & 248 pp.

G. HUMAN EMBRYOLOGY

Arey, L. B. 1954. Developmental Anatomy. W. B. Saunders Co., Philadelphia. 6th Ed. xi & 612 pp.

Brandt, W. 1949. Lehrbuch der Embryologie. S. Karger, Basel. xii & 648 pp.

Corner, G. W. 1944. Ourselves Unborn. Yale University Press, New Haven. xiv & 188 pp.

Corning, H. K. 1925. Lehrbuch der Entwicklungsgeschichte des Menschen. J. F. Bergmann, München, 2nd Ed. xi & 696 pp.

Fischel, A. 1929. Lehrbuch der Entwicklung des Menschen. Springer, Wien u. Berlin. viii & 822 pp.

Hamilton, W. J., J. D. Boyd, and H. W. Mossman. 1945. Human Embryology. Williams & Wilkins Co., Baltimore. viii & 366 pp.

Keibel, F., and F. P. Mall. 1910–12. Manual of Human Embryology. J. B. Lippincott Co., Philadelphia. Vol. 1, xviii & 548 pp., Vol. 2, viii & 1032 pp.

Patten, B. M. 1953. Human Embryology. 2nd Ed. The Blakiston Co., New York, Toronto. xvii & 798 pp.

Peter, K., G. Wetzel, and F. Heiderich. 1938. Handbuch der Anatomie des Kindes. J. F. Bergmann, München. 2 vols.

SPECIAL REFERENCES

The references in the following list are specifically related to material contained in the several chapters of this book, as indicated by the chapter numbers following each reference.

Abercrombie, M. 1950. The effects of anteroposterior reversal of lengths of the primitive streak in the chick. Phil. Trans. Roy. Soc. London, 234:317–338.
(Chaps. 14, 15)

———— *and R. Bellairs.* 1954. The effects in chick blastoderms of replacing the primitive node by a graft of posterior primitive streak. J. Embryol. & Exp. Morph., 2:55–72.   (Chap. 14)

———— *and J. E. M. Heaysman.* 1954. Observations on the social behaviour of cells in tissue culture. II. "Monolayering" of fibroblasts. Exp. Cell Res., 6:293–306.   (Chap. 14)

Addison, W. H. F. 1927. The centenary of the discovery of the mammalian ovum. Med. Life, 34:305–312.   (Chap. 26)

Alfert, M. 1950. A cytochemical study of oogenesis and cleavage in the mouse. J. Cell. & Comp. Physiol., 36:381–409.   (Chaps. 3, 4)

Allen, B. M. 1924. Brain development in anuran larvae after thyroid or pituitary gland removal. Endocrinology, 8:639–651.   (Chap. 11)

Atwell, W. J. 1939. The morphogenesis of the hypophysis cerebri of the domestic fowl during the second and third weeks of incubation. Anat Rec., 73:57–71.
(Chap. 19)

Austin, C. R., and J. Smiles. 1948. Phase-contrast microscopy in the study of fertilization and early development of the rat egg. J. Roy. Micr. Soc., 68:13–19.
(Chaps. 3, 4)

Baltzer, F. 1950. Chimären und Merogone bei Amphibien. Rev. Suisse Zool., 57: 93–114.   (Chaps. 4, 6, 7, 8)

Barclay, A. E., K. J. Franklin, and M. Prichard. 1945. The Foetal Circulation. Charles C Thomas, Springfield, Ill. xvi & 275 pp.   (Chap. 28)

Barott, H. G. 1937. Effect of temperature, humidity, and other factors on hatch of hens' eggs and on energy metabolism of chick embryos. U. S. Dept. Agr., Washington, D. C. Tech. Bull., 553:1–45.   (Chap. 20)

Bartelmez, G. W. 1912. The bilaterality of the pigeon's egg. J. Morph., 23:269–329. (Chap. 14)

Barth, L. G., and L. J. Barth. 1954. The Energetics of Development. A Study of Metabolism in the Frog Egg. Columbia University Press, New York. xviii & 117 pp. (Chap. 12)

Bellairs, R. 1953. Studies on the development of the foregut in the chick blastoderm. J. Embryol. & Exp. Morph., 1:115–124. (Chaps. 14, 15)

Birkmann, K. 1940. Morphologisch-anatomische Untersuchungen zur Entwicklung des häutigen Labyrinthes der Amphibien. Zeit. Anat. & Entwick., 110:443–488. (Chap. 11)

Boell, E. J., and J. S. Nicholas. 1948. Respiratory metabolism of the mammalian egg. J. Exp. Zool., 109:267–282. (Chaps. 21, 26, 28)

Böving, B. G. 1954. Blastocyst-uterine relationships. Cold Spring Harbor Symp. on Quant. Biol., 19:9–28. (Chaps. 21, 22, 26)

Boyden, E. A. 1918. Vestigial gill filaments in chick embryos, with a note on similar structures in reptiles. Am. J. Anat., 23:205–235. (Chap. 16)

———— 1953. Observations on the anatomy and development of the lungs. The Journal-Lancet, 73:509–512. (Chap. 28)

Brauns, A. 1940. Untersuchungen zur Ermittlung der Entstehung der roten Blutzellen in der Embryonalentwicklung der Urodelen. Arch. Entwicklungsmech., 140:741–789. (Chap. 7)

Briggs, R., and T. J. King. 1953. Factors affecting the transplantability of nuclei of frog embryonic cells. J. Exp. Zool., 122:485–506. (Chap. 5)

Bruner, J. A. 1951. Distribution of chorionic gonadotropin in mother and fetus at various stages of pregnancy. J. Clin. Endocr., 11:360–374. (Chaps. 25, 30)

Butler, E. G., and O. E. Schotté. 1949. Effects of delayed denervation on regenerative activity in limbs of urodele larvae. J. Exp. Zool., 112:361–392. (Chap. 9)

———— *and H. F. Blum.* 1955. Regenerative growth in the urodele forelimb following ultraviolet radiation. J. Nat. Cancer Inst., 15:877–889. (Chap. 9)

Chang, C. Y., and E. Witschi. 1955. Breeding of sex reversed males of *Xenopus laevis* Daudin. Proc. Soc. Exp. Biol. & Med., 89:150–152. (Chap. 10)

———————— 1955. Independence of adrenal hyperplasia and gonadal masculinization in the experimental adrenogenital syndrome of frogs. Endocrinology, 56:597–605. (Chap. 10)

Chang, M. C. 1954. Development of parthenogenetic rabbit blastocysts induced by low temperature storage of unfertilized ova. J. Exp. Zool., 125:127–150. (Chap. 4)

Clark, E. L. 1912. Injection and reconstruction of the jugular lymph "sac" in the chick. Anat. Rec., 6:260–264. (Chap. 18)

———— 1915. Observations of the lymph flow and the associated morphological changes in the early superficial lymphatics of chick embryos. Am. J. Anat., 18:399–440. (Chap. 18)

Clark, E. R., and E. L. Clark. 1920. On the origin and early development of the lymphatic system of the chick. Contr. to Embryol. 45, Carnegie, 9:447–482. (Chap. 18)

Cole, H. H., and H. Goss. 1943. The source of the equine gonadotrophin. Essays in Biology in honor of H. M. Evans. University of California Press, Berkeley, pp. 107–119. (Chaps. 21, 24)

———— *and G. H. Hart.* 1942. Diagnosis of pregnancy in the mare by hormonal means. J. Am. Vet. Med. Assoc., 101:124–128. (Chap. 24)

Congdon, E. D. 1922. Transformation of the aortic arch system during the development of the human embryo. Contr. to Embr. 68, Carnegie, 14:47–110. (Chap. 28)

Copenhaver, W. M. 1939. Initiation of beat and intrinsic contraction rates in the different parts of the Amblystoma heart. J. Exp. Zool., 80:193–224.
(Chaps. 7, 8, 28)

———— 1955. Growth of thyroid tissue in the gills of *Amblystoma punctatum* reared in propylthiouracil. J. Exp. Zool., 129:291–307.   (Chaps. 7, 8)

Corner, G. W. 1929. A well-preserved human embryo of 10 somites. Contr. to Embryol. 112, Carnegie, 20:81–102.   (Chap. 26)

Csapo, A., and H. Herrmann. 1951. Quantitative changes in contractile proteins of chick skeletal muscle during and after embryonic development. Am. J. Physiol., 165:701–710.   (Chap. 28)

Daniel, J. F., and E. A. Yarwood. 1939. The early embryology of *Triturus torosus.* Univ. California Publ. Zool., 43:321–356.   (Chap. 4)

Davies, J. 1954. Cytological evidence of protein absorption in fetal and adult mammalian kidneys. Am. J. Anat., 94:45–72.   (Chap. 29)

Davis, C. L. 1923. Description of a human embryo having twenty paired somites. Contr. to Embryol. 72, Carnegie, 15:3–51.   (Chap. 26)

Dean, B. 1937. Embryology of Chlamydoselachus. Dean Mem. Vol. II., American Museum of Natural History, New York.   (Chap. 13)

Dempster, W. T. 1930. The morphology of the amphibian endolymphatic organ. J. Morph. & Physiol., 50:71–126.   (Chap. 11)

Detwiler, S. R. 1936. Neuroembryology. The Macmillan Co., New York. x & 218 pp.   (Chaps. 7, 8, 11)

———— 1937. Observations upon the migration of neural crest cells, and upon the development of the spinal ganglia and vertebral arches in Amblystoma. Am. J. Anat., 61:63–94.   (Chaps. 7, 8, 11)

———— 1955. Experiments on the origin of the ventrolateral trunk musculature in the urodele (Amblystoma). J. Exp. Zool., 129:45–76.   (Chap. 8)

Dijkgraaf, S. 1952. Bau und Funktionen der Seitenorgane und des Ohrlabyrinths bei Fischen. Experientia, 8:205–216.   (Chap. 11)

DuShane, G. P. 1943. The embryology of vertebrate pigment cells. I. Amphibia. Quart. Rev. Biol., 18:109–127.   (Chap. 11)

Duval, M. 1889. Atlas d'embryologie. Masson & Cie, Paris. 116 pp., 40 plates.
(Chaps. 14–17)

Eakin, R. M., and collaborators. 1949–1953. Studies in protein metabolism of the amphibian embryo. J. Exp. Zool., 110:33–46; 124:263–278. Proc. Soc. Exp. Biol. & Med., 75:32–34; 78:502–504.   (Chap. 12)

Ebert, J. D. 1952. Appearance of tissue-specific proteins during development. Ann. New York Acad. Sci., 55:67–84.   (Chaps. 14, 20)

Erdmann, K. 1933. Zur Entwicklung des knöchernen Skelets von Triton und Rana. Zeit. Anat. & Entwicklungsgeschic., 101:566–651.   (Chap. 9)

Evans, H. M., and O. Swezy. 1929. The chromosomes in man: sex and somatic. Mem. Univ. California, 9:1–64.   (Chap. 30)

Fankhauser, G. 1932, 1934. Cytological studies on egg fragments of the salamander Triton. II. J. Exp. Zool., 62:185–235. III. J. Exp. Zool., 67:159–215.
(Chap. 4)

———— 1937. The development of fragments of the fertilized Triton egg with the egg nucleus alone (gyno-merogony). J. Exp. Zool., 75:413–469.   (Chap. 4)

———— 1937. The production and development of haploid salamander larvae. J. Hered., 28:2–15.   (Chap. 4)

———— and C. Moore. 1941. Cytological and experimental studies of polyspermy in the newt *Triturus viridescens.* J. Morph., 68:347–385.   (Chap. 4)

Fiske, C. H., and E. A. Boyden. 1926. Nitrogen metabolism in the chick embryo. J. Biol. Chem., 70:535–556.   (Chap. 20)

Flexner, L. B., D. B. Cowie, L. M. Hellman, W. S. Wilde, and G. J. Vosburgh.

1948. The permeability of the human placenta to sodium in normal and abnormal pregnancies and the supply of sodium to the human fetus as determined with radioactive sodium. Am. J. Obstet. & Gynec., 55:469–480.
(Chaps. 21, 22, 25)

Foote, C. L. 1941. Modification of sex development in the marbled salamander by administration of synthetic sex hormones. J. Exp. Zool., 86:291–319.
(Chap. 10)

Fraser, E. A. 1950. The development of the vertebrate excretory system. Biol. Rev., 25:159–187.
(Chap. 29)

Fugo, N. W. 1940. Effects of hypophysectomy in the chick embryo. J. Exp. Zool., 85:271–297.
(Chaps. 15, 19)

———— and E. Witschi. 1938. Removal of the hypophyseal primordium in the chick during the second day of incubation. Acta Biol. Latvica, 8:73–79.
(Chaps. 15, 19)

Gallien, L. 1950. Les hormones sexuelles dans la différenciation du sexe chez les amphibiens. Arch. Anat. micr. & Morph. exp., 39:337–366.
(Chap. 10)

Gayda, T. 1921. Richerche di calorimetria. Arch. fisiol., 19:211.
(Chap. 12)

Graves, A. P. 1945. Development of the golden hamster, Cricetus auratus Waterhouse, during the first 9 days. Am. J. Anat., 77:219–251.
(Chaps. 21, 22)

Green, W. W., and L. M. Winters. 1945. Prenatal development of the sheep. Techn. Bull. 169, Univ. Minn. Agr. Exp. Station.
(Chaps. 21, 22)

Grobstein, C. 1953. Epithelio-mesenchymal specificity in the morphogenesis of mouse sub-mandibular rudiments in vitro. J. Exp. Zool., 124:383–414.
(Chaps. 7, 14)

Gruenwald, P. 1952. Development of the excretory system. Ann. New York Acad. Sci., 55:142–146.
(Chap. 19)

Hadorn, E. 1936. Übertragung von Artmerkmalen durch das entkernte Eiplasma beim merogonischen Triton Bastard, palmatus-Plasma x cristatus-Kern. Verh. d. Zool. Ges. pp. 97–104.
(Chap. 4)

Hall, E. K. 1954. Further experiments on the intrinsic contractility of the embryonic rat heart. Anat. Rec., 118:175–184.
(Chap. 28)

Hamburger, V., and R. Levi-Montalcini. 1950. Some aspects of neuroembryology. In Genetic Neurology, P. Weiss, Ed., University of Chicago Press, pp. 128–160.
(Chaps. 16, 19)

Hamilton, H. L. 1952. Lillie's Development of the Chick. 3rd Ed. Henry Holt & Co., New York. 3rd Ed. xv & 624 pp.
(Chaps. 14–18)

Hammond, J., and F. H. A. Marshall. 1925. Reproduction in the rabbit. Edinburgh. 210 pp.
(Chaps. 4, 21, 22)

Harrison, R. G. 1921. On relations of symmetry in transplanted limbs. J. Exp. Zool., 32:1–135.
(Chap. 8)

———— 1925. The effect of reversing the medio-lateral or transverse axis of the fore-limb bud in the salamander embryo. Arch. Entwicklungsmech., 106:469–502.
(Chap. 8)

Hartmann, C. G. 1936. Time of Ovulation in Women. Williams & Wilkins Co., Baltimore. x & 226 pp.
(Chap. 26)

———— 1952. Possums. University of Texas Press, Austin. xiii & 174 pp.
(Chaps. 21, 22)

Helff, O. M. 1939. Studies on amphibian metamorphosis XVI. The development of forelimb opercular perforations in Rana temporaria and Bufo bufo. J. Exp. Biol., 16:96–120.
(Chap. 9)

Henderson, E. W., and R. Penquite. 1934. A comparison of embryonic growth rates of chickens, turkeys, ducks, and geese. Atti V. Congr. Mond. Pollicult., Roma. vol. II., 297–306.
(Chap. 18)

Henneberg, B. 1938. Normentafel zur Entwicklungsgeschichte der Wanderratte (*Rattus norwegicus* Erxleben). Keibel Normentafeln:15. Gustav Fischer, Jena.
(Chaps. 21–23)

Hertig, A. T. 1935. Angiogenesis in the early human chorion and in the primary placenta of the macaque monkey. Contr. to Embryol. 146, Carnegie, 25:39–81.
(Chap. 28)

———— *and J. Rock.* 1941. Two human ova of the pre-villous stage, having an ovulation age of about eleven and twelve days respectively. Contr. to Embryol. 184, Carnegie, 29:127–156. (Chap. 26)

———————— 1945. Two human ova of the pre-villous stage, having a developmental age of about seven and nine days respectively. Contr. to Embryol. 200, Carnegie, 31:65–84. (Chap. 26)

———, ————, *E. C. Adams, and W. J. Mulligan.* 1954. On the preimplantation stages of the human ovum. Contr. to Embryol. 240, Carnegie, 35:199–220.
(Chap. 26)

Heuser, C. H. 1930. A human embryo with 14 pairs of somites. Contr. to Embryol. 131, Carnegie, 22:135–154. (Chap. 26)

———— 1932. A presomite human embryo with a definite chorda canal. Contr. to Embryol. 138, Carnegie, 23:251–267. (Chap. 26)

———, *J. Rock, and A. T. Hertig.* 1945. Two human embryos showing early stages of the definitive yolk sac. Contr. to Embryol. 201, Carnegie, 31:85–99.
(Chap. 26)

———— *and G. L. Streeter.* 1941. Development of the macaque embryo. Contr. to Embryol. 181, Carnegie, 29:15–55. (Chaps. 26, 27)

Hill, J. P. 1910. The early development of the Marsupialia, with special reference to the native cat (*Dasyurus viverrinus*). Quart. J. Micr. Sci., 56:1–134.
(Chap. 5)

His, W. 1874. Unsere Körperform und das Problem ihrer Entstehung. Vogel, Leipzig. xiv & 224 pp. (Chaps. 12, 13, 14)

———— 1880–1885. Anatomie menschlicher Embryonen. Vogel, Leipzig. 3 vols. and atlas. (Chaps. 26, 27)

Hisaw, F. L. 1944. The placental gonadotrophin and luteal function in monkeys (*Macaca mulatta*). Yale J. Biol. & Med., 17:119–137. (Chap. 25)

Hodler, F. 1949. Untersuchungen über die Entwicklung von Sacralwirbel und Urostyl bei den Anuren. Rev. Suisse Zool., 56:747–790. (Chap. 9)

Hörstadius, S. O. 1950. The Neural Crest, Its Properties and Derivatives in the Light of Experimental Research. Oxford University Press, London, New York. viii & 111 pp. (Chaps. 7, 9, 11)

Hörstadius, S., and S. Sellman. 1946. Experimentelle Untersuchungen über die Determination des knorpeligen Kopfskelettes bei Urodelen. N. Acta Reg. Soc. Sci. Upsal. IV, 13:1–170. (Chap. 9)

Holtfreter, J. 1938. Differenzierungspotenzen isolierter Teile der Urodelengastrula. Arch. Entwicklungsmech., 138:522–738. (Chap. 7)

———— 1951. Some aspects of embryonic induction. Growth Sympos., 10:117–152. (Chap. 7)

Hunter, R. H. 1930. Observations on the development of the human female genital tract. Contr. to Embryol. 129, Carnegie, 22:91–108. (Chap. 30)

Irwin, M. R. 1949. Immunological studies in embryology and genetics. Quart. Rev. Biol., 24:109–123. (Chap. 14)

Janes, R. G. 1934. Histological changes in the alimentary tract of anuran larvae during involution. J. Exp. Zool., 67:73–91. (Chap. 9)

Jones, H. O., and J. I. Brewer. 1941. A human embryo in the primitive streak stage. Contr. to Embryol. 185, Carnegie, 29:157–165. (Chap. 26)

Jost, A. 1953. Problems of fetal endocrinology: The gonadal and hypophyseal hormones. Recent Progr. Hormone Res., 8:379–418. (Chap. 30)

Kappers, J. A. 1941. Kopfplakoden bei Wirbeltieren. Ergeb. Anat. & Entwicklungsgeschw., 33:370–412. (Chap. 15)

Kenneth, J. H. 1947. Gestation Periods. Edinburgh. 2nd Ed. 30 pp. (Chap. 22)

Knouff, R. A. 1935. The developmental pattern of ectodermal placodes in Rana pipiens. J. Comp. Neur., 62:17–71. (Chap. 14)

Kollros, J. J. 1942, 1943. Experimental studies on the development of the corneal reflex in amphibia. I. J. Exp. Zool., 89:37–67. II. Physiol. Zool., 16:269–279. III. J. Exp. Zool., 92:121–142. (Chap. 11)

——— 1953. The development of the optic lobes in the frog. J. Exp. Zool., 123: 153–188. (Chap. 11)

——— and J. C. Kaltenbach. 1952. Local metamorphosis of larval skin in Rana pipiens. Physiol. Zool., 25:163–170. (Chap. 11)

——— and V. M. McMurray. 1955. The mesencephalic V nucleus in anurans. J. Comp. Neur., 102:47–64. (Chap. 11)

Kopsch, F. 1952. Die Entwicklung des braunen Grasfrosches, Rana fusca Roesel. Georg Thieme, Stuttgart. vii & 70 pp. (Chap. 14)

Krediet, G. 1933. Uebergangsformen zwischen Follikeln und Samenkanaelchen in einem Ovariotestis. Zeit. Ges. Anat., 101:228. (Chap. 30)

Krehbiel, R. H. 1937. Cytological studies of the decidual reaction in the rat during early pregnancy and in the production of deciduomata. Physiol. Zool., 10:212–233. (Chap. 24)

Krogh, A., K. Schmidt-Nielsen, and E. Zeuthen. 1938. The osmotic behaviour of frog's eggs and young tadpoles. Zeit. Vergl. Physiol., 26:230–238. (Chap. 12)

Landauer, W. 1948. Hereditary abnormalities and their chemically induced phenocopies. Growth Symp., 12:171–200. (Chap. 14, 16, 17)

——— 1951. The hatchability of chicken eggs as influenced by environment and heredity. Storrs Agr. Exp. Station, Storrs, Conn., Bull., 262: 223 pp. (Chap. 14)

Leonard, S. L., and R. Kurzrock. 1945. A study of hyaluronidase effects on the follicle cells of ovulated rat ova. Endocrinology, 37:171–176. (Chaps. 4, 24)

Lillie, F. R. 1923. Problems of Fertilization. University of Chicago Press, Chicago. xii & 278 pp. (Chap. 4)

——— and M. Juhn. 1932. The physiology of development of feathers. I. Growth-rate and pattern in the individual feather. Physiol. Zool., 5:124–184. (Chap. 18)

Locy, W. A., and O. Larsell. 1916. The embryology of the bird's lung. Am. J. Anat., 19:447–504. (Chap. 18)

Ludwig, E. 1928. Über einen operativ gewonnenen menschlichen Embryo mit einem Ursegmente. Morph. Jahrb., 59:41–104. (Chap. 26)

——— 1929. Embryon humain avec dix paires de somites mésoblastiques. C. R. Assoc. Anatomistes, 24me Réunion. Bordeaux. 6 pp.

Luther, W. 1935. Entwicklungsphysiologische Untersuchungen am Forellenkeim. Biol. Zentralbl., 55:114–138. (Chap. 13)

Lutwak-Mann, C. 1954. Some properties of the rabbit blastocyst. J. Embr. & Exp. Morph., 2:1–13. (Chaps. 21, 22, 24)

Lutz, H. 1949. Sur la production expérimentale de la polyembryonie et de la monstruosité double chez les oiseaux. Arch. Anat. Micr. & Morph. Exp., 38:79–144. (Chap. 14)

Lynn, W. G., and M. Peadon. 1949. Situs inversus viscerum in conjoined triplets of the brook trout. J. Morph., 84:411–426. (Chap. 13)

Malan, M. E. 1953. The elongation of the primitive streak and the localization of

the presumptive chorda-mesoderm on the early chick blastoderm, studied by means of coloured marks with Nile blue sulphate. Arch. Biol., 64:149–188.
(Chap. 14)

Mangold, O. 1954. Entwicklung und Differenzierung der präsumptiven Epidermis und ihres unterlagernden Entomesoderms aus der Neurula von *Triton alpestris* als Isolat. Arch. Entwicklungsmech., 147:131–170. (Chaps. 7, 8)

———— 1955. Die Entwicklung kleinster und grösster Keime von *Triton alpestris* bei Fütterung und Hunger. Arch. Entwicklungsmech., 147:373–404.
(Chaps. 9, 21)

Mann, I. C. 1928. The Development of the Human Eye. Cambridge University Press, Cambridge. 306 pp. (Chap. 29)

McCrady, E. 1938. The embryology of the opossum. Am. Anat. Memoirs, 16: 1–233. (Chaps. 21, 22)

McCurdy, H. M. M. 1931. Development of the sex organs in *Triturus torosus*. Am. J. Anat., 47:367–403. (Chap. 10)

McKay, D. G., A. T. Hertig, E. C. Adams, and S. Danziger. 1953. Histochemical observations on the germ cells of human embryos. Anat. Rec., 117:201–219.
(Chap. 30)

McKenzie, F. F., J. C. Miller, and L. C. Bauguess. 1938. The reproductive organs and semen of the boar. Univ. Missouri Agr. Res. Sta. Res. Bull., 279:66–122.
(Chap. 24)

Meisenheimer, J. 1921. Geschlecht und Geschlecter im Tierreiche. Gustav Fischer, Jena. xiv & 896 pp. (Chaps. 23, 25)

Menkin, M. F., and J. Rock. 1948. In vitro fertilization and cleavage of human ovarian eggs. Am. J. Obst. & Gynec., 55:440–452. (Chap. 26)

Mintz, B. 1947. Effects of testosterone propionate on sex development in female Ambystoma larvae. Physiol. Zool., 22:355–373. (Chap. 10)

Moog, F. 1952. The differentiation of enzymes in relation to the functional activities of the developing embryo. Ann. New York Acad. Sci., 55:57–66. (Chap. 14)

Moore, K. L., M. A. Graham, and M. L. Barr. 1953. The detection of chromosomal sex in hermaphrodites from a skin biopsy. Surg., Gynec., & Obst., 96:641–648.
(Chap. 30)

Morita, S. 1936. Die künstliche Erzeugung von Einzelmissbildungen. Zwillingen, Drillingen und Mehrlingen im Hühnerei. Anat. Anz., 82:81–102. (Chap. 14)

Mossmann, H. W. 1937. Comparative morphogenesis of the fetal membranes and accessory uterine structures. Contrib. to Embryol. 158, Carnegie, 26:129–246.
(Chaps. 21, 22)

Neumann, H. O. 1925. Multiple Teratome in einem Ovarium. Zentralbl. Gynäkol., 46:1549–1560. (Chap. 4)

Newell, Q. U., E. Allen, J. P. Pratt, and L. J. Bland. 1930. The time of ovulation in the menstrual cycle as checked by the recovery of ova from the fallopian tubes. Am. J. Obstet. & Gynec., 29:180–185. (Chap. 26)

Nicholas, J. S. 1947. Experimental approaches to problems of early development in the rat. Quart. Rev. Biol., 22:179–195. (Chaps. 21, 22)

———— 1950. Development of contractility. Proc. Am. Phil. Soc., 94:175–183. (Chap. 28)

Nieuwkoop, P. D., and others. 1952. Activation and organization of the central nervous system in amphibians. J. Exp. Zool., 120:1–108. (Chaps. 6, 7, 11)

O'Connor, R. J. 1940. Experiments on the development of the amphibian mesonephros. J. Anat., 74:34–44. (Chap. 10)

Oppenheimer, J. M. 1936. Processes of localization in developing Fundulus. J. Exp. Zool., 73:405–444. (Chap. 13)

———— 1937. The normal stages of *Fundulus heteroclitus*. Anat. Rec., 68:1–15.
(Chap. 13)

Padget, D. H. 1948. The development of the cranial arteries in the human embryo. Contr. to Embryol. 212, Carnegie, 32:205–261. (Chaps. 26, 27, 28)

Painter, T. S. 1934. Salivary chromosomes and the attack on the gene. J. Hered., 25:465–476. (Chaps. 1, 2)

———— 1939. The structure of salivary gland chromosomes. Am. Nat., 73:315–330. (Chaps. 1, 2)

Pasteels, J. 1936. Étude sur la gastrulation des vertébrés méroblastiques. I. Téléosteens. Arch. Biol., 47:205–308. (Chap. 13)

III. Oiseaux. IV. Conclusions générales. Arch. Biol., 48:381–488. (Chap. 14)

Patten, B. M. 1948. Embryology of the Pig. The Blakiston Co., Philadelphia. 3rd Ed. xiv & 352 pp. (Chaps. 21, 22)

———— 1952. Early Embryology of the Chick. The Blakiston Co., New York. 4th Ed. xiii & 244 pp. (Chaps. 14–16)

Payne F. 1925. General description of a 7-somite human embryo. Contr. to Embryol. 81, Carnegie, 16:115–124. (Chap. 26)

Piatt, J. 1955. Regeneration of the spinal cord in the salamander. J. Exp. Zool., 129:177–207. (Chap. 11)

Pincus, G. 1936. The Eggs of Mammals. The Macmillan Co., New York. vii & 160 pp. (Chaps. 3, 4, 21, 24)

Potter, E. L., and F. L. Adair. 1940. Fetal and Neonatal Death. University of Chicago Press. xii & 207 pp. (Chap. 27)

Ramsey, E. M. 1937. The Lockyer embryo: An early human embryo in situ. Contr. to Embryol. 156, Carnegie, 26:99–120. (Chaps. 25, 26)

Rawles, M. E. 1936. A study in the localization of organ-forming areas in the chick blastoderm of the head-process stage. J. Exp. Zool., 72:271–315. (Chap. 14)

———— 1955. Pigmentation in autoplastic and homoplastic grafts of skin from fetal and newborn hooded rats. Am. J. Anat., 97:79–128. (Chap. 22)

Reynolds, H. C. 1952. Studies on reproduction in the opossum (*Didelphis virginiana virginiana*). Univ. California Publ. Zool., 52:223–284. (Chap. 22)

Rodgers, L. T., and T. L. Risley. 1938. Sexual differentiation of urogenital ducts of *Ambystoma tigrinum.* J. Morph., 63:119–141. (Chap. 10)

Rückert, J. 1899. Die erste Entwickelung des Eies der Elasmobranchier. Festschr. Von Kupffer. Gustav Fischer, Jena. pp. 581–704. (Chap. 13)

Rudnick, D. 1945. Limb-forming potencies of the chick blastoderm: including notes on associated trunk structures. Trans. Conn. Acad. Arts & Sci., 36:353–377. (Chaps. 15, 16)

Rugh, R. 1951. The Frog, Its Reproduction and Development. The Blakiston Co., Philadelphia. x & 336 pp. (Chaps. 4–9)

Saunders, J. W. 1948. The proximo-distal sequence of origin of the parts of the chick wing and the role of the ectoderm. J. Exp. Zool., 108:363–404. (Chap. 16)

Schechtman, A. M. 1932. Movement and localization of the presumptive epidermis in *Triturus torosus* (Rathke). Univ. California Publ. Zool., 36:325–346. (Chaps. 7, 8)

Segal, S. J. 1953. Morphogenesis of the estrogen induced hyperplasia of the adrenals in larval frogs. Anat. Rec., 115:205–230. (Chap. 10)

Sensenig, E. C. 1949. The early development of the human vertebral column. Contr. to Embryol. 214, Carnegie, 33:21–41. (Chap. 28)

———— 1951. The early development of the meninges of the spinal cord in human embryos. Contr. to Embryol. 228, Carnegie, 34:145–157. (Chap. 29)

Shettles, L. B. 1953. Observations on human follicular and tubal ova. Am. J. Obst. & Gynec., 66:235–247. (Chap. 26)

Smith, P. E. 1920. The pigmentary, growth, and endocrine disturbances induced in the anuran tadpole by the early ablation of the pars buccalis of the hypophysis. Am. Anat. Memoirs, *11*:1–151.   (Chap. 11)

Snell, G. D. 1941. The early embryology of the mouse. From: The Biology of the Laboratory Mouse. The Blakiston Co., Philadelphia. 54 pp.   (Chaps. 21, 22)

Spaulding, M. H. 1921. The development of the external genitalia in the human embryo. Contr. to Embryol. 61, Carnegie, *13*:67–88.   (Chap. 30)

Spemann, H. 1928. Die Entwicklung seitlicher und dorsoventraler Keimhälften bei verzögerter Kernversorgung. Zeit. Wiss. Zool., *132*:105–134.
                                                                         (Chaps. 4, 5, 7)

———— 1931. Über den Anteil von Implantat und Wirtskeim an der Orientierung und Beschaffenheit der induzierten Embryonalanlage. Arch. Entwicklungsmech., *123*:389–517.   (Chap. 7)

Spratt, N. T. 1947. Development in vitro of the early chick blastoderm explanted on yolk and albumen extract saline-agar substrata. J. Exp. Zool., *106*:345–366.
                                                                         (Chaps. 14, 20)

———— 1952. Localization of the prospective neural plate in the early chick blastoderm. J. Exp. Zool., *120*:109–130.   (Chap. 14)

Steiner, H. 1938. Der Archaeopteryx-Schwanz der Vogelembryonen. Nat. Forsch. Ges. Zürich, Vierteljahrsschrift, *83*:279–300.   (Chap. 17)

Stone, L. S. 1933. The development of lateral-line sense organs in amphibians observed in living and vital-stained preparations. J. Comp. Neurol., *57*:507–540.
                                                                         (Chap. 11)

———— 1955. Regeneration of the iris and lens from retina pigment cells in adult newt eyes. J. Exp. Zool., *129*:505–533.   (Chap. 11)

Streeter, G. L. 1908. The peripheral nervous system in the human embryo at the end of the first month. Am. J. Anat., 8:285–301.   (Chap. 29)

———— 1933. The status of metamerism in the central nervous system of chick embryos. J. Comp. Neurol. 57:455–475.   (Chap. 19)

———— 1942–1951. Developmental horizons in human embryos. Contributions to Embryol. 197, 199, 211, 220, 230, Carnegie Embryology Reprint Vol. II.
                                                                         (Chaps. 26–29)

Taylor, A. C. 1943. Development of the innervation pattern in the limb bud of the frog. Anat. Rec., 87:379–413.   (Chaps. 9, 11)

———— 1944. Selectivity of nerve fibers from the dorsal and ventral roots in the development of the frog limb. J. Exp. Zool., *96*:159–185.   (Chaps. 9–11)

Ten Cate, G. 1953. The Intrinsic Development of Amphibian Embryos. North-Holland Publishing Co., Amsterdam. xii & 188 pp.   (Chap. 6–8)

Theiler, K. 1947. Die Entwicklung der konstruktiven Form der Rückenmarkshäute beim Menschen. Schweizer Archiv Neurol. & Psychiatr., *61*:1–36.   (Chap. 29)

Tondury, G. 1948. Zur Genese der Hasenscharte. Pract. Oto-rhino-laryngol., *10*: 146–155.   (Chap. 27)

Torrey, T. W. 1954. The early development of the human nephros. Contr. to Embryol. 239, Carnegie, *35*:175–197.   (Chap. 29)

Townes, P. L., and J. Holtfreter. 1955. Directed movements and selective adhesion of embryonic amphibian cells. J. Exp. Zool., *128*:53–120.   (Chaps. 7, 26)

Trinkaus, J. P. 1951. A study of the mechanism of epiboly in the egg of *Fundulus heteroclitus*. J. Exp. Zool., *118*:269–320.   (Chap. 13)

———— and P. W. Groves. 1955. Differentiation in culture of mixed aggregates of dissociated tissue cells. Proc. Nat. Acad. Sci., *41*:787–795.   (Chap. 14)

Turner, C. L. 1940. Pseudoamnion, pseudochorion and follicular pseudoplacenta in poeciliid fishes. J. Morph., *67*:59–89.   (Chap. 13)

Turner, C. W. 1934. The causes of the growth and function of the udder of cattle. Univ. Missouri Agric. Exp. Sta. Bull., *339*:3–20.   (Chaps. 23, 25)

Tyler, A. 1948. Fertilization and immunity. Physiol. Rev., 28:180–219.
(Chap. 4)
Vandebroek, G. 1936. Les mouvements morphogénétiques au cours de la gastrulation chez *Scyllium canicula* Cuv. Arch. Biol. 47:499–584. Chap. 13)
Van Geertruyden, J. 1946. Recherches expérimentales sur la formation du mésonephros chez les amphibiens anoures. Arch. Biol., 57:145–181. (Chap. 9)
——— 1948. Les premiers stades de développment du mésonephros chez les amphibiens anoures. Acta Neerl. Morph. Norm. & Path., 6:1–17. (Chap. 9)
Vennings, E. H. 1946. Adrenal functions in pregnancy. Endocrinology, 39:203–220. (Chap. 25)
v. Eggeling, H. 1938. Allgemeines über den Aufbau knöcherner Skeletteile. In Bolk, Göppert, Kallius, and Lubosch: Handb. Vergl. Anat. Wirbelt. Vol. 5, pp. 275–304. Urban & Schwarzenberg, Berlin, Wien. (Chap. 9)
Waddington, C. H. 1952. The Epigenetics of Birds. Cambridge University Press. Cambridge. xvi & 272 pp. (Chap. 14)
Walls, G. L. 1942. The vertebrate eye and its adaptive radiation. Cranbrook Inst. Sci. Bloomfield Hills, Mich. xiv & 785 pp. (Chap. 29)
Walton, A., and J. Hammond. 1938. The maternal effects on growth and conformation in Shire horse-Shetland pony crosses. Proc. Roy. Soc. London, B, *125*:311–335. (Chap. 22)
Wang, H. 1943. The morphogenetic functions of the epidermal and dermal components of the papilla in feather regeneration. Physiol. Zool., *16*:325–349.
(Chap. 18)
Watterson, R. L. 1942. The morphogenesis of down feathers with special reference to the developmental history of melanophores. Physiol. Zool., *15*:234–259.
(Chap. 18)
——— 1949. Development of the glycogen body of the chick spinal cord. J. Morph., 85:337–390. (Chap. 19)
Weiss, P. 1950. Perspectives in the field of morphogenesis. Quart. Rev. Biol., 25: 177–198. (Chaps. 7, 9, 11)
——— 1952. Attraction fields between growing tissue cultures. Science, *115*:293–295. (Chaps. 7, 9, 11, 14)
——— *and G. Andres.* 1952. Experiments on the fate of embryonic cells (chick) disseminated by the vascular route. J. Exp. Zool., *121*:449–488. (Chap. 14)
Wells, L. J. 1954. Development of the human diaphragm and pleural sacs. Contr. to Embryol. 236, Carnegie, 35:107–134. (Chap. 28)
Wetzel, R. 1929. Untersuchungen am Hünchen. Die Entwicklung des Keims während der ersten beiden Bruttage. Arch. Entwicklungsmech., *119*:188–321.
(Chap. 14)
——— 1936. Primitivstreifen und Urkörper nach Störungsversuchen am 1–2 Tage bebrüteten Hünchen. Arch. Entwicklungsmech., *134*:357–465. (Chap. 14)
Willis, R. A. 1951. Teratomas. Atlas of Tumorpathology. Sect. III-Fasc. 9. Armed Forces Institute of Pathology, National Research Council, Washington, D. C.
(Chaps. 4, 25, 30)
Wills, I. A. 1936. The respiratory rate of developing amphibia, with special reference to sex differentiation. J. Exp. Zool., 73:481–510. (Chap. 12)
Wilson, J. L. 1952. Physiology of the newborn. Sharp & Dohme Seminar, *14*:3–19.
(Chap. 28)
Winters, L. M., and G. Feuffel. 1936. Studies on the physiology of reproduction in the sheep. IV. Fetal development. Univ. Minn. Agr. Exp. Sta., Techn. Bull. 118. (Chaps. 21, 22)
———, *W. W. Green, and R. E. Comstock.* 1942. Prenatal development of the bovine. Univ. Minn. Agr. Exp. Sta., Techn. Bull. 151. (Chaps. 21, 22)

Witschi, E. 1935. Origin of asymmetry in the reproductive systems of birds. Am. J. Anat., 56:119–141.   (Chaps. 17, 19)

———— 1935. Seasonal sex characters in birds and their hormonal control. Wilson Bull., 47:177–188.   (Chap. 19)

———— 1942. Temperature factors in the development and evolution of sex. Biol. Symp., 6:51–70.   (Chap. 12)

———— 1945. Quantitative studies on the seasonal development of the deferent ducts in passerine birds. J. Exp. Zool., 100:549–564.   (Chap. 19)

———— 1948. Migration of germ cells of human embryos from the yolk sac to the primitive gonadal folds. Contr. to Embryol. 209, Carnegie, 32:67–80.
(Chaps. 26–30)

———— 1949. The larval ear of the frog and its transformation during metamorphosis. Zeit. f. Naturforschung, 4b:230–242.   (Chaps. 9, 11)

———— 1949. Utilization of the egg albumen by the avian fetus. Contr. to Ornithologie als biologische Wissenschaft. Winter, Heidelberg. pp. 111–122.
(Chap. 18)

———— 1951. Embryogenesis of the adrenal and the reproductive glands. Recent Progr. Hormone Res., 6:1–27.   (Chaps. 10, 30)

———— 1952. Overripeness of the egg as a cause of twinning and teratogenesis. Cancer Research, 12:763–786.   (Chaps. 7, 12, 26)

———— 1953. The experimental adrenogenital syndrome in the frog. J. Clin. Endocr. and Metab., 13:316–329.   (Chaps. 10, 30)

———— 1955. On morphogenic capacities of the estrogens. J. Clin. Endocr. and Metab., 15:647–652.   (Chaps. 7, 25, 30)

———— 1955. The bronchial columella of the ear of larval Ranidae. J. Morph., 96: 497–512.   (Chap. 11)

———— *and H. M. McCurdy.* 1929. The free-martin effect in experimental parabiotic twins of *Triturus torosus.* Proc. Soc. Exp. Biol. & Med., 26:655–657.
(Chap. 10)

———— *and G. M. Riley.* 1940. Quantitative studies on the hormones of human pituitaries. Endocrinology, 26:564–576.   (Chap. 25)

———— *and R. P. Woods.* 1936. The bill of the sparrow as an indicator for the male sex hormone. II. Structural basis. J. Exp. Zool., 73:445–459.   (Chap. 18)

Wolff, E. 1936. Les bases de la tératogénèse expérimentale des vertébrés amniotes, d'après les résultats de méthodes directes. Arch. Anat. Hist. & Embr., 22:1–382.
(Chap. 14)

Yntema, C. L., and W. S. Hammond. 1955. Experiments on the origin and development of the sacral autonomic nerves in the chick embryo. J. Exp. Zool., 129: 375–414.   (Chap. 16)

Young, H. H. 1937. Genital Abnormalities, Hermaphroditism and Related Adrenal Diseases. Williams & Wilkins Co., Baltimore. xli & 649 pp.   (Chap. 30)

Zimmermann, A. A., and T. Cornbleet. 1948. The development of epidermal pigmentation in the Negro fetus. J. Investigative Dermat., 11:383–392.
(Chap. 22)

Zwilling, E. 1952. The effects of some hormones on development. Ann. New York Acad. Sci., 55:196–202.   (Chaps. 14, 16, 17)

Index

Page numbers in *italics* indicate references to illustrations.

567

Visceral arches (*continued*)
  fishes, *208, 211, 213*
  man, 492, *494*
Visceral cleft (gill slit), *211, 482*
Visceral membrane (pharyngeal), 263, *510*
Visual cells, 179
Vitelline membrane (fertilization membrane), 30, *36*, 53, *226*, 239, *387*
Vitreous body, *178*, 179, *497*
Viviparity, evolution, 373
von Baer, 224, 228

WALL, germ, *208, 213, 226, 231*
Warburg respiration technique, 194
Water, 188f., 336, 384
  intake in amphibian egg, 189
  reabsorption of, 343
Weber ossicles, 177
Weight of eggs, fetal and young birds, 318–320
  of human germs and fetuses, 498, 499
  of pre- and postnatal mammals, 401–406
Whale, 412
Wingbud, 270–274
Wings, fetal, 322
Wolff, 224

X-CHROMOSOME, 19, 547
X-rays, effect on chick blastoderm, 241
  effect on sperms, 59

Y-CHROMOSOMES, 19, 547
Yolk, 28, 29, 35–37, *64, 66*
  digestion of, 337
  platelets in amphibian egg, 29
Yolk plug
  amphibians, 70, *71, 79, 87*
  birds, *302*
  fishes, *215*
  man, *478*
Yolk sac, 75
  birds, *338*
  fishes, *208, 214*
  mammals, 379, *390*, 392–395
  man, *463–465, 467, 468, 483, 485, 490, 491*
  placenta, 381, *384*
Yolk stalk
  birds, 294, 307
  fishes, 207
  mammals, *384*
  man, *483, 484, 491*

ZONE OF junction, *66*, 74
Zygote, 4